NUCLEAR RESEARCH WITH LOW ENERGY ACCELERATORS

NUCLEAR RESEARCH WITH LOW ENERGY ACCELERATORS

Edited by

JERRY B. MARION

DEPARTMENT OF PHYSICS AND ASTRONOMY
UNIVERSITY OF MARYLAND
COLLEGE PARK, MARYLAND

AND

DOUGLAS M. VAN PATTER

BARTOL RESEARCH FOUNDATION OF THE FRANKLIN INSTITUTE
SWARTHMORE, PENNSYLVANIA

Proceedings of the Symposium on Nuclear Physics Research with Low Energy Accelerators held at the University of Maryland, June 1967

ACADEMIC PRESS New York and London 1967

ACADEMIC PRESS INC.
111 Fifth Avenue, New York, New York 10003

United Kingdom Edition published by
ACADEMIC PRESS INC. (LONDON) LTD.
Berkeley Square House, London W.1

LIBRARY OF CONGRESS CATALOG CARD NUMBER: 67-30257

PRINTED IN THE UNITED STATES OF AMERICA

PARTICIPANTS

Achor, W.	University of Maryland
Alford, W. L.	Auburn University
Armstrong, J. C.	Institute for Defense Analysis
Banerjee, M.	University of Maryland
Battist, L.	Catholic University
Becker, R. L.	Boston College
Behof, A.	De Paul University
Berg, R.	University of Maryland
Berkowitz, E.	Edgewood Arsenal, Maryland
Biggerstaff, J. A.	Oak Ridge National Laboratory
Bilaniuk, O.	Swarthmore College
Bilpuch, E. G.	Duke University
Blatt, S. L.	Ohio State University
Bonbright, D.	University of Maryland
Booth, E. C.	Boston University
Breckan, S. W.	Memorial University of Newfoundland
Brown, B.	Naval Ordnance Laboratory
Buccino, S. G.	Tulane University
Bunch, S. M.	Washington State University
Bygrave, W.	High Voltage Engineering Corp.
Carlson, A. D.	General Atomic
Carlson, R. R.	University of Iowa
Charyulu, V. P.	University of Tulsa
Chase, L. F., Jr.	Lockheed Palo Alto
Chasman, C.	Brookhaven National Laboratory
Chertok, B.	American University
Cherubini, J.	High Voltage Engineering Corp.
Choudhury, D. C.	Polytechnic Institute of Brooklyn
Cleland, M. R.	Radiation Dynamics, Inc.
Cohen, L.	Naval Research Laboratory
Connors, P. I.	University of Maryland
Cox, J.	Ohio University
Cranberg, L.	University of Virginia
Donoghue, T. R.	Ohio State University
Dotchin, L.	University of New Hampshire
Dunnam, F. E.	University of Florida
Durham, F. E.	Tulane University
Edge, R. D.	University of South Carolina
Eldridge, H. B.	University of Wyoming
Evans, A. E.	Los Alamos Scientific Laboratory
Finlay, R. W.	Ohio University
Firk, F. W.	Yale University

Fisher, R. A.	Northwestern University
Foster, B. P.	North Texas State University
Frisbee, P.	Catholic University
Gaigalas, A. K.	S. U. N. Y. Binghamton
Geiger, K. W.	National Research Council, Ottawa
Gertzman, H.	University of Rochester
Gibbons, J. H.	Oak Ridge National Laboratory
Goines, O. T.	Lamar State College
Goldman, D. A.	National Bureau of Standards
Gossett, C. R.	U. S. Naval Research Laboratory
Gray, T. J.	Florida State University
Hardie, G.	Western Michigan University
Harihar, P.	Lowell Technology Institute
Harris, G. I.	Wright-Patterson Air Force Base
Harris, W. R.	University of Maryland
Hayward, E.	National Bureau of Standards
Henkel, J.	Hillsboro, New Hampshire
Henning, P.	Varian Associates
Henrikson, A.	Queen's University, Ontario
Hill, M. W.	Brigham Young University
Holmgren, H. D.	University of Maryland
Huang, W. F.	University of Louisville
Irfan, M.	Memorial University of Newfoundland
Knox, H.	Ohio University
Kramer, P.	C. W. Post College, New York
Kroll, R.	University of Maryland
Krone, R. W.	University of Kansas
Latorre, V.	Lima, Peru
Lee, Y. K.	Johns Hopkins University
Lewis, A.	NASA/ERC-KIE, Massachusetts
Lin, J.	University of Georgia
Logan, B. A.	University of Ottawa
Long, H. C.	Dickinson College
Mandeville, C. E.	Kansas State University
Marion, J. B.	University of Maryland
Martin, P. W.	University of British Columbia
McEllistrem, M. T.	University of Kentucky
Mead, R. O.	University of Maryland
Mekjian, A.	University of Maryland
Mo, B. T.	University of Maryland
Montague, J. H.	Queen's University, Ontario
Morrison, G. C.	Argonne National Laboratory
Mruk, W.	Hamner Electronics Co.
Murphy, R.	Bristol, Rhode Island
Nellis, D. O.	Texas Nuclear Corp.
O'Brien, B. J.	Auburndale, Massachusetts
Owen, G. E.	Johns Hopkins University
Parker, P. D.	Yale University
Patterson, J. R.	Rockford College
Peck, R. A., Jr.	Brown University
Pegg, D.	University of New Hampshire
Perez, J. D.	University of Maryland

Perkons, A. K.	Centre of Forensic Science, Canada
Piltingsrud, W. T.	North Dakota State University
Pinkston, W. T.	Vanderbilt University
Plattner, R.	ORTEC, Oak Ridge
Plimpton, R. J.	Clayton, Missouri
Potziek, C.	National Bureau of Standards
Prasod, K.	Catholic University
Prosser, F. W.	University of Kansas
Richardson, A. C.	National Bureau of Standards
Ritter, R. C.	University of Virginia
Robinson, E. L.	University of Maryland
Robinson, W. K.	Canton, New Jersey
Rodberg, L. S.	University of Maryland
Roush, M. L.	University of Maryland
Russell, D. C.	Tulane University
Ruth, D.	Ohio University
Sayres, A. D.	Princeton Gamma-Tech
Seift, J.	Catholic University
Schectman, R. M.	University of Toledo
Schrack, R. A.	National Bureau of Standards
Shrader, E. F.	Case Western Reserve University
Shuster, M.	University of Maryland
Silverstein, E. A.	Case Institute of Technology
Simons, D. G.	Naval Ordnance Laboratory
Smith, A. B.	Argonne National Laboratory
Spiegel, V.	National Bureau of Standards
Steerman, C. E.	University of Maryland
Stelson, P. H.	Oak Ridge National Laboratory
Stephenson, G. J., Jr.	University of Maryland
Storey, R. S.	National Research Council, Ottawa
Sweeney, W. E., Jr.	University of Maryland
Thaxton, G. D.	Auburn University
Thomas, C. D.	West Virginia University
Thomas, H. C.	Texas Technological College
Tilley, D. R.	Duke University
Tombrello, T. A.	California Institute of Technology
Trail, C. C.	Brooklyn College
Treado, P. A.	Georgetown University
Tucker, W. E.	Texas Nuclear Corp.
Van Patter, D. M.	Bartol Research Foundation
Walker, J. C.	Johns Hopkins University
Warburton, E. K.	Brookhaven National Laboratory
Watson, J. W.	University of Maryland
Weigold, E.	Arlington, Virginia
Werntz, C. W.	Catholic University
Wilenzick, R. M.	Tulane University
Windham, P. M.	North Texas State University
Wolicki, E.	Naval Research Laboratory
Wooten, B. A.	Worchester Polytechnic Institute
Young, E. M.	High Voltage Engineering Corp.
Young, F. C.	University of Maryland
Yu, D.	Pennsylvania State University

PREFACE

This Symposium on Nuclear Physics Research with Low Energy Accelerators was conceived as somewhat of an innovation compared with the usual broad-range conference. It was felt that an unfulfilled need existed for a review in depth of the current experimental research using low energy accelerators—defined roughly as those operating below 5 MeV. At the same time, we hoped that such a symposium could be a source of stimulation to those who might be considering the initiation of nuclear structure programs at their own institutions. The idea for and the promotion of this Symposium originated in the Subcommittee on Nuclear Structure of the National Academy of Science—National Research Council and represents a continuation of this group's efforts to encourage topical conferences in nuclear physics.

Research using a low energy accelerator has advantages not usually enjoyed by larger facilities. For one thing, a more relaxed attitude toward scheduling is likely. Without a tight schedule involving many different experimental groups, problems can be tackled which require a great deal of machine time for set-up and data acquisition. A high degree of sophistication in one or more elements of the experiment can be evolved when a program receives emphasis over a period of time. For example, the ultra-high energy resolution achieved at Duke University required years of patient effort and continuing improvements. Another prime advantage is the greater opportunity for graduate students to assume responsibility for several aspects of an experiment, and to learn about the detailed operation of the accelerator and auxiliary equipment.

We are all familiar with the large international conferences which tend to accentuate the theoretical problems of current interest, together with the latest results from new higher energy facilities. Outside of private conversations, there is rarely an opportunity at such meetings for a vigorous discussion of the technical aspects of the experiments. Therefore we asked the invited speakers at this Symposium to include a discussion of some of the key technical problems which they had to overcome in the course of their work, as well as an evaluation of the present state of the art for their particular specialty.

After each lecture there followed a period of discussion during which many interesting and thought-provoking questions were raised. No recording of these discussions was made and so are not included in these Proceedings. In spite of the loss suffered thereby, the organizers felt that it was much more likely that there would be vigorous, lively discussion if microphones and tape recorders were absent. The effect, we believe, was much more relaxed and open discussion periods which were of considerable interest and benefit to the participants. Readers who did not attend the Symposium will therefore not be able to appreciate some of the apparent non sequiturs in, for example, Jack Gibbon's summary.

It is hoped that these review papers will not only furnish a good description of the various worthwhile programs currently underway using low energy accelerators, but will also indicate unsolved problems and areas needing further attention. Emphasis on the new techniques and instruments which are becoming available, such as beam pulsing and bunching, or the use of sophisticated high-resolution detecting systems, should serve to illustrate the vigor associated with many low energy accelerator research programs.

The organizers of the Symposium wish to express their appreciation to the National Science Foundation, the primary sponsor. Assistance was also received from the U. S. Atomic Energy Commission and the University of Maryland, and a group of commercial organizations contributed toward the entertainment expenses: Alpha Scientific Laboratories, Inc., High Voltage Engineering Corporation, Oak Ridge Technical Enterprises Corporation, Princeton Gamma Tech, Inc., Radiation Dynamics, Inc., and Texas Nuclear Corporation.

We also wish to express our thanks to the several session chairmen who ensured that the Symposium ran smoothly and who stimulated and contributed to the discussion:

M. Banerjee
E. G. Bilpuch
C. Chasman
L. Cranberg
L. Cohen
A. E. Evans
G. E. Owen
F. W. Prosser
L. S. Rodberg
C. W. Werntz

Thanks are also due to members of the panel who discussed recent developments in instrumentation at their laboratories:

J. A. Biggerstaff
L. F. Chase
C. Chasman
L. Cranberg
C. R. Gossett
M. L. Roush
A.B. Smith

Finally, these Proceedings could not have been prepared without the careful and patient work of many secretaries, particularly Janet Niebel and Marguerite Harpster, and the knowledgeable overseeing of our editorial assistant, Kathryn Ware.

Jerry B. Marion
Douglas M. Van Patter

June 1967
College Park, Maryland

CONTENTS

PARTICIPANTS v

PREFACE ix

Technical Problems in the Applications of Ge(Li) Gamma-Ray Detectors 1
Charles R. Gossett

Gamma-Ray Angular Correlation Studies and Isobaric Analog States in 2s-1d Shell Nuclei 17
Gale I. Harris

Electromagnetic Lifetimes 43
E. K. Warburton

Lifetime Measurements with Bremsstrahlung 75
Edward C. Booth

A Coincidence-Anticoincidence Ge(Li)-NaI(Tℓ) System 99
D. M. Van Patter

Uses of Magnetic Spectrometers 109
F. C. Young

Mössbauer Studies with Van de Graaff Accelerators 131
J. C. Walker and Y. K. Lee

(p, n) and (d, n) Time-of-Flight Experiments 141
P. H. Stelson

Gamma Rays from Neutron Inelastic Scattering 167
M. T. McEllistrem

Astrophysical Problems 195
T. A. Tombrello

Multiparticle Nuclear Reactions 213
H. D. Holmgren

Precision Elastic Scattering Experiments 247
J. C. Armstrong

Analog-State Experiments 275
George C. Morrison

Neutron Polarization Studies 311
Roger W. Finlay

Survey of (n, z) Reactions 337
R. A. Peck, Jr.

Neutron Inelastic Scattering by Time-of-Flight 359
A. B. Smith

Particle-Gamma Angular Correlation Experiments 389
D. R. Tilley

Shell Model Calculations 419
W. T. Pinkston

Theoretical Problems in Low Energy Reactions 433
G. J. Stephenson, Jr.

Triton-Induced Reactions 445
L. F. Chase, Jr.

Lithium-Induced Reactions 475
R. R. Carlson

Isobaric Spin Effects in Nuclear Reactions 497
Jerry B. Marion

Summary and Outlook 507
J. H. Gibbons

TECHNICAL PROBLEMS IN THE APPLICATIONS OF Ge(Li) GAMMA-RAY DETECTORS

Charles R. Gossett

U. S. Naval Research Laboratory
Washington, D. C.

Introduction

It is my purpose in this report to discuss the technique of the application of lithium-drifted germanium gamma-ray detectors in single detector systems from the point of view of obtaining optimum performance. It is my approach to discuss these devices and their associated electronic circuitry with regard to their individual properties, problems, and limitations, particularly with emphasis upon those factors over which the experimenter has choice or control to optimize the detector system to his particular requirements. For this purpose I will restrict the discussion, for the most part, to the capabilities of commercially available equipment. I will not discuss specific applications of this type of detector to various types of experiments, for these will be well brought out in succeeding papers of this symposium, and these papers will amply illustrate the importance of this relatively new tool to the field of low energy nuclear physics.

In the time alloted, it will only be possible to skim the surface of this extensive subject. Realizing that many of the audience may wish to obtain a better understanding of matters I will only touch upon, I would like to offer a few useful references: The most recent review of the state-of-the-art as well as listing of many applications is contained in a report by David Camp, issued as UCRL-50156. An excellent introduction to the workings of semiconductor detectors for non-solid-state physicists is a series of lectures by Fred Goulding, issued as UCRL-16231. Finally, an excellent introduction to nuclear pulse amplifiers is contained in a series of five articles by Fairstein and Hahn which are scattered through volumes 23 and 24 of Nucleonics.

In the present paper I will discuss, in outline, each of the major elements of the single detector system in the logical order beginning with the detector itself, carrying through the preamplifier, shaping amplifier, optional post amplification electronics including timing circuitry, and finally the analogue-to-digital converter of the multichannel analyzer or computer. Within each of these categories I will discuss, as appropriate, those factors with affect the principle characteristics of resolution, efficiency, counting rate, and timing capabilities.

Before beginning that discussion, however, I would like to place the relative importance of these characteristics in perspective. First, of course, it is the extremely high resolution capability of these detectors which distinguishes them from, and often makes them the detector of choice over the scintillation detector. The optimized germanium detector usually produces resolutions between a factor of ten and twenty better than NaI over most of the energy range of interest. This resolution is of course bought at a large loss of efficiency. The largest commercial single Ge detectors currently available are of only about 40 cm^3 volume compared to about 350 cm^3 for the standard 3" dia x 3" long NaI. Neglecting solid angle considerations, the intrinsic peak efficiency is also much lower for Ge, except at very low energies, due to the relative primary interaction cross sections and the reduced probability of multiple interactions in the smaller volumes.

The reason, of course, that this efficiency loss can be tolerated in many experiments is the considerably greater information content of the high resolution spectrum. It is in fact the very narrowness of the peak upon a relatively featureless background that permits a small number of counts in the peak to produce a peak height which is quite distinguishable from that background. In this sense greater resolution can substitute for greater absolute efficiency in the detection of the presence of a particular gamma ray. It is also obvious that improved resolution permits the detection of gamma rays closely spaced in energy: it is for instance, not at all uncommon for several gamma rays to be found present where only one was suspected from scintillation measurements. High resolution also implies, if adequate calibration is possible, more precise energy measurements. In addition the narrow peaks superimposed upon a relatively flat Compton background facilitate relative intensity measurements. These combined effects thus often make it possible to assign levels and branching ratios in complex gamma-ray decay schemes on the basis of a single spectrum alone to a much greater degree of certainty that is normally possible with scintillation detectors. In this application of course, the paramount consideration is optimum resolution and a great deal of the effort in developing both the detectors and associated electronics has been directed toward this end. Normally little interference from other considerations will be tolerated with the possible exception of efficiency considerations. In this regard much recent effort has been devoted to producing larger detectors which will not excessively degrade resolution. The question of the size of the detector used to gain efficiency, and of the influence of size and configuration on resolution, is a complex one which depends largely upon the application. I will discuss this question in more detail later. It may also be worth noting at this point that efforts at high resolution may often be defeated, particularly in accelerator applications with charged particle reactions, if Doppler spread or natural level widths become dominant.

Having thus stated the case for single detector spectroscopy with its preoccupation with resolution, I would like to point out that sooner or later many experimentalists will wish to use the high resolution germanium detectors in a more complex arrangement, usually involving coincidence arrangements with other detectors. Such arrangements require the consideration of characteristics of the detectors in the time domain and, because coincidence arrangements generally involve a further reduction of efficiency, may normally be expected to require the acceptance of higher counting rates. This latter effect, which may often be avoided in single detector spectroscopy, will almost inevitably produce some degradation of the system resolution. Here the experimentalist must make critical choices, to be discussed later, in order to affect the optimum compromise between conflicting requirements.

Therefore, in my discussion of each element of the single detector system, I will, after introducing some fundamental aspects of that element, first discuss the conditions for optimum resolution, followed by consideration of the other aspects with emphasis on their effects on the resolution.

Detector

It is possible to use single crystals of germanium as detectors due to the process of lithium drift which produces an intrinsic region in which the acceptor and donor atoms are effectively compensated and will remain so as long as the devices are maintained at reduced temperatures. Back biasing the P and N junctions of the resulting diode permits the collection without multiplication of all charge carriers, that is, electrons and holes formed in pairs in the intrinsic region. The detection of gamma-rays proceeds, as with all detectors, with one of the three types of primary interaction resulting in the gamma ray giving up all or part of its energy to the kinetic energy of an electron or electron-positron pair. This energy is dissipated in the crystal by both the creation of these electron-hole pairs and by thermal excitation of the lattice, or phonon excitation. The extremely high resolution capabilities of the germanium detectors arise from the small energy gap for this material which results in only about 2.9 eV being required on the average for the production of each electron-hole pair. The fact that the energy is partitioned bewteen the electron-hole creation and the phonon excitation processes in a statistical but partially correlated manner leads to a fluctuation in the number of electron-hole pairs created for a given energy deposited. This variance leads to a fundamental limitation on the minimum resolution that may be observed with an otherwise perfect detector. The effect of the degree of correlation in the energy partition is represented by the often quoted "Fano factor," which, although not adequately predicted theoretically does represent a useful concept in determining how well a detector compares to the ideal. Experimental estimates of this factor have tended to improve steadily over a period of time with technological improvement of the detectors and electronics, but a number of fairly recent measurements tend toward a figure of about 0.15. This figure leads to the following estimates of resolution expressed as the full width at half maximum, of 0.50 keV at 100 keV, 1.57 keV at 1 MeV, and 5.0 keV at 10 MeV as the theoretical best resolution of an ideal detector. Of course many other factors, such as noise, incomplete charge collection, lack of stability in amplification and pulse-height measurement, and counting rate effects, will also influence the observed resolution for a real detector system; but these sources, being statistically independent, may be added in quadrature to the ideal resolution to determine a reasonable representation of experimentally observed resolution as a function of energy.

Within the detector itself the chief source of noise is the leakage currents from the back biasing of the diode. These currents may arise from charge injection across the junctions, surface leakage on the edges of the intrinsic region, and bulk effects due to thermal excitation within the intrinsic region. In the latter case, due to the small energy gap of germanium, the devices are normally operated at very low temperatures, usually at that of liquid nitrogen. The leakage current at operating bias should ordinarily be less than a nanoampere and in many good detectors is considerably lower.

An additional factor due to the detector which may produce degradation of the performance is the problem of incomplete collection of the charge carriers. This problem is influenced by the strength of the impressed field which affects the charge collection time relative to the lifetime of the charge carriers. This lifetime is related to the basic quality of the material from which the detector was fabricated. Incomplete charge collection arises from the trapping of one or both types of charge carriers by impurities, dislocations, or other imperfections or deviations from perfect crystal structure. This effect generally manifests itself as a tailing of the peak to the low energy side. The extent to which this tailing is observed (particularly for gamma rays above 1 MeV) is one index of the quality of a detector. For this purpose a useful criterion sometimes applied is that the ratio of full width at one tenth maximum to that at half maximum should not exceed the factor of 1.82 predicted by the Gaussian shape by more than about 16%. When using detectors of less than ideal characteristics the resolution may often be improved by using higher bias voltages up to the point at which the increase in leakage current noise becomes significant. In practice the optimum bias voltage for a given detector is found empirically.

Another factor, which does not in itself degrade the detector but which does influence system resolution through its influence on the noise of the amplification system, is the inherent capacitance of the detector. For the simplest detector configuration, the planar or parallel plate type, the capacitance is readily calculated with the usual area and inverse depth dependence. The depth of the intrinsic region may depend on a number of factors. Some detectors have been offered commercially with depths up to 15 mm, but most manufacturers on the average drift to no more than 7-10 mm and most commercial detectors are in this range, although shallower depths are also available. The area of the detector is also limited by the size of the ingots in which it has been possible to grow detector grade germanium crystals. Thus planar detectors are usually restricted to volumes under 8 or 10 cm^3 with accompanying capacitances of a few picofarads.

One solution to the problem of larger volumes (and thus greater efficiencies) which has been widely adopted commercially is the technique of coaxial drift. In this case, instead of simply drifting from one face, the drift proceeds from several of the surfaces. Two cases are generally available commercially: the true coaxial, in which the drift takes place radially from a cylindrical outer surface toward the axis; and the five-sided, in which the drift is in from five of the six sides of a trapezoidal ingot shaped crystal. As both coaxial types are subject to drift depth limitations similar to those of planar devices, the added volume is achieved chiefly by increased area with consequently increased capacitance, which in some cases may amount to many tens of picofarads.

The choice of detector size and configuration will depend strongly on the expected use, particularly with regard to the range of gamma-ray energies to be studied. In the range below about 300 keV, electronic noise predominates, and low capacitance is an important factor. In addition, the higher peak efficiency of the photoelectric interaction and lower penetration due to greater absorption, also make the smaller planar detector oriented to present maximum area to the source the preferable choice. At the other end of the energy scale, above about 2 MeV where the pair production interaction predominates, a detector may be optimum which presents a long dimension in the gamma ray direction and moderate dimensions in the traverse direction in order to enhance the double annihilation escape peak. However, a too shallowly drifted detector may not show as good peak efficiency at the higher energies where the electron ranges become significantly large. Thus a properly oriented long planar or a cylindrical coaxial of average depths may be preferable. Also in this energy region noise effects, except for higher capacitance detectors, progressively become less significant to other factors. In the middle region of gamma-ray energies or in experiments covering a wide range the choice may well depend upon the experimental requirements of resolution vs. efficiency, keeping in mind that an increase in efficiency obtained at a loss of resolution may not produce the desired improvement of peak height to background. The optimum detector for resolution is a small area, moderately-deep planar detector, provided that all other conditions including detector quality are optimized. Deviations from optimum in any of a great number of variable quantities may produce larger effects upon the resolution than that due to small additional capacitance; thus frequently, a somewhat more efficient detector is quite tolerable from a resolution point of view in a not completely optimized system. It is clear, however, that from added capacitance alone, the larger coaxials will produce degraded resolution. In addition, deeper drifts and larger volumes place more stringent requirements on the quality of the germanium and the probability of achieving the ideal resolution may consequently be decreased.

Several other considerations may bear upon the detector configuration choice. At lower energies, due to self-absorption effects, coaxial types may not always be as effective as the increase in volume would suggest. Similarly, since germanium detectors are frequently used at rather short source-to-crystal-face distances, the back portions of a coaxial detector may be less effective, due to solid angle effects. On the other hand, the larger volumes of coaxial devices enhance the intrinsic full energy peak efficiency due to the greater probability of absorption through multiple interactions. Such an enhancement is generally useful up to the energy where the double-escape pair peak begins to predominate, but above such energies may actually lend added complexity to the spectrum. The coaxial devices currently available also have a residual core of inert P type material which may absorb radiation, particularly at lower energies and by contributing Compton scattered quanta, reduce the effectiveness of the detector.

It should be noted that the coaxial detectors always involve a degree of non-uniform field strength distribution in the active region. The five-sided detector, particularly with unrounded corners, is generally worse in this respect. The cylindrical detectors are more satisfactory, provided that the ratio of the outer and inner radii defining the active region is not too large. In both cases these non-uniform fields may affect the resolution and tailing for less than ideal detectors, as previously described. In addition, they also have an influence on the timing properties of the detector as I shall discuss later.

Finally, if the detector is to be used in angular distribution or correlation measurements, the use of a circular or cylindrical type, axially oriented, may be preferable from the point of view of solid angle corrections. The simpler geometries may also be preferred to permit efficiency calculations; although possible variations in the actual dimensions of the active region from the nominal values usually make the experimental measurement of efficiency with sources of calibrated activity a preferable technique.

The detector resolution, as contrasted to the system resolution, is generally experimentally determined by subtracting in quadrature the electronic noise as determined from the width of a nearby pulser peak. Detector resolution figures are usually quoted for Cs^{137} or Co^{60}. The latter may be more useful since it is at sufficiently high energy to show tailing effects. For the 1.33 MeV gamma ray of Co^{60}, the range of guaranteed values of detector resolutions which the various manufacturers may quote runs from about 5 keV down to perhaps 2.5 keV compared to the ideal of 1.8 keV. Commercial practice with regard to the purchase of the highest quality detectors apparently varies from one company to another, and the potential customer should determine this information from the manufacturer.

Before leaving the subject of detectors, I would like to make a few comments on the cryogenic arrangements which must necessarily accompany the use of germanium detectors. Because liquid nitrogen is readily available in many laboratories, most American manufacturers utilize this method of maintaining the detectors cooled as well as providing sufficiently low operation temperatures. Thus, the detector is factory mounted to a cold finger which is inserted into a reasonable sized (that is, 10 or 25 liter) liquid nitrogen reservoir. The detector and cold finger are surrounded by a chamber maintained at high vacuum. In best practice the vacuum is assured by a small appended ion pump, as well as the normal sorption pumping material. In this arrangement the detector is shipped, maintained and used at liquid nitrogen temperatures, and normally subject to damage only by failure to keep liquid nitrogen in the dewar or by vacuum failure due to accident. Another approach to the problem is to separately encapsulate the detector in a hermetically sealed container which permits handling of the device in air. The encapsulated device may then be shipped and maintained with dry ice or in a deep freeze and transferred to a liquid nitrogen system for use. This arrangement also provides some additional flexibility in the mounting arrangements in the cryostat which are thus more under the user's control. The encapsulation of a detector does, however, add some additional capacitance to the system. The choice between these two approaches will usually depend upon the user's needs in the handling of the detector, the need, if any, for additional flexibility in mounting arrangements and the local availability and cost of liquid nitrogen.

Preamplifier

The function of the preamplifier is to transform the low level current pulse from the detector to a voltage pulse, amplify it suitably, and provide a driver capable of transmitting the signal over the sometimes long lengths of coaxial cable to the input of the amplifier. Commercially this is normally accomplished with a charge-sensitive preamplifier utilizing an FET input stage. Because the signal is at its lowest level at the input of the preamp, it is at this point that most of the noise is introduced into the system; as noise introduced at this level is equally amplified with the signal, except for the band width limitations of successive amplifiers. From the user's point of view the noise performance of the preamplifier is characterized by two numbers, which are often conveniently stated in terms of their equivalent contribution to the FWHM for a germanium detector: the first being the noise for zero capacitance input and the second the amount of additional noise introduced per picofarad of detector capacitance. As of this writing, commercial FET preamps for room temperature operation will guarantee zero capacitance noise in the vicinity of 1.2 to 1.5 keV, with a slope figure of around 30 to 40 eV per picofarad for low capacitance detectors. There are also versions for use with devices of greater than about 25 picofarads which produce a higher zero capacitance value of about 1.6 keV but a lower slope of 25 eV per picofarad. It should be noted that such guaranteed values depend upon the succeeding shaping amplifier and are always quoted for optimum time constants. Some newer amplifier designs may reduce the effective noise levels from existing preamps.

It is interesting to note that one area in which commercial practice has lagged that of the national laboratories has been in the adoption of the use of the cooled FET. Although it has been well established that improvements of upward to 30 or 40 percent in the preamp noise figure can be obtained by cooling the FET to an optimum temperature, the industry has moved only reluctantly in this direction. Of course it is true that this is not a simple problem, for, among other difficulties, the optimum temperature for cooling the FET's is not at that of liquid nitrogen, but nearer 140°K on the average. Nevertheless, it is somewhat surprising that most manufacturers indicate that although they expect to offer this feature, the arrangements to cool FET's in their cryostats are still in the development stage. It should be noted, however, that at higher energies, except for large capacitance devices, the noise may not be a significant factor in resolution, in which case the quality of the preamp, and in particular the question of cooled FET's, may not be important. It is seldom, however, that a broad range device such as the germanium detector will be restricted to use solely in such a limited energy region.

Shaping Amplifier

It is in the shaping amplifier that the user has the greatest opportunity to optimize his equipment to the needs of his experiment. The high quality amplifier is not itself normally a source of noise significant in comparison to that of the detector and preamp, but it does strongly influence the systems resolution performance in that the shaping networks acting as high and low pass filters affect the quantity of this noise which is amplified along with the detector signal. In addition, the shaping networks, because they determine the form of the voltage _vs._ time of the pulses, strongly affect the capabilities of the system with regard to counting rate. That is, in any system registering events random in time, a certain proportion of the pulses will occur sufficiently close to the preceding pulse to be influenced by it, due to the fact that the voltage level has not completely returned to normal. The extent of the effect of this disturbance and the counting rates at which these effects become unacceptable may be largely determined by the shaping circuits.

I shall first address myself to the general type of amplifier which in several commercial versions has become a standard for high resolution work. This type of amplifier provides the capability for a single integration and one or two differentiations. Considering that the pulse from the preamplifier has a shape consisting of a relatively fast rise and a long tailed decay, it is to be remembered that integration affects the rise of a pulse. In its simplest form, that of the series resistor and parallel capacitor, the voltage will rise with a one minus an exponential form and a characteristic time dependent on the product of R and C. The differentiator, on the other hand, primarily affects the fall of a pulse. In the RC version a series capacitor with a parallel resistor provide an exponential fall with a characteristic time dependent on the product of R and C. Another form of differentiator is the use of a shorted delay line in which a reflected and delayed signal adds to cancel the remainder of the pulse and thus produce an essentially square shape. Each type of differentiator is used for the purpose of limiting the time extent of the pulse. The RC time constants used in these networks are usually in the range of a fraction to several microseconds, and the delay lines usually produce widths in the vicinity of one microsecond.

Two common combinations of shaping networks are used. The first, involving an integration and only one differentiation, produces a unipolar pulse, which rises, then (ideally at least) decays monotonically to the base line. The second common form is to use an integration and two differentiations to produce a bipolar pulse which has both a positive and negative lobe to the pulse, the latter (again ideally) returning monotonically to the base line. Often both the unipolar and bipolar pulses are simultaneously available. While these controls may appear to provide a bewildering number of possible combinations, they do provide the experimenter considerable range in the problem of resolution *vs.* counting rate.

The optimum conditions for resolution are usually obtained for this type of amplifier with the unipolar pulse produced by (often equal) RC time constants in the range of 1.5 to 3 microseconds. The optimum values for a particular system are of course found empirically. From the point of view of counting rate capability, this combination is among the worst possible, as it produces relatively long pulses, and often will require the use of counting rates under a thousand counts per second for optimum resolution.

At the opposite extreme the optimum combination for the highest counting rates is usually found with the bipolar mode with double delay line differentiation. With RC time constants the smaller values (again by producing shorter pulses) also permit higher counting rates. The preference in both cases for the bipolar pulses arises from the tendency for the equal positive and negative lobes of these pulses to leave any coupling capacitances in the system uncharged. Otherwise at higher counting rates there is a tendency for shifts in the base line to occur.

Unfortunately the factors which improve the counting rate response of an amplifier tend to increase its bandwidth and thus lead to higher noise transmission and worse resolution. Thus while shorter time constants, bipolar shaping, and double delay line clipping may each lead to successively worse resolution at low counting rates, it will be found that as higher counting rates are applied, rates will be successively reached where the degradation resulting from one mode of operation will cause the width to exceed that obtained by the next mode. The choice in a given situation will of course be determined empirically, and one of the strong points in this type of amplifier is its ability to achieve a wide range of possibilities for that compromise.

Fortunately there have been new design concepts which have improved the counting rate performance of high-resolution amplifiers. One of these developments has been the so-called "pole-zero cancellation" circuit. This term arises from an analytical technique wherein the effect of one shaping circuit may be modified or cancelled by an appropriate configuration in another circuit. In practice, in the shaping amplifier application, this technique is applied to remove the undershoot which occurs in unipolar operation. This undershoot arises from the fact that the pulse has actually undergone two differentiations: one in the amplifier and another in the output of the preamplifier. The latter leads to a shallow but long dip below the baseline, having the time constant of the preamplifier in the range of 40 to 100 microseconds. Successive pulses arising during this undershoot are regarded by the following circuitry as being of less than their full height, and thus contribute to the observed loss of resolution and a tailing toward lower energies. The pole-zero circuit by cancelling the effect of the preamp differentiation permits the pulse to show the ideal monotonic return to the base line expected from the single differentiation, and thus may produce a significant improvement in counting rate capability. The pole-zero technique is also effective with bipolar shaping by preventing an overshoot after the second lobe.

One interesting point with regard to pole-zero technique is that in removing the effect of the preamp differentiation a modification of the low pass frequency characteristics of the system is affected, which when used with a detector or preamplifier with excessive low frequency noise may degrade the observed resolution. In this case, if the system is to be used at low counting rates, it may be desirable to tune the pole zero for undershoot in order to achieve optimum resolution.

Other types of pulse shaping may theoretically produce better signal-to-noise characteristics than the RC shaping. Among those which have recently received additional attention commercially are active element shaping arrangements which results in a quasi-gaussian pulse shape. These amplifiers are available in versions providing a range of pulse widths as well as both unipolar and bipolar outputs. These amplifiers also incorporate the pole-zero concept and it is expected may produce better counting rate characteristics than RC shaping, although double delay lines may still be preferable in extreme cases.

Before leaving the subject of amplifiers I would like to comment that there are many other performance factors for amplifiers in addition to those that I have emphasized. Perhaps the most important among these are linearity and gain stability. The requirements for both these and other factors are generally much more stringent in high resolution systems than in other applications. This topic will be further discussed in connection with analogue-to-digital conversion.

Timing

I would at this point, before considering the general post amplifier circuitry and the related analogue-to-digital conversion problem, like to insert a brief discussion of the timing characteristics of germanium detectors.

The fundamental problem with developing a time signal from a germanium detector is that the shape of the leading edge of the output pulse is not constant for a given pulse height, but is dependent upon the site of the interaction within the detector. That this is so may be seen in a simple example. Consider a localized creation of electron-hole pairs, created at the center of a planar detector. If the mobilities of the charge carriers are equal (and they are nearly so at liquid nitrogen temperatures) the two carrier types will equally contribute to the slope of the induced pulse which will reach its maximum when both types reach their respective electrodes. Now consider a similar event, this time occurring quite close to one of the electrodes. Most of one type of charge carrier is thus collected almost immediately and the slope of the induced pulse, since it is due to only one type of carrier, will be only half of that of the previous case, reaching the maximum pulse height in twice the time. Of course, in an actual event many charge carriers are created and spread along the path of the primary electron; nevertheless, at all but the highest energies, the creation of the charge carriers is somewhat localized and leads to a dispersion in the rise times of pulses of the same height. This problem is of course compounded in the case of coaxial detectors where the spatially related non-uniform field distributions lead to further dispersion. The degree of the problem in either case is of course related to the field strengths which can be imposed before excessive leakage currents degrade resolution. It is interesting to note in this connection that deeper drifted detectors compound the timing problem. That is, to maintain the same charge collection time, the bias voltage must increase with at least the square of the depth of the intrinsic region.

The effects of this dispersion in rise times upon the timing capability of the system depend in part upon the technique used to generate the timing pulses. The two techniques commonly used are crossover pickoff and leading edge discrimination. The crossover pickoff technique has been widely used with scintillators where the pulse shapes are uniform and with charged particle semiconductor detectors where the dispersion in rise times is generally much smaller than in the drifted detectors. Because the crossover of the base line occurs (in the usual version) at the 50% charge collection point, the effect of the dispersion in rise times is strongly felt, and shorter resolving times are not possible with this method. Thus it is often stated that crossover pickoff timing is not satisfactory for germanium detectors. This statement is not strictly true since there are obviously many coincidence applications where resolving times of 50 nanoseconds or higher (depending on the detector configuration and bias voltages) produce quite acceptable accidental rates, particularly considering that counting rates may be severely limited by resolution considerations. This choice will clearly depend upon the application; however, where it is feasible to use it, crossover timing is easy to use and readily available commercially.

Leading edge timing on the other hand is capable of much shorter resolving times depending upon the relative height of the level at which discrimination may be applied. The germanium detector presents special problems in this regard, however. If the discrimination level is applied after the normal shaping amplifier, the slower rise times inherent in this amplifier for optimum resolution will degrade the timing capabilities and introduce additional problems of walk with pulse-height. On the other hand, at the output of the detector the signals are extremely small, and attempts to sample it before the preamp will generally lead to degradation in the system energy resolution. Thus the best solution may lie with sampling the signal following the preamp and accepting the rise time limitations of the preamp which may not become too severe except for large capacitance devices. At least one commercial system, adapted from a charge particle detection application, is available and other arrangements may be possible using circuits from the commercial category of "fast" electronics.

Post-Amplification Electronics

To return to the subject of optional post-amplification electronics, circuits in this category include: linear delays, linear gates, bias amplifiers, pulse stretchers, etc. Delay of the linear signal may be desirable particularly in more complex combinations where time must be alloted for logic decisions. This feature is sometimes available in the shaping amplifier itself. Linear gating, which is also sometimes available in a biased amplifier, may be used if it is desirable to restrict the number of pulses delivered to the ADC, either because high counting rates are degrading its performance or because of high dead-time losses. The biased amplifier is used to expand a region of interest and is particularly useful to permit high resolution work with a limited capacity ADC. A pulse stretcher is frequently needed when a biased amplifier is used or when very short time constants are required in the shaping amplifier. It serves to produce a pulse width more optimum for the input to the ADC. A stretcher may or may not be included with the biased amplifier.

All of the post amplifier electronics, which are inserted after the major amplification is complete, do not in general significantly introduce noise to the system. The two primary areas in which they may affect system performance are linearity and gain stability. In this regard their performance is generally comparable to that of the main amplifier itself, with the possible exception of the linearity performance of biased amplifiers.

Analogue-to-Digital Conversion

The high resolution germanium detectors place rather

severe requirements upon the analogue-to-digital converter and it is fortunate that these requirements have for the most part been met with the modern pulse-height analyzer. The most obvious requirement is that of a sufficient number of channels. If the usual criterion of five channels within the FWHM to adequately define a peak is applied to the ideal detector, it would appear that even the 4096 channels available in many ADC's is not completely adequate at higher energies. However, stability and charge collection problems will usually be found to degrade ideal performance to the point that 4096 channels are adequate even here. An analyzer of this size, however, becomes rather expensive and I would like to mention a couple of alternatives. Either a 4096 channel ADC may be coupled with a smaller capacity memory, or alternatively a biased amplifier may be used to expand the capability of a smaller capacity ADC and memory. Both techniques (particularly with gain stabilization with the latter) permit nearly equal resolution performance to the full 4096 channel analyzer; although, of course, only a limited portion of the total spectrum may be accumulated at one time.

One area in which the ADC may contribute to reduced resolution performance is in the stability of its conversion gain and zero level. Of course, as I have mentioned, various elements in the amplification system may also contribute through lack of gain stability. These effects, which primarily become apparent for medium to higher energy gamma rays where the noise contribution is relatively less, are generally kept small by the use of components carefully selected for their temperature stability. Thus if the ambient conditions in a laboratory are well controlled, satisfactory stability may be obtained, particularly over shorter time periods. It is my personal opinion, however, that because the counting rate may vary considerably in accelerator application, a system which is as nearly DC-coupled as possible, and which is in addition stabilized is probably optimum. In this connection I might add that when a pulser peak is used for the stabilization it is quite important that the pulser itself be exceptionally stable.

As the germanium detectors are themselves highly linear in their response, much effort has gone into preserving this linearity in both the amplification circuits and the ADC's. If, however, the high potential of determining accurately peak position with the very narrow peak widths is to be fully utilized for gamma-ray energy measurement, the residual nonlinearities must be carefully calibrated. For this purpose both a very high precision pulser and radioactive sources whose energies are well known may be used.

Summary

By way of summary I would like to review the principal sources of the line widths observed from a high resolution germanium system as function of gamma-ray energy. At low energies this width is dominated by noise. While the detector contributes some of this, the chief source is in the input stages of the preamplifier. The amount observed may generally be decreased by cooling the FET stage. The amount of noise observed for the system depends in part upon the capacitance of the detector and on the type and time constants of the pulse shaping used in the main amplifier.

For somewhat higher energy gamma rays the intrinsic resolution of the detector, which is of statistical origin begins to compete and finally predominates at high energy. Also evidenced, as the noise contribution becomes less significant, are certain effects due to incomplete charge collection and lack of gain stability in the system.

The efficiency of germanium detectors is quite low, although the larger coaxially drifted detectors offer some improvement at the cost of increased capacitance and poorer timing capability. Counting rate effects are generally detrimental to good resolution, and where higher rates must be tolerated the best compromise is achieved through proper choice of the amplifier-shaping networks. The timing characteristics of this type of detector are inherently not good, and where the best resolving times are required, leading edge timing is necessary. Finally, the narrow peak widths obtainable under optimum conditions require analogue-to-digital conversion in the range of 4000 channels or equivalent obtained by other means.

GAMMA-RAY ANGULAR CORRELATION STUDIES AND ISOBARIC ANALOG STATES IN 2s-1d SHELL NUCLEI

Gale I. Harris

Aerospace Research Laboratories
Wright-Patterson Air Force Base, Ohio

INTRODUCTION

The study of the γ-ray decay of resonance levels formed by proton capture at energies obtainable by small (2-3 MeV) accelerators has long been a valuable source of information on levels of nuclei with A less than about 50. Under these conditions, isolated resonance states are formed which, depending upon the Q-value, correspond to excitation energies roughly in the region 4-14 MeV in the compound nucleus. In this region, few channels are open for particle emission which would compete strongly with capture. Properties of lower-lying bound states can be obtained by studying γ-cascades from the resonance levels. Isolated resonances have the important advantage that the reaction mechanism is well understood and their formation and decay can be treated separately. This circumstance leads to a considerable simplification of the analysis of γ-ray angular correlation measurements.

Much, if not most, of the recent intensive study of isobaric analog states has been in medium and heavy weight nuclei. Here the analog states with $T = T_0 + 1$ in a nucleus with ground-state isobaric spin $T = T_0$ mix with the large number of densely spaced levels with $T = T_0$ and of the same spin and parity. Capture radiation is very difficult to observe due to the large number of open channels for particle emission. The situation is quite different, however, in the 2s-1d shell. The analog states appear in many cases as well-isolated resonances at lower excitation energies, and with much less isobaric-spin mixing. This has been found, as we shall see, to be especially true of analog states of the $1f_{7/2}$ and $2p_{3/2}$ configurations, which usually appear at several MeV excitation in s-d shell nuclei. Some of these are almost pure single-particle states with high isospin purity.

The special nature of the analog states with such properties leads to relatively easy identification in the proton capture reaction. As has been pointed out recently by P. M. Endt,[1] the analog resonances with dominant single-particle character and $T = T_0 + 1$ are easily distinguished from neighboring $T = T_0$ resonances in proton capture because: 1) they are exceptionally strong and often much broader than the average resonance; and 2) the γ-ray decay scheme is simple and unusual. In the best cases the resonance may decay entirely to just one particular bound state, often at a rather high excitation energy, and which is rarely excited at neighboring resonances.

In the common case where only the channels for proton and γ emission are open, the strength of a (p,γ) resonance can be given in terms of the yield $Y = (2J + 1)\,\Gamma_\gamma \Gamma_p / \Gamma$. In this case $\Gamma = \Gamma_\gamma + \Gamma_p$, and we see that a resonance can be strong only if both Γ_p and Γ_γ are relatively large. For a pure single-particle analog resonance the expected reduced proton width[2] is $\theta_p^2 = 1/(2T_0 + 1)$, in units of $\hbar^2/\mu a^2$, a value much larger than the average $\theta_p^2 = 0.001 \rightarrow 0.01$ found for the $T = T_0$ resonances.

The large value of the radiative width Γ_γ and the peculiar decay of the analog resonance can be explained by the observation that the resonance decays by the emission of an M1 transition to the state of the same configuration as the resonance, but with $T = T_0$ instead of $T = T_0 + 1$. This lower state is sometimes referred to as the "anti-analog" state of the same configuration. The strengths of such analog to anti-analog M1 transitions are easily computed and are found to be quite large (several Weisskopf units).

EXPERIMENTAL CONSIDERATIONS

The detailed study of these analog states requires the use of techniques which, in some cases, are not in very widespread use, but which, on the other hand, are ideally suited for the small accelerator. The things one need determine are the γ-decay schemes, the yields (which usually provide information on the radiative widths), the proton widths, and the spins and parities. The advent of the Ge(Li) detector has enormously simplified the task of deriving reliable decay schemes of capture resonances. Unique decay schemes can be derived in most cases without use of the extensive coincidence measurements normally required in NaI(Tl) work.

The absolute measurement of resonance yields has always been a difficult problem. However, many of the inherent difficulties can be circumvented by means of relative yield measurements provided reliable comparison resonances are available in the same target. The calibration may be performed with a resonance in the same nuclide, or with a resonance in another nuclide which exists in compound form with the target nuclide. Many such calibration resonances are now available in s-d shell nuclei as a result of an extensive set of yield measurements on targets in compound form by Engelbertink and Endt.[3]

The total width of a resonance can often be determined directly from the (p, γ) excitation curve. The requirements are good proton energy resolution and very thin targets. Recent work of this type is characterized by combined beam-energy and target-thickness spreads of less than 1 keV. Typical target thicknesses are in the range 1-5μ g/ cm^2, which correspond to thicknesses of less than about 100 atomic layers! In the case of a broad resonance, it is almost certainly the case that $\Gamma_p >> \Gamma_\gamma$. Then in the case that only the proton and γ emission channels are open, we have $\Gamma_p \simeq \Gamma$. (Under these conditions, the yield expression given above reduces to $Y = (2J + 1)\Gamma_\gamma$ and thus we are provided with both Γ_p and Γ_γ from the yield and width measurements.) The proton width can also be obtained from proton elastic scattering from the same resonance. This method has been used[1] on resonances having widths as narrow as 6 eV.

Since the techniques for these kinds of measurements have already been discussed in some detail in a paper[1] similar to this by Endt, I will concentrate here, instead, on the announced purpose of this talk — angular correlation measurements from which spins and parities are derived. That is, we shall assume that the decay schemes, strengths, and widths are known from the above kind of measurements, and that we have decided that our resonance is <u>probably</u> an analog state of single-particle character. The resonance of course must have the same spin and parity as its analog in the neighboring nucleus in order to qualify. In the case of a suspected analog to anti-analog Ml transition, the lower (bound) state must also of course have the same spin and parity as the resonance.

A brief, general review of the formalism and techniques of angular correlation measurements as they apply to proton capture will be presented and followed by some recently obtained data on $1f_{7/2}$ and $2p_{3/2}$ analog states in 2s-1d shell nuclei.

ANGULAR CORRELATION MEASUREMENTS

For our present purposes, we shall define angular correlations to include triple correlations (TC), angular distributions (AD), and linear polarizations (PC). An excellent review of this entire subject has been provided recently in textbook form by Ferguson.[4] We refer to that reference for foundations of the theory in terms of the efficiency tensors. Rather than to attempt to trace through a general formulation here, a summary will be given of a set of final formulas which we have adopted for specific use with capture reactions, but which could be applied to other situations as well.

The type of measurement considered can be regarded as a special case of "Method I" of Litherland and Ferguson.[5] In general, Method I applies to situations where a state of definite spin and parity is formed by a reaction involving both incident and outgoing particles proceeding through a compound state not necessarily having sharp spin and parity. The incident beam defines the quantization axis and the outgoing particles are not observed. Under these conditions, the magnetic substates of the system are symmetrically populated $[P(+m) = P(-m)]$ and are uncorrelated with each other. A state symmetrically populated in this manner is referred to as an aligned state. The measurement of the correlations of two cascade γ rays from an aligned state may provide sufficient information to determine the population parameters P(m), the level spins J, and the multipole mixtures δ of the two radiations. The γ-ray correlations are formulated in terms of the P(m), which can be considered as parameters to be adjusted in the analysis. They contain the information on the mechanism of formation of the aligned state.

The capture reaction is a special case in which no outgoing particle is involved and the γ-decaying state of sharp spin and parity is formed directly by the incident particle. The same general γ-ray correlation formalism applies since only the formation is different. In fact, the formation process is well understood in this case and can be specifically related to the P(m) which are obtained from the γ-ray correlations. Thus the analysis of capture γ-ray correlations is conducted in two basic steps: 1) the determination of the P(m), spins, and multipole ratios from the angular correlations, and 2) the determination of parameters relating to the formation of the aligned state from the P(m) obtained in the first step.

Triple Correlations

Consider the schematic diagram in Fig. 1 for a typical two-step γ-cascade from a state formed by proton capture. An aligned state with spin J_1 and substate populations P(m) is formed by capture of protons with orbital angular momenta ℓ and ℓ' by a target with ground state spin I. The capture proceeds through two channels with spins $s = I \pm 1/2$, and the aligned state decays by a double γ-cascade through two states with spins J_2 and J_3. The two transitions are denoted by γ_1 and γ_2, by their multipolarities L_1L_1' and L_2L_2', and by their multipole mixing ratios δ_1 and δ_2. The triple correlation measurement then consists of measurements of the coincidence counting rates of γ_1 and γ_2 over a set of angles defined in a polar coordinate system with a z-axis defined by the alignment axis (proton beam direction). If we define θ_1 and θ_2 as the angles between the directions of γ_1 and γ_2 and the z-axis, and ϕ as the difference $\phi = \phi_1 - \phi_2$ of the azimuthal angles of the two γ-rays, then the triple correlation intensity can be expressed by[6,7]

$$W(\theta_1, \theta_2, \phi) = \sum_m P(m) \sum_{KMN} A^N_{KM}(\delta_1, \delta_2, m)\, Q_K Q_M \times X^N_{KM}(\theta_1, \theta_2, \phi), \qquad (1)$$

where

$$X^N_{KM} = f(M, K, N)\, P^N_K(\cos\theta_1)\, P^N_M(\cos\theta_2) \cos N\phi. \qquad (2)$$

The f(M, K, N) is a factor depending only on K, M, and N, and the P^n_m are unnormalized, associated Legendre polynomials. The Q_K and Q_M are finite geometry correction factors.[4] (We shall refrain here from listing detailed definitions of all factors and coefficients which appear. They can be found in Refs. 4 through 7.) The coefficients A^N_{KM} are products of two factors, one for each transition γ_1 and γ_2,

$$A^N_{KM} = g^N_{KM}(J_1, J_2, \delta_1, m)\, H_M(J_2, J_3, \delta_2) \qquad (3)$$

where the g and H are given in terms of tabulated coefficients[7] as follows:

$$g_{KM}^{N} = (1 + \delta_1^2)^{-1} \sum_{L_1 L_1'} \delta_1^{p_1} E_{KM}^{N}(J_1 L_1 L_1' J_2 m), \tag{4}$$

and

$$H_M = (1 + \delta_2^2)^{-1} \sum_{L_2 L_2'} \delta_2^{p_2} h_M(J_2 L_2 L_2' J_3). \tag{5}$$

The interfering multipoles L and L' are taken to be L' = L + 1. The notation used here differs slightly from that used in Refs. 6 and 7 from which this was taken in that g_{KM}^N replaces the G_{KM}^N which included the X_{KM}^N coefficient. The exponents p_1 and p_2 take on the values 0, 1, or 2 for pure L, mixed L, L', or pure L' radiation, respectively.

Many other equivalent formulations of triple correlations are available which use a variety of tabulated coefficients. For example, the product $E_{KM}^N h_M$ is the same as the C_{KM}^N coefficients tabulated by Smith.[8] We have adopted this particular product form primarily for reasons associated with the extension to use with more general multiple-step cascades and with efficient computer analysis techniques (see Ref. 6).

Much effort has been devoted recently to the comparison of phases of the multipolarity mixing ratios δ determined from angular correlation measurements with those predicted in model calculations. We refer here to a recent extensive discussion of this difficult problem by Rose and Brink,[9] and note that the phases used in the present formalism are the same as those used by Ferguson[4] and by Smith.[8]

Angular Distributions

We refer again to Fig. 1. An angular distribution is a special case of a triple correlation in which the intensity correlation of only one member of the γ-cascade is measured relative to the alignment axis. The other member (or members), if present, are unobserved. The angular distribution (AD1) of γ_1 can be obtained from Eq. (1) by averaging over all directions of γ_2. Such an average results in a Kronecker delta $\delta_{M,0}$ and, thus, leaves only those terms for which M = 0. Similarly, the angular distribution (AD2) for γ_2 can be obtained from Eq. (1) by keeping only those terms for which K = 0. The two resulting AD formulas are:

$$W(\theta_1) = \sum_m P(m) \sum_K a_{Km}\, Q_K\, P_K(\cos\theta_1), \tag{6}$$

and

$$W(\theta_2) = \sum_m P(m) \sum_M b_{Mm}\, Q_M\, P_M(\cos\theta_2), \tag{7}$$

for AD1 and AD2, respectively. The coefficients a_{Km} and b_{Mm} are given by

$$a_{Km} = (2K+1)^{\frac{1}{2}} (1+\delta_1^{\,2})^{-1} \sum_{L_1 L_1'} \delta_1^{\,p_1}\, E^0_{K0}(J_1 L_1 L_1' J_2 m), \tag{8}$$

and

$$b_{Mm} = (2M+1)^{\frac{1}{2}} (1+\delta_1^{\,2})^{-1} (1+\delta_2^{\,2})^{-1} \sum_{L_1 L_1' L_2 L_2'} \delta_1^{\,p_1} \delta_2^{\,p_2}$$

$$\times\, E^0_{0M}(J_1 L_1 L_1' J_2 m)\; h_M(J_2 L_2 L_2' J_3). \tag{9}$$

It can be argued that there is no need to measure AD1 and AD2 since they are contained as a subset of the complete triple correlation, and thus provide in principle no additional information. However, because no coincidence counting is required, their measurement can often be conducted with greater precision than the TC. In cases where the decay scheme is relatively simple, the AD can provide very useful constraints on possible solutions. On the other hand, if the decay scheme is complex, the AD may be unreliable because of complex branching and the difficulty of "stripping" the spectrum accurately. In many cases of this type, it has been found that the TC are actually easier than the AD to obtain with a given precision.

Linear Polarizations

Once the level spins, multipolarity mixings, and the P(m) have been established by TC and AD measurements, the <u>relative</u> parities can be established, in favorable cases, by means of PC measurements of the γ transitions. Alternatively, the

PC measurements are sometimes used to remove remaining ambiguities in spins or in multipole mixings depending upon the specific problem and the available information.

The linear polarization correlation of γ_1 can be written as follows:

$$W(\theta_1, \phi) = W(\theta_1) \pm \sum_m P(m) \sum_K \cos 2\phi \; B_{Km} \times P_K^2 (\cos \theta_1), \qquad (10)$$

where $W(\theta_1)$ is given by Eq. (6) with $Q_K = 1$, and

$$B_{Km} = (1 + \delta_1^2)^{-1} \sum_{L_1 L_1'} \delta_1^{p_1} \eta_K(L_1 L_1') E^0_{K0}(J_1 L_1 L_1' J_2 m). \qquad (11)$$

The angle ϕ is defined as the angle between the electric vector of γ_1 and the plane defined by the γ-ray direction and the z-axis. The + sign is used if no parity change occurs in the transition and the - sign if parity change does occur. The coefficients $\eta_K(LL')$ consist of the factors $(2K+1)^{1/2}$ and the $\kappa_K(LL')$ tabulated by Fagg and Hanna[10] with signs chosen to conform with the present notation. The $\eta_K(LL')$ are tabulated for dipole through octupole radiation in Ref. 7. Expressions very similar to Eqs. (10) and (11) hold for the polarization of γ_2. The only changes are $\theta_1 \to \theta_2$, K→M and $\eta_K(L_1, L_1')$ E^0_{K0} $(J_1 L_1 L_1' J_2 m) \to \eta_M(L_2 L_2')$ $E^0_{0M}(J_1 L_1 L_1' J_2 m) h_M(J_2 L_2 L_2' J_3)$, with sums over $L_1 L_1'$ and $L_2 L_2'$ similar to that in Eq. (9). Explicit expressionsare given in Ref. 7.

The degree of linear polarization of γ_1 is defined as

$$\bar{P}(\theta_1) = \frac{W(\theta_1, 90) - W(\theta_1, 0)}{W(\theta_1, 90) + W(\theta_1, 0)}$$

$$= \pm [W(\theta_1)]^{-1} \sum_m P(m) \sum_K B_{Km} P_K^2 (\cos \theta_1). \; (12)$$

The polarization is commonly measured at $\theta_1 = 90°$ with a Compton polarimeter. In this case, the numbers of scattered quanta N_0 and N_{90} observed by a detector located in the plane defined by γ_1 and the z-axis and a detector perpendicular to this plane, respectively, are related by the expression

$$(N_{90} - N_0)/(N_{90} + N_0) = p(\beta)\,\overline{P}(90). \qquad (13)$$

The polarization efficiency $p(\beta)$ for "point" detectors and scatterers is given by

$$p(\beta) = (\sin^2\beta)/(k_0/k + k/k_0 - \sin^2\beta), \qquad (14)$$

where k_0 and k are the wave numbers of the incoming and scattered radiation, respectively, and β is the Compton scattering angle. Approximate efficiencies for the actual geometry of the Compton polarimeter (described below) used in the present work vary between 0.18 and 0.11 for γ ray energies between 1 and 5 MeV.[11]

Formation Analysis

A valid assumption is that only the lowest two possible proton orbital angular momenta ℓ and ℓ' will contribute significantly to the formation of the resonance level because of the rapid decrease of barrier penetrability with increasing ℓ. The interfering momenta ℓ and ℓ' must both be even or both odd depending upon the relative parities of the target state and the resonance if the resonance is isolated. In the case of capture in a channel with spin s, the population parameters $P_s(m)$ are related to ℓ and ℓ' as follows:

$$P_s(m) = (1+\epsilon^2)^{-1}\left[C_{sJ\ell m}^{\,2} + 2f\epsilon\, C_{sJ\ell m}C_{sJ\ell' m} + \epsilon^2 C_{sJ\ell' m}^{\,2}\right], \qquad (15)$$

where $C_{sJ\ell m} = k(sm\ J{-}m\,|\,\ell 0)$, and f is the Coulomb phase factor[4] $\cos(\xi_\ell - \xi_{\ell'})$. The normalization constant k in front of the Clebsch-Gordan coefficient is required because $P(m) = P(+m) + P(-m)$. $k = 1$ if $m = 0$ and $k = 2^{1/2}$ if $m \neq 0$. The amplitude ratio of capture with momentum ℓ' to capture with momentum ℓ is given by ϵ. In cases where two channels contribute to capture, the population parameters P(m) are an incoherent mixture of the contributions from each channel. Thus

$$P(m) = (1+t)^{-1}\left[P_{s_1}(m) + t\,P_{s_2}(m)\right], \qquad (16)$$

where t is the intensity ratio of capture in channel s_2 to that in channel s_1.

The formation imposes the important condition $m \leq s$ (channel spin limitation) on the number of populated magnetic substates. This condition is usually more restrictive than the primary limitation $m \leq J$. The population parameters are all positive and are normalized such that $\Sigma_m P(m) = 1$. It is easy to see that the formation will often be undetermined in capture since, in general, there are three parameters (t and the ϵ in each channel) which must be determined from the limited number of P(m).

It is useful in some situations to convert from the above channel-spin coupling scheme to jj-coupling. For example, in the $Si^{29}(p, \gamma)P^{30}$ reaction to be discussed below, $J\pi = 1^-$ resonances were formed by pure p-waves in channels with spins s = 0 and 1. One wishes to know the relative fractions of $2p_{1/2}$ and $2p_{3/2}$ contributions in the formation, and hence the dominant shell-model configuration of the resonance. The channel spin mixing t obtained from Eq. (16) can be related to the proton angular momenta $j_p = \ell - 1/2$ and $j_p' = \ell + 1/2$ as follows:[12]

$$t = \frac{1}{1 + x^2} \frac{(2s_2 + 1)}{(2s_1 + 1)} \left[a + 2xb + x^2 c \right] , \qquad (17)$$

where

$$a = \left[W^2(\ell \tfrac{1}{2} J_1 I; j_p s_2) \right] / \left[W^2(\ell \tfrac{1}{2} J_1 I; j_p s_1) \right] ,$$

$$c = \left[W^2(\ell \tfrac{1}{2} J_1 I; j_p' s_2) \right] / \left[W^2(\ell \tfrac{1}{2} J_1 I; j_p' s_1) \right] ,$$

and

$$b = \frac{W(\ell \tfrac{1}{2} J_1 I; j_p s_2) \, W(\ell \tfrac{1}{2} J_1 I; j_p' s_2)}{W(\ell \tfrac{1}{2} J_1 I; j_p s_1) \, W(\ell \tfrac{1}{2} J_1 I; j_p' s_1)}$$

The amplitude ratio of j_p' to j_p formation is given by x. We note that there are two possible solutions for x because of the quadratic form of Eq. (17). This ambiguity could be removed in principle by polarized beam measurements.

ANALOG STATES IN 2s-1d SHELL NUCLEI

For several years we have been studying proton capture reactions in several nuclei between A = 30 and 40 with a 2-MeV Van de Graaff accelerator. The original primary motivation for this work was to gain information on low-lying bound states by angular correlation measurements on γ cascades from highly-excited resonant states. Largely by accident, it was found that many of the resonant states were interesting in their own right. Excellent examples of these are the strong $J^{\pi} = 7/2^-$ resonances at E_p = 2187 keV and E_p = 1214 keV in the $Si^{30}(p,\gamma)P^{31}$ and $S^{34}(p,\gamma)Cl^{35}$ reactions, respectively.[13,14] These isolated resonances were both formed by pure f-wave capture on I = 0 targets and were obviously relatively pure $1f_{7/2}$ single-nucleon states. In each case the resonant state decayed by γ-emission entirely to a single lower lying state which was also shown to have $J^{\pi} = 7/2^-$ by angular correlation measurements. It is now known that the resonance levels are T = 3/2 analogs of $1f_{7/2}$ states in Si^{31} and S^{35} The lower states to which they γ-decay are the anti-analog states of the same configuration. The properties of these particular analog states have been reviewed elsewhere by Endt.[1] In the following, I will discuss an example of this type in Cl^{37}, and also some new data on similar, but slightly more complicated, cases in the odd-odd nucleus P^{30}.

$1f_{7/2}$, T = 5/2 Analog State in Cl^{37}

The ground state of S^{37} is expected to be a fairly pure $1f_{7/2}$, T = 5/2 configuration consisting of a neutron plus a S^{36} core which closes the $2s_{1/2}$ proton and $1d_{3/2}$ neutron subshells. The analog of this state in Cl^{37} ($T_Z = 3/2$) should lie near E_x = 10.2 MeV on the basis of the relative binding energies of S^{37} and Cl^{37}, Coulomb energy differences, and the n-p mass difference. A level near 10.2 MeV in Cl^{37} should appear as a resonance near E_p = 1.8 MeV in the $S^{36}(p,\gamma)Cl^{37}$ reaction. Based upon the previous experience with $1f_{7/2}$ analog states in P^{31} and Cl^{35} mentioned above, a strong $7/2^-$ resonance with simple γ-decay properties could be expected. The anti-analog state can be computed to lie near E_x = 3.2 MeV in Cl^{37} by use of the strength of the isospin interaction[15] obtained from Cl^{35}. Thus the resonance should be distinguishable in a (p,γ) excitation curve by 1) its strength, and 2) its probable decay by a simple two-step γ cascade through a level near 3.2 MeV.

A special search was conducted[16] for the analog resonance between E_p = 1640 and 1940 keV by detecting coincidences between pulses from two large NaI(Tl) detectors. Coincidence counts were recorded if pulses corresponding to $2.8 \leq E_\gamma \leq 3.2$ MeV from one detector and $6.8 \leq E_\gamma \leq 7.2$ MeV from the other detector were present. The resulting excitation curve is shown in Fig. 2. The prominent resonance at E_p = 1887 keV was shown, as discussed below, to possess the expected properties of the analog state. The weaker resonance just above the 1887 keV resonance is probably due to the $S^{34}(p,\gamma)Cl^{35}$ reaction.

The observed width of the resonance (Γ = 4 keV) can be attributed to beam-energy spread and target thickness. By means of a comparison measurement, the resonance yield was found to be $(2J+1)\Gamma_\gamma \Gamma_p/\Gamma = 130 \pm 20$ eV. Thus it is one of the strongest resonances observed in the entire 2s-1d shell. The decay scheme shown in Fig. 3 was derived from spectra obtained with an 8 in. x 8 in. NaI(Tl) detector and a 2 cc Ge(Li) detector. It should be noted that all measurements were conducted with targets enriched to only 3.5% S^{36}. The natural abundance is 0.014%!

AD and TC measurements were performed on the Res.→ 3.105→0 cascade using the setup shown schematically in Fig. 4. Detectors A and B are 5 in. x 5 in. NaI(Tl) crystals located with their front faces 6.25 in. from the target center. Detector C is an 8 in. x 8 in. crystal located 10 in. from the target. Spectra from Detector C are obtained in coincidence with appropriately chosen window pulses from Detector A <u>or</u> Detector B. The coincidence spectra thus obtained are stored in separate subgroups of a multi-channel analyzer. By use of this arrangement, measurements of the TC intensity can be made simultaneously at two or more of the angle combinations $(\theta_1, \theta_2, \phi)$. The measurements are normally performed in "geometries" in which two of the three angles are held fixed and the third varied in even steps in $\cos^2\theta$ between 0° and 90°. A typical "geometry" may be referred to as (90, V, 180) in which the fixed and variable angles in the set $(\theta_1, \theta_2, \phi)$ are denoted. An AD measurement is conducted by removing the coincidence conditions and recording singles spectra in Detector C at angles between 0° and 90°.

The TC and AD data obtained at the 1887-keV resonance are shown in Fig. 3 in which the various geometries are indicated. These data were analyzed using computer programs based upon the TC and AD formalism given above. The input data consists of the intensities observed at each point $(\theta_1, \theta_2, \phi)$

the finite geometry correction factors Q_K and Q_M, the maximum substate m which can be populated in the formation, and the level spins J_1, J_2, and J_3 to be tested. A χ^2 analysis based upon Eq. 1 is used in which the mixing ratios δ_1 and δ_2 are treated as parameters. For each spin sequence tested, a χ^2 surface is generated. That is, at each point (δ_1, δ_2), a value of χ^2 and the "best" values of the P(m) are computed. The projections of the χ^2 surface on the χ^2, δ_1 and χ^2, δ_2 planes are then displayed as shown in Fig. 3.

In the present case, the analysis is greatly simplified because S^{36} has I = 0 and hence formation occurs only in channel s = 1/2. Thus only m = $\pm 1/2$ substates are populated. The analysis of these data was performed for all spin combinations for J_1 and J_2 running from 1/2 through 9/2 with an octupole multipolarity limitation. (The ground state of Cl^{37} has J_3 = 3/2.) Only the combination J_1, J_2 = 7/2, 7/2 resulted in minimum values of χ^2 below the commonly adopted 0.1% χ^2 confidence "limit". The χ^2 projections for this combination and the next best-fitting combination J_1, J_2 = 5/2, 5/2 are shown in Fig. 3. The line through the data points in this figure is the theoretical angular correlation for J_1, J_2 = 7/2, 7/2 and for the values of δ_1 and δ_2 at the minima of the χ^2 projections. It is interesting to note that γ_1 is a pure dipole transition ($\delta_1 = 0.00 \pm 0.02$) as expected for an analog to anti-analog transition. γ_2 is a strongly mixed quadrupole-octupole transition ($\delta_2 = -0.18 \pm 0.01$).

The linear polarizations of γ_1 and γ_2 were measured with the Compton polarimeter setup shown schematically in Fig. 5. The scatterer, located vertically above the target, is a 2 in. x 2 in. NaI(Tl) crystal. The analyzing detectors, A and B, oriented as shown at $\phi = 90°$ and $\phi = 0°$, are 5 in. x 5 in. NaI(Tl) crystals. Standard electronic techniques are used to obtain sum spectra from the two scattering crystal-analyzing crystal combinations, which are recorded in separate memory subgroups of a multichannel analyzer. In practice, a measurement consists of several runs between which the entire polarimeter is rotated about its vertical axis through $\phi = 90°$, thus interchanging the effective positions of detectors A and B. The somewhat unusual analyzing detector orientation is used in order to provide a relatively sharp geometrical cutoff on the minimum scattering angle β. The maximum scattering angle is determined electronically. The polarizations obtained are compared with the theoretical values in Table I.

TABLE I

Polarization Results at E_p = 1887 keV in $S^{36}(p, \gamma)Cl^{37}$ for $J_1 = J_2 = 7/2$

Transition	$\overline{P}_{exp.}$	Parity Change	$\overline{P}_{th.}$
γ_1		Yes	-0.94
(Res. →3.105)	+ 0.95 ± 0.43	No	+ 0.94
γ_2		Yes	-0.84
(3.105→0)	-0.90 ± 0.27	No	+ 0.84

It is clear from the table that the resonance and 3.105 MeV levels both must have odd parity since the ground-state parity of Cl^{37} is even. The strength in Weisskopf units of the Ml, γ_1 transition is found from the yield measurement to be $|M|^2 = 1.7 + 0.3$. The theoretical value for a $(7/2^-, T = 5/2) \rightarrow (7/2^-, \overline{T} = 3/2)$ transition is $|M|^2 = 1.6$.

Two-particle Analog States in P^{30}

A number of strong resonances are found between E_p = 1300 and 1800 keV in $Si^{29}(p, \gamma)P^{30}$ which can probably be identified as members or fragments of the $(2s_{1/2}, 2p_{3/2})$ and $(2s_{1/2}, 1f_{7/2})$, T = 1 configurations. In the following, four of these resonances will be briefly discussed. One, the 1505 keV resonance, has been described previously.[17] The other three have not been dealt with in detail.

The (p, γ) excitation curve in the region of interest is shown in Fig. 6. This curve was obtained by the same method used in Fig. 2. In this case, the coincidence channels were set between 0.6→3.25 MeV and between 3.5→8 MeV in the two detectors, respectively. This coincidence procedure was used here to remove the contributions from the strong $F^{19}(p, \alpha\gamma)O^{16}$ resonance at 1375 keV and the broad $Si^{28}(p, \gamma)P$ resonance at 1650 keV. Although the target used in this run was thicker (≈ 4 keV) than one would ideally wish to have, the broad natural widths of the resonances at 1375, 1640, and 1686 keV resonances clearly stand out. After correction for instrumental resolution, the widths of these three resonances are found to be Γ = 7.1, 17.2, and 5.9 keV, respectively. These resonances have also been observed in proton elastic scattering[18] with widths in close agreement with these. The elastic scattering data show that these three resonances all have odd parity. This result is confirmed in the cases of the 1375 and 1686 keV resonances by polarization measurements in the present work. Polarizations were not measured at the 1640 keV resonance. A summary of the angular correlation measurements at all four resonances follows.

1375 and 1640 keV resonances. The predominant modes of decay of the 1375 keV resonance (E_x = 6.93 MeV) are to the 0^+, T = 1 level at 0.680 MeV and to the newly discovered level at 4.468 MeV which we have previously suggested[19] to be the T = 1, J = 0 analog of the 3.79 MeV level of Si^{30}. The present results strengthen considerably the earlier arguments. The resonance spin was measured by means of TC measurements on the Res.→.680→0 cascade. The data are shown in Fig. 7. Only J(Res.) = 1 resulted in an acceptable value of χ^2. In the analysis of angular correlation data on this reaction, one must consider both m = 0 and m = 1 resonance substates since the target spin is 1/2. The analysis yields P(0) = 0.94 ± 0.02 and P(1) = 0.06 ± 0.02. A PC measurement of the Res.→.680 transition gave $\overline{P}_{exp.}$ = 1.13 ± 0.23. The theoretical values are + 0.99 and -0.99 with and without parity change, respectively. The 1375 keV resonance is thus a $J^\pi = 1^-$ level. Using the observed P(m) and Eqs. (16) and (17), we find the two solutions x^2 = 1.9 or 10.2 for the ratio of $p_{3/2}$ to $p_{1/2}$ formation. In either case, it is clear that the resonance is predominately a ($2s_{1/2}$, $2p_{3/2}$) two-particle state. (The ground state of Si^{29} is mainly $2s_{1/2}$.)

It was found that TC measurements alone on the Res.→4.468→0 cascade were not sufficient to fix the spin of the 4.468 MeV level. For certain values of δ_1 and δ_2, J(4.468) = 0, 1, or 2 would fit the data. However, by combining the TC results with PC measurements of γ_1 and γ_2, a unique spin and parity is obtained. The experimental results $\overline{P}(\gamma_1)$ = 0.73 ± 0.20 and $\overline{P}(\gamma_2)$ = -0.37 ± 0.36 agree only with $J^\pi(4.468) = 0^+$, for which the theoretical polarizations are $\overline{P}_{th.}(\gamma_1)$ = + 0.99 and $\overline{P}_{th}(\gamma_2)$ = 0. This 0^+ level is thus almost certainly the T = 1 analog of the 3.79 MeV, J = 0 level[20] in Si^{30}.

The broad resonance at E_p = 1640 keV (E_x = 7.18 MeV) is known from elastic scattering[18] to have $J^\pi = 1^-$. The resonance decays by γ emission to the ground state and 0.680, 0.709, and 3.02 MeV levels. TC data (not shown) on the Res.→3.02→0.680 cascade confirm the resonance spin, but agree with either J(3.02) = 1 or 2. These TC data, combined with AD data on Res.→0, fix the population parameters of the resonance as P(0) = 0.51 ± 0.02 and P(1) = 0.49 ± 0.02. This result corresponds to solutions $x^2 = 0.21$ or 23.2 for the ratio of $p_{3/2}$ to $p_{1/2}$ formation. The latter value is probably correct for this resonance since it is expected that the main strength of the $2p_{1/2}$ configuration should lie considerably higher in excitation energy.

A detailed examination of the γ-decay schemes of these two resonances based upon the isospin selection rule $\Delta T = 1$ for El transitions shows that the 1375 and 1640 keV resonances must be predominately T = 0 and T = 1, respectively. Their proton reduced widths in units of $\hbar^2/\mu a^2$ are $\theta_p^2 = 0.21$ and 0.19, respectively, where a nuclear radius of $1.4(A^{1/3}+1) \times 10^{-13}$ cm. has been assumed. Their sum is close to the maximum expected value $\theta_p^2 = 0.5$. Much of the remaining $2p_{3/2}$ strength lies in the 1686 keV resonance.

<u>1686 keV Resonance.</u> The γ-decay scheme of this strong resonance ($Y = 9.1 \pm 1.4$ eV) at $E_x = 7.23$ MeV is dominated by a (41%) two-step cascade through a level at 4.14 MeV, characteristic of an analog to anti-analog transition. TC and PC measurements were performed on this cascade. The extensive TC data are shown in Fig. 8. All reasonable spin combinations for the resonance and 4.14 MeV levels were examined with the result that only J(Res.) = J(4.14) = 2 would give acceptable solutions. The χ^2 projection curves for this combination are shown in Fig. 9. Both γ_1 and γ_2 are almost pure dipole. (The high solution for γ_2 was eliminated by the PC measurements.) The experimental PC results are $\overline{P}(\gamma_1) = 0.65 \pm 0.11$ and $\overline{P}(\gamma_2) = 0.20 \pm 0.11$. These results agree only with odd parity for the resonance and 4.14 MeV levels for which the theoretical polarizations are $\overline{P}_{th}(\gamma_1) = 0.64$ and $\overline{P}_{th}(\gamma_2) = 0.15$.

A 2^- resonance can be formed in proton capture by Si^{29} only in channel s = 1 and with a possible mixture of p and f waves. It is easy to show that the f-wave contribution is very small by reduced-width arguments. Such a conclusion is supported by the observed values of P(m) in the angular correlation measurements which agree with P(0) = 0.4 and P(1) = 0.6 expected for p-wave capture. In jj-coupling, we find that only $p_{3/2}$ protons can form the 2^- state. Thus we arrive at the conclusion that this resonance is also a member of the $(2s_{1/2}, 2p_{3/2})$ two-particle configuration, but with coupling such that J = 2. The reduced width $\theta_p^2 = 0.06$ for this resonance, when added to those for the 1375 and 1640 keV resonances, gives a total $\theta_p^2 = 0.46$; a value very close to $\theta_p^2 = 0.5$ expected for the configuration. The strength of the Res.$\rightarrow$4.14, Ml transition is 1.2 Weisskopf units; a value much higher than normal. From the observations that the resonance decays only to T = 0 levels, is exceptionally strong, has a reasonably large reduced width, and exhibits a characteristic analog to anti-analog transition, it can be concluded that it is the T = 1 analog of a level near 6.55 MeV in Si^{30}.

1505 keV Resonance. We conclude with a summary of results at this interesting, but complicated, resonance at E_x = 7.05 MeV. The decay scheme and results of numerous TC and PC measurements are shown in Fig. 10. The J^π assignments for all levels shown except the ground state and 0.680 MeV levels result from the measurements at this resonance. For the TC analysis, an extended form[6,7] of the angular correlation formalism for multiple-step γ cascades is required. The 4^- resonance decays by a typical analog to anti-analog transition to the 4^-(T = 0) level at 4.23 MeV. The strength of this (pure) Ml transition is 0.55 Weisskopf units. The resonance is thus surely a T = 1 analog. It is formed by $f_{7/2}$ protons. The width Γ is too small to be observed with presently available resolution even if it were of pure single-particle character. The resonance is very probably the 4^-, T = 1 member of the ($2s_{1/2}$, $1f_{7/2}$) configuration. It would be very interesting to locate the 3^-, T = 1 member. A possible candidate for this state lies at E_p = 1748 keV. However this "resonance" is a doublet and has not yet been studied in detail. The J assignments for this doublet shown in Fig. 6 are, at best, preliminary values based upon TC measurements obtained before the doublet structure was known.

The experimental data given in this paper were obtained in collaboration with A. K. Hyder, Jr.

REFERENCES

1. P. M. Endt, Proceedings of the 1967 Dacca Seminar on Nuclear Structure (to be published).

2. H. E. Gove, in Nuclear Reactions, edited by P. M. Endt and M. Demeur (North-Holland Publishing Company - Amsterdam, 1959) p. 270.

3. G.A.P. Engelbertink and P.M. Endt, Nucl. Phys. 88 12 (1966).

4. A.J. Ferguson, Angular Correlation Methods in Gamma-Ray Spectroscopy, (North-Holland Publishing Company - Amsterdam, 1965).

5. A. E. Litherland and A. J. Ferguson, Can. J. Phys. 39, 788 (1961).

6. G. I. Harris, H. J. Hennecke, and D. D. Watson, Phys. Rev. 139, B1113 (1965).

7. D. D. Watson and G. I. Harris, Nuclear Data (to be published).

8. P.B. Smith, in Nuclear Reactions, edited by P.M. Endt and P.M. Smith (North-Holland Publishing Company Amsterdam, 1962), Vol. II.

9. H.J. Rose and D.M. Brink, Rev. Mod. Phys. 39, 306 (1967).

10. L.W. Fagg and S.S. Hanna, Rev. Mod. Phys. 31, 711 (1959).

11. H. Willmes and G.I. Harris (to be published).

12. W.T. Sharp, J.M. Kennedy, B.J. Sears, and M.G. Hoyle, Atomic Energy of Canada, Ltd., CRT-556, AECL-97, 1957 (unpublished).

13. G.I. Harris, H.J. Hennecke, and F.W. Prosser, Jr., Phys. Letters 9, 324 (1964).

14. D.D. Watson, Phys. Letters 22, 183 (1966).

15. J. B. French, in Proc. Conf. on Nuclear Spectroscopy with Direct Reactions, edited by F.E. Throw, ANL-6878, (1964) (unpublished).

16. A.K. Hyder, Jr. and G.I. Harris, Phys. Letters 24B, 273 (1967).

17. G.I. Harris and A.K. Hyder, Jr., Phys. Letters 22, 159 (1966).

18. A.N. L'vow, A.I. Popov, P.V. Sorokin, and V.E. Storizhko, Bull. Acad. Sci. USSR, (English Translation) Phys. Ser. 30, 447 (1966).

19. G.I. Harris and A.K. Hyder, Jr., Phys. Rev. 157 (1967).

20. C. Broude, P.J.M. Smulders and T.K. Alexander, Nucl. Phys. A90, 321 (1967).

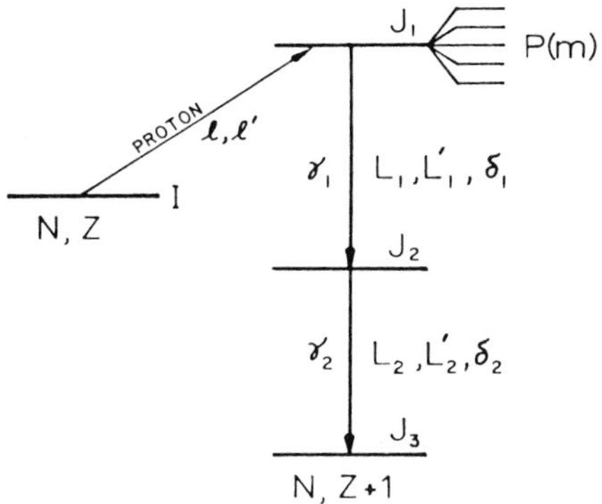

Fig. 1 Parameters associated with a typical double γ cascade from an isolated resonance formed by proton capture.

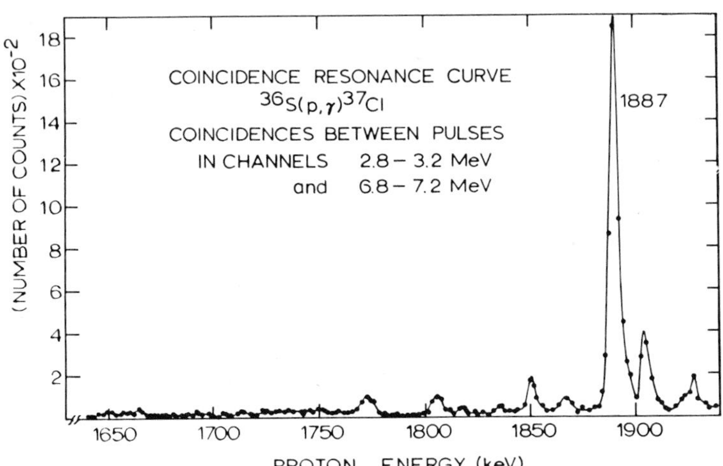

Fig. 2 Coincidence γ-ray excitation curve in the S^{36} (p, γ)Cl^{37} reaction. The coincidence conditions are shown. The dominating resonance at E_p = 1887 keV is the 7/ 2^-, T = 5/ 2 analog of the S^{37} ground state.

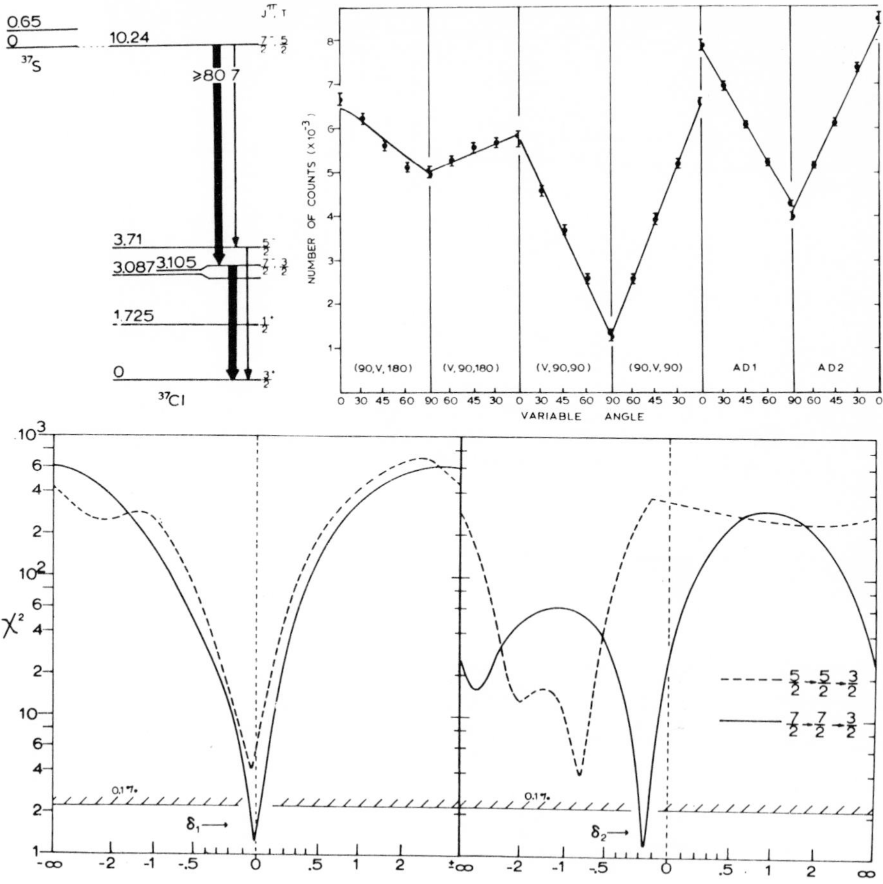

Fig. 3 Decay scheme of the $S^{36}(p,\gamma)Cl^{37}$, E_p = 1887 keV resonance, the TC and AD data on the Res.→3.105→0 cascade, and the corresponding χ^2 projection curves.

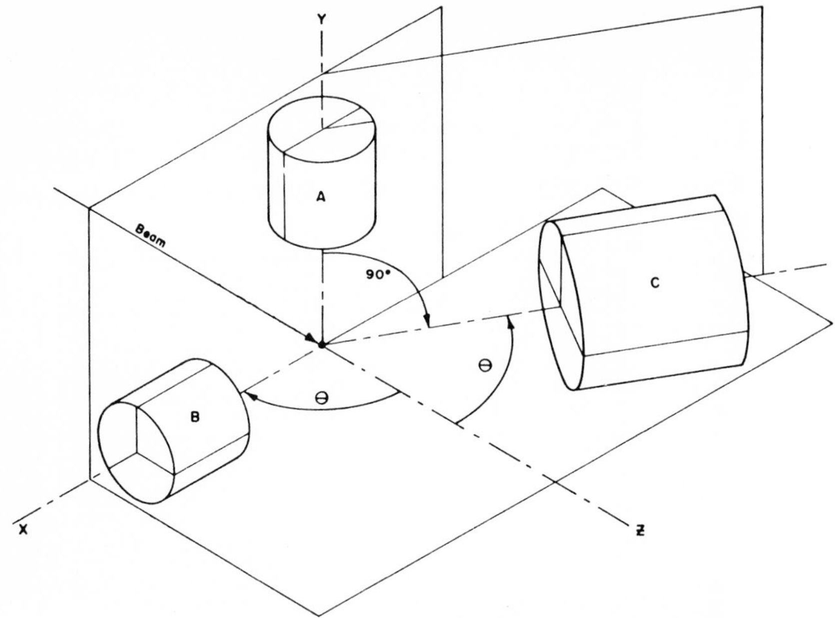

Fig. 4 Schematic diagram of the NaI(Tl) detector arrangement used for γ-ray triple correlation and angular distribution measurements.

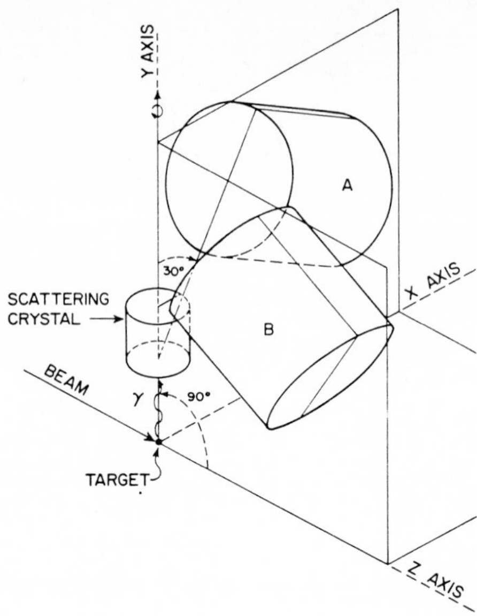

Fig. 5 Schematic diagram of the Compton polarimeter arrangement used for γ-ray linear polarization measurements.

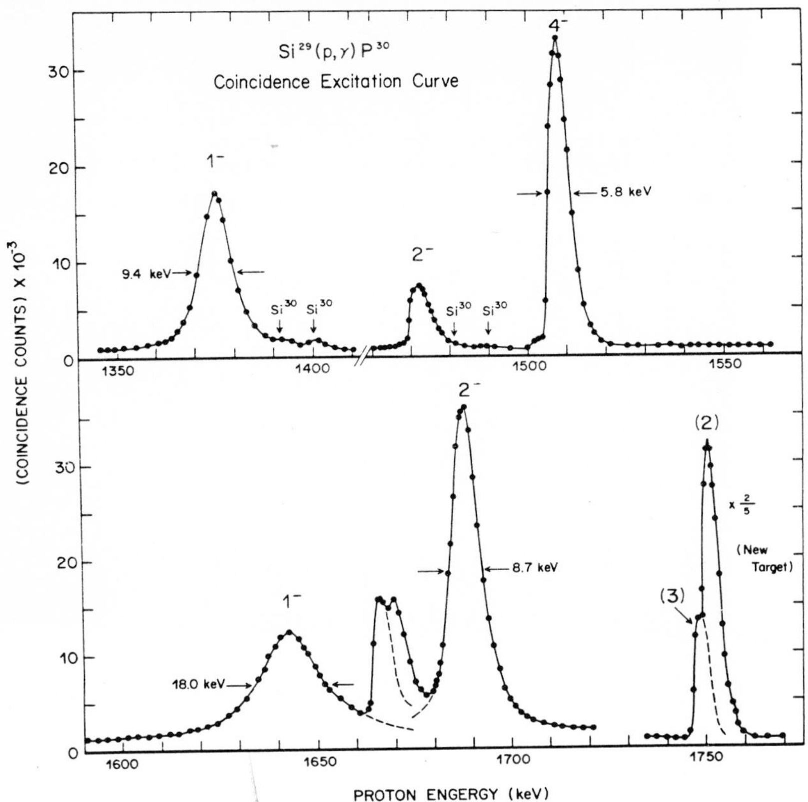

Fig. 6 Portions of a coincidence γ-ray excitation curve in the $Si^{29}(p, \gamma)P^{30}$ reaction. Three unusually broad resonances appear in the energy range shown which are associated with T = 1 analog state structure. The 4^- resonance is a member of the $(2s_{1/2}, 1f_{7/2})$, T = 1 configuration.

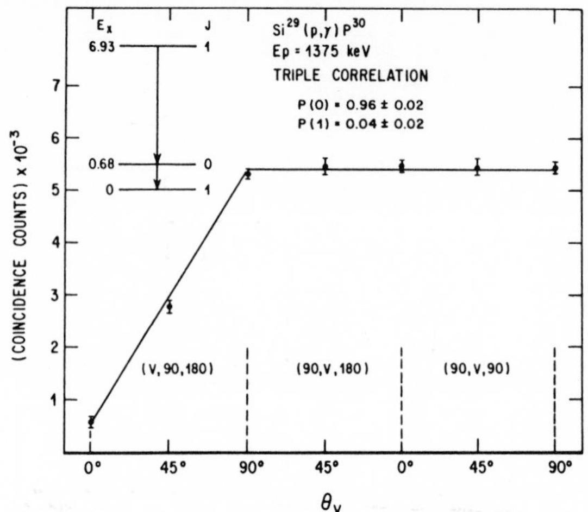

Fig. 7 Triple angular correlation data for the Res.→0.680→0 γ-cascade at the E_p = 1375 KeV resonance in $Si^{29}(p, \gamma)P^{30}$. The solid line is the theoretical correlation for J(Res.) = 1.

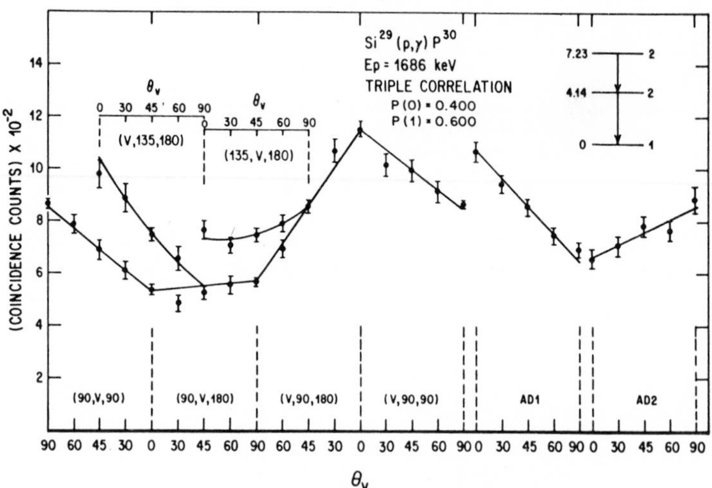

Fig. 8 Triple correlation and angular distribution data for the Res.→4.14→0 γ-cascade at the E_p = 1686 keV resonance in $Si^{29}(p, \gamma)P^{30}$.

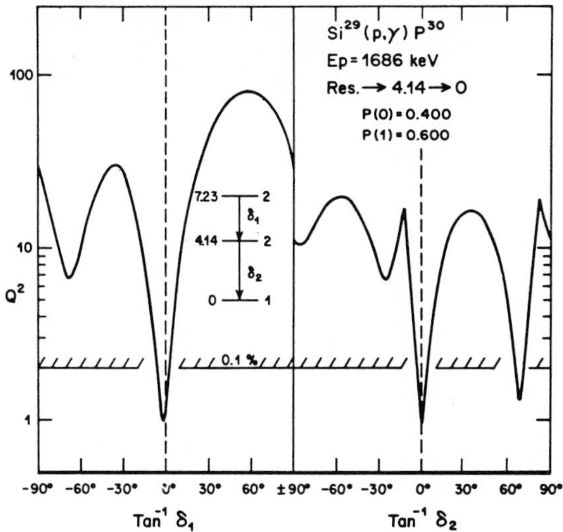

Fig. 9 The χ^2 projection curves for the data in Fig. 8, and for J = 2 for the resonance and 4.14 MeV levels.

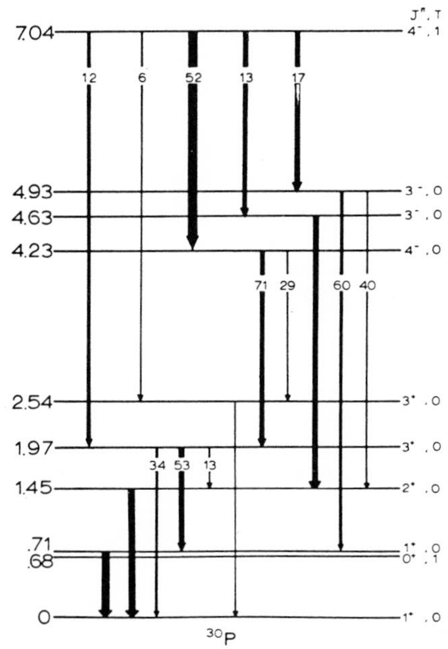

Fig. 10 γ-ray decay scheme of the 1505 keV resonance in $Si^{29}(p,\gamma)P^{30}$.

ELECTROMAGNETIC LIFETIMES*

E. K. Warburton

Brookhaven National Laboratory
Upton, New York

I. INTRODUCTION

Historically, the first test of a particular nuclear model has usually been to see whether it can reproduce the experimental spectra of energy levels of given spin and parity for a set of nuclei. It often turns out that the calculated relative binding energies are not too sensitive to the model wave functions, and so more direct and sensitive tests of these wave functions are desirable.

The most important and direct ancillary test has been provided in the past by the properties of the electromagnetic transitions connecting the nuclear levels. The particular parameters of interest are the matrix elements for the multipole orders allowed by the spins and parities of the levels connected by the transitions. The usefulness of these matrix elements rests in large part on the rigor of the underlying theory—namely, the description of the multipole radiation field and its interaction with nuclei. Because of the accommodating nature of this interaction and our excellent understanding of it, the uncertainty in our calculations of electromagnetic matrix elements is due almost entirely to the crudities of the nuclear wave functions we wish to test. This is in contrast to the situation pertaining when nuclear forces are involved, e.g., the calculation of nucleon reduced widths. In short, electromagnetic matrix elements are important mainly because they test nuclear wave functions directly and accurately without any dependence on nuclear forces or reaction mechanisms and because they are relatively quite sensitive to these wave functions.

In general, it is not the total radiative width (remember $\Gamma\tau = \hbar$) of a bound nuclear level or the partial radiative width for γ-decay of a virtual level that is of

---

* Work performed under the auspices of the United States Atomic Energy Commission.

direct interest to us. Nor is it the radiative width for a particular decay mode. Rather it is the matrix element of a particular multipole operator between two nuclear states. It is this quantity which I refer to as an electromagnetic matrix element. The square of this matrix element is proportional to the partial radiative width (for a particular multipole order) of the initial state for decay to a given final state. We obtain the magnitude of the matrix element by measuring this partial radiative width. In general, then, the measurement of an electromagnetic matrix element goes in three steps: 1) the determination of the total radiative width of a nuclear level, 2) the measurement of the fractional γ-decay (branching ratio) of the level to a given final state, 3) the separation of this partial radiative width into contributions from different multipoles. (We have just heard in Harris' paper of the very sophisticated techniques used in this latter endeavor.) Obvious exceptions to this general procedure involve selective phenomenon such as Coulomb excitation and inelastic electron scattering which measure the radiative width of a specific multipole order directly.

I have dwelled somewhat lengthily on what we are after because it is important to keep in mind just why we measure the electromagnetic lifetimes of nuclear levels. I reiterate: It is because we wish to compare electromagnetic matrix elements to the predictions of theory. Thus, because it also leads to the determination of the magnitude of a matrix element, the mundane measurement of a branching ratio is often ultimately as important as a measurement of the lifetime of a level by the most sophisticated and advanced technique. Even more importance can be claimed for the multipole mixing ratios which are measured by γ-ray angular correlation techniques (Harris' paper). For these mixing ratios have a sign and thus they tell us the relative phase of two matrix elements as well as the magnitudes of both (if we have carried out the first two steps given above).

II. SOME ADVANCES IN EXPERIMENTAL TECHNIQUES

A. Introduction

The emphasis in this talk will be on lifetimes which can be measured using small ($\lesssim$ 4 MeV) accelerators. It shall also be on light and medium-weight nuclei, this limitation following naturally from the first. I do not intend to present a review of all methods but shall concentrate on those which are new or changing rapidly.

I have listed in Table I the most common methods used to measure the electromagnetic lifetimes (or radiative widths) of nuclear levels. All of these methods have gained in recent years by general technical improvements. The most startling

Table 1. Methods for measuring the lifetimes of nuclear states.

Method	Limits on Mean Life
ELECTRONIC TIMING (pulsed beam techniques, delayed coincidences)	$\tau \gtrsim 5\times10^{-11}$ sec.
RECOIL DISTANCE	$5\times10^{-9} \gtrsim \tau \gtrsim 5\times10^{-12}$ sec.
DOPPLER-SHIFT ATTENUATION (including Doppler-shape measurements)	$10^{-11} \gtrsim \tau \gtrsim 5\times10^{-15}$ sec.
CAPTURE CROSS SECTION (p,γ), (n,γ), (α,γ), etc.	
RESONANCE FLUORESCENCE (scattering, self-absorption, or transmission)	
COULOMB EXCITATION	
INELASTIC ELECTRON SCATTERING	
INELASTIC PARTICLE SCATTERING (p,p'), (n,n'), (α,α'), etc.	

of these is the advent of the lithium-drifted germanium γ-ray detector (Gossett's paper) the steady improvement of large memory multi-channel analyzers, on-line computers, and electronic circuitry in general, has also been important.

The last four methods listed in Table 1 have the limitation that they can only be used to investigate stable (or semi-stable) nuclei. Nevertheless they have proved very powerful and are the only methods listed which can be used in determining lifetimes of bound states in the range $\tau \lesssim 5\times10^{-15}$ sec. I shall say no more about the last two methods since they are not very suitable for use with small accelerators. Nor shall I discuss resonance fluorescence since it is the subject of Booth's paper.

The remaining method of the last four listed, Coulomb excitation, has been the subject of several recent reviews (see, e.g., Ref. 1) and I shall pass it by only noting that the improvement in doubly-ionized alpha beams and the advent of Ge(Li) detectors has given this method a renaissance, so that a large number of heretofore unknown E2 rates in medium and heavy nuclei can be measured using Ge(Li) detectors in conjunction with alpha beams below 8 MeV.

I now shall consider the first four methods listed in Table 1, these being the main subject of this section. We shall first consider, briefly, the lifetimes of virtual nuclear states. That is, those states which are unbound against the emission of nucleons or clusters of nucleons.

B. Virtual Levels

The procedure for determining the radiative widths of virtual states by measuring the cross section for their formation in (particle,gamma) reactions is well-known and has not changed much in 20 years (see, e.g., Refs. 2 and 3). What has changed is our ability to measure accurately the γ-ray branching ratios of isolated resonances in (particle,gamma) reactions, and our ability to extract, from angular distribution and correlation measurements, the amplitude ratio of competing multipoles in a given transition. We have just been shown (Harris' paper). Some examples of the latter type of work.

Our ability to disentangle the γ-ray spectra from the decay of such resonances and thus to extract branching ratios has increased greatly in recent years on two fronts. First, there is the use of large Na(Tℓ) detectors with or without anti-coincidence shields, together with computer-implemented spectrum-stripping programs (see, e.g., Refs. 4 and 5). Second, there is the use of Ge(Li) detectors with the enormous gain in γ-ray energy resolution that follows. Extensive programs to investigate (p,γ) and (α,γ) resonances with Ge(Li) detectors have just begun at Toronto[6] and Utrecht and certainly at other laboratories as well, and already this has been shown to be extremely fruitful research. I submit that is is worthwhile to re-investigate with Ge(Li) detectors practically all resonances previously studied with NaI(Tℓ) detectors. This should provide a lot of work for all of us.

Before leaving virtual states let me show an example of a simple γ-ray angular distribution measurement which illustrates that the old methods are sometimes the best. The example is the angular distribution of the ground-state transition from the B^{10} 6.03-MeV level after formation by the $Li^6(\alpha,\gamma)B^{10}$ reaction. The α-particles are captured in a well-isolated resonance at an energy of 2.61 MeV with $\ell=4$ and the level γ-decays ~100% to the B^{10} ground state. The angular distribution of the γ rays uniquely determines[7] the spin-parity of the 6.03-MeV level to be 4^+. The cross section for formation of the resonance has been measured,[8] and assuming $\Gamma_\gamma \ll \Gamma_\alpha$, gives the radiative width of the 6.03-MeV level. The B^{10} 6.03 → 0 transition is an E2/M1 admixture and the problem is to measure the amplitude ratio, x, of these two components. This is done by measuring the γ-ray angular distribution which has recently been done at Lockheed[9] with care and good statistics. Preliminary results are illustrated in Figs. 1 and 2 which show the measured angular distribution and analysis of the Legendre-polynomial coefficients of this distribution, respectively. The E2 and M1 matrix elements are found to be in the ratio 10:1. This result agrees with earlier work[7] but is considerably more accurate.

I have chosen to show this example in a talk purportedly on electromagnetic lifetimes in order to emphasize my contention that our concern should be with the measurement of matrix elements and not simply lifetimes.

C. Electronic Timing

The vast majority of nuclear levels have lifetimes too short for measurement by direct electronic timing. Nevertheless the method is an important one. It is so far the most accurate method and thus provides us with calibration standards for use with less exact methods. Also, many of the lifetimes that can be measured by this means are important ones, being those of low-lying levels (i.e., transition energies of $\lesssim$100 keV and $\lesssim$1.2 MeV for M1 and E2 transitions of average strength so qualify).

Essentially, two different methods are used to mark the population of a given nuclear state in time-delayed measurements. These are the pulsed beam and associated particle techniques. The associated particle in the latter technique may be a γ ray, as in conventional radioactive investigations, or the particle feeding the state, such as the proton in a (d,p) reaction. Usually a γ ray determines the decay of a state. I am not competent to review the advances in the technology of pulsed beams nor of delayed-coincidence circuitry. Instead I shall only mention two inovations in experimental techniques which have yielded improvements in the accuracy of lifetime measurements.

The first is the use of two-dimensional analysis, one axis displaying the time-delay distribution and the other the γ-ray energy spectrum. In pulsed beam experiments the γ-ray energy spectrum is gated by the beam pulse while in the associated particle method it is in coincidence with the detector which determines the population of the state. The reason for the two-parameter display is to allow a more accurate subtraction of background. This is important since background-associated uncertainties are often the limiting error in lifetime measurements of accelerator-induced activities. If the γ-ray detector is an organic scintillator, as is usually the case if fast timing is necessary, then not much is gained by this method. However, if the lifetime can be used, then the advantage can be considerable (see, e.g., Ref. 10). Use of two-dimensional analysis should also be of great use in survey work.

The second inovation is the use, already alluded to, of charged particles to provide a time signal in the associated particle technique. In the first application of this method[11] the charged particles were detected in a silicon surface-barrier detector and the γ rays in a plastic scintillator. A time resolution of about 450 picosecs FWHM was achieved with this system, a large fraction of which was associated with the γ-ray detection (a 2x2-in. plastic scintillator was used for the γ rays). The great advantage of this scheme is that the energy resolution of the particle detector allows a much greater selectivity of states, and thus lower background than the conventional pulsed-beam technique or the γ-γ coincidence techniques. For instance, in both of these latter techniques, when plastic organic scintillators are used, the Compton distributions of all higher-energy γ rays contribute to the background under the γ ray of interest. Two examples[11] of lifetime measurements using a silicon surface barrier detector for protons in (d,p) reactions are shown in Fig. 3. Of course, the two improvements I have chosen to discuss can be combined. Then one displays the charged particle spectrum on one axis of a two-parameter analyzer and the time distribution of γ rays on the other.

D. The Recoil Distance Method

As is the case for several other ingenious inovations in nuclear physics, the use of the recoil distance method, in the form in which we shall consider it, was suggested by A.E. Litherland (see Ref. 12). It bears some resemblance to earlier recoil distance techniques[13,14], but is considerably more accurate and is especially adapted for use with Ge(Li) γ-ray detectors. It has been applied at Chalk River[12,15,16] and at Oxford.[17] The examples I shall show are taken largely from these references.

The principle of the method is illustrated schematically in Fig. 4. A heavy-ion beam impinges on a target thin enough to permit the residual nuclei to recoil freely into vacuum with velocity v. By placing a metal plate at a distance D = vt (D is referred to as s in Fig. 4) and observing the intensity of the γ rays from nuclei slowed down in it, the number of excited nuclei surviving for a time t can be determined. The γ rays from nuclei that decay before reaching the metal plate are Doppler-shifted according to Eq. (1),

$$E = E_0\left[1+(v/c)\cos\theta)\right], \tag{1}$$

and are separated into a second peak in the spectrum from the Ge(Li) detector which is located at an angle $>90^\circ$ (or at 0° in the Oxford work[17]). Thus the intensity of the Doppler-shifted peak is,

$$I_s = I(1-e^{-D/v\tau}), \tag{2}$$

where I is the total number of reaction-produced γ rays and the intensity of the unshifted peak is,

$$I_o = Ie^{-D/v\tau} . \tag{3}$$

Hence a measurement of the ratio $I_o/(I_o+I_s) = e^{-D/v\tau}$ as a function of D gives the lifetime τ if v is known. The effective recoil velocity v may be determined directly from the Doppler shift at a given angle (Eq. 1) or calculated from the kinematics of the reaction.

The experimental apparatus used for this work at Oxford is shown in Fig. 5. As in the Chalk River apparatus, the plunger is moved by a micrometer screw.

Results obtained at Chalk River[12] for the lifetime of the first-excited state of O^{17} at 0.871 MeV are illustrated in Fig. 6. The graphs on the left-hand side of Fig. 6 are spectra of the 0.871-MeV γ ray showing the Doppler-shifted line and the unshifted line. The spectra have been normalized so that the total area under the two peaks is a constant, thereby showing the relative change in intensity of the unshifted peak as the plunger displacement is increased. The measured Doppler shift was (16.5 ± 1) keV for $\theta_\gamma = (122 \pm 1)^o$. The resolution was 5 keV (FWHM) on the unshifted peak. The shifted peak, corresponding to nuclei decaying in flight at full initial velocity, shows Doppler broadening due to lateral motion of the O^{17} ions caused by the associated protons in the $H^2(O^{16},p\gamma)O^{17}$ reaction. From the measured Doppler shift the average recoil velocity is $\overline{v}/c = (3.58 \pm 0.24)\%$, where c is the velocity of light.

The relative intensity of the unshifted peak to the total intensity as a function of the plunger displacement is plotted in the graph at the top right of Fig. 6. The intensity decreases exponentially with the plunger displacement and falls by a factor of e in a distance $D_m = 2.50 \pm 0.22$ mm. The error in D_m is from counting statistics and background uncertainties; no error has been included for the relative plunger-displacement measurement.

The center-of-mass velocity, calculated from the reaction kinematics, is $v/c = 3.68\%$, assuming an incident O^{16} ion energy of 12.8 MeV. Although the angular distribution of the protons will change the average value of the forward recoil velocity from the center-of-mass velocity, the effect is small. From the measured values of D_m and $\overline{v}/c$, the mean lifetime of the first-excited state of O^{17} was found to be[12]

$$\tau = (2.33 \pm 0.26)\times 10^{-10} \text{ sec.}$$

The most accurate electronic timing result is $(2.587 \pm 0.042) \times 10^{-10}$ sec.[18]

A second example is illustrated in Fig. 7 which shows portions of spectra obtained for different plunger displacements, D, in the $H^3(O^{16},n\gamma)F^{18}$ reaction. From this data lifetimes were obtained for the F^{18} 0.937- and 1.082-MeV levels. In later work a lifetime was also obtained for the 2.103-MeV level. The decay curve (i.e., $I_o/(I_o+I_s)$ versus D) of the 1.082-MeV γ ray is shown in Fig. 8.

Recently the recoil distance method has been adapted for use with gas targets.[19] In this variation a heavy-ion beam enters a gas chamber through a thin nickel window, traverses the gas target, which is at a pressure of 0.1 to 15 mm, and impinges on the plunger. Neglecting second-order corrections, which were all less than 10%,[19] the method differs from the conventional recoil method only in the use of an extended source of reactions. The ratio of stopped peak to the total number of decays is now given by

$$I_o/(I_o+I_s) = \int_0^D e^{-x/v\tau}\,dx \Big/ \int_0^D dx = \frac{v\tau}{D}\left[1-e^{-D/v\tau}\right] \qquad (4)$$

where D is the gas target thickness. The ratio $D/v\tau$, from which τ is extracted, is still obtained from the measured quantity $I_o/(I_o+I_s)$. In the first application[19] of this method the $H^2(O^{16},p\gamma)O^{17}$ and $H^2(O^{16},n\gamma)F^{17}$ reactions were used with the Ge(Li) detector at 0° to a 33-MeV O^{16} beam ($v/c \simeq 5.8\%$). A typical Ge(Li) spectrum is shown in Fig. 9 and plots of $D/v\tau$ versus D are shown in Fig. 10. From the latter $v\tau$ was extracted, while v is obtained from the observed Doppler shifts (Fig. 9). These measurements gave mean lifetimes of $(2.32 \pm 0.08) \times 10^{-10}$ and $(3.96 \pm 0.10) \times 10^{-10}$ sec. for the first-excited states of O^{17} and F^{17}, respectively (the former disagrees somewhat with electronic timing results[18]). Note that the experimental uncertainties are 3.4% and 2.5%, quite competitive with those of electronic timing.

So far, the recoil distance technique has been used almost exclusively in conjunction with heavy-ion bombardment of light targets. Can it be applied using conventional nuclear reactions and thus with low-energy accelerators? The answer is yes. The recoil velocities obtained so far with heavy ions vary from $\sim$3.2 to 5.8% of the velocity of light. Recoil velocities about 1/5 of these are associated with conventional reactions. For instance, with 5-MeV α-particles, the $F^{19}(\alpha,n)Na^{22}$ reaction produces Na^{22*} recoils with 0.9% the velocity of light. Thus, since $D/\bar{v}$ is the determining parameter, it is necessary to work with plunger displacements of ~1/5 of those in the examples shown here and this is possible (see, e.g., Ref. 20).

One major difficulty to be overcome is the spread in angle of the recoiling nuclei which pertains when the light particle is accelerated. There are two different ways to overcome this. One is to work close to threshold in an endothermic reaction. In this case a neutron producing reaction is to be preferred since the yields are often quite strong close to threshold if neutrons are emitted. An example here is the $F^{19}(\alpha,n)Na^{22}$ reaction. The other way to produce a narrow cone of recoiling nuclei is to count γ rays in coincidence with the reaction particles observed in the backward direction. An annular counter is admirably suited for this purpose. By this means the Doppler shift is also increased; the major difficulty to overcome is that of the low coincidence yield.

Because of the very good inherent accuracy of the method and because it bridges the gap between electronic timing and the Doppler shift attenuation method, the recoil distance method is extremely valuable. It is therefore important to develop its application to conventional nuclear reactions. This is especially true since there are many nuclei which cannot be easily formed by heavy-ion bombardment of light particles.

E. The Doppler Shift Attenuation Method

General Considerations

The Doppler shift attenuation method (hereinafter referred to as DSAM) has come a long way since the pioneer work of Devons[21] and his collaborators. The development of the Ge(Li) γ-ray detector, in particular, has transformed the measurements of nuclear lifetimes by the DSAM from difficult experiments, possible in a few special cases, into routine experiments that can be carried out as part of an overall plan of study. In the DSAM, the nuclear lifetime is compared to the slowing down time of the recoiling excited nuclei. This time is of the order of 5×10^{-13} sec in a solid and about 5×10^{-10} sec in a gas so that the DSAM may be used over a range of lifetimes from about 10^{-11} to 5×10^{-15} sec in the former case and from about 10^{-8} to 5×10^{-12} sec in the latter.

Equation 1 is the fundamental equation for the DSAM. Two basic variants of the method are commonly used.[22] In one, the energy difference for γ rays emitted at two different angles θ_1,θ_2 with respect to the recoiling ion direction is measured for one stopping material. In the other, the difference in γ-ray energies is measured for the recoiling nuclei slowing down in different stopping materials while the emission angle of the γ rays is kept constant. In either method, the lifetime is calculated from the observed shift in γ-ray energy. Of course, the two methods may be combined to check on systematic errors and to improve the accuracy by over-determining the problem. For lifetimes long compared to the stopping time the first variant is the more accurate; while for lifetimes short compared to the stopping time the second variant is the more appropriate.[23]

The principle of the DSAM can be viewed as a measurement of the ratio of the average velocity of the recoiling ions to the average velocity of these ions at the instant of formation. The former is always measured, the problem we now consider is the determination of the latter. It is because the best way to determine this average velocity depends strongly on the case of interest that there exist so many variants of the DSAM. One method which is quite straightforward is to view the γ rays in coincidence with the associated particle detected in a particular direction, or two different directions. This has been used often (see, e.g., Ref. 24) with NaI(Tℓ) γ-ray detectors. However, because of the lower efficiency of Ge(Li) detectors, the trend today is to do singles measurements and to define the kinematics in some other way (see, however, Ref. 25). Again, there are two basic variants. In the first of these, a reaction is used which produces, in general, a large spread of velocities (direction and magnitude) and the <u>average</u> initial velocity in the beam direction is determined either from a measurement of the angular distribution of the reaction or by observing the Doppler shift for the ions recoiling into vacuum. The second of these is to use a reaction which approximates closely a uni-directional, mono-energetic beam. Three types of reactions which are used nowadays, so qualify. These are (particle,gamma) capture reactions such as $Al^{27}(p,\gamma)Si^{28}$, heavy ion reactions, such as $H^{3}(O^{16},n\gamma)F^{18}$,[26] and endothermic neutron-producing reactions used near threshold, such as $F^{19}(\alpha,n\gamma)Na^{22}$.[27]

Energy Loss and Scattering of Ions in Matter

At the present time, the basic limitation to the accuracy of lifetime measurements via the DSAM is in our inexact knowledge of the process for energy loss and scattering of heavy ions in matter from which we deduce the slowing down time of the ions. The limitation imposed is about 10%, no matter how careful and accurate a measurement is made.

Why does this limitation exist? The fact is that we do not have an accurate quantitative theory for the energy loss and scattering process. Work of Lindhard and his collaborators (see e.g., Ref. 28) has provided us with a qualitative understanding of the general features of the process; that is, the dependence on ion velocity of the energy loss and scattering of an ideal ion traversing an ideal stopping material. There are two practical difficulties. First, this theory has not been tested adequately at low ion velocities ($v/c < 0.5\%$) and second, at higher ion velocities ($v/c \simeq 1$-6%), fluctuations with Z of the moving ion about the predicted magnitude of the energy loss of up to 20% are observed experimentally.[28]

Recently, several formulations[22,24,27,29] of the DSAM have been presented which go considerably further than previous work in utilizing our knowledge of the energy loss and scattering process. These formulations have reduced the error of analysis to an amount which is small compared to the uncertainties in the magnitude and form of the energy loss and scattering process. Since the experimental error involved in measuring Doppler shifts are also relatively small, it is clear that the frontier in our attempt to improve the DSAM is in our knowledge of the energy loss and scattering process itself. It seems to me that the crucial need here from the experimental point of view is for careful measurements of the energy loss and scattering process for different ion-stopping material combinations—especially at ion velocities ($v/c < 0.5\%$) where nuclear events are important.

Some Examples of the DSAM

The use of the Ge(Li) γ-ray detector allows the observation of considerably smaller Doppler shifts than were possible with NaI(Tℓ) detectors. Thus, measurements are now feasible for smaller recoil velocities and can therefore be made with low-energy accelerators on heavier nuclei than were heretofore possible. The work of the Argonne group using the (p,n) reaction is an example of this trend. Figure 11 illustrates results obtained at Argonne using the $O^{18}(p,n)F^{18}$ reaction at $E_p = 3.76$ MeV.[23] This energy corresponds to a resonance ~70 keV above threshold for production of the F^{18} 1.042-MeV level. So close to threshold, the F^{18} recoils are emitted in a narrow cone about the beam direction and variations in the kinematics of the reaction can be neglected. The F^{18} ions have an initial velocity, $v/c = 0.47\%$. The difference in the Doppler shift of the 1.042-MeV γ rays in TaO_2 and H_2O vapor was observed to be (0.124 ± 0.035) keV, leading to a mean lifetime of $(0.4^{+0.3}_{-0.2}) \times 10^{-14}$ sec. This is, to my knowledge, the shortest lifetime measured by the DSAM.

Another example of the observation of smaller Doppler shifts is the work by the Toronto group[6] using the (p,γ) reaction. Here the Doppler shifts are about the same magnitude as in the work at Argonne. The advantage of capture reactions is that a mono-energetic, uni-directional beam of recoiling ions is naturally produced since there is no outgoing particle to carry off momentum.

In Fig. 12 are illustrated results of a Doppler shift measurement of the Na^{22} 0.891 → 0 transition formed in the $F^{19}(\alpha,n)Na^{22}$ reaction.[30] This work was part of a study of the Na^{22} levels and was completed in a few hours. Again, the measurements were done just above threshold for production of the state under investigation. In the top and bottom parts of the figure are shown full-energy peaks of the 0.891-MeV γ ray observed at 0° and 90° to the beam using a $CClF_2$ gas target at 1-atm pressure. The full Doppler shift was observed. With a solid target, no Doppler shift was observed[27] which explains the middle part of the figure. Thus, upper and lower limits (gas and solid targets, respectively) could be placed on the mean lifetime of this level. These give $8 < \tau < 52$ picosecs.

Doppler Line Shapes

Since the resolution of the Ge(Li) detector is comparable to or less than the Doppler shifts observed in conventional nuclear reactions, it is possible to observe the γ-ray energy distribution which, so far, we have integrated over to obtain the Doppler shift attenuation. This opens a very promising method of lifetime measurements. Lifetimes can be obtained more accurately and, most importantly, the heavy ion energy loss and scattering process can be simultaneously studied as will be shown.

The dependence of the γ-ray line shape on the nuclear lifetime is exemplified in Fig. 13. Here we show the expected line shapes of a 4.50-MeV γ ray emitted at 0° in a semi-hypothetical case in which the excited nuclei (Si^{28}) are mono-energetic, are emitted toward the Ge(Li) detector, and are stopped in a nickel backing. The line shapes shown cover the approximate range of lifetimes (a factor of ~700) which could be measured in this case. Of course, this range could be increased by changing the stopping material. The line shapes of Fig. 13 were generated using the phenomenological representation of the stopping and scattering process of Ref. 27.

Figures 14 and 15 illustrate the application of this line shape analysis[27] to two γ-ray transitions in Na^{22}. Here, a least-squares fit was made of the theoretical line shape to the observed line shapes with two free parameters—the ratio of the mean life (τ) to the electronic stopping time (α), and a parameter, γ_1^2, which characterizes the nuclear stopping and scattering processes. The fits are essentially perfect; the mis-match on the low side of the distribution being due to neglect of a low-energy tail in the response function of the Ge(Li) detector. In Fig. 16 are shown more details of this least-squares fitting. In this figure the abscissa, K_n/K_e, is related to γ_i^2 while the ordinate for the lower part of the figure represents the goodness-of-fit of Figs. 14 and 15. From this figure it is seen that α/τ (and thus τ) and K_n/K_e (and thus γ_i^2) can be obtained simultaneously from line shape analysis. This is nice since it means we can investigate the energy loss and scattering process by observation of line shapes; while, at the same time, we extract lifetime information. This is true, of course, no matter which representation of the energy loss and scattering process we use. (The dashed curve in the lower part of Fig. 16 illustrates how well K_n/K_e would have been determined from the line shape of Fig. 15 if it were known that α/τ was exactly equal to 0.44 in this case.)

The line shapes of Figs. 14 and 15 are all for negligible deviation from a mono-energetic uni-directional beam of recoiling ions. Now let us consider some line shapes observed when these conditions are not fulfilled; that is, when an endothermic reaction is used. The results I shall discuss are from the Stanford group.[31] Figure 17 shows the line shape[32] of the C^{13} 3.09 → transition observed with the C^{13} ions recoiling into vacuum for two different incident deuteron energies in the $C^{12}(d,p)C^{13}$ reaction. The line shapes are entirely due to the angular distribution of the reaction. If now the recoils were allowed to stop in a solid any lifetime effect would be superimposed on those of Fig. 17. Such a situation is illustrated in Fig. 18 which shows the two-escape peak of the Be^{10} 3.36 → 0 transition observed in singles at 0° to the beam with the Be^{10} ions recoiling into vacuum and nickel.[33] The shape of the upper line is entirely due to the angular distribution of the reaction. The solid line is a least-squares fit to the line shape. The procedure is to least-squares fit the lower curve (solid curve) starting with the upper curve, with the lifetime of the level as a free parameter. Preliminary results of this procedure gave a mean life of $(2.45 \pm 0.4)\times10^{-13}$ sec for the Be^{10} 3.36-MeV level.

Figure 17 was specifically shown to illustrate a particular danger of this method. The difference in the two line shapes shown is due to the change in the angular distribution associated with the 10-keV change in bombarding energy. Thus it is clear that good energy control is necessary before an analysis such as that of Fig. 18 is made.

III. COMPARISON TO MODEL PREDICTIONS

I shall close by giving two examples of the comparison of observed electromagnetic matrix elements to the predictions

Table 2. Comparison between the measured M1 radiative widths and E2/M1 mixing ratios and the effective interaction results [(8-16) POT.] of Cohen and Kurath (Ref. 35).

Transition	Γ_γ(M1) Experiment (eV)	Γ_γ(M1) Theory (eV)
N^{14} 7.03 → 0	0.091 ± 0.013	0.11
N^{13} 3.51 → 0	0.65 ± 0.12	0.83
B^{11} 4.46 → 0	0.54 ± 0.10	0.54
N^{15} 6.32 → 0	~2.7	4.88

Nucleus	Transition	x(E2/M1)[a]	x(E2/M1)[b]	x_{exp}
C^{13}	3.68 → 0	-0.054	-0.100	$-(0.096^{+0.030}_{-0.021})$
N^{13}	3.51 → 0	+0.030	+0.068	+(0.092 ± 0.02)
O^{15}	6.18 → 0	0	-0.048	-(0.16 ± 0.016)
N^{15}	6.32 → 0	+0.081	+0.122	+(0.12 ± 0.015)
B^{11}	4.46 → 0	-0.123	-0.224	-(0.20 ± 0.02)
C^{11}	4.32 → 0	+0.090	+0.204	+(0.17 ± 0.02)
N^{14}	7.03 → 0	+0.361	+0.722	+(0.60 ± 0.1)

a. No collective enhancement for E2 rates.
b. Collective enhancement for E2 rates calculated via the weak surface coupling approximation with $\beta = 0.5$.

of specific nuclear models. My first example is of some mixed E2/M1 transitions in the 1p-shell. The comparison[34] is given in Table 2 which lists some measured M1 radiative widths and some measured E2/M1 mixing ratios. These are compared to the predictions of the recent effective interaction calculations of Cohen and Kurath.[35] There are two points I wish to make. First, this comparison supports the use of the effective charge approximation to characterize collective enhancement of E2 rates. Second, it shows perfect agreement between the predicted and observed relative phases of the M1 and E2 matrix elements. Such a comparison of phases can be routinely made since the work of Rose and Brink[36] and there is no reason to ignore these phases as has been done in the past.

My second example concerns the M1 and E2 transitions connecting the bound T=0 s^4p^{10} states of N^{14}. The comparison[37] to theory is shown in Tables 3 and 4 which give the experimentally observed M1 and E2 radiative widths together with the predictions of five model calculations. Again, the comparison (Table 4) supports the effective charge approx-

TABLE 3

Magnetic dipole radiative widths (in mev) connecting the four lowest s^4p^{10} states of N^{14}

Calculation	Transition					
	2.31 → 0 (1)	2.31 → 0 (2)	3.95 → 2.31	3.95 → 0	7.03 → 0	7.03 → 3.95
Soper[a]	54.9	103.0	105	5.26	103	1.035
Elliott[b]	16.9	10.8	159	0.49	120	0.026
Visscher and Ferrell[c]	23.7	16.2	137	0.56	106	0.056
Cohen and Kurath I[d]	18.1	11.8	180	0.41	115	0.002
Cohen and Kurath II[d]	41.5	9.6	185	1.32	115	0.052
Experiment[f]	8.1 ± 1.4		140 ± 13	0.58 ± 0.12	91 ± 13	≲(1.1 ± 0.3)

For the 2.31 → 0 transition, column (1) is calculated from the wave functions given by the indicated calculations. Column (2) includes the effects of admixtures of the $p^8(2s,1d)$ configuration using the results of True (Ref. e) and, for the last four rows, has the spin part of the matrix element set equal to zero.

a. J.M. Soper (private communication). Intermediate coupling with a/K=7.
b. J.P. Elliott, Phil. Mag. 1, 503 (1956).
c. W M. Visscher and R.A. Ferrell, Phys. Rev. 107, 781 (1957).
d. S. Cohen and D. Kurath, Nucl. Phys. 73, 1 (1965), explained in Ref. 37.
e. W.W. True, Phys. Rev. 130, 1530 (1963).
f. See J.W. Olness, A.R. Poletti, and E.K. Warburton, Phys. Rev. 154, 971 (1967) for references to the measurements.

Table 4. Electric quadrupole radiative widths (in mev) connecting the four lowest s^4p^{10} states in N^{14}

Calculation	Transition						
	3.95 → 0		7.03 → 0		7.03 → 3.95		7.03 → 2.31
	(a)	(b)	(a)	(b)	(a)	(b)	
Soper	1.47	5.89	18.46	73.8	0.16	0.62	1.33
Elliott	1.14	4.58	10.45	41.8	0.37	1.47	0.78
Visscher and Ferrell	1.33	5.32	6.58	26.3	0.20	0.81	0.94
Cohen and Kurath I	1.21	4.83	9.70	38.8	0.34	1.35	0.57
Cohen and Kurath II	1.11	4.43	8.35	33.4	0.37	1.47	0.50
Experiment	4.81 ± 0.33		33 ± 9		$\leq (1.1 \pm 0.3)$		0.62 ± 0.14

The columns headed (a) have no collective enhancement of E2 rates, while those designated (b) have collective enhancement with $\beta=0.5$. The origin of the calculations is stated in Table 3.

imation to characterize collective enhancement of E2 rates. The last four model calculations include a tensor force, while the first does not. Although it may not be obvious without a detailed discussion, the comparison also gives strong evidence for the existence of a tensor force. It is certainly not obvious, but nevertheless true, that the comparison also leads to the conclusion that configuration mixing cannot be responsible for the long lifetime of C^{14}; rather, the tensor force causes the C^{14} beta decay matrix element to vanish (almost).

REFERENCES

1. P. Stelson, Proceedings of the Summer Study Group on the Physics of the Emperor Tandem Van de Graaff Region, Vol. III, edited by J. Weneser and E.K. Warburton (BNL Report 948, 1965), p. 1005; R.L. Robinson, in Nuclear Spin-Parity Assignments, edited by N.B. Gove and R.L. Robinson (Adademic Press, N.Y., 1966), p. 205.
2. H.E. Gove, in Nuclear Reactions, Vol. I, edited by P.M. Endt and M. Demeur (North-Holland Publishing Co., Amsterdam, 1959), p. 259.
3. E.K. Warburton, in Electromagnetic Lifetimes and Properties of Nuclear States, National Academy of Sciences, National Research Council Publication no. 974, (1962) p. 180.
4. A.E. Evans, Phys. Rev. 155, 1047 (1967).
5. F.D. Lee, R.W. Krone, and F.W. Prosser, Jr., Nucl. Phys. A96, 209 (1967).
6. L.E. Carlson and R.E. Azuma, Phys. Letts. 24B, 462 (1967).
7. S.S. Hanna and L. Meyer-Schützmeister, Phys. Rev. 108, 1644 (1957).
8. P.D. Forsyth, H.T. Tu, and W.F. Hornyak, Nucl. Phys. 82, 33 (1966).
9. D.E. Alburger, L.F. Chase, Jr., R.E. McDonald, and D.H. Wilkinson, to be published.
10. J.A. Becker, J.W. Olness, and D.H. Wilkinson, Phys. Rev. 155, 1089 (1967).
11. R.E. McDonald, D.B. Fossan, L.F. Chase, Jr., and J.A. Becker, Phys. Rev. 140, B1198 (1965); D.B. Fossan, R.E. McDonald, and L.F. Chase, Jr., Phys. Rev. 141, 1018 (1966).
12. T.K. Alexander and K.W. Allen, Can. J. Phys. 43, 1563 (1965).
13. J. Thirion and V.L. Telegdi, Phys. Rev. 92, 1253 (1953).
14. J. Burde and S.G. Cohen, Phys. Rev. 104, 1093 (1956).
15. T.K. Alexander, K.W. Allen, and D.C. Healey, Phys. Letts. 20, 402 (1966).
16. K.W. Allen, T.K. Alexander, and D.C. Healey, Phys. Letts. 22, 193 (1966).

17. K.W. Allen, in Lithium-Drifted Germanium Detectors, IAEA, Vienna (1966), pp. 142-153.
18. J.A. Becker and D.H. Wilkinson, Phys. Rev. 134, B1200 (1964).
19. P.G. Bizzeti, A.M. Bizzeti-Sona, S. Kalbitzer, and B. Povh, Z. Phys. 201, 295 (1967).
20. D.R. Goosman and R.W. Kavanagh, Phys. Letts 24B, 507 (1967).
21. S. Devons, G. Manning, and D. St. P. Bunbury, Proc. Phys. Soc. (London) A68, 18 (1955); D. St. P. Bunbury, S. Devons, G. Manning, and J.W. Towle, ibid. A69, 165 (1956); S. Devons, G. Manning, and J.W. Towle, ibid., A69, 173 (1956).
22. E.K. Warburton, D.E. Alburger, and D.H. Wilkinson, Phys. Rev. 129, 2180 (1963).
23. A.E. Blaugrund, D.H. Youngblood, G.C. Morrison, and R.E. Segel, Phys. Rev., to be published.
24. R.E. Pixley and W. Benenson, Nucl. Phys. A91, 561 (1967)
25. J.R. MacDonald, D.F.H. Start, R. Anderson, A.G. Robertson, and M.A. Grace, Bull. Am. Phys. Soc. 12, 682 (1967).
26. A.E. Litherland, M.J.L. Yates, B.M. Hinds, and D. Eccleshall, Nucl. Phys. 44, 220 (1963).
27. E.K. Warburton, J.W. Olness, and A.R. Poletti, Phys. Rev., to be published.
28. J. Lindhard, M. Scharff, and H.E. Schiott, Kgl. Danske Videnskab. Selskab, Mat.-Fys. Medd. 33, no. 14 (1963); B. Fastrup, P. Hvelplund, and C.A. Sautter, ibid., 35, 10 (1966).
29. A.E. Blaugrund, Nucl. Phys. 88, 501 (1966).
30. A.R. Poletti, E.K. Warburton, J.W. Olness, and S. Hechtl, to be published.
31. T.R. Fisher, P. Paul, and S.S. Hanna, private communication.
32. F. Reiss, private communication.
33. T.R. Fisher and D.C. Healey, private communication.
34. A.R. Poletti, E.K. Warburton, and D. Kurath, Phys. Rev. 155, 1096 (1967).
35. S. Cohen and D. Kurath, Nucl. Phys. 73, 1 (1965).
36. H.J. Rose and D.M. Brink, Revs. Mod. Phys. 39, 306 (1967).
37. H.J. Rose, O. Haüsser, and E.K. Warburton, to be published.

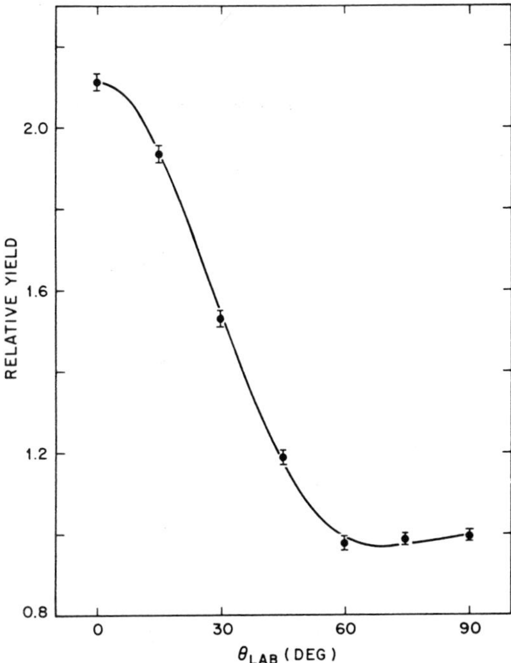

Fig. 1. Angular distribution of the ground-state transition in the $Li^6(\alpha,\gamma)B^{10}$ reaction proceeding through the B^{10} 6.03-MeV level.

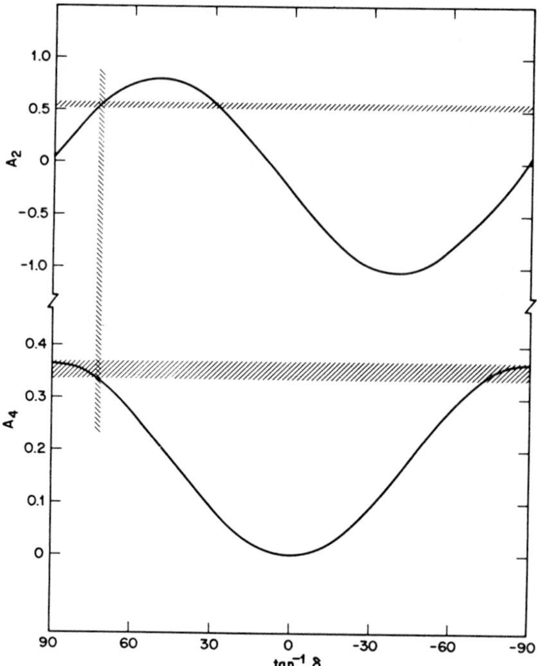

Fig. 2. Comparison of the experimental and theoretical Legendre polynomial coefficients describing the angular distribution of Fig. 1.

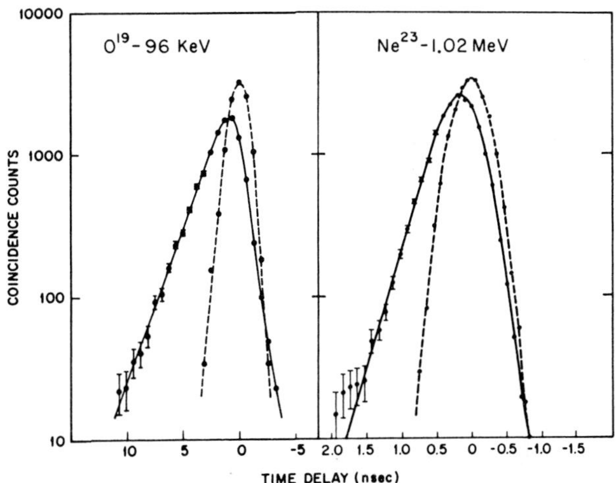

Fig. 3. Experimental decay curves for the 96-keV level in O^{19} and the 1.02-MeV level in Ne^{23}. The dashed curves represent the prompt-resolution function. The left slopes correspond to half-lives, $t_{1/2}$, of 1.39 $\pm$ 0.05 and 0.178 $\pm$ 0.010 nsec, respectively.

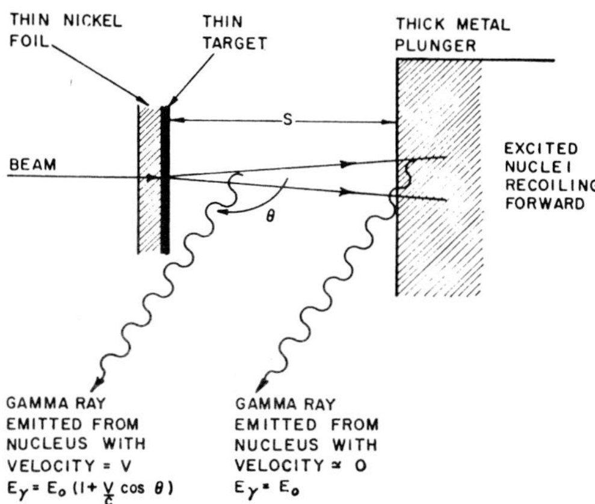

Fig. 4. Recoil method of measuring lifetimes of excited states.

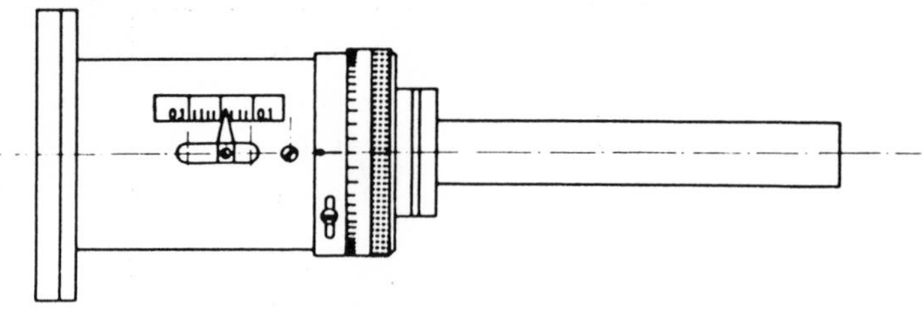

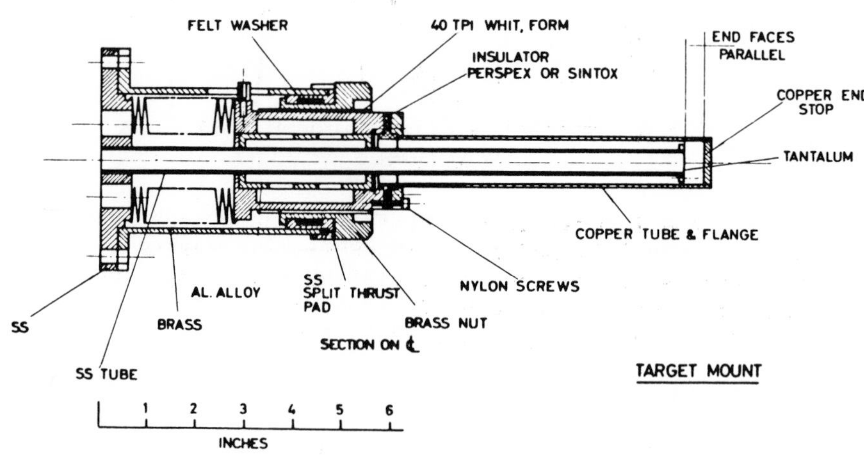

Fig. 5. The Oxford plunger apparatus for measuring lifetimes via the recoil distance method. (Ref. 17)

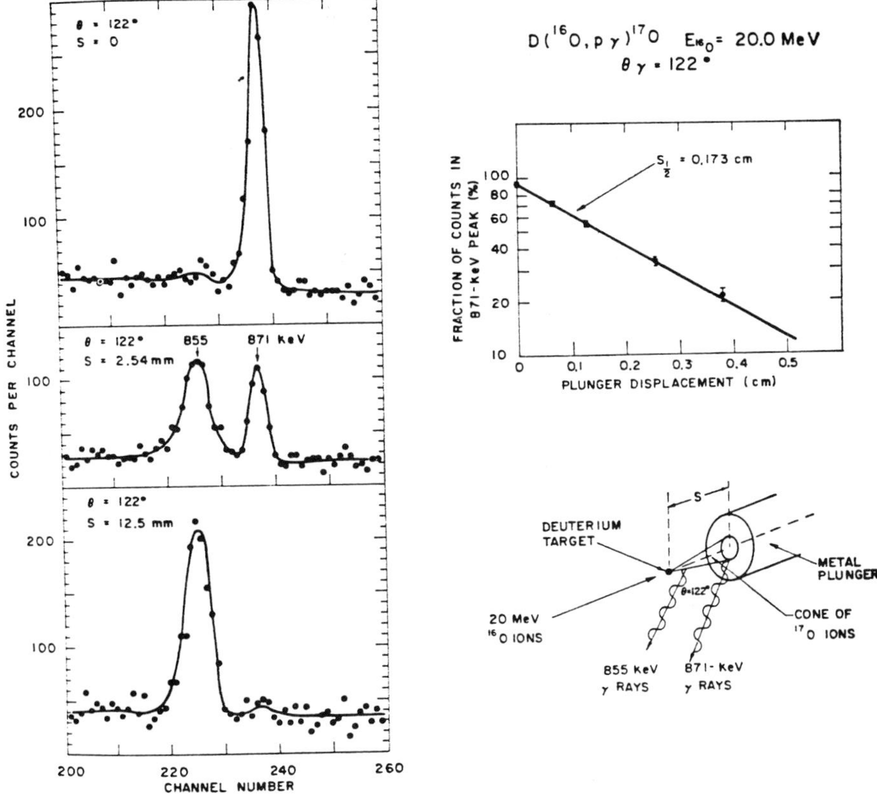

Fig. 6. The lifetime measurement of the 0.871-MeV level of O^{17}. The γ-ray spectra at the left show the relative intensity of the 0.871- and 0.855-MeV peaks as the plunger displacement is increased. The logarithm of the relative intensity of the 0.871-MeV peak is plotted as a function of the plunger displacement in the graph at the top right.

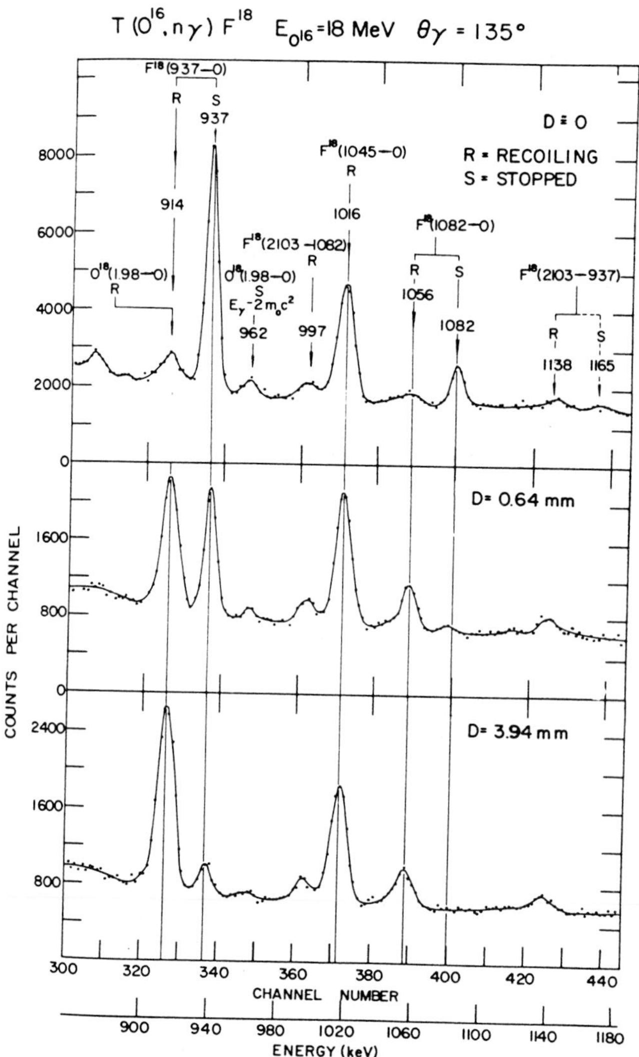

Fig. 7. Gamma-ray spectra from the reaction $O^{16}+H^3$. D is the distance from the tantalum stopper to the target.

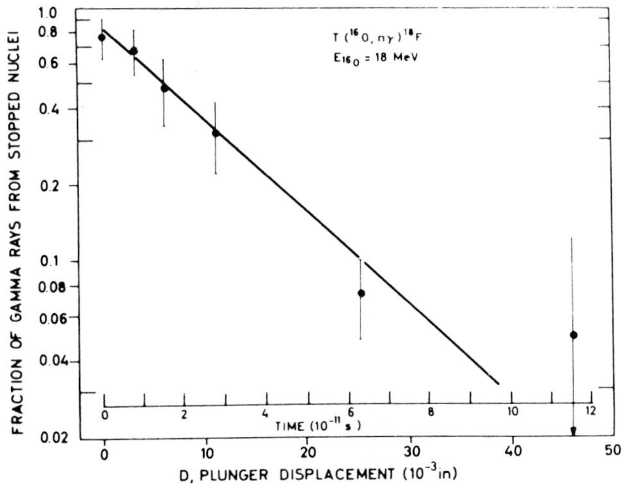

Fig. 8. Decay of the 1082-keV state of F^{18}.

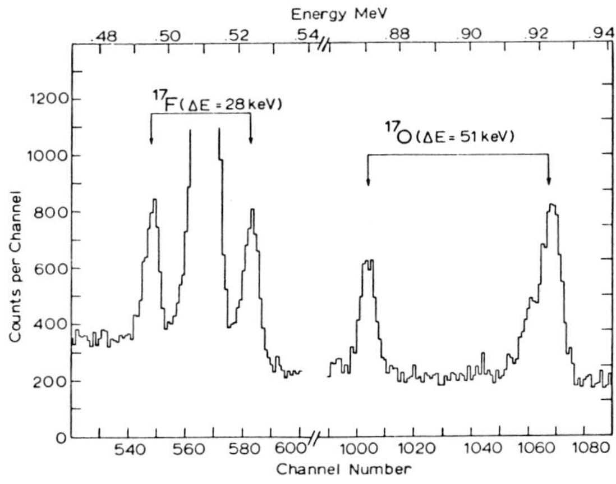

Fig. 9. Gamma-ray spectrum from the reaction $O^{16}+H^2$. The O^{16} energy was 33 MeV and the Ge(Li) detector was at 0° to the beam. The intense peak between the F^{17} peaks is annihilation radiation.

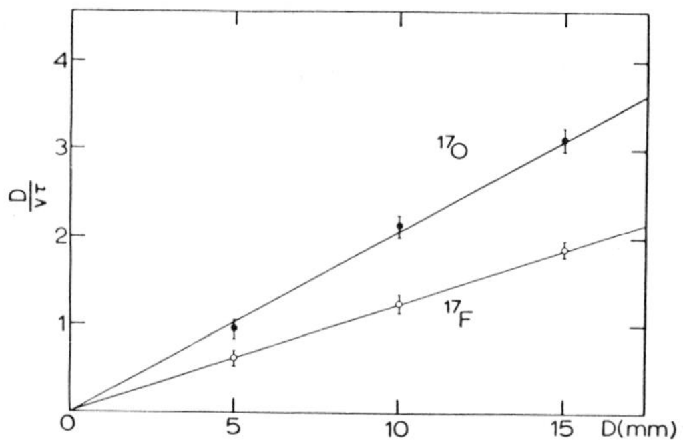

Fig. 10. Experimentally obtained values of $D/v\tau$ versus the target thickness D (Ref. 19).

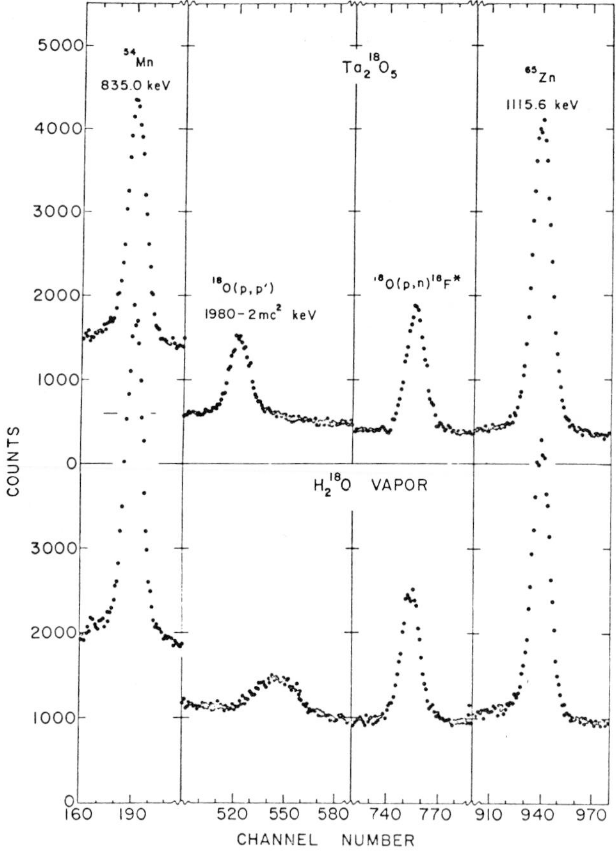

Fig. 11. Relevant portions of the γ-ray spectra from a solid $Ta_2O_5^{18}$ and H_2O^{18} vapor target at 0° to the beam. The energy dispersion is 0.374 keV/channel.

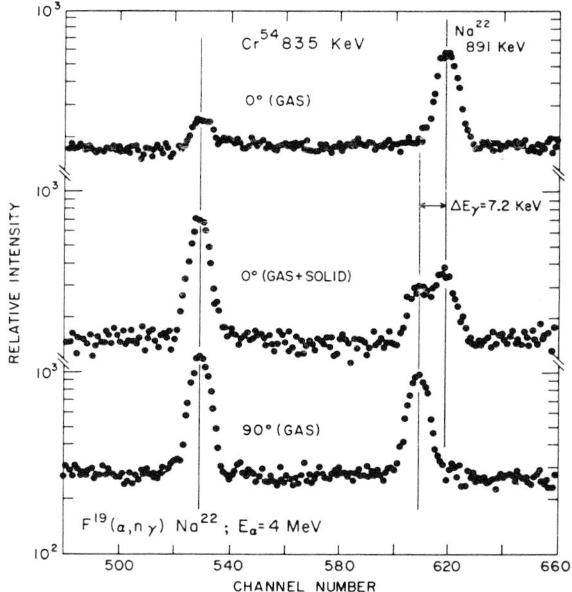

Fig. 12. Doppler shift of the ground-state transition from the Na^{22} 0.891-MeV level observed via the $F^{19}(\alpha,n)Na^{22}$ reaction. The angle of the Ge(Li) detector to the beam is indicated. The Cr^{54} line is from a Mn^{54} radioactive source. In the upper and lower curves the recoils stopped in gas while for the middle curve they stopped partially in a gas and partially in nickel.

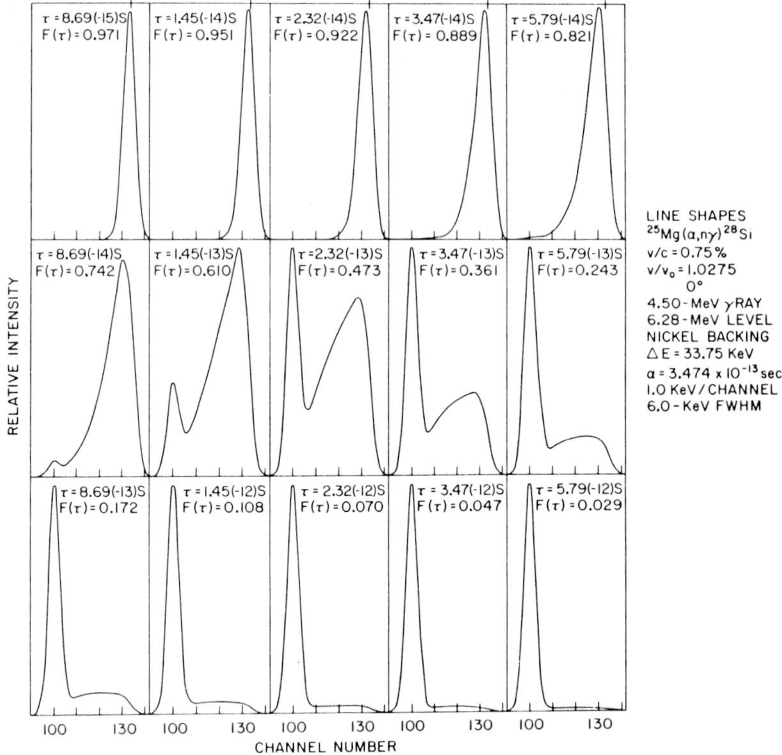

Fig. 13. Hypothetical Doppler line shapes as a function of assumed mean lifetime. F(τ) is the ratio of the average Doppler shift to the full shift for recoil into vacuum. Calculated following Ref. 27.

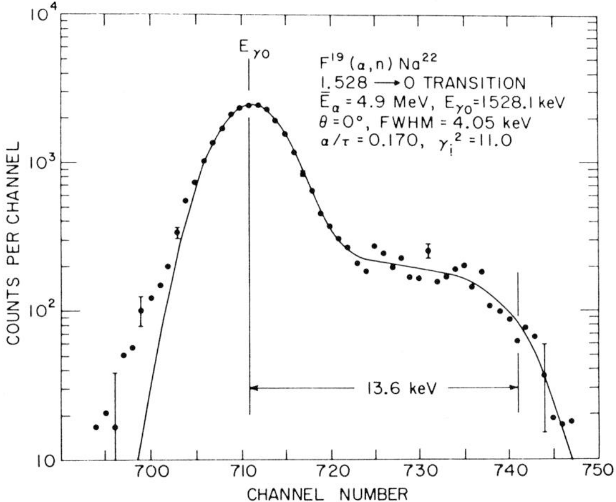

Fig. 14. Doppler line shape of the Na^{22} 1.528 → 0 transition observed at 0° to the beam in the $F^{19}(\alpha,n)Na^{22}$ reaction. Background has been subtracted.

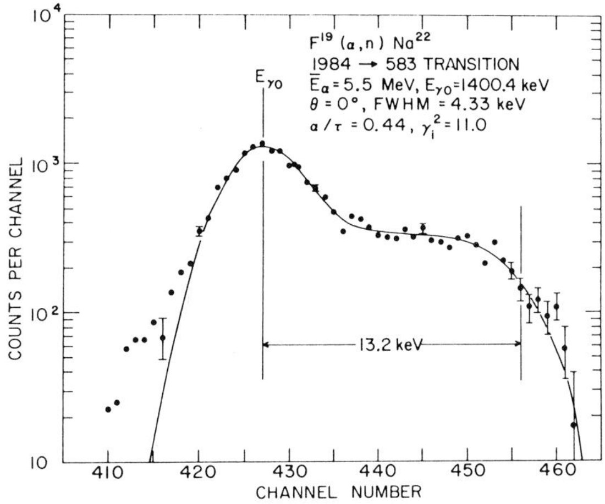

Fig. 15. Doppler line shape of the Na^{22} 1.984 → 0.583 transition observed at 0° to the beam in the $F^{19}(\alpha,n)Na^{22}$ reaction. Background has been subtracted.

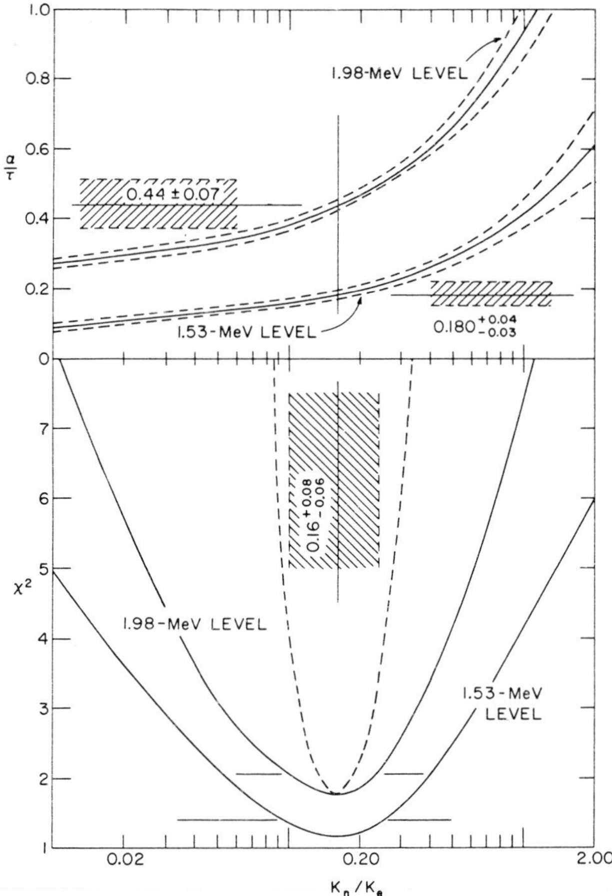

Fig. 16. Resume of the results of a two-parameter search for the best fits to the line shapes of Figs. 14 and 15.

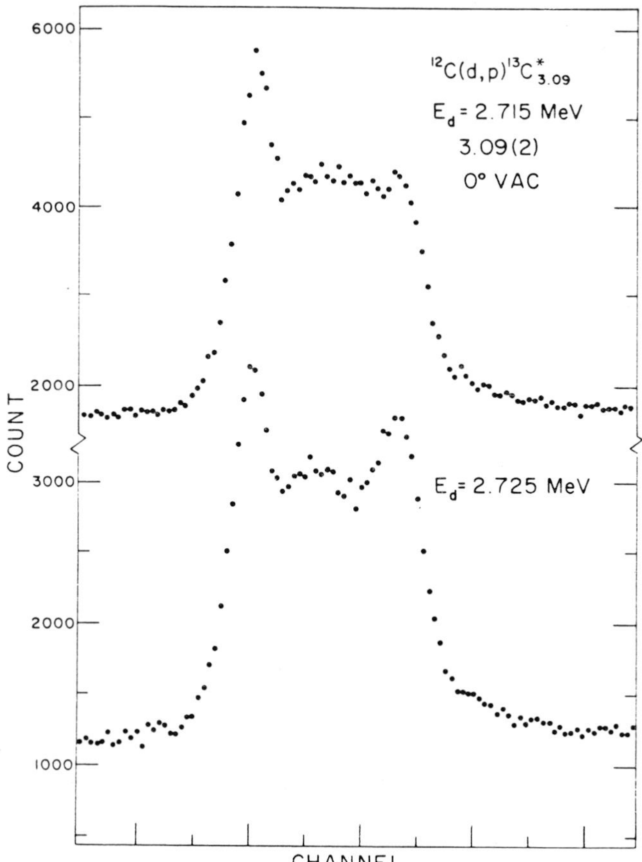

Fig. 17. Doppler line shape of the two-escape peak of the C^{13} 3.09 → 0 transition observed in singles at 0° to the beam in the $C^{12}(d,p)C^{13}$ reaction at two different deuteron energies. The C^{13} ions are recoiling into vacuum.

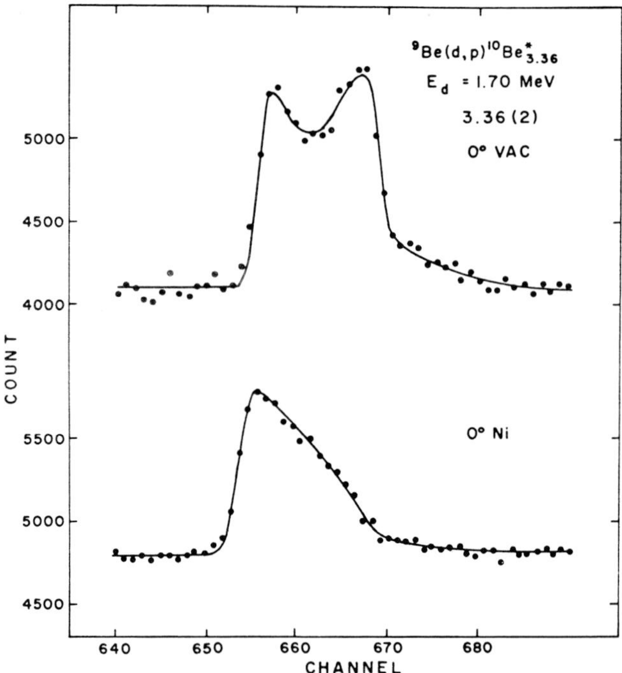

Fig. 18. Doppler line shape of the two-escape peak of the Be^{10} 3.36 → 0 transition observed in singles at 0° to the beam in the $Be^9(d,p)Be^{10}$ reaction. The Be^{10} ions are recoiling into vacuum (upper) and nickel (lower). The solid lines are least-squares fits from which the lifetime of the Be^{10} 3.36-MeV level is extracted.

LIFETIME MEASUREMENTS WITH BREMSSTRAHLUNG*

Edward C. Booth

Boston University
Boston, Massachusetts

Introduction

Nuclear electromagnetic transition probabilities can be measured by various methods including electron scattering, Coulomb excitation, and nuclear resonance fluorescence. This paper describes the use of 3 MeV electron accelerators in such experiments, with special emphasis on the last method.

For transitions with no parity change, the quantities measured at low energies are listed in Table 1.

TABLE 1

Ref	Method	Measured
1),2)	$\sigma_{ee'}(\theta)$	$\frac{g}{m_o c^2}[\Gamma_o(E0)F(E0,\theta)+\Gamma_o(M1)F(M1,\theta)+\Gamma_o(E2)F(E2,\theta)]$
1)	Coulomb	$g\,\Gamma_o(E2)F'(E2,\theta)/m_o c^2$
3)	$\sigma_{\gamma\gamma'}(\theta$	$\{g(\Gamma_o(M1)+\Gamma_o(E2))\}W'(\theta)\Gamma_o/\Gamma$

In Table 1, $g = (2I+1)/(2I_o+1)$, F is a factor in units of cm^2 which can be calculated, $\Gamma_o(E2)$ is the partial width for an electric quadrupole transition to ground state, and $W'(\theta) = \pi W(\theta)/\int W(\theta)d\theta$, where $W(\theta)$ is the usual expression for the angular distribution in a $I_o\to I\to I_o$ gamma-ray cascade. The low energy electron scattering cross sections yield the quantities shown only in the limit of zero momentum transfer; at high energy the terms are momentum dependent. The angular dependence of the electron scattering data can be used to determine the relative amounts of the various multipoles, but at low energies the cross sections are usually too low to permit

*Work supported by the National Science Foundation and Department of Army Research, Durham.

such measurements. Only those multipoles have been included that we are likely to observe in the 0-3 MeV region. The odd-parity E1 transitions are seldom seen because of selection rules and because most of the E1 strength is at higher energies. The Coulomb excitation process preferentially excites E2 transitions, whereas the relativistic electron interaction has appreciable contributions from M1 and E0 multipoles.

Table 1 applies to scattering experiments in which the angular distributions depend on the multipolarities of the transitions. Excitation and absorption measurements can be performed which yield angle-integrated results, but the ratio of charged-particle to photon excitation still depends on the multipolarity of the transitions.

Resonance Fluorescence

1) Scattering and Absorption

Resonance fluorescence is the absorption of on-energy photons, raising the nucleus to an excited saate, with the subsequent emission of de-excitation photons: (γ,γ) or (γ,γ'). For widely separated states, as in the 0-3 MeV region of excitation, the absorption cross section is

$$\sigma_{ab} = g\lambda^2\Gamma_o\Gamma/8\pi[(E-E_r)^2+\Gamma^2/4]$$

where

$$\lambda = c\nu^{-1}$$

and E_r is the energy of the excited state.

The scattering cross section is $\sigma_{ab}\Gamma_o W'(\theta)/\Gamma$, where Γ_o/Γ is the branching ratio for the de-excitation photon. At low energies, $\Delta(I)>>\Delta>>\Gamma$ where $\Delta(I)$ is the instrumental energy resolution and Δ is the Doppler width, and the scattering experiment measures

$$\int(E)dF = \frac{1}{4}\lambda^2 g\Gamma_o[\Gamma_o W'(\theta)/\Gamma]$$

if the incident flux, N(E), is known over the energy region Δ. In a scattering measurement it is ncesssary to determine Γ_o/Γ, $N(E_r)$, $W(\theta)$ (or δ^2) as well as counter efficiencies, in order to find $g\Gamma_o$. Conversely, a measurement of $W(\theta)$ can be made to determine δ^2. The scattered intensity can be attenuated by an absorber by an amount depending on the maximum value of the Doppler broadened absorption cross section; that is,

$$\sigma_r = 0.1\ \lambda^2 g\Gamma_o/\Delta$$

where Δ can be calculated, so that $g\Gamma_o$ can be obtained in this way.

2) Gamma-Ray Sources

The large nuclear recoil energy $E_{rec} = E_r^2/2MC^2$ is of order 10 eV compared to a Doppler width of order $\Delta \simeq 1$ eV and prevents the use of unshifted gamma rays from radioactive sources, so that various techniques are used to obtain photons on resonance. Some of these techniques are mentioned below together with the names of a few workers in the field.

TABLE 2

Category	Technique	Author	Location
Doppler shift	Centrifuge	Metzger[4)]	Bartol
	Thermal	Metzger[4)]	Bartol
	Reaction	Skorka[5)]	Hamburg
Compton shift	n,γ,γ'	Knowles[6)]	Chalk River
	Co^{60},γ,γ'	McIntyre[7)]	Texas
Bremsstrahlung		Booth[8)]	Boston

In any technique it is necessary to obtain a sufficient photon intensity at resonance and also to insure an adequate signal-to-noise ratio, since there is always a background from elastic scattering and from other sources. The signal-to-noise ratio in the case of a background continuous in energy is inversely proportional to the energy resolution of the gamma-ray detector, or to the energy spread of the incident flux in the case of an incident beam with a narrow range of energies. The best detector energy resolution, of order 10 keV, is obtained with Ge(Li) detectors. Doppler- and Compton-shifted photons can be obtained in an energy range from an electron volt up to tens of kilovolts, depending on the method. Another consideration is the total scattered flux, which can degrade the energy resolution at high counting rates. The bremsstrahlung spectrum and the multiple gamma rays of the neutron capture gamma $(n,\gamma\gamma')$ spectrum are bad in this respect, but they have great flexibility in energy and intensity.

3) Bremsstrahlung Resonance Fluorescence

The first successful bremsstrahlung resonance fluorescence measurements were reported by Beckman and Sandstrom[9)] in 1958 using a 0.5-MeV Cockcroft-Walton accelerator. Cohen and Toben[10)] used a linear accelerator to excite the 3.56-MeV state of Li^6 in 1959 and seven cases of resonance fluorescence obtained with a 3-MeV Van de Graaff were reported by Booth[11)] in 1960. Low duty-cycle electron accelerators are not suited to resonance fluorescence measurements since the experiments are count-rate limited at 3 MeV even with a D.C. machine. Tandem Van de Graaffs now have a single-stage capability of 8 MV or more, and should be very useful for bremsstrahlung work provided that the terminal can be made negative. The CW microtron, a cyclic linear accelerator[12)] promises to be a relatively inexpensive source of electrons, but the device is still in development.

Some experimental details of the bremsstrahlung method will now be given. Ideally, thin bremsstrahlung targets are used to take advantage of the square shape of the upper end of the spectrum, and to decrease the total flux at low energies. The resonance energy E_r is set at the tip of the spectrum, eliminating half of the background due to poor energy resolution and avoiding the Compton edge of the spectrum. The Notre Dame group resolved the 3.00 and 2.98-MeV states of a $A\ell^{27}$ by taking an excitation function with a thin bremsstrahlung radiator so that the energy resolution depended on the machine rather than the NaI detector. Electrons emerging from a thin target are largely within a cone of half angle $\theta = m_o c^2/E$ and can be "dumped" magnetically.

The B.U. - M.I.T. group uses targets of 70-keV thickness backed by water, and relies on the detector for energy resolution. Considerable effort was put into a bremsstrahlung monochromator of the type designed by O'Connell[13)], but this was found to be marginal at 3 MeV and was replaced by the Ge(Li) detector for high resolution work. Both ring and point geometry were used with a NaI detector while the 3 cc Ge(Li) crystal required ring geometry for adequate counting rates at 200 μA of beam. Fig. 1 shows the Ge(Li) crystal in ring geometry. Target weights are a kilogram or two, ruling out separated isotopes. Fig. 2 shows the entire spectrum of scattered radiation from 1.6 kg of manganese in ring geometry together with the radiation from the same weight of iron. One can see the 2.564-MeV state of Mn^{55}, as well as indications of the 2.252- and 2.197-MeV states. The 0.51-MeV annihilation radiation dominates the low energy part of the spectrum. Table 3 gives some typical counting conditions for a 3 cc Ge(Li) and a 2"x2" NaI detector.

The data are taken at the highest rate compatible with good energy resolution, which deteriorates above 2 MeV at 200 μA for both detectors. The low-energy Compton scattered photons are attenuated by a 3-cm lead filter, but the annihilation radiation leaks through. The ratio of peak counts to total counting rate is optimized by adjusting the filter

TABLE 3

Counting Rates for the 2.564-MeV State of Mn^{55} with a 1.6 kg target, a 2"x2" NaI and a 3cc Ge(Li) Detector

Detector	Beam	Peak ct.	Resolution	Peak/Total	Total
Ge(Li	100 μA	0.04/sec	15 keV	3×10^{-7}	$1.3\text{x}10^{5}$/sec
NaI	6 μA	1/sec	230 keV	4×10^{-5}	$3\text{x}10^{4}$/sec

thickness, by a thin bremsstrahlung radiation and by large scattering angles. The background rate was measured as a function of energy and atomic number of the target, and is found to have a Z^3 dependence, but is rather independent of energy, unlike Rayleigh scattering. The necessary lifetimes to give a signal/noise ratio of Q = 1 for 100% isotopic abundance and $\{gW'(\theta)\Gamma_o/\Gamma\} = 1$ for NaI are shown as the solid lines in Fig. 3. Since NaI has a high peak counting rate, the experimental errors are largely due to difficulties in matching the target to a dummy target in order to subtract the atomic scattering, so that the Q = 1 line corresponds to matching errors of about 10%. The dotted lines show the 10% statistical limits imposed on the Ge(Li) detector in a 5-hour run at 250 μA beam. The Ge(Li) detector becomes saturated at about 2 MeV where the total rate reaches 2×10^5/sec as shown in Fig. 3. A baseline restoration circuit designed by R.L. Chase[14] permits a factor of two or three increase in total rate. The NaI detector is used to search for cases of resonance fluorescence which are then examined with the Ge(Li) detector. Excitation functions are obtained and target/dummy ratios are computer-plotted to reduce human error. The limits at which one can just detect resonance fluorescence is about a factor of 10 above the curves shown in Fig. 3 for both detectors. In the scattering measurements with large signal/noise ratio, (Q), the principal error is in the determination of the flux $N(E_r)$, which is measured directly or by comparison with previous measurements. Fig. 4 shows the flux at an angle suitable to the ring geometry at an energy 10% below the electron energy. This estimate is believed to be accurate to within ± 20% and is supported by direct measurements. In cases where g is known, $W'(\theta)$ can be calculated only if the mixing ratio δ^2 is known, which is the case if only one multipole is allowed by angular momentum or if the $\Gamma(E2)$ is known from Coulomb excitation measurements. $W'(\theta)$ is nearly the same for pure M1 or E2, but can decrease by a factor of 2 for $\delta^2 \approx 1$. The scattered intensity is corrected for resonance absorption as described by Metzger[4]. The Debye temperatures, θ, were calculated from specific heat measurements in order to find the effective temperature, T_{eff}, needed to calculate the Doppler width $\Delta = E(2k\ T_{eff}/mc^2)^{1/2}$. We have $\Delta/\Gamma > 50$, allowing the use of a pure Doppler shape in the calculation of absorption, which requires a computer solution of a transcendental equation.

4) Bremsstrahlung Absorption

The absorption cross section for thin targets is given to within 5% by $\sigma_r = 0.1\ g\Gamma_o \lambda^2/\Delta$ for $\sigma_r ndx < 1$. For thick absorbers the coefficient decreases, and the procedure described above must be used on both absorber and target. A dummy absorber, as well as a dummy scatterer, is used to account for the atomic effects. It is possible to match the absorbers to $\pm$ 1% using gamma-ray sources, but errors in target matching and instrumental instabilities caused background errors of about 10%, requiring a 50% absorption to give $g\Gamma_o$ to $\pm$20% at Q = 1, using NaI. The Ge(Li) detector has a larger Q by a factor of 10, but a reduction of $g\Gamma_o$ by a factor of 10 requires a similar increase in absorber thickness as well as a large reduction in the counting rate, which was low to begin with. These measurements are feasible with high beam currents and large Ge(Li) detectors. The interpretation of the absorption results is simple, since the incident spectrum is flat across the line width. Corrections for Compton scattering back into the resonance are only a few percent.

5) Angular Distributions

The angular distribution for a mixed transition of L and L+1 for $I_o \to I \to I_o$ is $W(\theta) = 1 + A_2P_2(\cos\theta) + A_4P_4(\cos\theta) + \text{---}$ where

$$A_\nu = [F_\nu(I,I_o,L,L) + 2\delta F_\nu(I,I_o,L,L+1) + \delta^2 F_\nu(I,I_o,L+1,L+1)]^2$$

where $\delta^2 = \Gamma(L+1)/\Gamma(L)$. The ratio $W(\theta_1)/W(\theta_2)$ is measured in hope of determining δ and perhaps I, if I is unknown. Angular correlation studies were made with an accuracy of $\pm$10% where Q > 1, although we incurred needless errors by using NaI crystals of different sizes. Two Ge(Li) detectors could be used to good advantage provided the counting times of order ten hours are acceptable. Fig. 5 shows the $W(\theta)$ ratios as a function of δ^2 for I = 7/2, 5/2 with I_o = 5/2. The cross-hatched area shows the experimental limits on the 1.86-MeV state of Mn^{55} where the 3/2 state was rejected from beta-decay evidence, and the 9/2 state appears as a single point with $\delta^2/(\delta^2 + 1) = 1$. The measurement is inconclusive without an improved accuracy by an order of magnitude, and is typical of cases where the mixing ratio is either small or large.

Table 4 shows the results of our angular distribution measurements.

TABLE 4

Angular Distribution Results

Nucleus	Energy(MeV)	A_2	A_4	Allowed Spins
Mn^{55}	1.884	-0.06 ± 0.07	-0.02 ± 0.07	5/2,7/2
Mn^{55}	2.564	$+0.06\pm0.08$	$+0.11\pm0.06$	3/2,5/2,7/2
Y^{89}	1.53	$+0.6\pm0.3$		3/2
Na^{23}	2.98	0.33 ± 0.05	-0.27 ± 0.07	3/2,5/2
Si^{28}	1.78	0.2 ± 0.1	0.7 ± 0.2	2

6) Discussion of Results

The results of our resonance fluorescence and absorption measurements are shown in Table 5 and are plotted in Fig. 6 where the circles are Coulomb excitation measurements on 2^+ states in even-A nuclei[15], the circles with crosses are our resonance fluorescence measurements in even-A nuclei, the triangles are the results of B(E2) measurements in odd-A nuclei by Coulomb excitation, and the crosses are resonance fluorescence measurements in odd-A nuclei. A number of the crosses contain the factor $(\Gamma_o/\Gamma)^2$ and will move down for $\Gamma_o/\Gamma < 1$. In addition to these cases of resonance fluorescence, a large number of states were examined with negative results, and for these, limits can be assigned to the integral cross section $\int\sigma dE$. One can plot reduced transition probabilities as a frequency distribution in the manner of Wilkinson[16] in the hope of distinguishing between M1 and E2 transitions, but the range is sufficiently broad so that our measurements fit both distributions, although none of the highly enhanced E2 transitions are seen. These frequency plots are not to be taken as a basis for predicting the probability of observing resonance fluorescence in a particular case; otherwise we would have observed more cases than we did, especially at higher energy where many states occur. Aside from the fact that the plots reflect experimental bias toward fast transitions, one expects lower branching ratios at higher energy, a spreading out of transition strength among several states, and larger required multipoles. No resonance fluorescence was observed for states not reported in the 1-2.5 MeV region of the nuclei listed in Table 5. One may estimate the limits using Fig. 3.

The points in Fig. 6 show that, while the E2 transitions to first excited states of even-A nuclei ($A < 100$) lie in a fairly narrow band, there exists a large set of transitions in odd-A nuclei which are faster by an order of magnitude. It is tempting to ascribe this difference to a large M1 component, but a plot of the partial lifetimes from Coulomb excitation measurements in odd-A nuclei shows that even the E2 part of the transition in odd-A nuclei is faster than the average E2 rate in even-A nuclei. More Coulomb excitation work in odd-A nuclei should be forthcoming, so that additional measurements of the total width will be useful in determining $\Gamma_o(M1)$.

The situation with regard to model calculations of these transition probabilities in light and medium-weight odd-A nuclei is not very satisfactory. Individual particle calculations have been made for particular states in the lightest nuclei;[17)] Nilsson model calculations have been applied to $A\ell^{27}$; the particle-core coupling model[18)] has been applied to Cu^{63} and others; and $f_{5/2}$ shell calculation have been made using a strong-coupling symmetric-rotator with Coriolis coupling between bands[19)].

7) Future Work

Our measurements were done under the restriction of limited machine time, and considerable improvement is possible. The energy resolution of the Ge(Li) detector can be increased from the 15 keV we used, and one can obtain detectors larger than 3 cc and beam currents higher than 200 μA. Bremsstrahlung measurements should be extended to higher energy, especially in light nuclei. Resonance fluorescence measurements can be done in nuclei with $A > 90$ using a longer running time and better energy resolution. It may be possible to measure $g\Gamma_o$ for low-lying states in odd-A deformed nuclei, and more Coulomb excitation measurements of $\Gamma_o(E2)$ should be made to combine with $\Gamma_o(E2) + \Gamma_o(M1)$ measurements. Absorption measurements can be made on many of the cases of resonance fluorescence reported in Table 5.

Isomer Excitation

1) Introduction

It is possible to excite long-lived isomeric states in stable nuclei by inducing electromagnetic transitions to a higher state which then decays, in part, to the isomeric state. The activity of the isomeric state can be counted with the beam off, avoiding background from elastic scattering The normal room background can be reduced by the usual low-level counting techniques. This method was an early tool of nuclear spectroscopy, having been used by Pontecorvo in 1938, and it was used in a series of experiments at Notre Dame[21)].

2) Photo-excitation

Isomer excitation by bremsstrahlung measures $g\Gamma_o\Gamma_{iso}/\Gamma$, provided the flux and the counter efficiency are known. Γ_{iso}/Γ is the probability that the short-lived excited state populates the isomeric state. The isomeric states have a large spin difference from the ground state and are of opposite parity. The usual situation is an M1-E2 transition to the excited state, which should be of intermediate spin in order that Γ_{iso}/Γ be greater than zero. For example, in In^{115} one has $9/2^+ \rightarrow 7/2^+ \rightarrow 3/2^+ \rightarrow 1/2^-$. An E1 transition is always required to provide the parity change, since M2 would give a small Γ_{iso}/Γ. A survey shows that little is known about the states picked out by isomer excitation, and indeed we found five new states of In^{113} and Hg^{199}. The photo-excitation measurements are not very useful for determining the transition probability to the excited state, since Γ_{iso}/Γ is often unknown in order of magnitude. Absorption measurements sometimes can be performed inserting an absorber in front of the target, so that $g\Gamma_o$ can be found. It is necessary to "peel" the photo-excitation curves to find values of $g\Gamma_o\Gamma_{iso}/\Gamma$ from successive states, and each absorption measurement must allow for absorption due to a lower state. For example, if one has absorption from three states, the observed resonance cross section is $\sigma''' = = (1 + a)\ \sigma'' + b\sigma_3/(1+a+b)$ where σ_3 is the resonance cross section for the third state, $\sigma''$is the observed cross section for the second state,

$$a=N(E_2)\int\sigma_2(E)\,dE/N(E_1)\int\sigma_1(E)\,dE$$

and

$$b=N(E_3)\int\sigma_3(E)\,dE/N(E_1)\int\sigma_1(E)\,dE.$$

The same corrections must be applied to the photo-absorption data as in the resonance fluorescence experiment, but the criteria for the thin target approximation can always be fulfilled.

3) Electron Excitation

Low energy (3-MeV) electron inelastic scattering measurements are possible for the lightest nuclei[22)], but the signal/noise ratio is very poor in heavy nuclei where the electron cross sections are $\sigma_{ee'}$ 10^{-32} cm^2. It is possible to measure isomer cross sections of $\sigma_{iso}=\sigma_{ee'}\Gamma_{iso}/\Gamma\simeq10^{-35}cm^2$, a fact well known to the early workers. It is only recently that the low energy electron cross sections could be related to the radiative transition probabilities, and problems still remain in the theoretical treatment. For even-parity transitions

$$\sigma_{iso} = g[\Gamma_o(M1)F(M1)+\Gamma_o\ (E2)F(E2)]\Gamma_{iso}/m_oc^2\Gamma.$$

The theoretical F factors are in units of cm^2, and depend on E_r and T, the kinetic energy. A monopole term, $\Gamma_o(E0)F(E0)$, can occur for I_o = I, no parity change. The ratio of the electron to the photon excitation cross section determines F for unmixed transitions, allowing the theoretical value for F to be confirmed if the multipolarity is known. For mixed transitions, the ratio is $[\delta^2F(E2)+F(M1)]/(\delta^2+1)$, determining δ^2 if the F factors are known theoretically. δ^2 can also be found if a photon absorption measurement is made and a Coulomb excitation measurement of $g\Gamma_o(E2)$ exists. The low energy E0 cross section has not been estimated theoretically, except in Born approximation[1)] and by Ter-Martirosyan[23)], who found $\sigma_{ee'}(E0)>10^{-30}cm^2$ at threshold, but cross sections from high energy electron scattering are no larger than E2 cross sections. Isomer excitation including an E0 part will have abnormally large F values, but the experimental situation is unfavorable since Γ_{iso}/Γ is small for I_o = I.

Electron targets are thin and in spite of that, target heating problems occur resulting in counting rates lower than for photo-excitation.

4) Discussion of Results

Photon and electron excitation data are shown for $In^{113,115}$ in Figs. 7 and 8, and the results listed in Table 6.

The electron cross sections have not yet been calculated, but it should be possible to identify multipolarities in the 1-MeV region once the theory is firm near threshold. At energies above 2 MeV, the difference between the F(M1) and F(E2) factors shrinks to about 10%, so that experimental errors preclude multipole assignment; but at least an electron excitation can predict $g\Gamma_o\Gamma_{iso}/\Gamma$ regardless of multipolarity. The principal virtue of the isomer technique is that one can measure $g\Gamma_o$ for the heaviest nuclei in cases which are nearly fluorescence.

TABLE 6

Isomer excitation results. The errors in $g\Gamma_o\Gamma_i/\Gamma$, and σ_e are about $\pm30\%$. The electron energy is $T = 1.1\ E_r$. (nb $=10^{-9}$ barn.)

Nucl.	E_r MeV	J_r	$\sigma_{ee'}$ nb	$\frac{g\Gamma_o\Gamma_i}{\Gamma}$ 10^{-3}eV	B.U. $g\Gamma_o$ 10^{-3}eV	Other $g\Gamma_o$ 10^{-3}eV	$\frac{g\Gamma_o}{\Gamma_w(E2)}$
Sr^{87}	1.22	?	1.0	0.003			
	1.88	?	1.4	0.15			
	2.66	?	4.1	6.9	~50		20
In^{113}	1.01	$(7/2^+)$	0.3	0.003			
	1.13	$(5/2^+)$	1.4	0.025			
	1.58	$(7/2^+)$	3.4	0.58			
In^{115}	.935	$7/2^+$	0.2	0.002	$0.3^{+.3}_{-.2}$	0.08 ± 0.03 [24]	15
	1.08	$(5/2^+)$	1.8	0.035	0.28 ± 0.08	0.6 ± 0.3 [24]	7
	1.45	$(7/2^+)$	2.8	0.32	$1.5^{+.6}_{-.5}$		8
	1.57	?	2.0	0.16	small		
Hg^{199}	1.49	?	0.4	0.004			
	1.61	?	0.4	0.006	~3		5

No calculations have been made for these transition probabilities. The isomers are supposed to be spherical nuclei, and their even-A neighbors exhibit vibrational transitions with strengths of order 10(E2) single particle units, in agreement with Table 6. The models coupling single-particle motion to even-A core excitations apparently become complex above 1 MeV.

5) Future Work

A few long-lived isomers remain to be studied, as well as half a dozen in the 1-second to 10-minute lifetime region. A large number of cases might be studied by pulsing the electron accelerator and extending the technique to the microsecond or nanosecond region. This is a more difficult experiment but will allow one to study a class of nuclei different from the spherical isomeric cases. The direction of development will be toward machines of high current with good pulse capability.

Coulomb Excitation of Isomers

Isomeric states can be excited with ions to measure $g\Gamma_o(E2)\Gamma_{iso}/\Gamma$, which can be compared to the photo-excitation results to find δ^2. Calculations show that the 1.08-MeV state of In^{115} will be excited by a 10μA beam of 2.5-MeV protons. Unfortunately the excitation function will show no "breaks", since the upper end of the virtual photon spectrum is not square as it is for relativistic electrons. Nevertheless, the method could be used for isolated states or to set limits on the $\Gamma_o(E2)$ strength over several states.

ACKNOWLEDGMENTS

This work was performed using the proto-type 4 MeV electron Van de Graaff at the High Voltage Engineering Laboratory of M.I.T. The author is grateful to Dr. John Trump for his interest in the project, which has lasted somewhat longer than we thought. Mr. Kenneth A. Wright of M.I.T. has been active in the data taking and in solving machine problems. Dr. Benson Chertok and Mr. Henry Wilson played a large role in the isomer and resonance fluorescence experiments. Dr. William Alston and Mr. John Brownson are currently contributing to the experiments, while Dr. Bernard Chasan joined in the ill-advised monochromator project.

TABLE 5

Partial widths measured by bremsstrahlung, including old measurements with recent spin assignments and compared to recent averages of partial widths. The mean lifetime in units of 10^{-14} sec is nominal and should not be taken as a measurement. "T" refers to total width and "abs" means measured by absorption.

Nucl	E_r MeV	J_r	Γ_o/Γ	$gW\Gamma_o\Gamma_o/\Gamma$ 10^{-3}eV	Err %	Γ_o(BU) (10^{-3}eV)	Γ_o(other) (10^{-3}eV)	δ^2 (%)	τ 10^{-14} sec
Li^7	0.000	$3/2^-$							
	0.478	$1/2^-$	1.0	abs	14	7.1	T 5.9	0.005	11
							E2 0.0003		
B^{11}	0.000	$3/2^-$							
	2.124	$1/2^-$	1.0	55	33	110	M1 135		0.51
N^{14}	0.000	0^+							
	2.312	1^+	1.0	3.0	36	6.8	M1 8.3		8.2
F^{19}	0.000	$1/2^+$							
	1.460	$3/2^-$	(0.15)	$2.4\Gamma_o/\Gamma_1$	30	$1.8\Gamma/\Gamma_1$	M1 $6.5\Gamma_o/\Gamma_1$	7	36
							E2 $0.45\Gamma_o/\Gamma_1$		
	1.560	$3/2^+$	(0.04)	$6.0\Gamma_o/\Gamma_2$	36	$3.0\Gamma/\Gamma_2$	M1 <3.6	5	22
				abs	15		E2 0.15		
Na^{23}	0.000	$3/2^+$							
	3.000	$(3/2^+)$	0.46	47	35	100-200	M1 48	50	0.44
				abs	30	140			
Mg^{24}	0.000	0^+							
	1.368	2^+	1.0	1.6	31	0.45	E2 0.37		180
Mg^{25}	0.000	$5/2^+$							
	1.611	$7/2^+$	1.0	31	24	23-36	T 27		2.4
Mg^{26}	0.000	0^+							
	1.805	2^+	1.0	5.5	42	1.6	E2 1.0		66
Al^{27}	0.000	$5/2^+$							
	2.212	$7/2^+$	0.98	abs	15	16.5	T 13		4.7
	2.908	$3/2^+$	0.90	abs	18	86	T 100		0.7
Si^{28}	0.000	0^+							
	1.772	2^+	1	3.7	27	1.1	E2 0.89		0.73
Si^{29}	0.000	$1/2^+$							
	1.277	$3/2^+$	1.0	7.7	35	3.9-7.1	T 1.5		40
	2.425	$3/2^+$	?	6.0	35	$(30\text{-}55)\Gamma/\Gamma_o$	—		1.6
P^{31}	0.000	$1/2^+$							
	1.265	$3/2^+$	1.0	1.2	31	0.6-1.1	T 0.84	6	80
							E2 0.055		
	2.232	$5/2^+$	1.0	3.5	35	1.5-2.6	E2 1.5		33
	3.133	$3/2^+$	?	66	35	$(33\text{-}61)\Gamma/\Gamma_o$	—		
S^{32}	0.000	0^+							
	2.236	2^+	?	7.7	33	$2.1\Gamma/\Gamma_o$	E2 2.6		25

TABLE 5 (cont.)

Nucl	E_r MeV	J_r	Γ_o/Γ	$gW\Gamma_o\Gamma_o/\Gamma$ 10^{-3}eV	Err %	Γ_o(BU) (10^{-3}eV)	Γ_o(other) (10^{-3}eV)	δ^2 (%)	τ 10^{-14} sec
$C\ell^{35}$	0.000	$3/2^+$							
	1.220	$1/2^+$	1	1.1	35	0.55	M1 5.0		
	1.762	$5/2^+$	?	1.6	35	(1-2)Γ/Γ_o	—		
	2.70	?	?	21	35	21/$gW\Gamma_o/\Gamma$	—		3.0
	3.01	?	?	18	35	18/$gW\Gamma_o/\Gamma$	—		3.5
K^{39}	0.000	$3/2^+$							
	3.02	?	?	18	35	18/$gW\Gamma_o/\Gamma$	—		3.6
	3.90	?	?	47	35	47/$gW\Gamma_o/\Gamma$	—		1.4
Ti^{47}	0.000	$5/2^-$							
	2.58	?	?	146	40	146/$gW\Gamma_o/\Gamma$	—		0.45
Ti^{48}	0.000	0^+							
	0.99	2^+	1.0	0.60	36	0.17	E2 0.11		60
	2.30	(2^+)	1	9.8	40	2.8Γ/Γ_o	—		2.3
V^{51}	0.000	$7/2^-$							
	1.609	$(11/2^-)$	(1)	0.60	26	0.40-0.70	—		120
Cr^{52}	0.000	0^+							
	1.434	2^+	1	1.9	30	0.55	E2 0.67		100
Cr^{53}	0.000	$3/2^-$							
	2.32	$(1/2^-)$	(1)	105	32	210	—		
Mn^{55}	0.000	$5/2^-$							
	1.527	$(3/2^-)$	0.9	4.7	25	8-12	—		10
				abs	40	8.2			
	1.884	?	(0.6)*	37	25	45-130	—		1.2
				abs	10	55/g			
	2.197	?	(0.8)*	16	25	9-27	—		4
				abs	20	17/g			
	2.252	?	(0.9)*	15^+	25	10-31	—		5
				abs	20	13/g			
	2.365	?	?	3.1	36	(2-7)Γ/Γ_o	—		13
	2.564	?	(1)*	44	25	27-100	—		1.1
				abs	20	61/g			
	2.751	?	?	6.0	42	(4-14)Γ/Γ_o	—		7
Fe^{56}	0.000	0^+							
	0.847	2^+	1	0.26	50	0.075	E2 0.063		900
Ni^{58}	0.000	0^+							
	1.452	2^+	(1)	35	32	1.0	E2 0.76		86
Co^{59}	0.000	$7/2^-$							
	1.189	$(7/2^-)$	(1)*	6.2	25	7.5	E2 0.33	5	8
				abs	25	12			
		$(9/2^-)$	(1)*	6.2	25	5.0	E2 0.27	6	13
				abs	25	10			
	1.458	?	?	1.6	33	1.6/$gW\Gamma/\Gamma_o$	—		41
	2.477	?	?	8.7	40	8.7/$gW\Gamma/\Gamma_o$	—		8

TABLE 5 (cont.)

Nucl	E_r MeV	J_r	Γ_o/Γ	$gW\Gamma_o\Gamma_o/\Gamma$ 10^{-3}eV	Err %	Γ_o(BU) (10^{-3}eV)	Γ_o(other) (10^{-3}eV)	δ^2 (%)	τ 10^{-14} sec
Cu^{63}	0.000	$3/2^-$							
	0.668	$1/2^-$	1	0.90	25	1.8	T 2.1 E2 0.025	0.12	31
	0.961	$5/2^-$	1	0.94	25	178	T 0.76 E2 0.16	27	88
	1.327	$7/2^-$	0.91	1.3	32	0.75	E2 0.72		91
	1.412	$3/2^-$	?	1.4	30	(1.4-2.6) x Γ/Γ_o	—		33
		$5/2^-$	?	1.4	30	0.9-1.6Γ/Γ_o	—		53
	1.547	$(5/2^-)$	?	1.5	37	1.0-1.7Γ/Γ_o	—		49
Cu^{65}	0.000	$3/2^-$							
	0.771	$1/2^-$	1	2.4	25	4.7	T 5.0 E2 0.045	0.9	13
	1.114	$5/2^-$	1	1.6	36	1.3	T 1.25 E2 0.25	25	53
	1.482	$7/2^-$	0.76	3.0	47	2.1	E2 1.1		60
Ga^{69}	0.000	3.2^-							
	0.87	?	?	0.8	35	.8$\Gamma/gW\Gamma_o$			36
	1.117	?	?	7.5	20	7.5$\Gamma/gW\Gamma_o$			5
As^{75}	0.000	$3/2^-$							
	0.86	?	?	1.5	20	3.4$\Gamma/gW\Gamma_o$	—		19
	1.07	?	?	1.2	30	2.3$\Gamma/gW\Gamma_o$			
	1.35	?	?	3.5	20	6.0$\Gamma/gW\Gamma_o$	—		11
Br^{79}	0.000	$3/2^-$							
	0.833	$(1/2^-)$	0.70	0.72	25	2.1	T 3.2 E2 0.004	0.2	12
Sr^{88}	0.000	0^+							
	1.84	2^+	1.0	7.5	50	2.1	E2 4.4		25
Y^{89}	0.000	$1/2^-$							
	1.53	?	?	42 abs	15	42$\Gamma/gW\Gamma_o$ 45/ g	 —		1.6 1.5
	2.52	?	?	33	50	33$\Gamma/gW\Gamma_o$	—		2.0
Ce^{140}	0.000	0^+							
	1.596	2^+	1.0	13	33	3.7	E2 5.3		18

*Measured with Ge(Li) detector; accuracy ± 10%.
+Transitions between the 2.365 → 0.126 states may have contributed to this transition strength.

REFERENCES

1. K. Alder, A. Bohr, T. Huus, B. Mottelson, and A. Winther, Rev. Mod. Phys. 28 432 (1956).
2. H. Robl, Nucl. Phys. 2, 641 (1956/1957).
3. F. Metzger, in Progr. in Nucl. Phys., Vol. 7, p. 53; ed. by P. Frische (Pergamon Press, New York, 1959).
4. F. Metzger, Phys. Rev. 139B, 1464 (1965).
5. S. Skorka, R. Hübner, T. Retz-Schmidt and H. Wahl, Nucl. Phys. 47, 417 (1963).
6. J. Knowles, Canadian Assoc. of Physicists Conf., Vancouver, 1965. (CONF 650664).
7. Jack McIntyre (preprint).
8. E. C. Booth, B. Chasan and K. A. Wright, Nucl. Phys. 57, 403 (1964).
9. A. Beckman and R. Sandstrom, Nucl. Phys. 5, 595 (1958).
10. L. Cohen and R. Tobe, Nucl. Phys. 14, 243 (1959).
11. E. C. Booth, Nucl. Phys. 19, 426 (1960).
12. P. Wintersteiner and D. Edmonds, Proc. 1967 Accel. Conf. Washington.
13. J. O'Connell, P. Tipler and P. Axel, Phys. Rev. 126, 228 (1962).
14. R. Chase and L. Paulo, BNL 10649.
15. P. Stelson and L. Grodzins, Nuclear Data 1, 21 (1965).
16. D. H. Wilkinson, in Nuclear Spectroscopy, ed. by F. Ajzenberg-Selove (Academic Press, New York, 1960).
17. D. Kurath and S. Cohen, Nucl. Phys. 73, 1 (1965).
18. B. Bayman and L. Silverberg, Nucl. Phys. 16, 625 (1960).
19. W. Sholz and F. Malik, Phys. Rev. 147, 836 (1966).
20. B. Pontevorco, Compt. Rend. 208, 99 (1938).
21. W. C. Miller and B. Waldman, Phys. Rev. 75, 425 (1949).
22. B. Chertok and E. C. Booth, Nucl. Phys. 66, 230 (1965).
23. K. Ter-Martirosyan, ZHETF (USSR) 20, 925 (1950).
24. Y. Cauchois, Y. Heno and M. Boivin, Compt. Rend. 259, 3233 (1964).

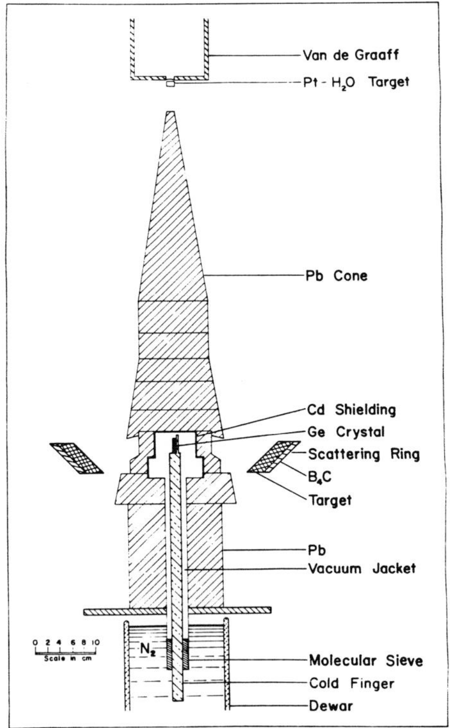

Fig. 1 Resonance fluorescence scattering assembly for the Ge(Li) detector.

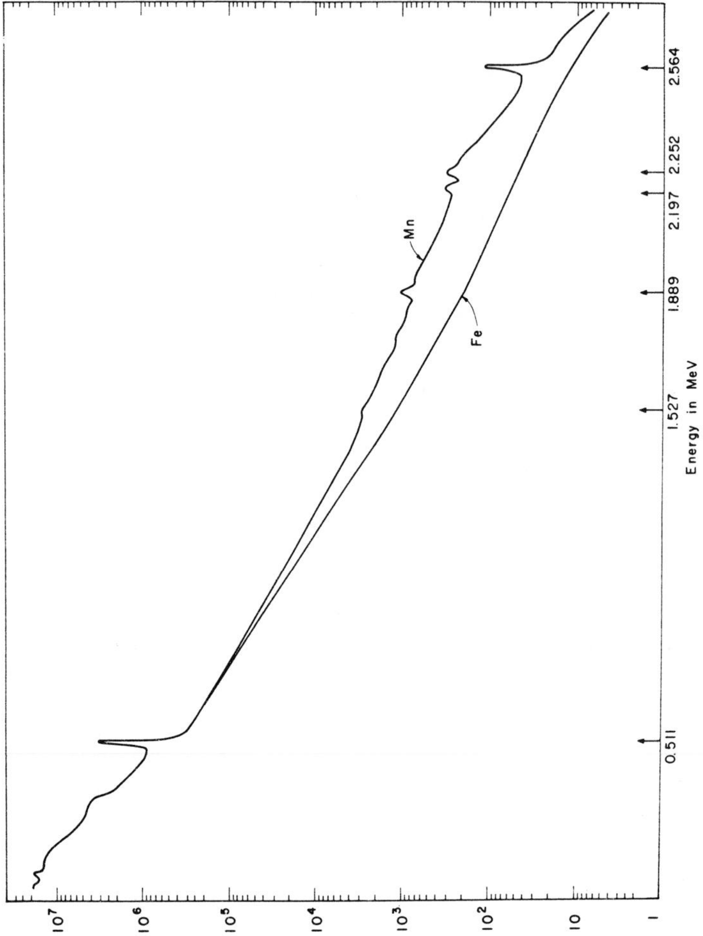

Fig. 2 Scattered radiation from 1.6 kg of manganese showing resonance fluorescence from the excited states of Mn^{55}. The lower line is the scattering from iron.

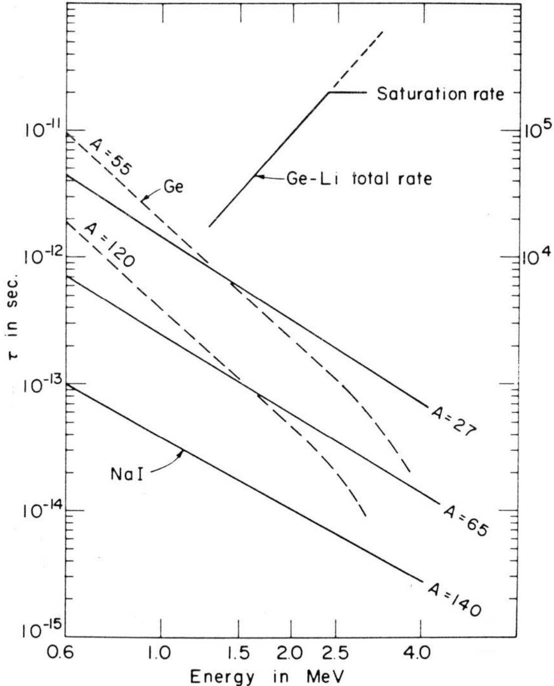

Fig. 3 The solid lines show the lifetime necessary to obtain a signal-to-noise ratio of Q=1 at E_r=0.9 T (where T is the bombarding kinetic energy) using NaI with 100% isotopic abundance and $\{gW(\theta)\Gamma_o/\Gamma\}=1$. The lifetimes required to give a 10% measurement with a 3 cc Ge(Li) detector are shown by the dotted lines. The total counting rates with Ge(Li) are shown at the upper right using a 250 μA beam.

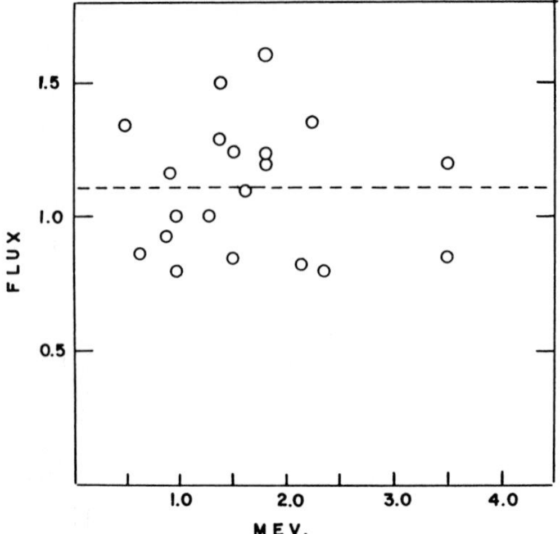

Fig. 4 This figure shows the incident proton flux in 10^{10} photons/MeV-sr·sec·μA at $\theta = 11^{o}$ from a 0.001 in. platinum foil backed by water at a photon energy of $E_r = 0.9$ T, as found by measuring the resonance fluorescence from states of known values of $g\Gamma_o{}^2 W(\theta)/\Gamma$.

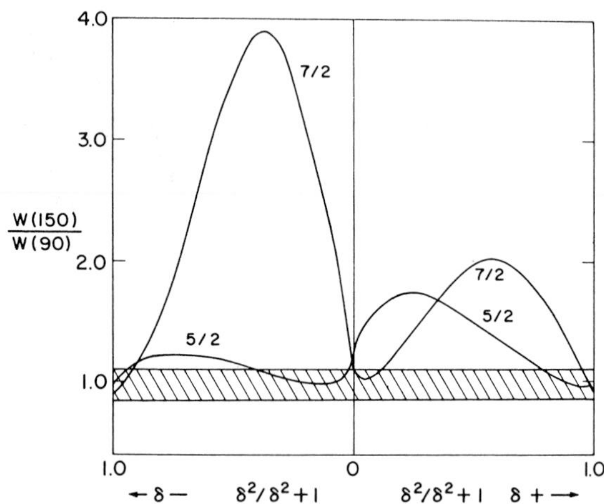

Fig. 5 $W(\theta_1)/W(\theta_2)$ calculated for E1 or mixed E2+M1 radiation for $I_o = 5/2$, I = 7/2, 5/2, as a function of the mixing ratio δ^2. The shaded areas are the experimental limits for the 1.89-MeV state of Mn^{55}.

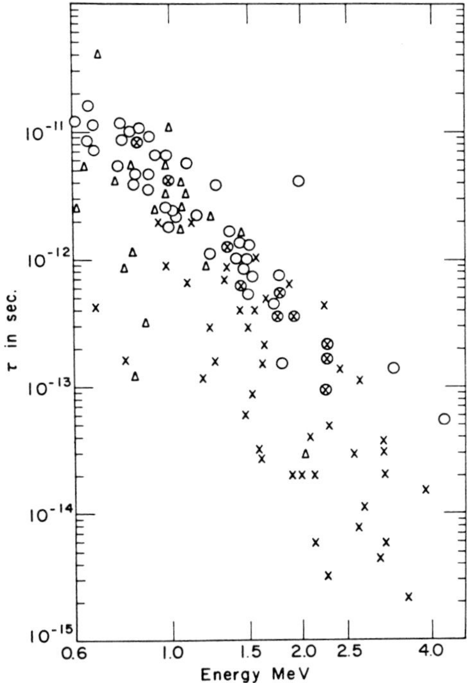

Fig. 6 Experimental values of E2 lifetimes are shown as open circles for coulomb excitation and crosses for resonance fluorescence in even-A nuclei. Δ is for partial lifetimes from coulomb excitation of odd-A nuclei and crosses are for resonance fluorescence lifetimes in odd-A nuclei.

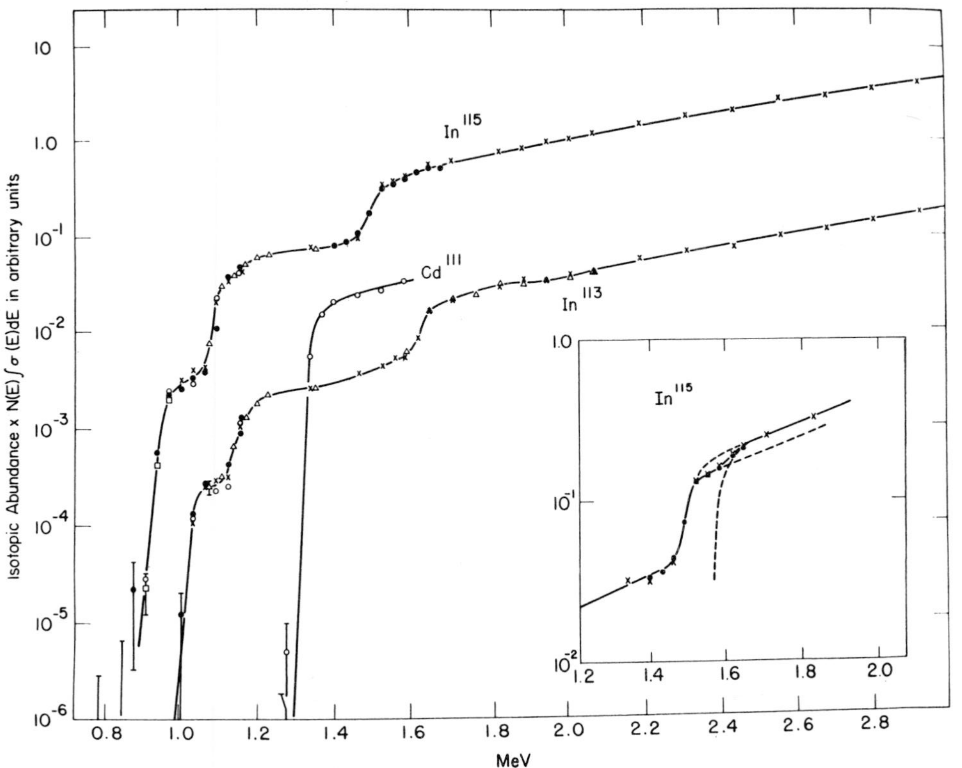

Fig. 7 Photo-excitation curve for the isomeric excitation of In^{115}, In^{113}, and Cd^{111}. The shape of the function reflects the bremsstrahlung intensity at resonance. Recent measurements have lowered the thresholds on the left by a factor of 20.

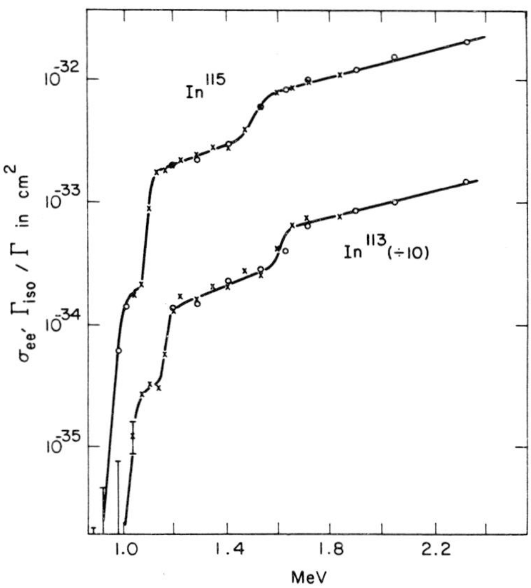

Fig. 8 Electron-excitation functions for In^{113} and In^{115}.

A COINCIDENCE-ANTICOINCIDENCE Ge(Li)-NaI(Tℓ) SYSTEM*

D. M. Van Patter

Bartol Research Foundation of the Franklin Institute
Swarthmore, Pennsylvania

INTRODUCTION

In dealing with complex spectra containing many γ rays of varying intensities, the usefulness of a Ge(Li) counter can be substantially enhanced if it is operated in conjunction with one or more NaI(Tℓ) crystals placed in close proximity. There has been a marked trend lately in this direction, for there have been several recent reports of Ge(Li)-Na(Tℓ) spectrometers, consisting of one or more NaI(Tℓ) detectors surrounding a central Ge(Li) diode[1-11].

Some of these systems were designed primarily to provide an anticoincidence shield, such as a single NaI(Tℓ) annular or well-type detector, in order to suppress Compton events in the central Ge(Li) detector[2-5]. I wish to concentrate on systems which can also be employed as a pair spectrometer, where those annihilation quanta which escape are recorded in coincidence with pair producing events in the Ge(Li) detector[1,5-11]. A system with a particularly high overall performance has been reported by D.C. Camp[7]. It has an especially favorable geometry consisting of two 9.0" OD x 4.5" thick NaI(Tℓ) crystals, which fit snugly around a planar 7-cc Ge(Li) detector. I recommend his excellent monograph in which he discusses this system, as well as the basic principles of Ge(Li) detectors and their associated electronics.

A point of interest concerns the comparative performance of two-crystal and three-crystal pair spectrometers. In the two-crystal arrangement, it is necessary to set a gate on the 511-511 keV sum peak in the surrounding NaI(Tℓ) detector[5]. This mode of operation has been shown by Auble et al.[8] to be clearly inferior to a geometry utilizing triple coincidences. Using a split NaI(Tℓ) annulus, they

* Work supported by the U.S. Air Force Office of Scientific Research and the National Science Foundation.

compared directly two-escape coincidence spectra from Co^{56} for both situations. The improvement in the peak-to-background ratio for the three-crystal spectrometer was quite marked, especially for γ-ray energies below 2 MeV.

EXPERIMENTAL APPARATUS

A coincidence-anticoincidence spectrometer has been recently constructed at the Bartol Research Foundation. Its geometry and general characteristics are similar to several of the other new systems at other laboratories. A preliminary report of its performance has been given by P.F. Hinrichsen[11], who has been chiefly responsible for the design and development of this facility.

The present configuration of the system is shown in Fig. 1. It consists of a 20-cc Ge(Li) detector, placed at the center of a split NaI(Tℓ) annulus of standard Trail-Raboy[12] dimensions (12" long x 8" OD x 2.75" ID), supplied by the Harshaw Chemical Company. Each optically-isolated half is coupled to three phototubes, which are offset to provide space for the Ge(Li) cold finger. Energy resolutions of 11 and 12% for Cs^{137} 662-keV radiation were obtained, considerably better than the 15-20% resolution achieved for prior annuli[12,13].

A six-inch collimator ($\Omega/4\pi=5\times10^{-4}$) of Mallory metal is used to shield the annulus from direct γ radiation, and provides a minimum attenuation of 5000 at E_γ=3 MeV. With this geometry, counting rates in the annulus have proved to be satisfactorily low for external neutron-free sources. Under such conditions, the timing characteristics of the central Ge(Li) detector are not critical.

The central Ge(Li) detector (five-sided drift) has a depth of 20 mm with very little dead volume, but its timing characteristics are rather poor. Consequently, large time windows were required for both the coincidence (57 ns) and anticoincidence (110 ns) modes.

The entire system is mounted on a turntable for the purpose of measuring angular distributions of γ radiations from nuclear reactions. It is located on one beam line of the University of Pennsylvania tandem accelerator.

One of the most attractive features of this system concerns Hinrichsen's method of storing various types of Ge(Li) counter events. Each event is tagged with a logic pulse, which is fed into the Y input of an analyzer, operated in the 1024x4 two-dimensional mode. The net result is the simultaneous accumulation of four spectra, stored under identical gain and linearity conditions, which is a particularly desirable feature from the viewpoint of data analysis.

The four spectra obtained with a Y^{88} source are shown in Fig. 2. The original singles spectrum (top curve) is obtained from a sum of the three lower spectra. The full energy spectrum shows those events in which there was no count in either NaI(Tℓ) crystal. The Compton-suppressed events are shown in the spectrum of rejected counts. This spectrum, which is normally not exhibited, is useful for identifying single-escape peaks, and contains as well a large fraction of the two-escape peaks. The lowest spectrum represents the triple 511-511-γ coincidences, which in this case represent about 30 percent of the counts in the two-escape peak (814 keV) registered in the singles spectrum.

One great advantage of this four-spectra display is the ease in which two types of γ-ray peaks (full energy, single or double escape) can be identified even though they may happen to have the same energy. One glance at the relative intensities of a given peak in the four spectra will reveal immediately whether or not a single peak in the singles spectrum may have more than one type of contribution.

A Compton suppression factor of 3.8 was obtained for this system, as shown by the two normalized spectra for Co^{60} in Fig. 3. This result appears to be normal for this geometry. It should be pointed out that the important criterion for Compton suppression of such a system is the suppression factor achieved for complex spectra, which may be less than that quoted for a single source[7].

APPLICATIONS

Figure 4 shows the low energy portions of γ-ray spectra observed from the decay of 52-min As^{70}. Since the activity was produced by bombardment of an enriched Ge^{70} target on a platinum backing, some lines from contaminant activities of As^{72} and $Au^{194,6,8}$ are present. The lower curve shows the effect of Compton suppression, which enhances the weaker peaks up to a factor of ≃4 relative to background. A weak 834-keV As^{72} peak is clearly visible on the Compton edge of the 1040-keV γ ray, which could be easily overlooked in the singles spectrum. At the bottom of the figure are shown a few prominent two-escape peaks in the three-crystal coincidence spectrum. This investigation[14] has established that the main decay (≃70%) of As^{70} proceeds through a 13-keV doublet (3047, 3060 keV) rather than a single state as was previously thought[15].

Another interesting facet of this study concerns the 3-keV doublet (2154,2157 keV), which was recently established by a high resolution (p,p') study using a broad-range magnetic spectrograph[16]. Here the capability of the system for studying (p,p'γ) spectra proved to be of value. Figure 5 shows a comparison of portions of spectra for the Ge^{70}(p,p'γ) and $As^{70}(\gamma)Ge^{70}$ reaction taken under nearly identical gain conditions. From detailed analysis of such spectra, the decay properties of this doublet have been determined. The 2157-keV member has a larger branch to the anomalous $0^{+'}$ state (1216 keV) than to the ground state of Ge^{70}. When the $E_{\gamma}{}^{5}$ dependence for quadrupole transitions is taken into account, the ratio of B(E2) values becomes about 300:1. This is persuasive evidence that the 2157-keV state is the first 2^{+} member of a new band which starts with the $0^{+'}$ state.

As indicated in Fig. 1, the Ge(Li)-NaI(Tℓ) spectrometer can be rotated about the target; this provides the possibility of measuring energy-averaged (p,p'γ) angular distributions[17] for determination of spins of excited states as well as γ-ray multipole admixtures. In our first application, we have examined Ni^{58}(p,p'γ) spectra at E_p=7.0 MeV for $\theta=0^{o}$ to 90°. Initial examination of the triple coincidence spectra revealed a previously unsuspected ground-state branch (4±1%) from the 2.77-MeV level, which had been thought to be a 0^+ state. The initial angular distribution results are consistent with J=2 assignment[18]. Identification of this level as the 2_2^+ level then produces a discrepancy of $\sim 10^4$ with the E2 branching predicted by Cohen et al.[19]

I hope I have demonstrated the tremendous capability of such a Ge(Li)-NaI(Tℓ) system. It is really satisfying to see a complex γ-ray spectra decomposed into four parts, and to realize how far we've come from the days of using a single NaI(Tℓ) detector for spectral analysis.

REFERENCES

1 G.T. Ewan and A.J. Tavendale, Can.J.Phys. 42, 2286 (1964).

2 Y. Sever and J. Lippert, Nucl. Instr. and Meth. 33, 347 (1965).

3 M.W. Hill, Nucl. Instr. and Meth. 36, 350 (1965).

4 J. Kantele and P. Suominen, Nucl. Instr. and Meth. 41, 41 (1966).

5 J.B. Ashe, G.H. Williams and J.D. Hall, Bull. Am. Phys. Soc. 11, 102 (1966).

6 V.J. Orphan and N.C. Rasmussen, Nucl. Instr. and Meth. 48, 282 (1967).

7 D.C. Camp, UCRL-50156 (March 1, 1967).

8 R.E. Auble et al., Nucl. Instr. and Meth. 51, 61 (1967).

9 R.K. Smither and A.I. Namenson, Rev. Sci. Instr. 38, 52 (1967).

10 P.H. Stelson, Phys. Rev. 157, 1098 (1967).

11 P.F. Hinrichsen and T. Bardin, Bull. Am. Phys. Soc. 12, 462 (1967).

12 C.C. Trail and S. Raboy, Rev. Sci. Instr. 30, 425 (1959).

13 C.O. Bostram and J.E. Draper, Rev. Sci. Instr. 32, 1024 (1961).

14 D.M. Van Patter and P.F. Hinrichsen, Bull. Am. Phys. Soc. 12, 510 (1967).

[15] P. Born, C. Bobeldijk, W.A. Oost, and J. Blok, Physica 29, 277 (1963).

[16] P.F. Hinrichsen, D.M. Van Patter and M.H. Shapiro, Bull. Am. Phys. Soc. 12, 129 (1967).

[17] E. Sheldon and D.M. Van Patter, Revs. Mod. Phys. 38, 143 (1966).

[18] R.N. Horoshko, P.F. Hinrichsen and D.M. Van Patter, private communication.

[19] S. Cohen, R.D. Lawson, M.H. Mcfarlane, S.P. Pandya and M. Soga, Phys. Rev., to be published.

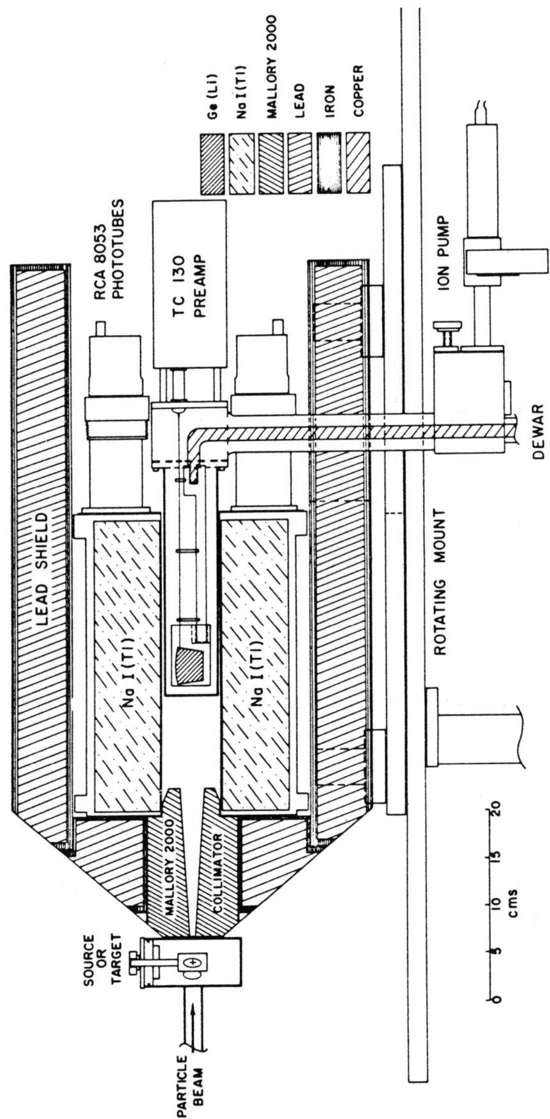

Fig. 1 Assembly of the Ge(Li)-NaI(Tℓ) spectrometer, including its shield, mount and cooling system.

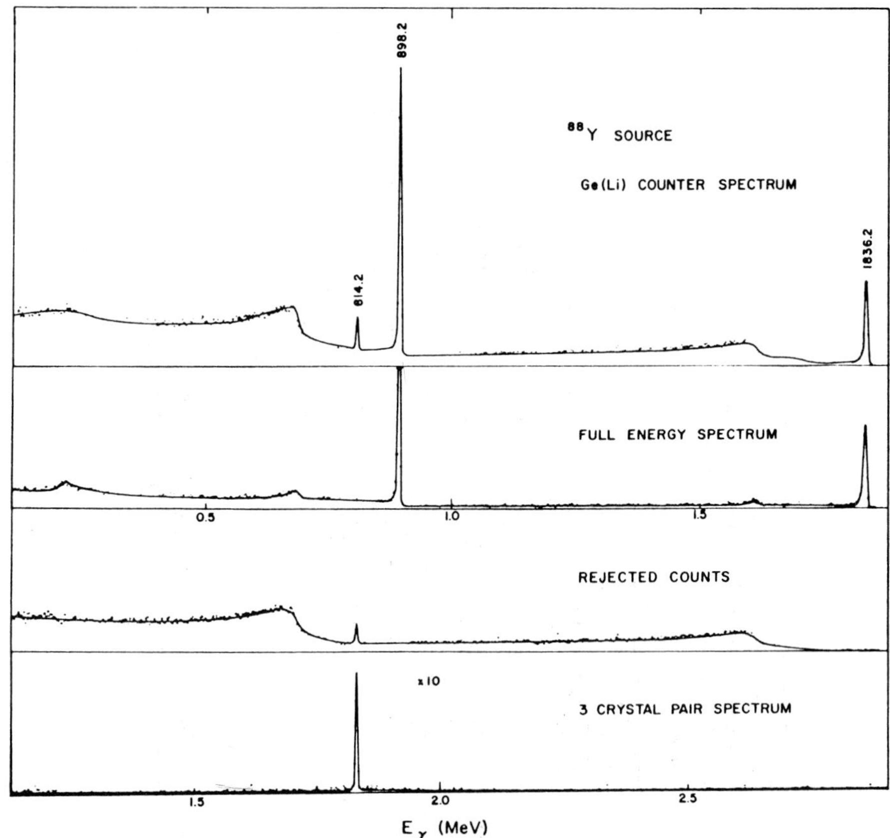

Fig. 2 Four simultaneous spectra from a Y^{88} source. Note the enhancement of the 814.2-keV two-escape peak in the three-crystal pair spectrum, and its suppression in the full energy spectrum.

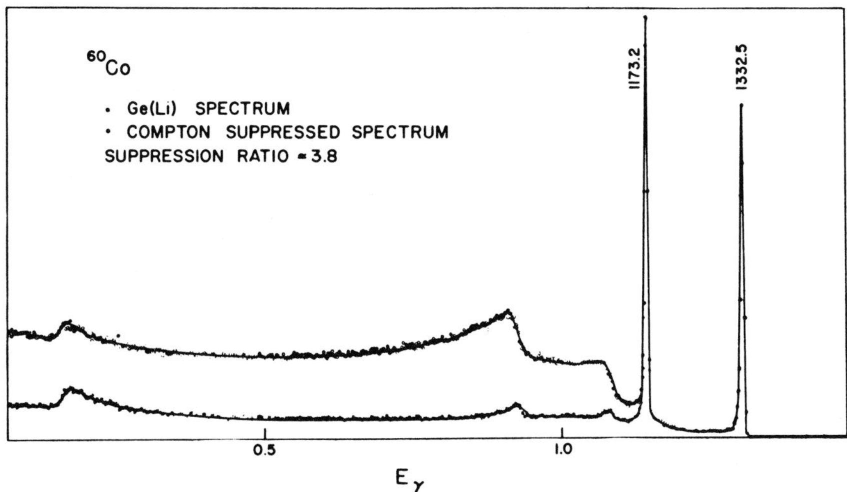

Fig. 3 Effect of Compton suppression for a Co^{60} source.

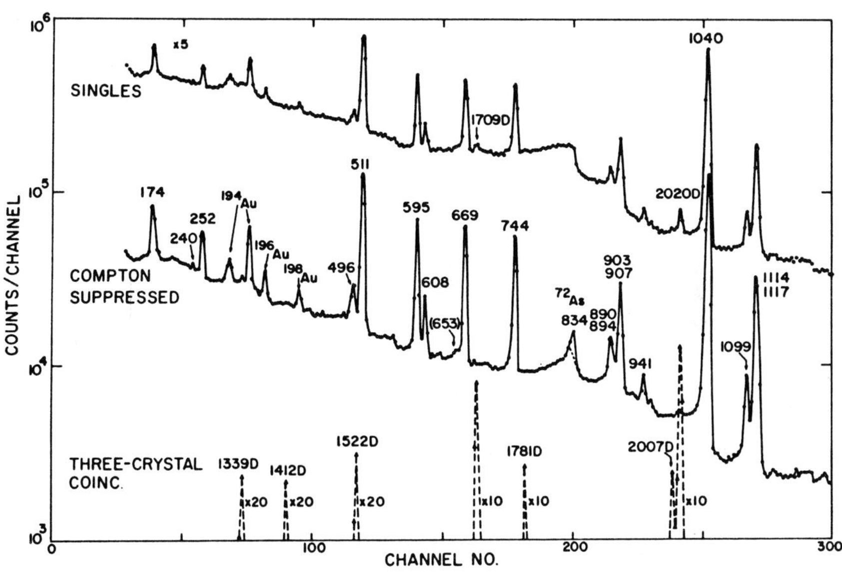

Fig. 4 Low-energy portion of spectra observed for a source of 52-min As^{70}. Contaminant activities include As^{72} and $Au^{194,6,8}$.

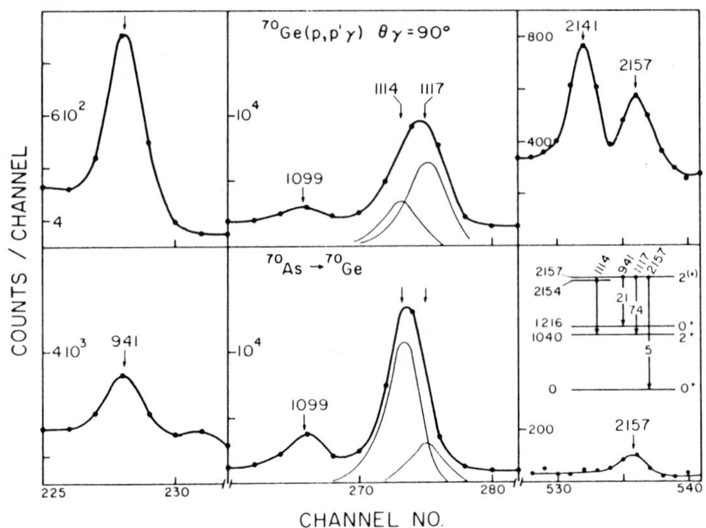

Fig. 5 Comparison of selected portions of γ spectra from the $Ge^{70}(p,p'\gamma)$ and $As^{70}(\gamma)Ge^{70}$ reactions, emphasizing the γ-ray decays of a 2154, 2157 keV doublet in Ge^{70}.

USES OF MAGNETIC SPECTROMETERS*

F. C. Young

University of Maryland
College Park, Maryland

INTRODUCTION

Magnetic spectrometers have been used for many years in experimental studies of nuclear physics. In particular, I am sure that you are familiar with the application of magnetic spectrometers in making absolute energy determinations and in identifying nuclear excited states. This application of spectrometers has been valuable in extending our knowledge of nuclear structure and is still being profitably pursued. However, today I would like to talk about some further applications of magnetic spectrometers which have been made in the past few years in nuclear physics research with low energy accelerators. These considerations will be limited to the magnetic analysis of positive ions. First a few pertinent properties of magnetic spectrometers will be discussed. Then some uses of spectrometers (1) in conjunction with silicon surface-barrier detectors and (2) in conjunction with NaI γ-ray detectors will be considered. These uses are motivated by a variety of research objectives and I shall only briefly indicate the significance of the experiments which can be conducted in each instance. The presentation will be devoted mainly to the experimental aspects of these applications.

ADVANTAGES OF A MAGNETIC SPECTROMETER COMBINED WITH A SOLID-STATE DETECTOR

It is well known that a magnetic spectrometer of radius ρ selects charged particles of momentum p according to the relation $B\rho = p/q$ (Mks units) where B is the magnetic field and q is the charge on the particle of momentum p. $B\rho$ is frequently referred to as the magnetic rigidity. For a non-

* Supported by the U. S. Atomic Energy Commission

relativistic particle of mass M it follows that $(B\rho) = 2ME/q^2$ where E is kinetic energy of the particle. Thus for a given magnetic rigidity particles of different mass and charge will have different energies with the energy proportional to q^2/M.

If a silicon surface-barrier detector is used for energy analysis following magnetic analysis of nuclear reaction products, it is possible to separate and identify various reaction products from the knowledge that $E \propto q^2/M$. Figure 1 shows a solid-state detector spectrum measured at the exit of a magnetic spectrometer for a $Be^9 + He^3$ bombardment using the 9 MeV He^3 beam from the U. S. Naval Research Laboratory 5 MV Van de Graaff.[1] The magnetic rigidity was adjusted so that 2.5 MeV deuterons were focussed onto the solid-state detector. Twelve particle groups have been separated and identified in this spectrum. The q^2/M value for each group is given by the right hand scale. Further checks on the particle identification can be made by (1) inserting thin foils before the solid-state detector or (2) adjusting the depletion depth of the detector by changing the bias voltage. These techniques can also be used to separate particles which happen to have the same magnetic rigidity, such as proton, alpha (q = +2) and Be^9 (q = +3) particles which occur at about 5 MeV (channel 128) in Fig. 1.

In the $Be^9 + He^3$ bombardment, a self-supporting Be^9 target of about 130 $\mu gm/cm^2$ thickness was used. A small oxygen contaminant was present in the target, but the majority of the observed particles arise from reactions induced in the Be^9. By using the magnetic spectrometer combined with the solid-state detector, it is possible to detect not only proton, deuteron, He^3, and alpha particles, but also heavier ions such as Li^6, Li^7, and B^{10}. However, it is essential to combine the good resolution in magnetic rigidity of the spectrometer with the good energy resolution of the solid-state detector in order to separate and identify the host of particle types that are emitted. Confusion in identifying ions of nuclei of the same mass such as $Li^7(+3)$ and $Be^7(+3)$ can frequently be eliminated by reaction-kinematic considerations. For example, the $Be^9(He^3, Li^7)p,\alpha$ reaction has a Q-value of 2.73 MeV, but the $Be^9(He^3, Be^7)n,\alpha$ reaction has a Q-value of only 1.09 MeV. Therefore the mass 7(+3) ions of 6.4 MeV probably originate from the $Be^9(He^3, Li^7)p,\alpha$ reaction. Note again that all of the particles identified in Fig. 1 have the same magnetic rigidity.

These particles of the same magnetic rigidity do have different velocities and hence different flight-times through the magnetic spectrometer. This time difference can be used to resolve ions which are not already resolved by energy and magnetic rigidity. This technique has been recently exploited by Denes and Daehnick[2] and a typical energy spectrum (for a given magnetic rigidity and summed over the time-of-flight dimension) is shown in Fig. 2. By energy and magnetic rigidity the particles are not resolved, but with the additional time-of-flight dimension the particles are completely separated and identified in mass. Note that the heavier ions Mass 14(+4)and C^{14}(+4) do not quite give the pulse height expected from their Z^2/A ratio. Presumably this could be due to greater energy losses for these ions either in the Au layer on the surface-barrier solid-state detector or in the target foil backing.

STUDIES INVOLVING NUCLEAR IONS

A magnetic spectrometer combined with a solid-state detector can be used to study reactions which produce nuclear ions. This application is illustrated by considering a recent study of the $B^{11}(He^3,Li^6)Be^8$ reaction.[3] Figure 3 shows a pulse-height spectrum measured by a solid-state detector at the exit of a magnetic spectrometer for a 5.2-MeV He^3 beam incident on a B^{11} target. The magnetic rigidity was fixed at a momentum per unit charge corresponding to 4.33-MeV Li^6(+3) ions. Five different types of particles are separated and identified in this spectrum

In order to obtain the yield of Li^6 ions in the reaction, a momentum scan of the particle group was measured by changing the magnetic field of the spectrometer. Figure 4 shows a portion of three different momentum spectra which were obtained with different pulse-height windows for 3 MeV bombarding energy and at an observation angle of 35°. At this energy and angle the alpha particles and B^{10}(+3) recoil ions are well separated in pulse height and are measured with separate windows. The momentum spectra for these ions reflect the energy-level structure of B^{10} through the $B^{11}(He^3,\alpha)B^{10}$ reaction. Only excited states in B^{10} that predominately γ decay are observed in the B^{10}(+3) momentum spectrum. The $C^{12}(He^3, \alpha_o)$ group arises from reactions in the carbon backing of the target. The pulse-height window used for the Li^6(+3) ions also included the B^{10}(+4) ions. The non-zero valley between the B^{10}(+4) (ground state) and Li^6(+3) (ground state) corresponds to the tail of the Be^8 first excited state. With a good resolution particle-detection system it is possible to extract the yield of the Li^6(+3) ions even in the presence of B^{10}(+4) ions by measuring pulse-height spectra as in Fig. 3. Well defined momentum profiles for heavy ions are obtained by using thin self-supporting targets or thin targets on thin self-supporting backings to minimize straggling of the heavy ions.

To obtain meaningful results from these Li^6 yield measurements, corrections must be made for the number of lithium ions emerging from the target in the +3 charge state. To establish charge-state equilibrium for the ions detected the target is oriented so that the carbon backing is between the B^{11} target and the spectrometer. A compilation of equilibrium charge-state fractions for ion beams from hydrogen through neon as a function of ion velocity has been made by C. S. Zaidins.[4] The results for lithium ions are shown in Fig. 5. The curves are a semi-empirical fit to available experimental data for solid materials. The celluloid data is from Ref. 5 and the carbon data was taken during the $B^{11}(He^3,Li^6)$ measurements[3] as a check of the semi-empirical curves. There is only a limited amount of this kind of data available and the dependence of the equilibrium charge state on the material through which the ions pass is not well understood. Clearly, magnetic spectrometers can be very useful in making measurements of equilibrium charge-state fractions for ion beams.

Momentum spectra extended to lower Li^6 energies correspond to $B^{11}(He^3,Li^6)Be^8$ reactions with Q-values less than the ground state Q-value, 4.56 MeV. Extended momentum spectra measured at 5.2-MeV bombarding energy indicate an appreciable yield for this reaction with Be^8 nuclei left in the 2.9-MeV first excited state and with Li^6 nuclei emitted in the 3.56-MeV second excited state, which decays only by γ radiation. The 2.18-MeV first excited state decays by particle emission and hence could not be observed. A typical energy distribution obtained from a momentum distribution is shown in Fig. 6. The momentum distribution is obtained experimentally by measuring the number of counts n(p) at a fixed momentum (fixed magnetic field) for a fixed exit slit width δx as a function of momentum (magnetic field). For a spectrometer of radius R and dispersion D, the slit width is related to the momentum interval accepted by the slit δp by $\delta x = DR\ \delta p/p$. (A discussion of the focusing properties of magnetic spectrometers may be found in Ref. 6.) The measured distribution $n(p)\delta x$ is proportional to $n(p)\delta p/p$ for a constant dispersion. Since $p^2=2ME$, it follows that $n(E) = n(p)/p^2$. Therefore the momentum distribution is converted to an energy distribution by dividing the number of counts measured at a fixed magnetic-field setting by the square of the magnetic-field setting.

Excitation curves from 1.4 to 5.8 MeV for the $B^{11}(He^3,Li^6)Be^8$ reaction are shown in Fig. 7. Angular distributions at 5.2 MeV for the ground-state reaction and for reactions leaving the residual nuclei in excited states are given in Fig. 8. The smooth energy variation of the excitation curves and the forward peaking of the angular distribution suggest that the ground-state reaction proceeds via a direct process. The ground-state reaction has been interpreted in terms of a "cluster pickup" process.[3] In this description B^{11} is considered to consist (partially) of the cluster configuration (Be^8_0 + t). The incident He^3 particle picks up the triton and emerges as Li^6. The ground state of Li^6 is required to consist (partially) of the configuration (He^3 + t). Further information about the cluster structure of B^{11} and Li^6 may be obtained from the $B^{11}(He^3,Li^6)Be^8$ reaction for which the residual nuclei are left in excited states.[3]

Magnetic spectrometers can be used to make accurate Q-value determinations for neutron-producing reactions by precision magnetic analysis of nuclear recoil ions. This technique has been used by Fisher and Whaling[7] to determine the Q-value of the $B^{10}(He^3,N^{12})n$ reaction by observing N^{12} (+5) recoil ions. Measurements at 1.7° and 7.0° laboratory angle for 10-MeV bombarding energy gave a Q-value of 1.570 ± 0.025 MeV (1.6% uncertainty). This value differs considerably from the value 1.46 ± 0.06 MeV (4.1% uncertainty) obtained from neutron spectroscopy[8] and has a significantly smaller uncertainty than the neutron measurement.

USES IN CONJUNCTION WITH γ-RAY DETECTION

A knowledge of the properties of NaI scintillation detectors is necessary for the use of these devices in the study of γ rays from nuclear reactions. In order to derive relative γ-ray intensities from a measured spectrum the efficiency of the detection equipment as a function of γ-ray energy must be known. Frequently, only the full-energy peak can be reliably extracted from a measured γ-ray spectrum so that it is also necessary to know the photofraction (i.e., peak-to-total ratio) as a function of the γ-ray energy.

Peak-to-total ratios and efficiencies for γ-ray detectors can be measured by using a magnetic spectrometer to isolate nuclear states that decay by only one γ-ray transition. Coincidence measurements between particles from a nuclear reaction in the spectrometer and γ rays in a NaI crystal, provide pulse-height spectra for discrete γ-ray energies. The detector efficiency is determined by detecting in the spectrometer only those particles leading to the nuclear state which provides the desired monoenergetic γ rays. The efficiency is given by the ratio of the coincidence counts in the γ-ray detector to the particle counts in the spectrometer. The spectrometer counts must include only particles leading to the desired nuclear state. Peak-to-total ratios are extracted directly from the measured γ-ray pulse-height spectra.

This technique has been used to measure peak-to-total ratios and efficiencies for a 5-in.-diam x 5-in. NaI crystal.[9] The experimental geometry is shown in Fig. 9. The γ-ray detector was located as close to the target as possible in order to increase the coincidence yield, as well as to integrate over angular correlation effects which are present in many experimental situations. The axis of the γ-ray detector was located perpendicular to the plane defined by the incident beam and the mean spectrometer acceptance direction. The distance between the γ-ray detector and the target is limited to a minimum of 3/4 in. by the vertical acceptance angle of the spectrometer. An aluminum plate of only 0.05 in. thickness was used between the target and the detector to minimize γ-ray absorption effects. The entire NaI crystal and associated photomultiplier was placed inside a cast iron cylinder to provide magnetic shielding of the phototube and some radiation shielding of the crystal.

For the efficiency measurements, excited states were used that are known to decay isotropically, or with known angular correlations so that appropriate corrections could be made. Table I lists the sources of γ rays that were used. Where possible, an incident energy corresponding to a known resonance was used. Some γ-ray sources and (p,γ) reactions were used to supplement the peak-to-total ratio data. Peak-to-total ratios computed from the measured pulse-height spectra are plotted in Fig. 10. It was possible to clearly discriminate and detect particles leading to the nuclear state of interest only for the four reactions corresponding to γ-ray energies of 0.432, 1.63, 2.31, and 6.13 MeV. The total efficiencies determined at these energies are plotted in Fig. 11. The calculated efficiencies of Vegors, Marsden and Heath[10] are also shown.

By interpolating the calculated curves, a fit to the experimental data was obtained for a source distance of 2.5 cm (dashed curve). The distance from the center of the target to the front face of the NaI detector is 2.0 cm. The 0.5 cm-increase in the source distance may be ascribed to the thickness of the 0.032-in. Aluminum body and reflector packing in which the crystal is mounted and to small absorption effects arising from these thicknesses and the 0.05 in.- aluminum plate which have not been included. The two measurements at 2.31-MeV γ-ray energy were made at different times under different experimental conditions and indicate the reproductibility of the experimental set up.

This experimental arrangement of the NaI crystal and magnetic spectrometer can be used to study γ-ray branching ratios of excited states. This method is illustrated by a recent study of the $C^{13}(He^3,p\gamma)N^{15}$ reaction.[11] A magnetic spectrometer was used to resolve protons from states in N^{15} from 8- to 11-MeV excitation. The protons were detected by a solid-state counter at the exit of the magnet. Aluminum foils were positioned in front of the detector at the exit of the magnet to allow protons leading to the level of interest in N^{15} to be detected, but to prevent heavier particles from competing reactions from reaching the detector. A momentum profile taken at 5 MeV incident He^3 energy and at an angle of 20° is shown in Fig. 12. The proton groups labeled p_7 through p_{19} correspond to excited states in N^{15} from 8.31 to 10.80 MeV inclusive. Proton groups from the $C^{12}(He^3,p)N^{14}$ and $O^{16}(He^3,p)F^{18}$ reactions from carbon and oxygen contamination in the target are also identified in the profile.

The proton group (p_{11} in Fig. 12) to the 9.22-MeV state in N^{15} is resolved from the group (p_{10} in Fig. 12) to the 9.16-MeV state and has a sufficient yield for performing coincidence measurements. A γ-ray spectrum measured by the 5-in.-diam x 5-in. NaI detector in coincidence with protons to the 9.22-MeV state in N^{15} is shown in Fig. 13. The prominent γ-ray peaks in these figures are identified and the straight lines give the γ-ray energy calibration. In order to minimize pile-up in the γ-ray singles spectrum, a beam current of only 0.04 μA was used. The proton-singles counting rate at this beam current was about 4 cps; while the real coincidence counting rate was about 1 cps. The accidental counting rate was less than 3% of the real coincidence rate for a resolving time 2τ = 180 nsec. The coincidence spectrum in Fig. 13 was accumulated in about 11 hours.

The decay scheme deduced from the coincidence spectrum is indicated in Fig. 13. Branching ratios were extracted from the measured spectrum using the previously measured efficiencies and peak-to-total ratios for the NaI crystal. The branching ratios obtained for the 9.22-MeV level are given in Table II. It is possible to observe branches as small as one percent and to set upper limits of one percent for most unobserved branches involving a γ ray of energy greater than about 1 MeV.

The theory of particle γ-ray angular correlations as a tool for determining spins and multipole mixing ratios of nuclear excited states has been developed by Litherland and Ferguson.[12,13] Method II of these authors requires the detection of reaction particles emitted along the beam direction (i.e., either 0° or 180°). It is difficult to use a solid-state detector near 0° because these detectors cannot withstand the intense radiations from the incident beam and still function as useful counters. Therefore it is customary to use an annular detector near 180°. However, it is possible to use a magnetic spectrometer combined with a solid-state counter to detect charged particles at exactly 0° in order to make angular correlation measurements in the geometry of Method II. The incident beam intensity to which the solid-state counter is exposed can be greatly reduced or eliminated by magnetic analysis prior to energy analysis, as well as by the use of thin foils in front of the solid-state detector.

This technique is illustrated by a proton-γ-ray angular correlation measurement[11] for the $C^{13}(He^3,p\gamma)N^{15}$ reaction leading to the state at 9.22-MeV excitation. Measurements were made at a beam energy of 2 MeV and a thin aluminum foil was placed in front of the solid-state detector to stop the scattered He^3 beam from reaching the detector. The experimental arrangement used for the measurement is shown in Fig. 14. Because the theoretical correlation depends only on even powers of cos θ, it is necessary to take data only in one quadrant. Three 3-in.-diam x 3-in. NaI detectors were placed with their axes at angles relative to the beam direction of 90°, 135°, and 160° (chosen as close as practical to 180°) and at a distance of 6.6 in. from the center of the target (measured from the face of the crystal). To minimize γ-ray absorption, the walls of the target chamber and beam tube were constructed from 1/16-in. brass, but there is still some dependence of γ-ray absorption on the angle of the NaI detector. The proper correction for this effect was determined by measuring the angular distribution for the isotropic γ ray from the 3.56-MeV level in Li^6.

The angular correlation was measured for the ground-state decay of the 9.22-MeV level and corrections (of the order of 10%) were included for γ-ray absorption effects. The measured correlation was used in chi-squared analysis as described by Poletti and Warburton.[14] In Fig. 15 is shown the best theoretical fit (smallest chi-square) to the measurements for each value of the initial spin as a function of the multipole mixing ratio x for possible excited state spins from J = 1/2 to J = 7/2. Larger J values can be eliminated from lifetime considerations.[15] The 9.22-MeV level probably has J = 3/2; however J = 1/2 is ruled against with only 90% certainty by the chi squared analysis.[11] The multipole mixing ratio is not determined by the measured correlation.

Finally let's consider a somewhat unusual way in which coincidence measurements between charged particles analyzed with a magnetic spectrometer and γ rays detected by a NaI crystal have been used to identify an energy-level doublet without actually resolving the doublet.[16] In this experiment the $Be^9(d,p)Be^{10}$ reaction with 2.8-MeV deuterons was used to populate the 5.96-MeV level in Be^{10}. The protons were detected with a solid-state detector at the exit of a magnetic spectrometer. The γ rays were detected by a 3-in.-diam x 3-in. NaI crystal located 5 cm from the target in the same geometry as the 5-in.-diam x 5-in NaI crystal previously. By adjusting the magnetic field of the spectrometer, coincident γ-ray spectra were measured over the proton group corresponding to the 5.96-MeV level. Figure 16 shows the sum of all coincident γ-ray spectra measured with the spectrometer at 20°. The yields of the cascade γ rays (2.59 and 3.37 MeV) and crossover γ ray (5.96 MeV) were extracted from the measured spectra. Figure 17 shows the cascade and crossover yields as a function of magnetic-field setting. The peak of the cascade yield occurs at a greater magnetometer setting than the peak of the crossover yield by 0.025 mV which corresponds to about 1-keV excitation energy in Be^{10}.

The ratio of the cascade strength to the crossover strength (corrected for the efficiency of the γ-ray detector) is plotted in Fig. 18. This variation of the branching ratio measured across the proton group corresponding to the 5.96-MeV state is interpreted as evidence for the existence of two closely-spaced levels at 5.96 MeV. To determine the separation of these two levels more accurately, an actual line profile for the spectrometer was determined by fitting the cascade and crossover yields to a single line shape. This line shape was used to calculate the ratio of the cascade to crossover yield for various energy separations of the two levels. The calculated curves are shown in Fig. 18. The calculated ratio is normalized to the experimental ratio at the peak of the proton yield curve. A separation of 1.1 $\pm$ 0.4 keV provides the best fit to the data. In using this procedure to determine the separation, it is assumed that the cascade and crossover yields arise from distinct levels. The branching ratios of Warburton and Alburger[17] indicate that the upper member of the doublet decays primarily by the crossover transition and the lower member decays primarily by the cascade transition.

CONCLUSION

The dispersive property of magnetic spectrometers was not utilized to its fullest in the applications which have been considered. A variety of position-sensitive detectors have been developed to take advantage of this property, but various drawbacks limit their universal acceptance. For example, photographic emulsions are reliable and widely used, but do not provide on-line output. An array of small detectors requires extensive associated electronics to provide on-line output. Position-sensitive solid-state detectors are of limited length and do not seem to have the desired linearity in position. Spark chambers are insensitive to short range particle It is hoped that future development in using position-sensitive detectors in conjunction with magnetic spectrometers will allow the dispersive property to be utilized to a greate extent.

Some advantages of magnetic spectrometers have been pointed out and several different applications have been discussed with the aim of showing that the magnetic spectrometer is a versatile and valuable instrument to use in nuclear research with low energy accelerators. It is hoped that these examples will motivate further innovations in the use of magnetic spectrometers as a research tool.

REFERENCES

1. P. D. Forsyth, A. R. Knudson, and F. C. Young, Nucl. Phys. 85, 153 (1966).

2. L. J. Denes, and W. W. Daehnick, Phys. Rev. 154, 928 (1967).

3. F. C. Young, P. D. Forsyth, and J. B. Marion, Nucl. Phys A91, 209 (1967).

4. C. S. Zaidins, Ph.D. thesis, California Institute of Technology, 1967 (unpublished).

5. Ia. A. Teplova, I. S. Dmitriev, V. S. Nikolaev, and L. N Fateeva, Soviet Phys. JETP 5, 797 (1957).

6. D. L. Judd, Rev. Sci. Instr. 21, 213 (1950).

7. T. R. Fisher and W. Whaling, Phys. Rev. 133, B1502 (1964

8. F. Ajzenberg-Selove, M. L. Bullock, and E. Almqvist, Phy Rev. 108, 1284 (1957).

9. F. C. Young, H. T. Heaton, G. W. Phillips, P. D. Forsyth and J. B. Marion, Nucl. Instr. and Methods 44, 109 (1966

10. S. H. Vegors, Jr., L. L. Marsden, and R. L. Heath, Calculated Efficiencies of Cylindrical Radiation Detectors, Phillips Petroleum Co. Report ICO-16370, 1958 (unpublished).

11. G. W. Phillips, F. C. Young, and J. B. Marion, Phys. Rev. (to be published).

12. A. E. Litherland and A. J. Ferguson, Can. J. Phys. 39, 788 (1961).

13. A. J. Ferguson, Angular Correlation Methods in Gamma-Ray Spectroscopy, North-Holland, Amsterdam, 1965.

14. A. R. Poletti and E. K. Warburton, Phys. Rev. 137, B595 (1965).

15. E. K. Warburton, J. W. Olness, and D. E. Alburger, Phys. Rev. 140, B1202 (1965).

16. F. C. Young, P. D. Forsyth, M. L. Roush, and W. F. Hornyak, in Nuclear Spin-Parity Assignments, edited by N. B. Gove and R. L. Robinson (Academic Press Inc., New York, 1966), p. 179.

17. E. K. Warburton and D. E. Alburger, in Nuclear Spin-Parity Assignments, edited by N. B. Gove and R. L. Robinson (Academic Press Inc., New York, 1966), p. 114.

TABLE I. γ-Ray Sources

E (MeV)	Source	E(MeV)	Source
0.432	$B^{10}(p,\alpha_1\gamma)Be^7$	3.09	$C^{12}(d,p_1\gamma)C^{13}$
0.661	Cs^{137} source	3.56	$Be^9(p,\alpha_2\gamma)Li^6$
0.835	Mn^{54} source	4.43	$N^{15}(p,\alpha_1\gamma)C^{12}$
1.63	$Na^{23}(p,\alpha_1\gamma)Ne^{20}$	6.13	$F^{19}(p,\alpha_1\gamma)O^{16}$
2.14	$Be^9(He^3,p_1\gamma)B^{11}$	7.48	$Be^9(p,\gamma)B^{10}$
2.31	$C^{12}(He^3,p_1\gamma)N^{14}$	9.17	$C^{13}(p,\gamma)N^{14}$

TABLE II. Branching Ratios for the Level at 9.22 MeV in N^{15} from $C^{13}(He^3,p\gamma)N^{15}$.

E_f (MeV)	E (MeV)	Branching Ratio (%)
0	9.22	41.5 ± 2.2
5.27	3.95	31.2 ± 1.7
5.30	3.92	
6.32	2.90	24.7 ± 1.5
7.15	2.07	<1
7.30	1.92	2.6 ± 0.7
7.56	1.66	<1
8.31	0.91	

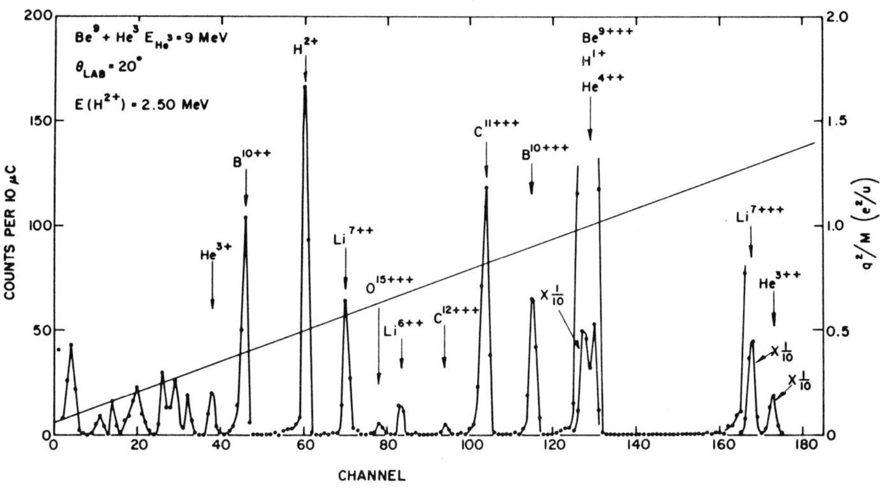

Fig. 1. Pulse-height spectrum measured by a solid-state detector at the exit of a spectrometer for 9-MeV He^3 ions on Be^9.

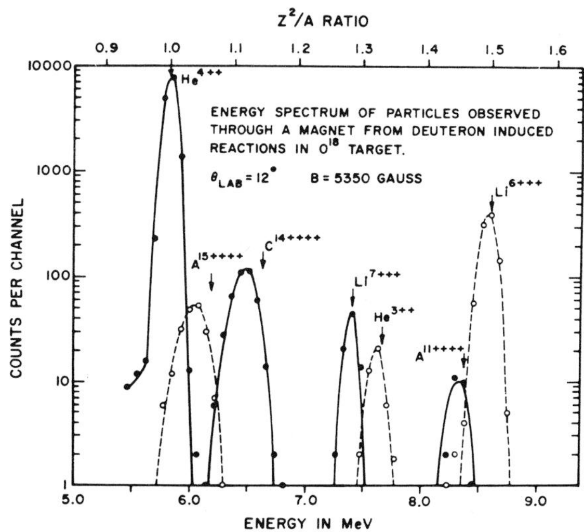

Fig. 2. Pulse-height spectrum (for a given magnetic rigidity and summed over the time-of-flight dimension) observed at the exit of a magnet for 15-MeV deuterons on O^{18}.

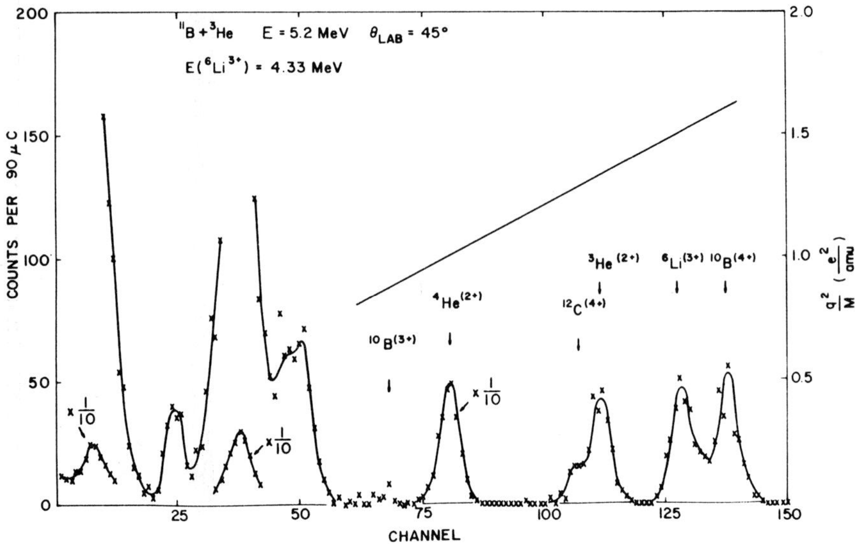

Fig. 3. Pulse-height spectrum measured by a solid-state detector at the exit of a spectrometer for 5.2-MeV He^3 on B^{11}.

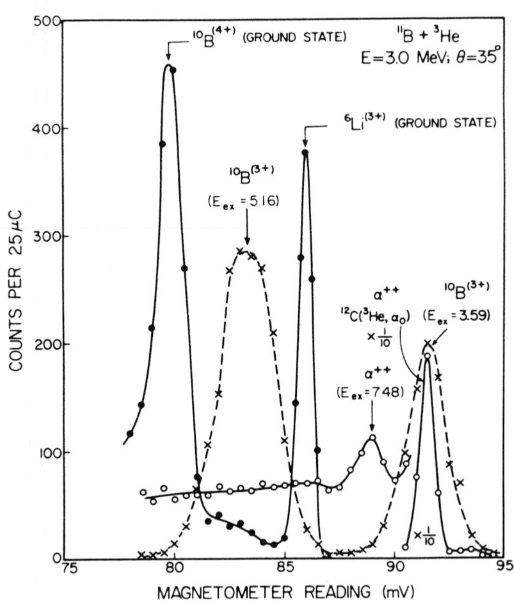

Fig. 4. Momentum spectra of α-particles, $B^{10}(3+)$ and $Li^6(3+)$ and $B^{10}(4+)$ combined at an observation angle of 35°.

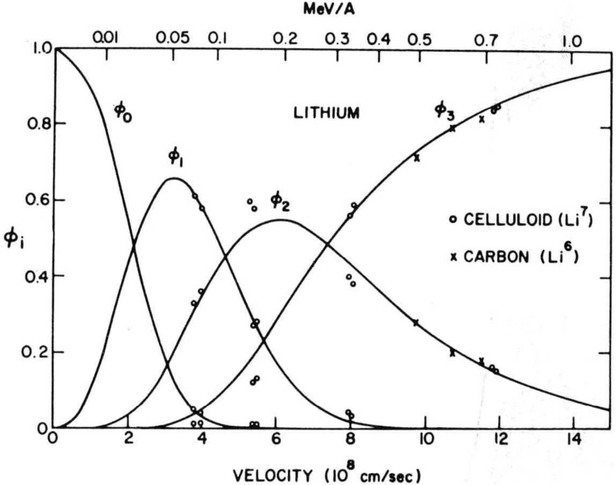

Fig. 5. Equilibrium charge-state fractions for lithium ions in solids.

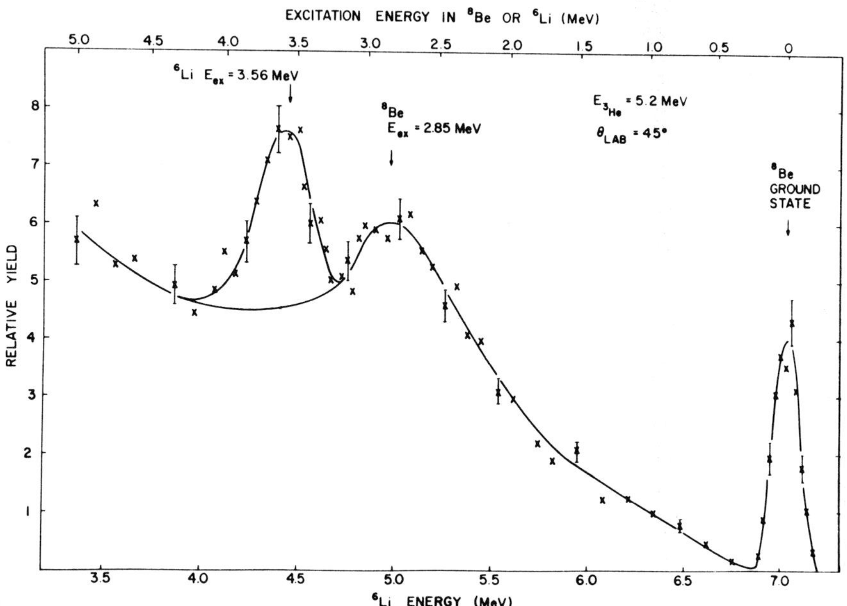

Fig. 6. Energy spectra of Li^6 nuclei for 5.2-MeV He^3 incident on B^{11} and at an angle of observation of 45°.

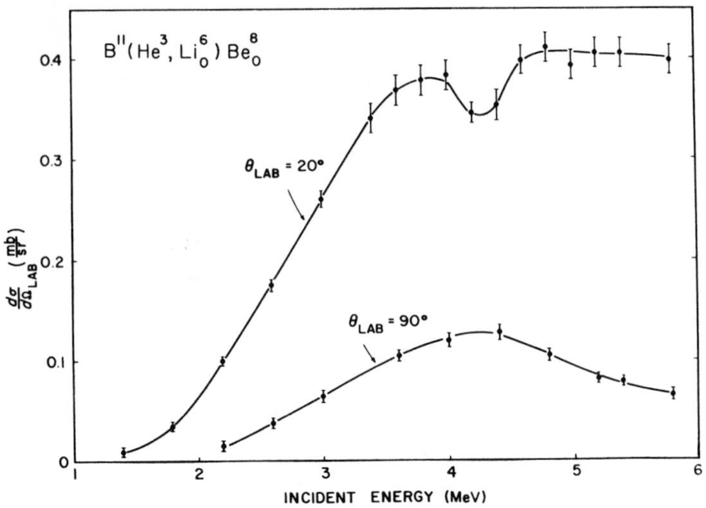

Fig. 7. Excitation curves for Li^6 (ground state) nuclei at 20° and 90°.

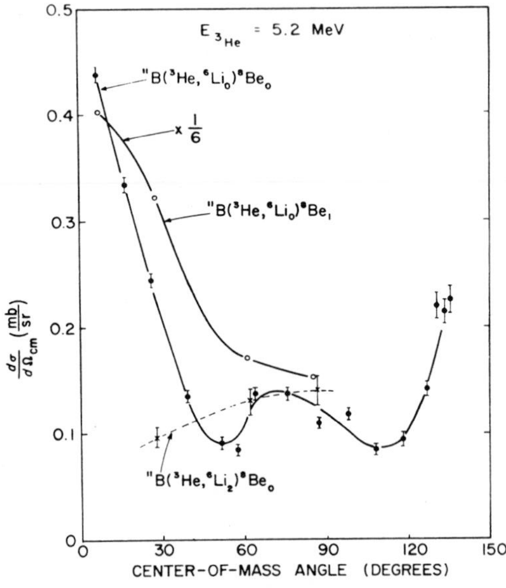

Fig.8. Angular distributions for various $B^{11}(He^3,Li^6)Be^8$ reactions at 5.2-MeV He^3 energy.

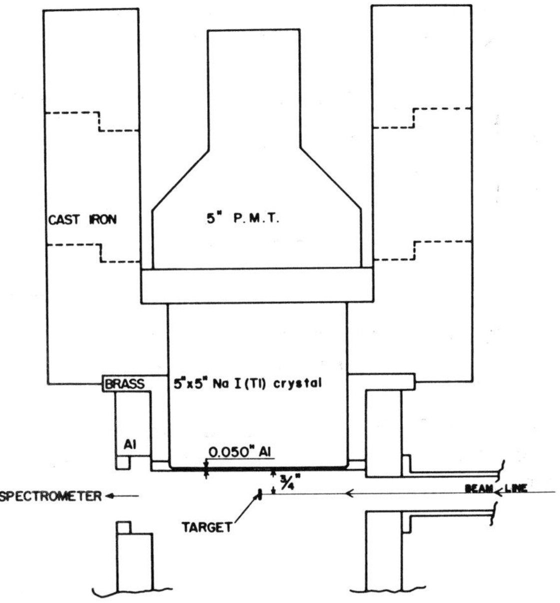

Fig. 9. Experimental geometry for the 5-in.-diam x 5-in. NaI crystal.

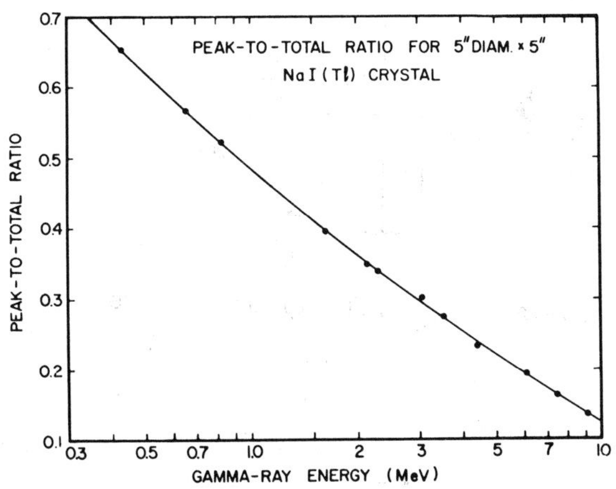

Fig. 10. Experimental peak-to-total ratios for a 5-in.-diam x 5-in. NaI crystal 2.5 cm from the source.

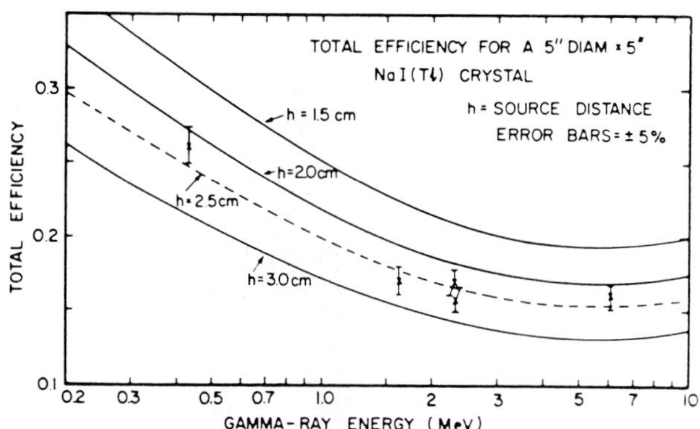

Fig. 11. Total absolute efficiencies for a 5-in.-diam x 5-in. NaI crystal. The solid curves are theoretical calculations.

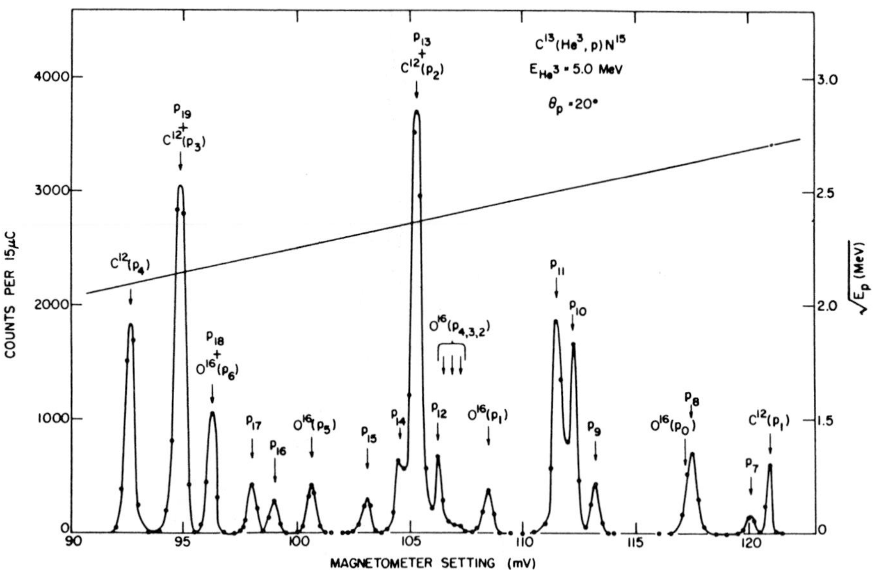

Fig. 12. Proton momentum profile for the $C^{13}(He^3,p)N^{15}$ reaction. Proton groups from O^{16} and C^{12} in the target are labeled by the target nucleus.

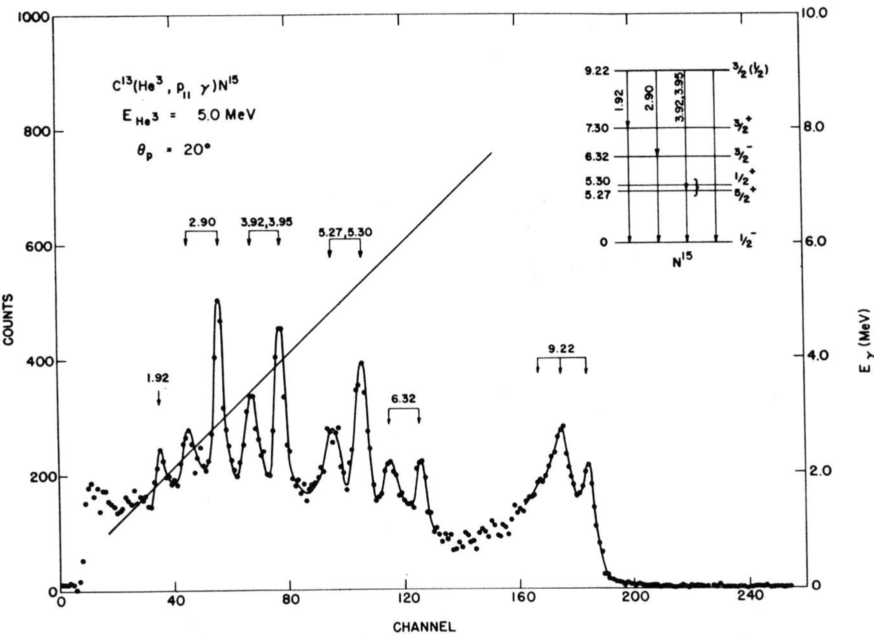

Fig. 13. γ-ray coincidence spectrum for the 9.22-MeV level in N^{15} from the $C^{13}(He^3,p\gamma)N^{15}$ reaction.

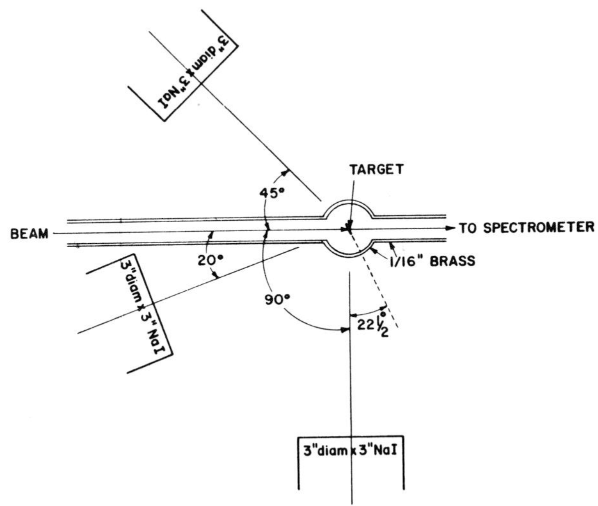

Fig. 14. Geometry for the proton-γ-ray angular correlation measurement.

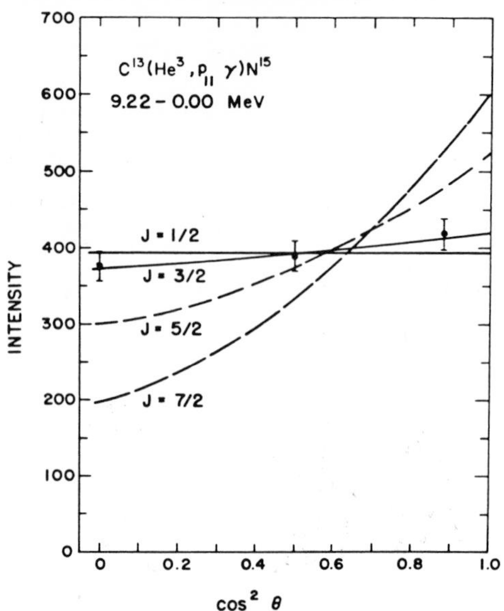

Fig. 15. Proton-γ angular correlation for the 9.22-MeV level in N^{15}. The curves are the best theoretical fits to the measured correlation for each value of the spin J.

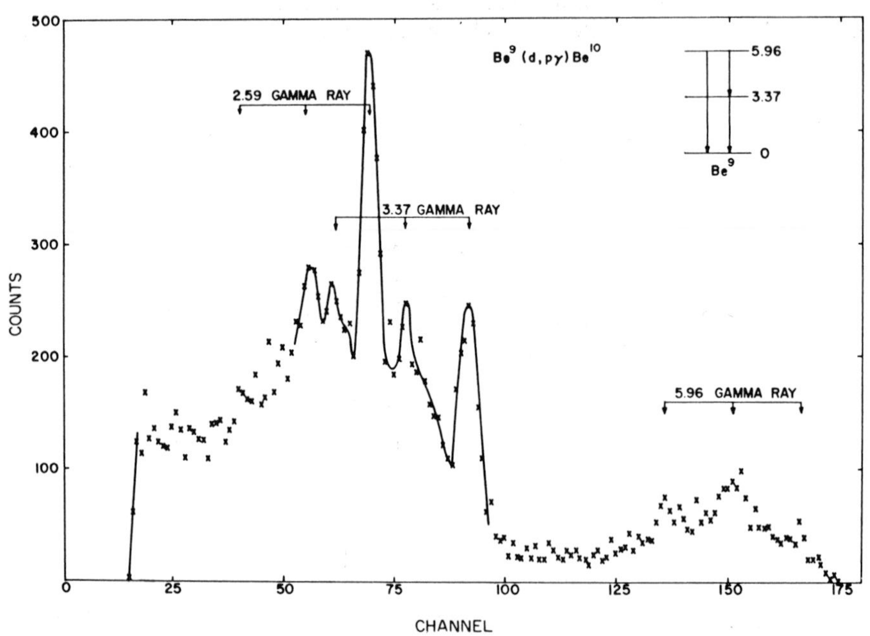

Fig. 16. $Be^9(d,p\gamma)Be^{10}$ γ-ray coincidence spectrum measured on the proton group corresponding to the 5.96-MeV level in Be^{10}.

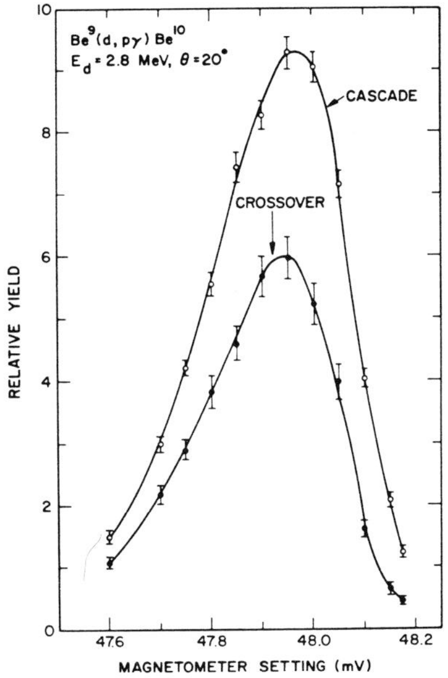

Fig. 17. Cascade and crossover γ-ray yields as a function of magnetic field for $\theta_p = 20°$.

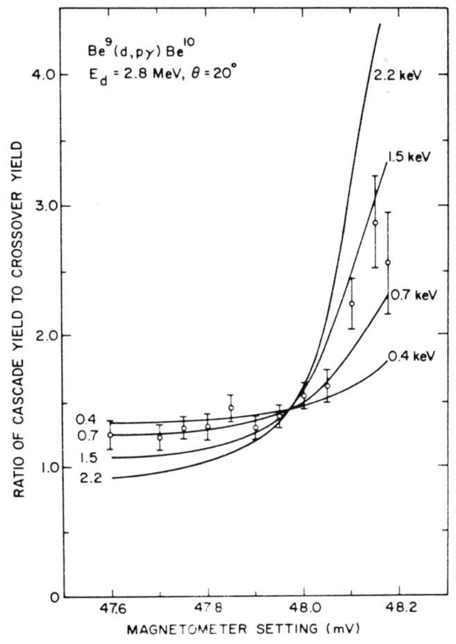

Fig. 18. Ratio of cascade yield to crossover yield for $\theta_p = 20°$. The solid curves are calculated ratios for various separations of two levels.

MÖSSBAUER STUDIES WITH VAN DE GRAAFF ACCELERATORS

J. C. Walker* and Y. K. Lee

The Johns Hopkins University
Baltimore, Maryland

Abstract

The use of low energy accelerators for excitation of nuclear levels whose decays can show Mössbauer effects is discussed. The application of these techniques to determinations of nuclear moments of several even isotopes of ytterbium is mentioned. A brief discussion of initial experiments to observed Mössbauer effects in U^{238} is given.

Introduction

It is well known that the Mössbauer effect can be used to obtain information about nuclear moments. A number of measurements have been made of nuclear magnetic dipole and electric quadrupole moments using Mössbauer hyperfine spectra. The technique is particularly useful in that it makes possible the relatively accurate determinations of moments of nuclei in excited states. In general, the accuracy of such measurements exceeds those made with integral perturbed angular correlation techniques. The Mössbauer effect measurements are restricted to states of energy less than 150 KeV above the ground state, and to nuclei which are stable or have relatively long half-lives.

A more serious restriction in the past has been the requirement that there be an easily produced radioactive source for populating the excited state of interest. The source should not have other radiations with energies near that of the transition of interest, and the lifetime of the radioactive parent should be long enough to permit the experiments to be carried out. While new techniques of radioactive source production have increased the number of levels from which a Mössbauer effect can be observed, this source

*Alfred P. Sloan Foundation Fellow.

requirement has tended to severely restrict the study of nuclear properties using the Mössbauer effect. Since each case presented a new source problem, the observation of Mössbauer effects in several isotopes of the same element in order to observe trends in nuclear moments was usually not possible. It was with this problem in mind that the attempts to observe Mössbauer effects from nuclear levels populated by means other than radioactive decay were made.

General Considerations

Among the various techniques used to populate Mössbauer levels other than by radioactive decay were (d, p) reactions, neutron capture, and Coulomb excitation. In each of these cases, the nucleus of interest had recoil energies much greater than those following the usual β-decay excitation. These energies were orders of magnitude greater than the energy required to displace the atom of interest from a normal lattice position in the target material. Because the Mössbauer effect involves the lattice in which the excited nucleus is bound, as well as the nuclear γ-decay itself, there was some concern about the efficacy of these more energetic nuclear excitation processes. Following the observation[1] of Mössbauer effects in Np^{247} following α-decay, which imparted very large recoil energies to the nucleus, renewed interest in these other excitation processes produced success in several cases. Mössbauer effects were observed[2,3] following (d, p) and (n, γ) reactions producing K^{40}, as well as following Coulomb excitation[4] of Ni^{61} and Coulomb excitation and (d, p) reactions[5,6] in Fe^{57}. Effects were also seen[7] following (n, γ) reactions in Gd^{156} and Gd^{158}.

The work of Lee and collaborators[5] on Fe^{57} established that it was possible to observe Mössbauer effects and to see hyperfine structure following Coulomb excitation and (d, p) reactions which were unchanged from those seen following β-decay population of the relevant nuclear level. Other, more detailed work on Fe^{57} has substantiated these early findings.[8,9] It was found that in close-packed metallic lattices, radiation effects were not observed in the Mössbauer spectra; while in oxides, a reduction of the Mössbauer fraction f, and some indication of changes in hyperfine field were seen.

Of all of the methods of excitation of Mössbauer levels besides radioactive source decay, Coulomb excitation seems to be the most generally applicable. This arises from the fact that a large number of levels can be reached by Coulomb excitation using accelerators of modest energies. In particular, it has been possible to achieve satisfactory Coulomb excitation of low-lying levels in U^{238} using 3-MeV He^4 nuclei from a Van de Graaff accelerator as the bombarding particles. There is also the consideration that collective nuclei such as the rare earths have Coulomb excitation cross sections which are about twenty times larger than single-particle values, which is an additional advantage in studying these species. Using Coulomb excitation, we have been able to observe Mössbauer effects in a number of cases in which such effects had not previously been seen. One case in which a systematic study has been carried out is the even isotopes of ytterbium. These nuclei are highly deformed and their lowest lying levels are rotational. We have obtained information about the quadrupole moments of Yb^{172}, Yb^{174}, and Yb^{176}. Measurements of the magnetic moments of Yb^{174} and Yb^{176} have also been made.

Experimental Considerations

The energies of the $2+ \rightarrow 0+$ transitions in the even ytterbium isotopes are all about 80 KeV. In order to observe appreciable Mössbauer effects, it was necessary to cool both the target and the resonant absorber to temperatures near that of liquid helium. A schematic view of the apparatus used to do this is shown in Fig. 1. The resonant absorber was moved with constant acceleration over each half cycle of the motion. Counts from a scintillation detector were recorded in a 256 channel analyzer operating as a multiscalar. Analyzer channel and absorber velocity were directly related so that a Mössbauer effect hyperfine spectrum was recorded in the analyzer. Two target materials were investigated. Most easily obtainable was Yb_2O_3, enriched to greater than 90% in the isotope of interest. This material was fastened to the cold finger, using a small amount of epoxy resin. While no discernible radiation damage appeared in the spectra, these targets were inferior to the enriched ytterbium metal foils available for the later experiments. The metal targets produced approximately 1000 counts per second in the energy selection window for the gamma ray of interest with a beam current of 0.1 microampere of 3-MeV protons from an electrostatic accelerator. A typical Coulomb excitation spectrum appears in Fig. 2.

The question of radiation effects in the metal targets was answered by using a metallic absorber with a metallic target. The metal is cubic and diamagnetic, so that no hyperfine structure is expected. The resulting spectrum shown in Fig. 3 confirms that this is the case. The line width is about 30% greater than natural width, but this can all be accounted for by the thickness of target and absorber.

With the beam currents used in these experiments, liquid helium was consumed at a rate of about ¾ liter per hour. Recently we have installed a closed cycle refrigerator which enables us to operate with target and absorber at 25° K with no liquid coolants.

Results

To study the trend of quadrupole moments of the even isotopes of ytterbium, hyperfine spectra characteristic of Yb_2O_3 were obtained. This material is not simple, as there are two nonequivalent sites for the ytterbium. Three quarters of the ytterbium atoms are in sites of C_2 symmetry, while one quarter are in sites of C_{3i} symmetry. We could not observe any effects of the latter sites in our spectra due to marginal resolution. Because of this resolution and the great difficulty in calculating reliable electric field gradients, the ratios of quadrupole moments of Yb^{172}, Yb^{174}, and Yb^{176} to that of Yb^{170}, which could be studies with a radioactive source, were obtained. A typical spectrum from which this information was obtained is shown in Fig. 4. One can predict these ratios from measurements of the E2 transition rates for the $2+ \rightarrow 0+$ decays, if the collective model is assumed valid. In Fig. 5 the directly measured ratios are compared to the ratios inferred from Coulomb excitation measurements of E2 transition rates.[10]

Perhaps of greater interest is the measurement of magnetic moments for the 2+ rotational levels of the even ytterbium isotopes. Some work has been done using radioactive sources.[11] Using as absorber $YbCl_3 \cdot 6H_2O$ in which the magnetic field at the nucleus is known, purely magnetic hyperfine spectra, shown in Fig. 6, were obtained for Yb^{174} and Yb^{176}. From these data values of g_R, the rotational gyromagnetic ratio, were obtained. In its simplest form, the collective model predicts a value of $Z/A \sim 0.4$ for these quantities. Nilsson and Prior[12] have applied the formalism of the BCS theory of superconductivity to this problem to allow for a residual pairing interaction associated with the gap in intrinsic excitation energies of such nuclei. The results of these calculations compared with measured g_R values are shown in Fig. 7. We have found that by reducing the energy gap parameters by 10%, agreement between theory and experiment is achieved. This is not unreasonable considering that these parameters are thought to be uncertain by 10-20% due to the uncertainties in the experimental data from which they are taken. Certainly the trend is correct in the Nilsson and Prior calculation.

A recent experiment to observe the Mössbauer effect in the decay of the 45 KeV level of U^{238} illustrates how successful one can be with very modest accelerator energies. There is great interest in observing Mössbauer effects in the actinide region, because the chemistry of actinide compounds is not well understood. Nuclear information is also of interest, as this is another region of collective nuclear behavior. The difficulties in the present experiment come from the very large ($\sim$600) internal conversion coefficient for the transition of interest. Other experimenters have tried to overcome the low gamma yield by using higher energy oxygen nuclei as bombarding particles to increase the Coulomb excitation cross-section. We now believe that severe radiation damage effects prevented success in these cases.

In the present experiment, the target was at 50° K and the absorber at 75° K. With a beam current of 2.5 microamperes on a uranium metal target, a count rate of 40 per second in the energy selection window was obtained. Fig. 8 shows the spectrum obtained using 3 MeV He^4 nuclei as bombarding particles. The effect is small, but clear evidence of structure in the spectrum exists. The line spectrum beneath the experimental spectrum indicates what would be expected for the case in which the metal target and U_3O_8 absorber had similar quadrupole hyperfine structure. The poor understanding of the structure of U_3O_8 and the relatively poor statistics of the data preclude drawing any firm conclusions at this point.

Conclusion

It can be seen that nuclear excitation using particle accelerators of modest energy greatly extends the usefulness of the Mössbauer effect for studying nuclear structure. Studies of radiation damage effects using these techniques would probably shed new light on this aspect of solid state physics.

References

1. J. A. Stone and W. L. Pillinger, Phys. Rev. Letters 13, 200 (1964).
2. S. L. Ruby and R. E. Holland, Phys. Rev. Letters 14, 591 (1965).
3. D. W. Hafemeister and E. B. Shera, Phys. Rev. Letters 14, 593 (1965).
4. G. Czjzek, J. L. C. Ford, Jr., F. E. Obenshain, and D. Seyboth, Physics Letters 19, 673 (1966).
5. Y. K. Lee, P. W. Keaton, Jr., E. T. Ritter, and J. C. Walker, Phys. Rev. Letters 14, 957 (1965)
6. D. A. Goldberg, P. W. Keaton, Jr., Y. K. Lee, L. Madansky and J. C. Walker, Phys. Rev. Letters 15, 418 (1965).

7. J. Fink and P. Kienle, Physics Letters 17, 326 (1965).
8. J. Christiansen, E. Recknagel, and G. Weyer, Physics Letters 20, 46 (1966).
9. Felix Obenshain, private communication.
10. B. Elbek, M. C. Olesen, and O. Skilbreid, Nucl. Phys. 19, 523 (1960).
11. S. Hüfner and P. Quitmann, private communication.
12. S. G. Nilsson and O. Prior, Kgl. Danske Videnskab Selskab Mat-fys. Skr. 32, No. 16 (1961).

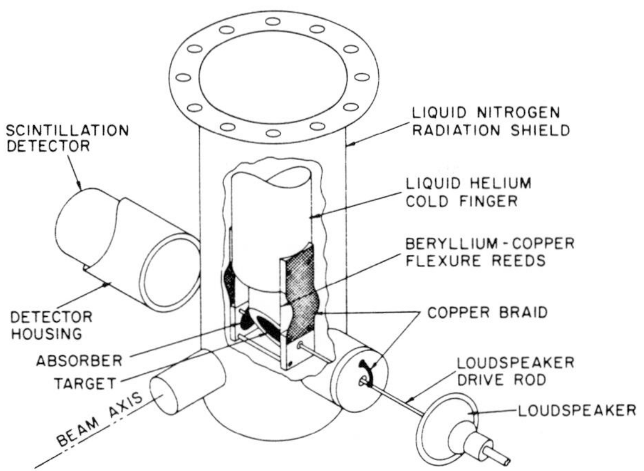

Fig. 1 Schematic view of target and absorber arrangement.

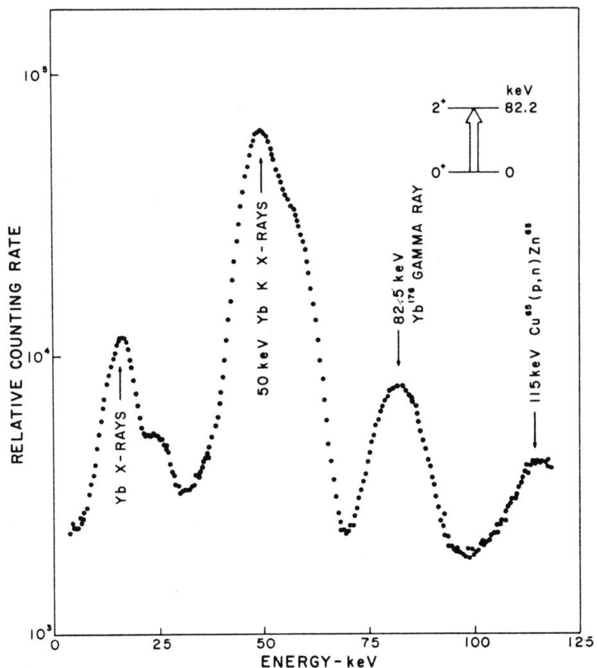

Fig. 2 Coulomb excitation spectrum for Yb^{176}, Ep=3 MeV.

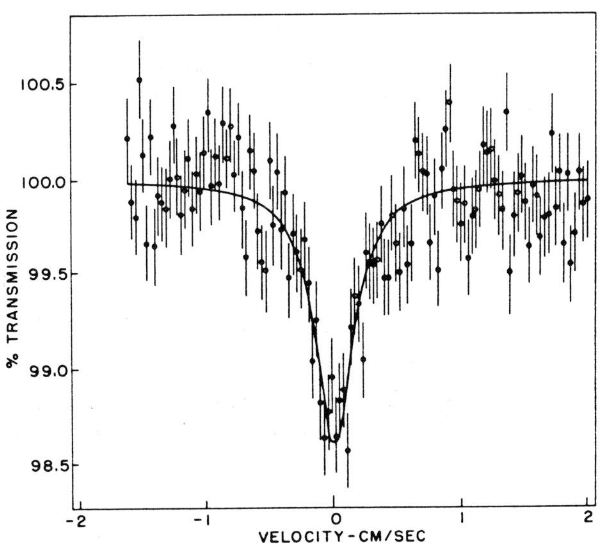

Fig. 3 Spectrum for Yb^{174} metal target and natural ytterbium metal absorber.

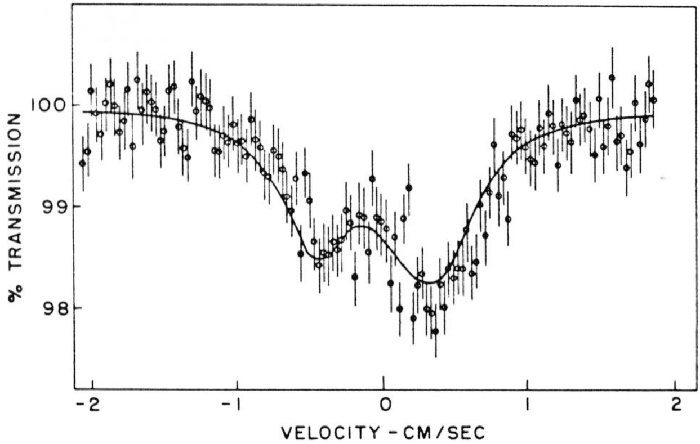

Fig. 4 Spectrum for Yb^{172} oxide target and natural ytterbium metal absorber.

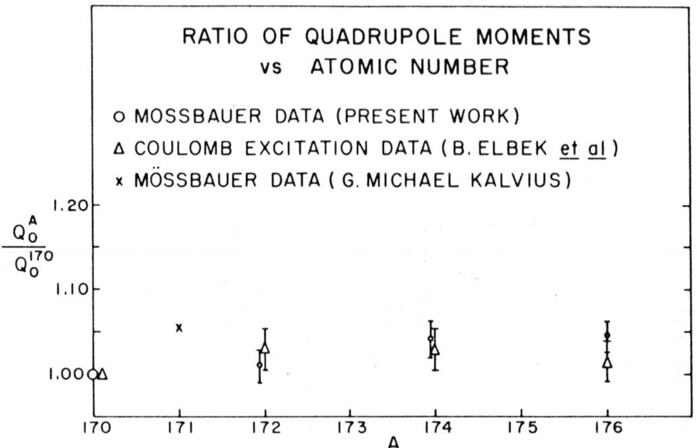

Fig. 5 Comparison of quadrupole moment ratios of even Yb isotopes with ratios inferred from B(E2) measurements from Coulomb excitation.

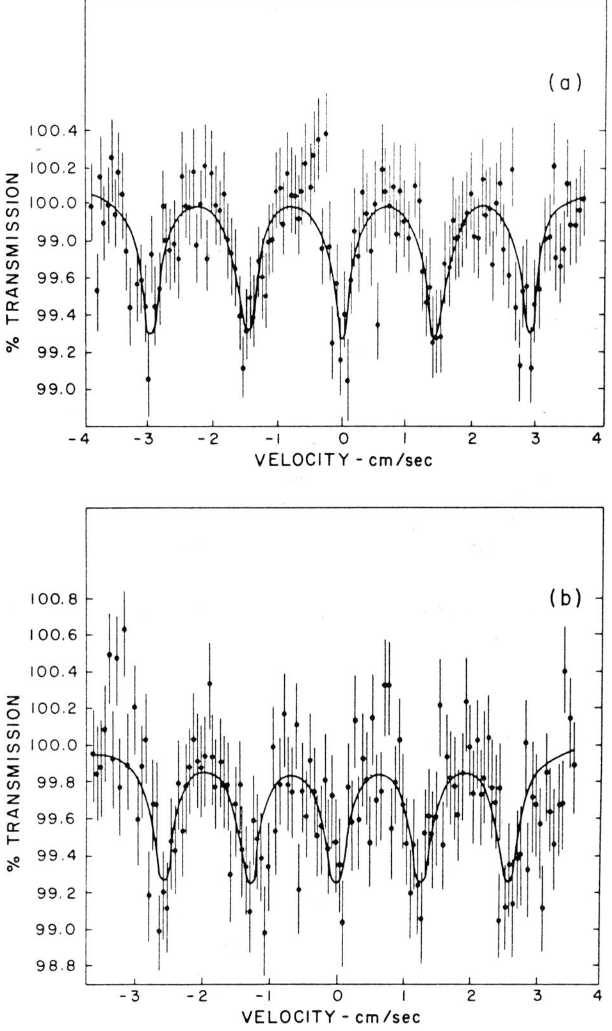

Fig. 6 Magnetic hyperfine structure for Yb^{174} and Yb^{176}.

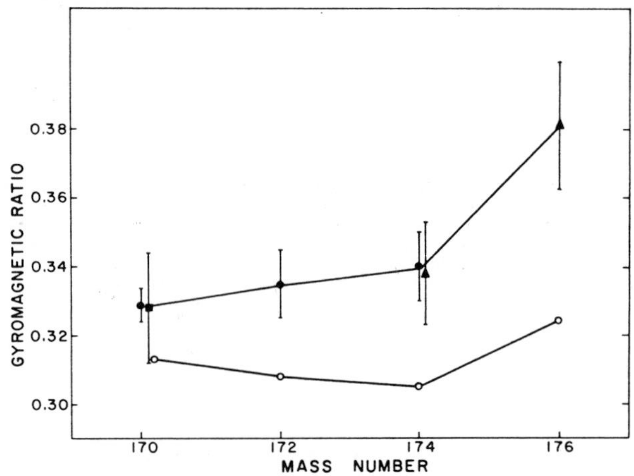

Fig. 7 Experimental and theoretical values of g_R for even Yb isotopes.

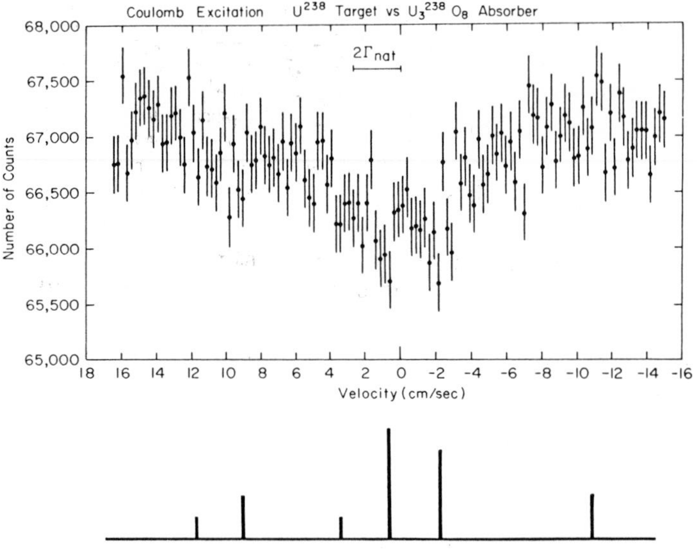

Fig. 8 Spectrum for U^{238} metal target and U_3O_8 absorber. Lines below represent purely quadrupole spectrum.

(p,n) AND (d,n) TIME-OF-FLIGHT EXPERIMENTS*

P. H. Stelson

Oak Ridge National Laboratory
Oak Ridge, Tennessee

Nanosecond beam pulsing and precise flight timing techniques are now widely used for investigating nuclear reactions in which fast neutrons are emitted. The gradual improvements in time-of-flight techniques are such that it is possible in many cases to resolve neutron groups with a precision comparable to that obtained by the magnetic analysis of charged particles from nuclear reactions. I will confine my discussion to recent results obtained for (p,n) and (d,n) reactions which have so far received the most attention. Similar techniques apply and have been used to study (He^3,n) and (α,n) reactions. In fact future work with the (He^3,n) reaction might be especially rewarding because it involves the transfer of a pair of protons and is analogous to the interesting (t,p) reaction. Of course, pulsed (p,n) and (d,n) reactions are widely used as neutron sources for measurements of neutron reactions. The use of this technique for inelastic neutron scattering measurements will be discussed at this conference by A. B. Smith.

A survey of recent literature indicates that nanosecond beam pulsing work is done on about a dozen Van de Graaffs (single-ended or tandem), on several cyclotrons and on at least one linear accelerator. The different accelerators produce pulse widths which vary from several nanoseconds down to a fraction of a nanosecond and peak currents which vary from 5 mA down to 30 μA. The spacing of pulses varies from 200 nsec to 2000 nsec.

What are the limitations on energy resolution obtained by the time-of-flight method? The answer must necessarily be rather complicated because there are at least nine factors which must be considered and balanced

*Research sponsored by the U.S. Atomic Energy Commission under contract with Union Carbide Corporation

judiciously to obtain a near optimum situation. Even so, the particular arrangement chosen probably won't be optimum for all neutron energies of interest. There are of course limitations such as target thickness and intrinsic energy spread of the accelerated beam which are common to other types of experiments. Of special interest to us are those factors which involve time measurement. Since the energy resolution, $E_n/\Delta E_n$, depends on $t_n/\Delta t_n$ we can increase the resolution either by increasing t_n (increasing the flight path) or by decreasing Δt_n. Bearing in mind that the neutron flux varies inversely with the square of the flight path, it becomes clear that it is advantageous to decrease Δt_n rather than to increase t_n. Although the above argument is an oversimplification of the actual situation, it is nevertheless roughly correct and hence it explains the strong emphasis of trying to achieve small Δt_n values in time-of-flight work.

It is straightforward to calculate the expected neutron energy spread, ΔE_n, which results from a given overall timing uncertainty, Δt_n, for a given neutron energy and flight path. Some typical values are shown in graphical form in Fig. 1. The straight lines on the log-log scale give the values of ΔE_n as a function of E_n for several different flight paths. We assume a timing width of 1 nsec; the values can be directly scaled up or down for other values of Δt_n. Of central importance in time-of-flight work is the fact that ΔE_n is proportional to $E_n^{3/2}$. For example, if the flight path is 5 meters and Δt_n is 1 nsec, then ΔE_n changes from 6 to 500 keV as E_n changes from 1 to 20 MeV. A flight path of 40 meters is required to give 60 keV for ΔE_n at E_n = 20 MeV.

The timing spread of a monoenergetic neutron group is caused by a) the time width of the beam pulse, b) the finite detector thickness, and c) the timing accuracy of the detector and associated electronics system. Of these the simplest to discuss is the time spread caused by the finite detector thickness. Plastic scintillators of 1- to 2-inch thickness are typical in fast neutron time-of-flight work. It takes a 1-MeV neutron 1.8 nsec to move 1 inch. A 20-MeV neutron will move 1 inch in 0.4 nsec. In Fig. 1 we show a dashed curve for a 5-meter flight path in which an additional time spread due to a 1-inch thick detector is folded into the basic 1 nsec width. In this example the detector thickness is the chief limitation for neutron energies below 1 MeV. In many experiments we wish to detect a wide range of neutron energies. We see that it is then difficult to achieve a well-matched system. We want a thick detector for high energy neutrons to increase the detection efficiency and yet a thick detector severely limits the energy resolution for low-energy neutrons. If the detector thickness is an important contributor to the energy resolution for a given neutron energy and it is desired to decrease ΔE_n, it is advantageous from a counting rate point-of-view to decrease the detector thickness rather than to increase the flight path.

Plastic or liquid scintillators coupled to fast photomultipliers are almost universally used to detect the fast neutrons and hence the time response of these detectors is of great importance to time-of-flight work. I will not have the time to discuss this subject in detail; there are several good articles on this subject.[1-4] A rather flat continuous distribution of pulse heights result from the fast neutron interaction with the scintillator and in order to maintain a high counting rate it is desirable to use a wide dynamic range of pulse heights for timing. In considering the time response of the detector it is useful to distinguish "time jitter" from "time walk." By time jitter we mean the variation in timing of pulses which have the same pulse height. If the scintillator area is not large and if the pulses used for timing are restricted to a small range of the larger pulses, then it is possible to detect neutrons of several MeV energy with a time jitter well under 1 nsec. Time jitter increases for lower energy neutrons and for larger area detectors.

The rise time of the pulse from the detector is governed by a) the decay time of the scintillator (typically 2 to 4 nsec), b) the time taken by the photons to arrive at the photocathode (not negligible when large area scintillators and light pipes are used), and c) the rise time of the photomultiplier (typically 2 nsec). The rise time of the pulses is therefore several nanoseconds and if we measure time by triggering at a given pulse height there will be appreciable time walk for pulses of different size. In principle, time walk is not a limitation on timing accuracy, it merely requires an elaborate system for recording the information. At Oak Ridge we use leading edge timing and we store a 2-dimensional array in which the time spectra are sorted according to scintillator pulse height. The individual time spectra are then appropriately walk corrected and collapsed into a single time spectrum.

There are timing systems in use which do not require two-dimensional storage. By the use of the "fast crossover" technique one can eliminate time walk but only at the expense of increased time jitter.

In our work at Oak Ridge we have used an NE-213 liquid scintillator with 1-inch thickness and 4-1/2-inch diameter which is mounted directly onto a 58 AVP photomultiplier. When we set the trigger level to respond to energy pulses greater than 0.5 MeV we find that the timing resolution for several MeV energy neutrons is approximately 1 nsec. Similar results are obtained by others, for example, C. J. Oliver, et al.[5]

The final necessary ingredient for fast neutron time-of-flight work is an accelerated pulsed beam. A Van de Graaff accelerator produces a dc beam characterized by a certain energy homogeneity, angular divergence, spot size and intensity which taken together indicates the quality of the ion beam. Fowler and Good[6] have emphasized that the production of a time-modulated beam invariably reduces the quality of the beam. Careful consideration should be given to the pulsing system to achieve a desirable balance between the beam burst duration and the decrease in beam quality. For example, in an attempt to achieve better energy resolution by producing sharp time bursts through strong klystron bunching one might in fact find poorer energy resolution because the bunching process produces an appreciably larger energy spread in the incident ion beam.

The Mobley magnetic compression method has proved to be a popular and reliable method for achieving sharp ion bursts with Van de Graaff accelerators. The actual performance of a Mobley system has been described by Cranberg, et al.[7] An rf ion source and a beam chopper, located in the high voltage terminal, produce pulses of 10 nsec width and 1000 nsec spacing. After acceleration the Mobley magnet system compresses the pulses to about 1 nsec width. The peak current is several mA.

It is well-known that Mobley time compression is paid for by an increase in the beam divergence. However, one should also note that in the system described by Cranberg, et al. there is a considerable increase in ion energy spread caused by the electrostatic beam deflector needed to fan out the beam prior to entrance into the Mobley magnet. The energy homogeneity is decreased to 1 part in 250. This is to be compared with values of 1 part in 1000 to 2000 which are commonly realized with dc beams from Van de Graaffs.

An alternative method for producing nanosecond pulsing for Van de Graaffs has been developed at Oak Ridge. A duoplasmatron ion source, a beam chopper, and a klystron buncher are located in the terminal of the Van de Graaff. The characteristics of this system for our 3-MV Van de Graaff has been described in detail by Moak, et al.[8] This system produces a pulse with width $\leq$ 1 nsec and a peak current of 10 mA. Since one achieves time compression by energy modulation of the particles within a given pulse, one expects to pay for the time compression by an increase in the energy spread of the ion beam. In Fig. 2, I show a test made a couple of years ago. The narrow resonance in the $C^{13}(p,\gamma)$ reaction was measured with a chopped beam of 9 nsec pulse width. The indicated beam energy spread was 0.4 keV. The klystron buncher was then turned up until the pulses on the scope had a width of 1.5 nsec and the narrow resonance was again measured. The measured energy spread was 1.8 keV. Thus the klystron buncher reduces the energy homogeneity from 1 part in 4000 to 1 part in 1000.

A beam pulsing system similar to that described by Moak, et al. has been in operation for about two years on the 6-MV Van de Graaff at Oak Ridge. One recent improvement made to both machines was the installation of a beam pulse diverter or "count down" system in each terminal. This allows the experimenter to turn a knob on the control console and thereby select the time interval between pulses from among the values 500, 1000, 2000, ---, to 16,000 nsec.

Nanosecond pulsing systems have been developed for several tandem Van de Graaffs. Because one must work with a negative ion beam, the peak currents for tandems are down 1 to 2 orders of magnitude from those obtained with single-ended Van de Graaffs. An early pulsing system is described by Lefevre, et al.[9] The negative ions are obtained by charge exchange. The beam is klystron bunched at the low-energy end of the tandem and is then rf chopped at the high-energy end. The system produced pulses of 2 nsec width and peak current of 30 μA. The Aldermaston tandem[10,11] also uses a negative ion beam obtained by charge exchange. However in the Aldermaston system the beam is first chopped and then klystron bunched at the low-energy end. They report pulses of 2.5 nsec width and about 50- to 90-μA peak current. The pulsing system which has recently become operational for the Oak Ridge tandem[12] uses direct extraction of a negative ion beam from a duoplasmatron ion source. The beam is then chopped and klystron bunched at the low-energy end of the tandem. This pulsing system produces pulses which are 0.8

nsec wide and 400 μA peak current and spot size of 5 mm.

The natural phase bunching in cyclotrons results in a time-structured accelerated beam which may be quite suitable for neutron time-of-flight work. Anderson and co-workers have done extensive neutron time-of-flight work with the small variable energy cyclotron at Livermore.[13] I do not know the characteristics of their pulsed beam.

(p,n) Reactions

I now want to discuss some (p,n) measurements done with the 6-MV Van de Graaff at Oak Ridge. Figure 3 shows a time-of-flight spectrum (converted to pulse height) observed when 3-MeV protons hit a thin Cu^{65} target. Four neutron groups are observed which result from the excitation of the ground state and 3 low-lying excited states in Zn^{65}. Although γ-n pulse shape discrimination was used (liquid scintillator NE213), there is still a small residual γ-ray peak. For this experiment the spacing between beam pulses was 222 nsec and the flight path was about 9 meters. Whenever the time difference between the fastest and slowest neutrons detected is larger than the time between beam pulses then we have what we call a "wrap around" situation. In Fig. 3, the γ rays actually get to the detector 3 cycles earlier than the ground state neutrons. The γ-ray peak is narrow compared to the neutron peaks and this shows that the beam pulse width and electronic time spread are small contributions to the width of the neutron peaks. The flight time of the ground state neutron group is about 700 nsec (E_n = 0.88 MeV). The observed width is 3.4 nsec or 9 keV. This width is believed to be the result of 3 approximately equal contributions: a) the energy spread from target thickness (nominal value 5 keV or 1.9 nsec), b) the energy spread in the beam pulse (estimated at 5 keV or 1.9 nsec), and c) the timing spread caused by the 1-inch thick detector (1.9 nsec or 5 keV).

One can therefore obtain a neutron energy resolution of about 10 keV for neutron groups with energies between 0.5 and 1 MeV. As we have seen the resolution becomes less impressive for higher energy neutrons. This is illustrated in Fig. 4 which shows once again a time-of-flight spectrum for Cu^{65} but at a higher bombarding energy of 4.36 MeV. Now the neutron groups labelled 0, 1, 2 and 3 are not nearly so well resolved (E_n = 2.2 MeV). On the other hand neutron groups labelled 15 and 16 correspond to neutrons leaving the Zn^{65} nucleus in excited states at 1.6 MeV with an energy separation of only 15 keV. By bombarding at successively higher proton energies we can gradually move up the region of good energy resolution and in this way examine the level structure in the residual nucleus. This has been done for the targets V^{51}, Co^{53}, Mn^{55}, Co^{59}, and Cu^{65} all of which have fairly low (p,n) thresholds.

To illustrate the results I will discuss the $Co^{59}(p,n)Ni^{59}$ reaction. High resolution work on the states in Ni^{59} is also available from the $Ni^{58}(d,p)Ni^{59}$ reaction.[14] Figure 5 shows a time-of-flight spectrum for E_p = 4.359 MeV (the (p,n) threshold is about 1.8 MeV). There is some "wrap around" complication in this spectrum. Neutron group 10 is merged with group 1. The "wrap around" groups can be disentangled because the data is recorded in a 2-dimensional array. Those peaks due to lower energy neutrons have smaller pulse heights. The peak labelled 7 and 8 is too wide for a single neutron group and is assumed to be a close doublet.

Figure 6 is a time-of-flight spectrum taken at the higher proton energy of 4.765 MeV. Notice that there is a weak peak (5) on the side of the strong peak (6). Figure 7 is a composite of 3 time-of-flight spectra taken at the still higher energies of 5.771, 5.866, and 6.045 MeV. The peaks are labelled with the excitation energies in the Ni^{59} nucleus. These spectra serve to examine the level structure in Ni^{59} at excitation energies of 2.9 to 3.6 MeV. The close-lying states at 3.035 and 3.047 MeV are resolved in the top spectrum but are merged to a single peak at the next higher proton energy. Similarly the states at 3.298 and 3.305 MeV are a broad peak in the top spectrum, then separate in the center spectrum and again merge in the bottom spectrum. We note that new groups corresponding to higher excited states emerge as the proton energy is increased.

The ground state of Co^{59} is $7/2^-$. Assuming the validity of the statistical model, we can use proton penetrabilities from the optical model to calculate the relative populations of different J^π states in the compound nucleus. Such a distribution is shown for 5-MeV protons in Fig. 8. States with spins 3 to 5 are the most likely. The $Ni^{58}(d,p)Ni^{59}$ results have shown that the state labelled 5 in Fig. 6 has an ℓ = 1 stripping pattern. It must then be a $3/2^-$ or $1/2^-$ state. The small intensity of this state in the (p,n) reaction strongly suggests that the state is a $1/2^-$ state. Other known $3/2^-$ states are more strongly excited. Higher ℓ waves and hence lower neutron penetrabilities are required to excite a $1/2^-$ residual state. For example the compound nucleus state 4^- can decay to a $1/2^-$ state only by g-wave neutrons whereas it can decay to a $3/2^-$ state by d-wave neutrons.

Figure 9 is a graphical summary of the excited states in Ni^{59} observed with the (p,n) reaction. We have also shown the level structure obtained by Cosman, et al. who used the (d,p) reaction on Ni^{58}. There is good agreement for the first 6 excited states. At higher energies there are definite differences in the level structures obtained in the two experiments.

Figure 9 also shows some preliminary results obtained by looking at the γ rays with a Ge detector when protons bombard a Co^{59} target. At these low proton energies neutron emission is strongly favored and hence most of the observed γ rays come from the decay of excited states in Ni^{59}. The $Co^{59}(p,n\gamma)$ results in Fig. 9 indicate the levels for which γ rays have been identified.

Next I want to briefly discuss the $Y^{89}(p,n)Zr^{89}$ reaction which has been studied by Kim and Robinson.[15] Figure 10 shows the low-lying states of Zr^{89}. The ground state and first excited state are known to be $9/2^+$ and $1/2^-$, respectively. Goodman[16] has measured the $Zr^{90}(p,d)Zr^{89}$ reaction and found $\ell = 1$ for the transferred neutron to the second excited state at 1095 keV. The $Y^{89}(p,n)Zr^{89}$ was used to try to decide whether this second excited state was $1/2^-$ or $3/2^-$. The relative differential cross sections were measured at several proton energies. An example of these results is shown in Fig. 11. Hauser-Feshbach predictions are shown for $3/2^-$ (solid curve) and $1/2^-$ (dashed curve). Clearly the shape and magnitude of the differential cross section indicate that the second excited state is $3/2^-$.

As a final topic on (p,n) reactions I will briefly discuss some work by Kim, Kernell, Robinson, and Johnson[17] which uses the neutron decay of an analog resonance to make spin and parity assignments to residual excited states. Figure 12 shows the $Sn^{119}(p,n)Sb^{119}$ yield as a function of proton energy. The strong resonance is identified as the analog of the 0^+ ground state in Sn^{120}. The idea of the experiment is to measure the neutron spectra both on and off the analog resonance. When off the resonance the compound states from which the neutrons decay will be typically distributed over a range of J^π. However, the analog resonance selectively enhances 0^+ compound states. As a result the neutron decay to the residual states in Sb^{119} would be expected to differ when on and off the analog resonance. This is illustrated in Fig. 13. For example, the groups n_3 and n_4 have different relative heights when on resonance and off resonance. This type of experiment plus some additional angular distribution measurements has led to spin and parity assignments for the levels fed by the neutron groups n_{10}, n_{11}, n_{12}, and n_{13}.

(d,n) Reactions

The Q-values for (p,n) reactions for many nuclei are so negative that the (p,n) reaction cannot be studied with a low-energy accelerator. In contrast, the (d,n) reaction generally has a positive Q-value and hence (d,n) reactions offer a more extensive range of application for low-energy accelerators. The problem with (d,n) reactions is that the Q-value may be so large and positive that the neutron groups with high energy may not be adequately resolved by the time-of-flight method. Long flight paths are required. The (d,n) work done with the 3-MV Van de Graaff at Harwell has used a 15-meter flight path.

In the recent (d,n) work done at Oak Ridge we have used the experimental arrangement shown in Fig. 14. The 6-MV Van de Graaff is a vertical machine. The beam analyzing magnet is on a gun mount which permits the beam to be sent in different directions. To change the angle at which the neutrons from a (d,n) reaction are detected we rotate the beam analyzing magnet. The shielded detector which is mounted on a polar coordinate system (carriage mounted on a horizontal beam which is in turn supported by a pivot point and circular rail) requires only slight adjustment to allow the detector to view the new target position. This system allows flight paths of up to 15 meters.

Now the simplest thing to do with the (d,n) reaction is to use it to locate levels in the residual nucleus. However, one would also like to use stripping theory to get information on the spins and parities of the states and possibly also spectroscopic factors. The difficulty is that at low bombarding energy the reaction is likely to be a mixture of direct and compound nucleus reactions. If this is the case one may still be able to make a qualitative interpretation which will select ℓ values. The spectroscopic factors will be more difficult. As an example, Paul and Montague[18] have studied the $Ne^{22}(d,n)Na^{23}$ reaction at E_d = 3 MeV and have used the strong peaking at forward angles to pick out ℓ = 0 proton transfer.

Davies, et al.[19] have studied the $Si^{28}(d,n)P^{29}$ reaction at both 4 and 5 MeV incident deuteron energy. They found a j-dependence for the stripping patterns. It is also interesting to note that they found different spectroscopic factors at 4 and 5 MeV. They believe that at 5 MeV the spectroscopic factors are probably reliable (relatively small compound nucleus contribution). Buccino, et al.[20] also studied the $Si^{28}(d,n)P^{29}$ reaction at the higher energies of 7, 9, and 10 MeV. Their results are in agreement with those obtained by Davies, et al.

It is clear that a great deal more (d,n) work on nuclei is desirable in order to have information on the proton states in nuclei which is comparable in quality and quantity to what is now known for the neutron states. In recent years the (He^3,d) reaction has proved to be an attractive alternative to the (d,n) reaction. At present the theoretical interpretation of the (d,n) reaction is probably more reliable than that for the (He^3,d) reaction. The study of (d,n) reactions on the medium and heavy weight nuclei will probably require deuteron energies in the tandem Van de Graaff range.

Lawergren, Morrison, and Ferguson[21] have used the (d,n) reaction to study the excitation of analog states. The $Na^{23}(d,n)Mg^{24}$ and $Al^{27}(d,n)Si^{28}$ reactions excite states in Mg^{24} and Si^{28} which are the analogs of the low-lying states in Na^{24} and Al^{28}. They have compared the spectroscopic factors for excitation of the analog states to those previously obtained for the states in Na^{24} and Al^{28} from the (d,p) reaction. Lawergren, et al. point out that the energy resolution available for investigation of the analog states is especially good because the neutrons leading to these states (for the cases studied) have low energy.

An example of a (d,n) time-of-flight spectrum taken recently at Oak Ridge is shown in Fig. 15 for a Ni^{58} target. The neutron groups leading to the low-lying states of Cu^{59} are very well resolved. Some preliminary angular distributions for the ground state and first three excited states of Cu^{59} are shown in Fig. 16. The ground and first excited states are $p_{3/2}$ and $p_{1/2}$ states and one sees a strong stripping pattern for the neutrons going to these states.

Blair[22] has used the (He^3,d) reaction to look at states in Cu^{59}. A strong state at 3.9 MeV was identified as the analog of the ground state of Ni^{59}. Rosner, et al.[23] concluded that states at 3.90, 4.32, and 4.37 MeV are excited in the (He^3,d) reaction and are to be identified as the analogs of the first 3 states in Ni^{59}. However, Morrison and Schiffer[24] also studied the (He^3,d) reaction and found a somewhat more complicated situation. Our results from the (d,n) work are in general agreement with the work of Morrison and Schiffer. The spectrum shown in Fig. 15

indicates a number of strong peaks in the region from 3.5 to 4.5 MeV. In fact, Morrison and Schiffer found states at 3.56, 3.59, 3.76, 3.90, 3.92, 4.01, 4.06, 4.12, 4.32 and 4.36 MeV and these values correspond quite well with those shown in Fig. 15.

During this talk I have referred to (p,n) and (d,n) work at Oak Ridge. I therefore want to acknowledge my co-workers, Y. Cassagnou, F. Perey, J. Biggerstaff, A. Marusak, K. Dickens, W. Kinney, and J. McConnell.

References

1. A Schwarzschild, Nucl. Instr. and Methods 21, 1 (1963).

2. G. Present, A. Schwarzschild, I. Spirn, and N. Wotherspoon, Nucl. Instr. and Methods 31, 71 (1964).

3. E. Gatti and V. Svelto, Nucl. Instr. and Methods 30, 213 (1964).

4. C. W. Williams, "Timing with Photomultipliers", ORTEC News (March 1967). Oak Ridge, Tennessee.

5. C. J. Oliver, B. Collinge, and G. Kaye, Nucl. Instr. and Methods 50, 105 (1967).

6. T. K. Fowler and W. M. Good, Nucl. Instr. and Methods 7, 245 (1960).

7. L. Cranberg, R. A. Fernald, F. S. Hahn, and E. F. Shrader, Nucl. Instr. and Methods 12, 335 (1961).

8. C. D. Moak, W. M. Good, R. F. King, J. W. Johnson, H. E. Banta, J. Judish, and W. H. duPreez, Rev. Sci. Instr. 35, 672 (1964).

9. H. W. Lefevre, R. C. Borchers, and C. H. Poppe, Rev. Sci. Instr. 33, 1231 (1962).

10. J. H. Anderson and D. Swann, Nucl. Instr. and Methods 30, 1 (1964).

11. D. Dandy and D. P. Hammond, Nucl. Instr. and Methods 30, 23 (1964).

12. C. D. Moak (private communication).

13. See, for example, C. Wong, J. D. Anderson, J. W. McClure and B. Pohl, Phys. Rev. 156, 1266 (1967).

14. E. R. Cosman, C. H. Paris, A. Sperduto, and H. A. Enge, Phys. Rev. 142, 673 (1966).

15. H. J. Kim and R. L. Robinson (submitted to Phys. Rev.).

16. C. D. Goodman, Bull. Am. Phys. Soc. 9, 106 (1964).

17. H. J. Kim, R. L. Kernell, R. L. Robinson, and C. H. Johnson (private communication).

18. E. B. Paul and J. H. Montague, Nucl. Phys. 54, 497 (1964).

19. W. G. Davies, W. K. Dawson, G. C. Neilson, and K. Ramavataram, Nucl. Phys. 76, 65 (1966).

20. S. G. Buccino, D. S. Gemmell, L. L. Lee, Jr., J. P. Schiffer, and A. B. Smith, Nucl. Phys. 86, 353 (1966).

21. B. Lawergren, G. C. Morrison, and A. T. G. Ferguson, page 739, Conference on Isobaric Spin, Academic Press (1966).

22. A. G. Blair, page 115 Proceedings of "Nuclear Spectroscopy with Direct Reactions" ANL-6878 (1964).

23. B. Rosner, C. H. Holbrow, and D. J. Puller, page 595, Conference on Isobaric Spin, Academic Press (1966).

24. G. C. Morrison and J. P. Schiffer, page 748, Conference on Isobaric Spin, Academic Press (1966).

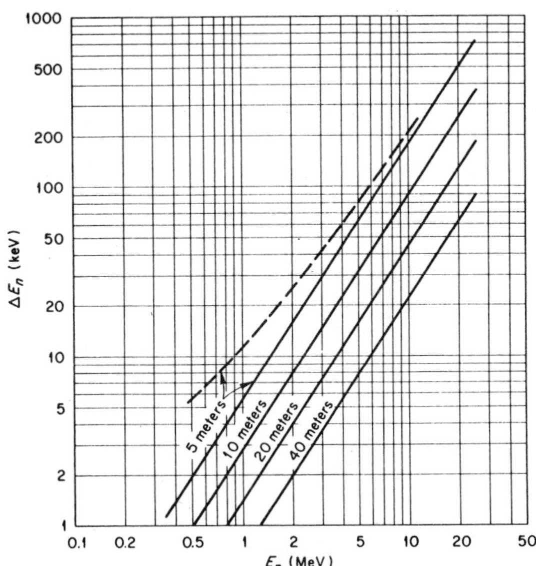

Fig. 1 Plots of the neutron energy spread ΔE_n (in keV) as a function of neutron energy (in MeV) for different flight paths which results from a timing uncertainty Δt_n of 1 nsec. The dashed curve shows the ΔE_n for a 5 meter flight path which results from an additional timing spread caused by a 1 inch thick detector.

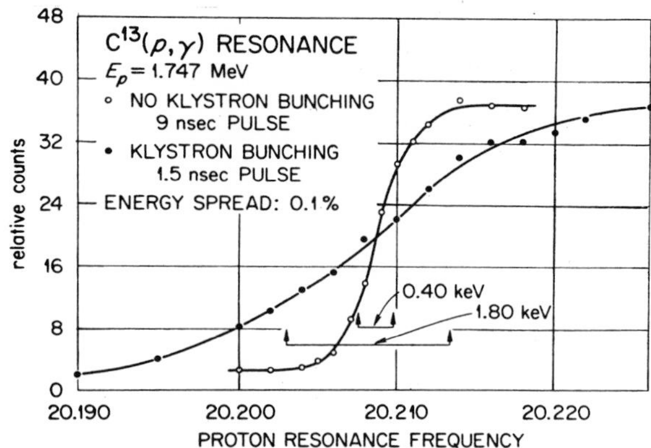

Fig. 2 Narrow $C^{13}(p,\gamma)$ resonance which was measured with and without klystron bunching to study the increase in beam energy spread caused by the bunching.

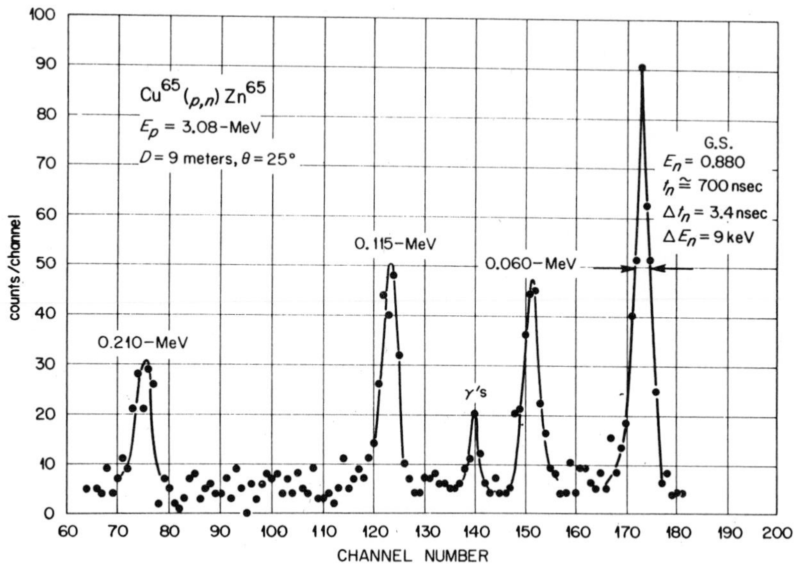

Fig. 3 Time-of-flight spectrum for the $Cu^{65}(p,n)Zn^{65}$ reaction.

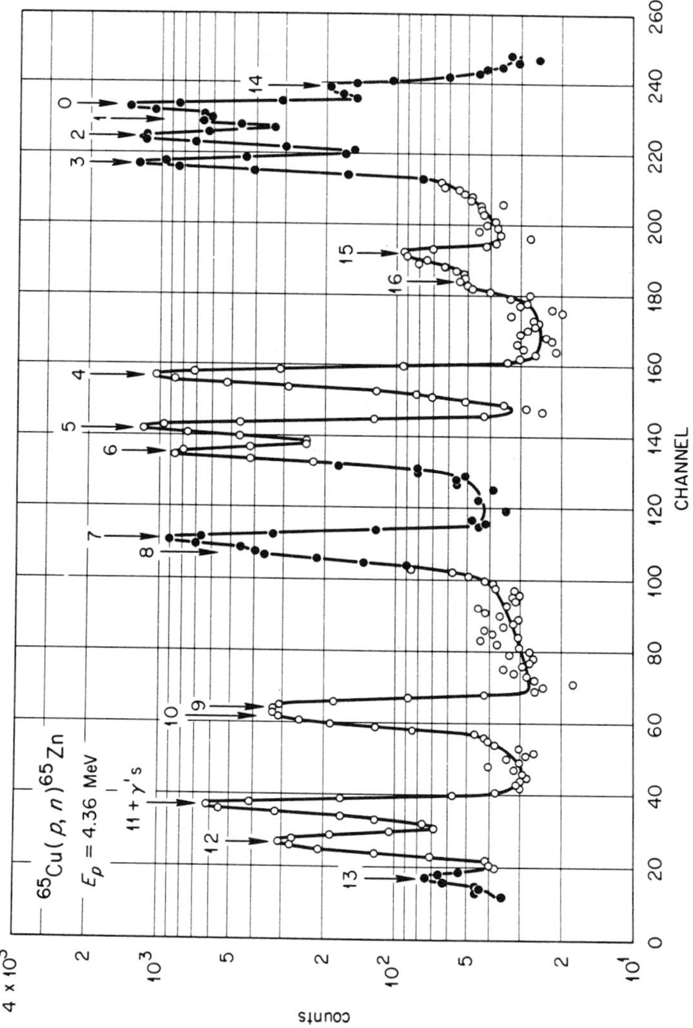

Fig. 4 Time-of-flight spectrum for the $Cu^{65}(p,n)Zn^{65}$ reaction. The flight path was about 6 meters. The arrows indicate the neutron groups going to excited states in Zn^{65} (ground state group labelled 0).

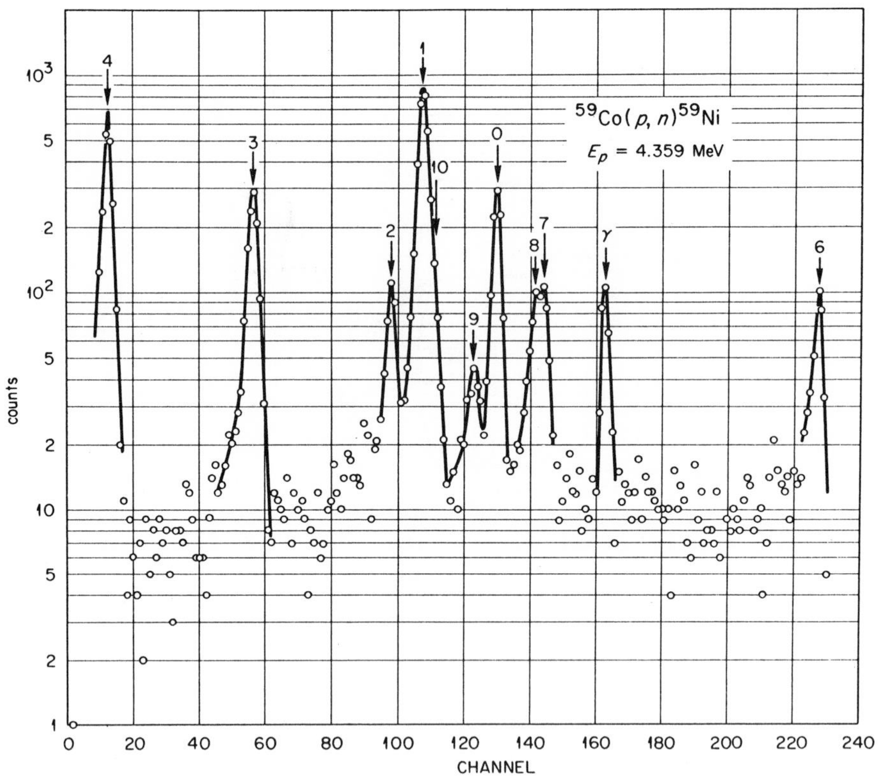

Fig. 5 Time-of-flight spectrum for the $Co^{59}(p,n)Ni^{59}$ reaction. Flight path is 6 meters.

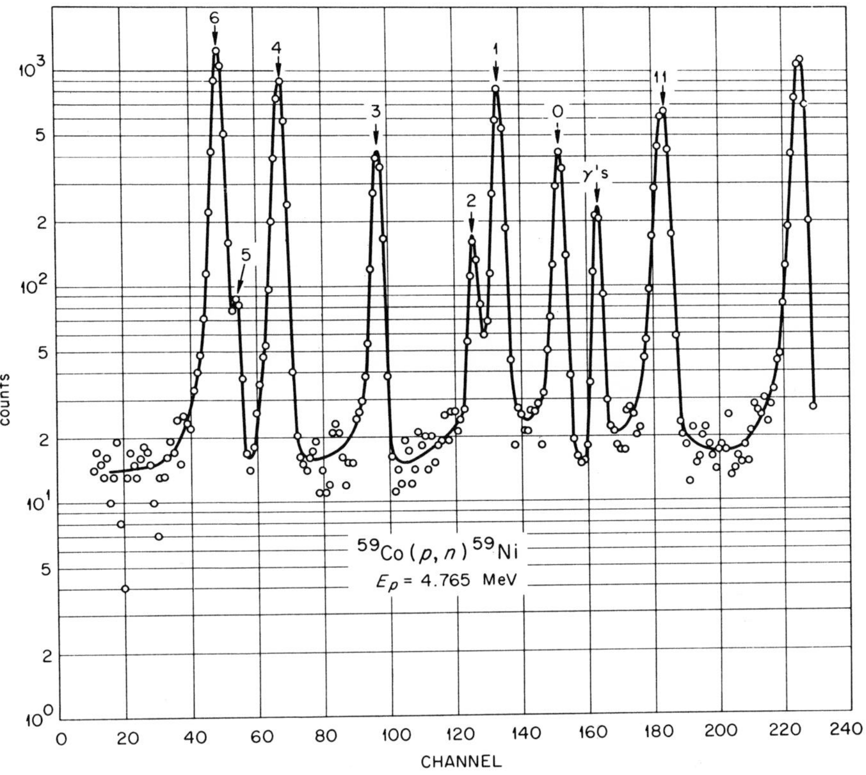

Fig. 6 Time-of-flight spectrum for the $Co^{59}(p,n)Ni^{59}$ reaction. Flight path is 6 meters.

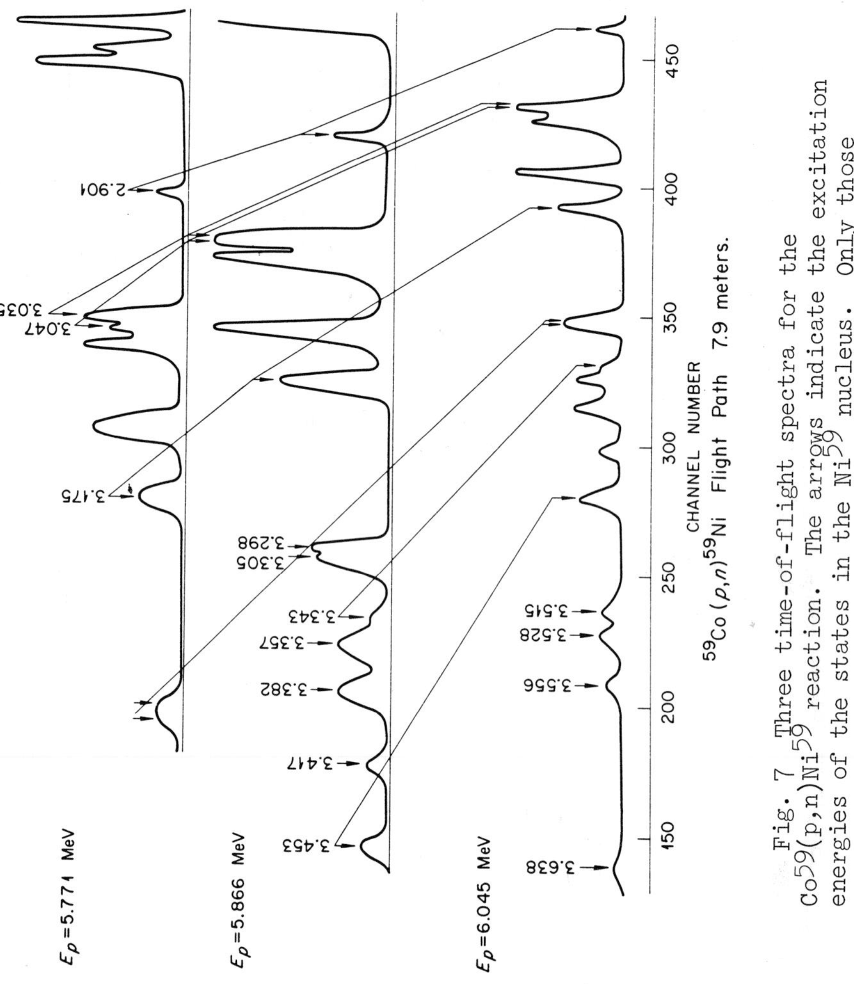

Fig. 7 Three time-of-flight spectra for the $Co^{59}(p,n)Ni^{59}$ reaction. The arrows indicate the excitation energies of the states in the Ni^{59} nucleus. Only those neutron groups leading to rather high excited states are shown.

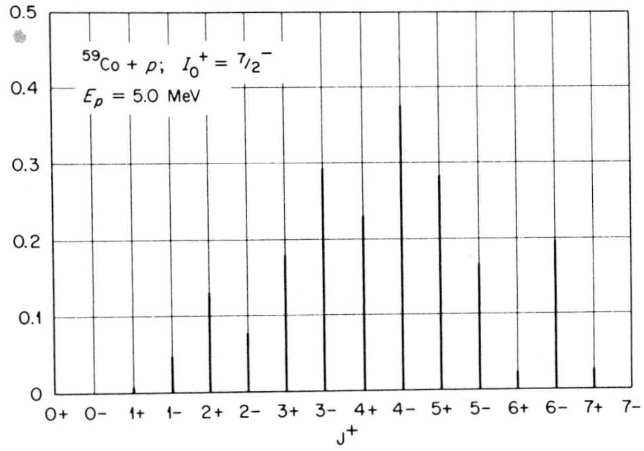

Fig. 8 Relative population of J^{π} states for 5 MeV protons on Co^{59}. The statistical assumption is made and the transmission coefficients are obtained from an optical model.

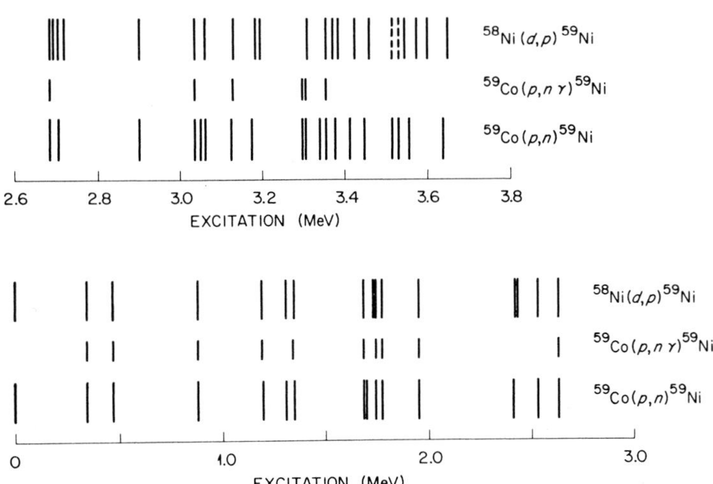

Fig. 9 Summary of levels in Ni^{59} observed by the Co^{59}(p,n) reaction. The levels obtained by the Ni^{58}(d,p) reaction are also shown. Levels identified by observing the γ rays in a Ge detector spectrum are shown.

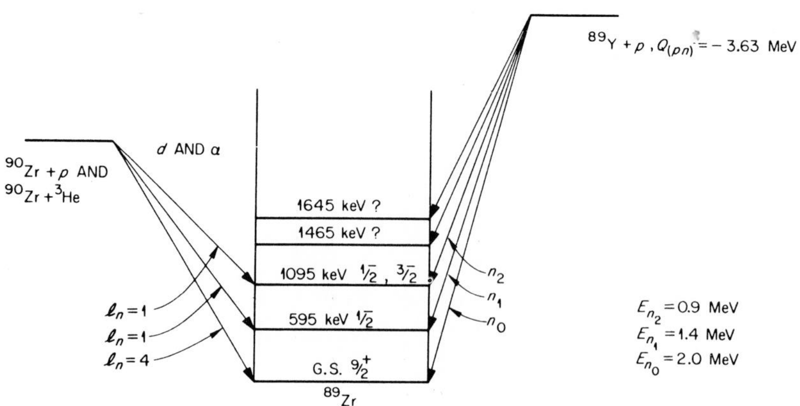

Fig. 10 Level diagram for Zr^{89}.

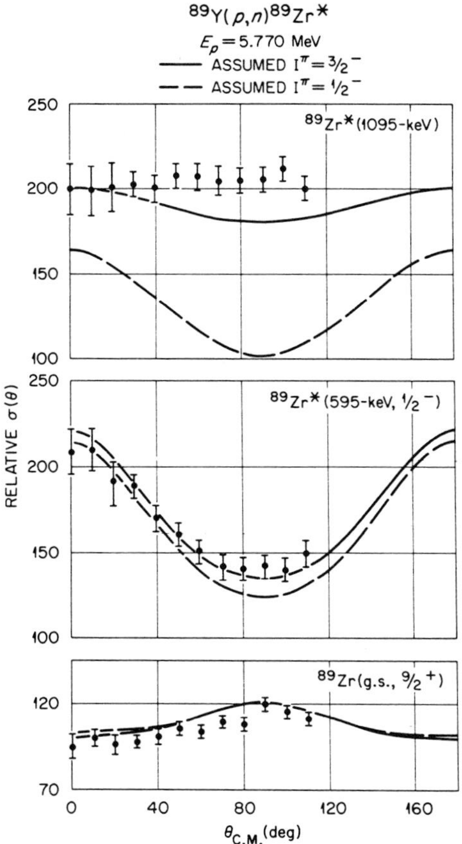

Fig. 11 Relative differential cross sections for the neutron groups leading to the ground state and first two excited states in Zr^{89}. The curves are theoretical predictions of the Hauser-Feshbach theory. The dashed curve is for the assignment $1/2^-$ and the solid curve is for the assignment $3/2^-$ for the second excited state.

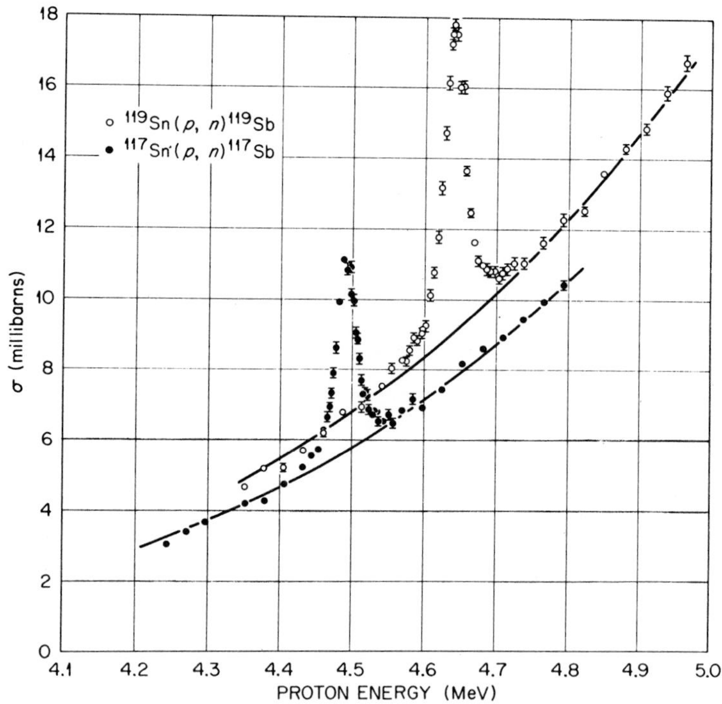

Fig. 12 (p,n) reaction cross sections for Sn^{117} and Sn^{119} in the vicinity of the 0^+ analog resonance.

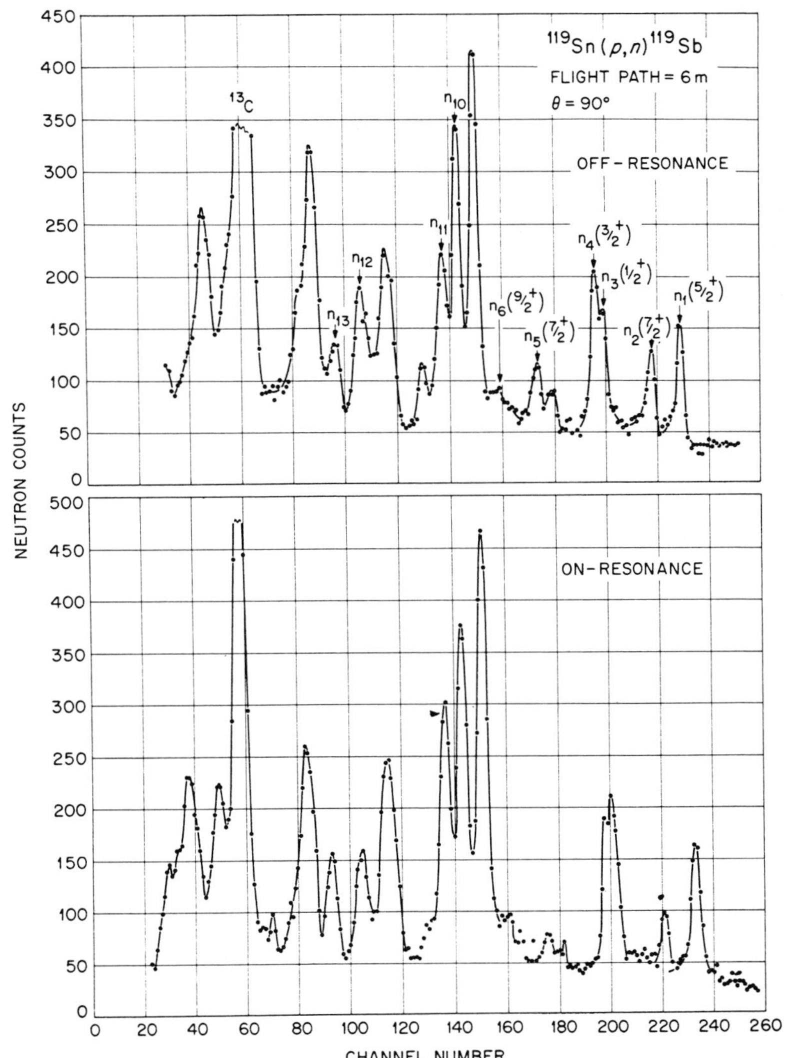

Fig. 13 Neutron time-of-flight spectra for the $Sn^{119}(p,n)$ reaction taken on-resonance and off-resonance.

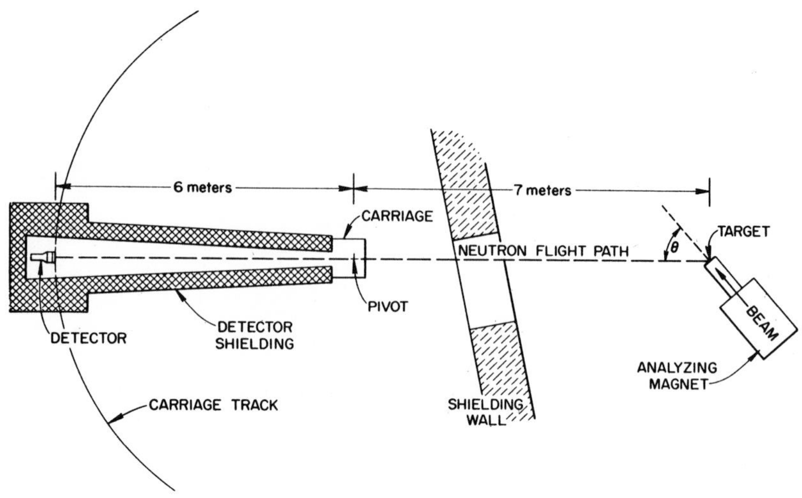

Fig. 14 Schematic diagram of the experimental neutron time-of-flight arrangement on the Oak Ridge 6 MV Van de Graaff. The observation angle is changed by rotating the beam analyzing magnet.

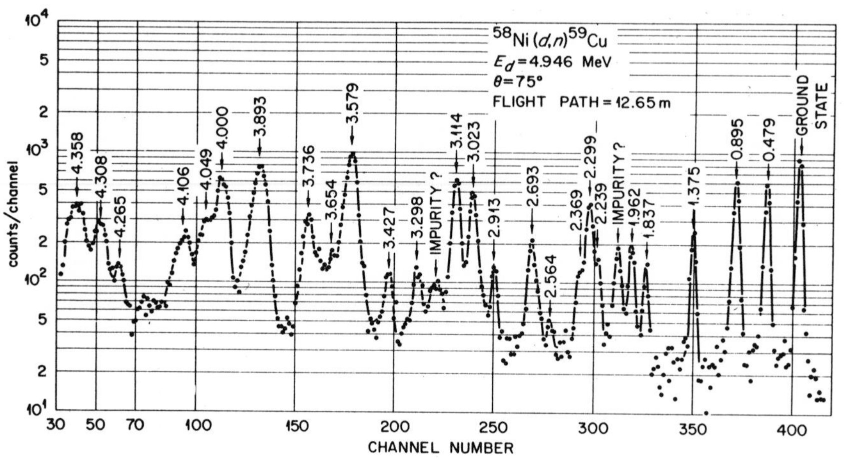

Fig. 15 An example of a $Ni^{58}(d,n)$ time-of-flight spectrum. This spectrum was obtained with 1 hour of running time.

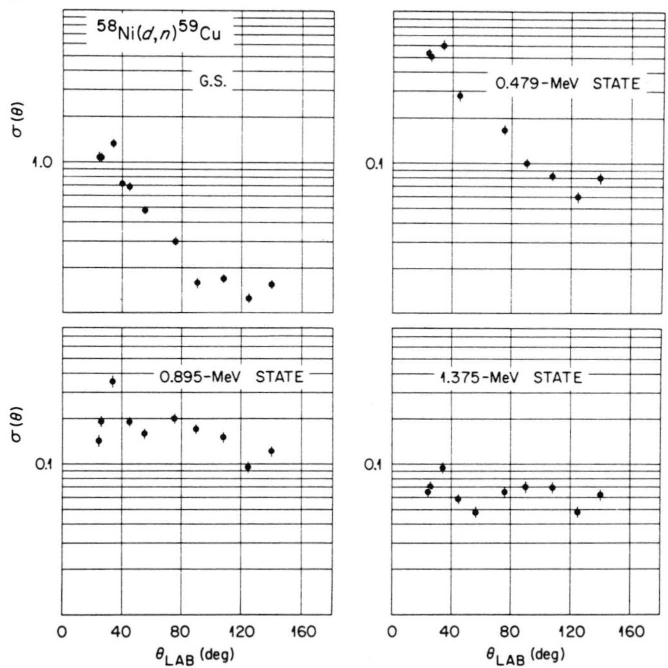

Fig. 16 Some preliminary angular distributions for the ground and first 3 excited states in Cu^{59} obtained from the Ni^{58}(d,n) reaction at E_d = 4.946 MeV.

GAMMA RAYS FROM NEUTRON INELASTIC SCATTERING*

M. T. McEllistrem

University of Kentucky
Lexington, Kentucky

INTRODUCTION

This paper reviews measurements made on prompt gamma rays following neutron inelastic scattering and the information extracted from the measurements. The techniques used to measure differential production cross sections and gamma-ray energies will be described. The precision and accuracy of presently available data and the interpretations used to extract information will be briefly reviewed.

Most of the effort on (n,n'γ) reactions to data has been with incident neutron energies $\lesssim$ 5 MeV and directed toward the spectroscopy of excited levels. The properties of levels sought in these experiments are their excitation energies, gamma-ray decay-schemes, and their angular momenta or "spins." In some cases of mixed-multipole transitions the mixing ratio $\delta \equiv \langle|L + 1|\rangle/\langle|L|\rangle$ can be determined.

When the gamma-ray branching ratios and production cross sections have been measured, the neutron inelastic scattering cross sections are determined. The (n,n'γ) reactions are thus an important source of neutron inelastic scattering cross sections at low energies. The comparison of these with the predictions of a statistical model helps to establish the mechanism of neutron inelastic scattering at low energies. The remarkable success of the model has greatly enhanced the effectiveness of the reactions for nuclear spectroscopy, as will be shown later. A small amount of work has been completed on (n,n'γ) angular correlations, with the purpose of testing the statistical model. This work has been reviewed in detail by E. Sheldon,[1] and will not be included here.

---

*Supported in part by the National Science Foundation

MEASUREMENTS NEAR THRESHOLD

The primary power of the (n,n'γ) reaction as a spectroscopic tool comes from the fact that the (n,n') cross sections rise rapidly above threshold and the detection efficiency has its full value, independent of incident energy. This means that careful cross section measurements are conveniently made a few hundred keV above threshold. The excited levels can be studied without having to contend with radiation from many levels above the level of interest.

EXCITATION FUNCTIONS

The sharp rise of the cross section above threshold makes the identification of a gamma ray as either a ground-state or cascade transition a very simple matter. Fig. 1, taken from the work of D. E. Velkley et al.[2] illustrates the clarity of threshold determinations. In this case all four lines are clearly ground state transitions, so that the data immediately identifies four levels in the two stable isotopes of Ga. Two of these levels were unknown prior to this data, although all of the lines had been observed in other studies[3] of Ga. Excitation functions of this type together with accurate measurements of the transition energies yield very directly portions of the level structure and gamma-ray decay scheme. Unfortunately, sensitivity limitations will cause weak transitions to be missed entirely. As a sort of general rule, transitions which account for less than 15% of the decay of a level can be missed. When the weak branch is a higher energy line than the more intense decay, lines corresponding to only 3% of the decay of a level have been measured.[4]

GAMMA-RAY ANGULAR DISTRIBUTION

A second important advantage of the ability to work only a little above threshold arises in the measurement of angular distributions. Near threshold, the inelastic scattering will be dominated by s-wave outgoing neutrons. Since $m_\ell = 0$ for the incoming plane wave, where m denotes magnetic quantum number, the excited level must have $m_J < |J_0 + 1|$, with J_0 denoting ground level spin, and J denoting the spin of the excited level. Hence if $J > |J_0 + 1|$, the excited state is a highly aligned state with high occupation only for $|m_J|$ small. This alignment depends little upon the mechanism of neutron inelastic scattering. The anisotropy of the subsequent gamma-ray decay depends therefore on the spins of the emitting and final states and the multipole character of the gamma ray. For $J > |J_0 + 1|$ the anisotropies are large and often permit unique determination of an unknown J.

At neutron energies near and well above thresholds for exciting particular levels the gamma-ray angular distributions and the neutron inelastic scattering cross sections are usually analyzed by comparison to statistical model predictions. The excellent agreement characteristically achieved enables spin assignments to excited levels. The formal framework of the model has been carefully reviewed by Sheldon,[1] and a subsequent review by Sheldon and Van Patter[5] contains many detailed calculations of gamma-ray angular distributions and comparisons with measured distributions. The model itself will thus not be reviewed here, but a later section will show results to illustrate points made in the above paragraphs.

EXPERIMENT DESIGN--D. C. BEAM

Ring Geometry Experiments

A high degree of interest in the (n,n'γ) reactions developed in the late 1950's. It was inspired largely by the extensive study of gamma-ray transitions completed by R. B. Day and collaborators.[6] Extensive work was completed also by the group working with D. M. Van Patter. Most of the work of these groups was carried out in "ring geometry" and was reviewed in some detail by R. B. Day[6] in 1963. The experimental arrangement is shown in Fig. 2, taken from the work of Van Patter et al.[7]. The scatterer is in the form of a ring with rectangular cross section surrounding a detector located on the axis of the ring. The detector is shielded from source neutrons by a cone of iron, tungsten, or other high density material.

As is clear from Fig. 2, the compactness of the geometry means that work must be done with poor angular resolution. This arrangement is especailly well suited to measurements of gamma-ray excitation functions, as displayed for example in the extensive series of such measurements completed by Lind and Day,[8] and has enough sensitivity to permit work with neutron inelastic cross sections[7,8] $\gtrsim$ 20 mb. The ring geometry is not well suited to gamma-ray angular distribution work, both because of the poor angular resolution and because changing the detection angle changes the detection geometry. If the angle is changed by moving the detector, the background is also quite angle dependent. If it is changed by moving the ring, the neutron flux at the sample undergoes a substantial change.

The principal difficulties of all ring geometry experiments are high backgrounds caused by neutron inelastic scattering in the detector, the requirement of large samples , and the importance of neutron multiple scattering and gamma-ray absorption corrections. With NaI(Tl) detectors, the principal backgrounds are those from $^{127}I(n,n'\gamma)^{127}I$ in the detector, and neutrons scattered by the sample into the detector contribute significantly to the production of that background. Since a NaI(Tl) detector with reasonable efficiency has a diameter of at least 1 inch, the sample I. D. will be $\gtrsim$ 2 inches. These ring samples contain from 5 to 10 moles of material. For angular distribution work,[9] they have usually been 50% larger than this. Corrections for absorption and neutron multiple scattering are important and angle dependent, because of the changes in detection geometry with angle. If the axial thickness of the sample is adjusted to give a neutron transmission of 0.75, Day[6] has shown that to within a few percent the effect of multiple scattering approximately cancels the attenuation caused by single scattering. This result was confirmed by Nishimura, _et al_.[10] The sample absorption of gamma rays has also been carefully studied experimentally by Nishimura, _et al_,[10] who used granular samples containing a small amount of a radioactive source mixed into the sample. By comparing source yields with and without the sample present they determined that the effective absorption ranged from 70% to 90% of that implied by the total photon absorption cross section[11] for gamma rays ranging in energy from 300 keV to 1 MeV. In spite of the difficulties mentioned, angular distribution measurements carried out[9] in ring geometry showed the usefulness of the distributions as a method of determining spins.

PULSED BEAM METHODS

NaI(Tl) Gamma-Ray Detection

In 1957 L. Cranberg[12] suggested that an extremely effective method of reducing background would be to detect the gamma-rays in coincidence with source neutrons. In his 1963 review, Day[6] included some work with separated isotopes using this technique. Two shielded NaI(Tl) detection systems have been used at Kentucky.[13,14] Both shields have detectors mounted in Pb containers with a wall thickness of 7.6 cm. The Pb cases are imbedded in a mixture of Li_2CO_3 and paraffin. A large shield houses a Raboy-Trail[15] or anti-Compton spectrometer and is shown in Fig. 3. The thickness of Pb in front of the NaI(Tl) annulus can be changed, and is usually made twice the wall thickness. The shield is 1.1 m long with a 1.1 m rear diameter and a 0.68 m front diameter. Its mass is 2700 kg and it is mounted on a movable carriage so that both detection angle and distance can be varied. An adjustable wedge and block of tungsten are used to shadow the detector from the neutron source. The whole arrangement[14] is called "System II". A small shield has dimensions of approximately 0.5 the larger, and it houses a single 6.35 cm x 6.35 cm NaI(Tl) detector. The collimating aperture of that shield is 4 cm, so that only the central 4 cm of the 6.35 cm scintillator is illuminated by gamma rays from the sample. This simple detection system is called "System I". A shielded anti-Compton spectrometer very similar to the one shown in Fig. 3 has been in use by I. L. Morgan's group[16] at Texas Nuclear Corporation for several years. Some of the results of work with that detector were reviewed in Ref. 5.

The neutron source of Fig. 3 was a 3.5 cm long gas cell containing T at 1 atm. It was sealed with a 0.3 mil Mo entrance foil and had a Pt beam stop. The incident proton beam was pulsed at 5 Mc with a pulse width of 5.5 ns and a time averaged beam current near 4 μa. The neutron energy spread was nearly gaussian in shape with a FWHM of 65 keV at a neutron energy of 3.5 MeV. Time reference pulses were derived through capacitive coupling of the beam pulses to a cylinder mounted in the beam tube. Run times, for the data to be shown here, ranged from 20 min to 40 min, but each spectrum to be shown corresponds to a superposition of three runs. The time distribution of radiation at the detector is measured with respect to the beam pulses using conventional[17] time-of-flight techniques. The time spectra obtained with a Cl sample are shown in Fig. 4. The discriminator for the time-to-amplitude converter is set near 100 keV. The spectra are gated by a slow side channel which permits display for radiation above 400 keV. The flight path used for the data of Fig. 4 was 1.15 m. The importance of the coincidence technique is seen to be the complete elimination of background caused by prompt neutron inelastic scattering in the detector, and 90% of the time-uncorrelated background. Those eliminations are implemented by gating the pulse-height analysis of the gamma-ray detector's pulses with portions of these time spectra. Single channel analyzers are used to select the two portions indicated by the heavy tic-marks in the 135° spectrum. One "time-window" is set over the prompt γ-peak and the other, labeled B, is a displaced window used to provide a simultaneous record of the time uncorrelated background. The consistency of this method of recording background is checked by comparing it to the background recorded in the prompt gamma-ray window when the sample is removed. Except for some small differences at 35°, the backgrounds measured in these two ways are the same.

The system used at Los Alamos by Conde et al[18] is shown in Fig. 5. Fig. 6 shows a time spectrum obtained with the system, with display of all radiation[18] above 100 keV. The excellent timing achieved shows the capacity of this technique even when working with a large spread of gamma rays. The data were taken with a flight path of 1.3 m, but it is clear that that distance could easily be cut in half to provide a very sensitive detection geometry. The gamma-ray spectrum obtained with an Al sample is shown in Fig. 7. The triangles show data without Compton rejection, and the dots are the result of both time and anti-coincidence gating, showing the importance of the anti-Compton feature with a complex pulse height spectrum.

At Kentucky we have taken data with the single NaI(Tl) detector, System I, and with the Raboy-Trail detector. Pulse height spectra taken with a Cl sample are shown in Fig. 8. The run time is about the same for both spectra, and the backgrounds shown were recorded with the displaced time gate as indicated in Fig. 4. Although the advantages of the anti-Compton spectrometer are evident, quite satisfactory yields can be obtained with a simple detector if the gamma spectra are not too complex. What this means in practice is that a single NaI(Tl) scintillator will work quite nicely for incident neutron energies $\lesssim$ 2.5 MeV.

An advantage of the (n,n'γ) technique for neutron inelastic scattering cross sections is its sensitivity. Fig. 9 shows a 90° pulse height spectrum taken with a KOH sample. The elemental differential cross section for the 1.291 MeV line is approximately 0.35 mb/sr, and its angular distribution was readily measured. All of the lines shown are transitions in the 6.88% abundant ^{41}K. A typical spectrum obtained with incident neutron energies near 4 MeV is shown in Fig. 10. The cross section for the 3.603 MeV line is approximately 1 mb/sr. Angular distributions have been measured for lines having half this cross section with incident energies near 4 MeV. To achieve this sensitivity, spherical samples containing 3-4 moles of the element to be studied are used. For the K and Cl samples, the spheres were ~5.7 cm in diameter and mounted ~9 cm from the gas cell. The angular resolution was ±19°.

Ge (Li) Detectors

The use of Ge(Li) detectors for (n,n'γ) experiments was first explicitly tested by C. Chasman, et al[19] who showed the feasibility of their use. A recent arrangement in use at Kentucky was developed with the collaboration of J. D. Brandenberger and is shown in Fig. 11. The 15cc detector has 2 cm of paraffin immediately in front of it. The shield contains a Pb case 6.5 cm thick surrounded by a mixture of

Li_2CO_3 and paraffin. The paraffin mixture is cut back on one side to permit use of the tungsten shadow bar and adjustable wedges. To see the differences in detection geometry from that employed with large NaI(Tl) detectors, the bar shown here appears in Fig. 3 labeled "W". Because the detector is small, data have been taken without the shield, relying only upon the tungsten bar. Time spectra obtained are shown in Fig. 12, both with and without the shield. Shielding the detector lowers the time uncorrelated background by more than a factor of 1.7.

Since the concern here is the measurement of differential production cross sections from 35° to 145°, the data of Fig. 12 and the spectrum of Fig. 13 have a 2 mole Ga sample located 7 cm from the neutron source and the detector located 57 cm from the sample. Ga has 60% ^{69}Ga and 40% ^{71}Ga, so the lines observed are similar to those of a 1 mole sample of a monoisotopic element. The side channel gate permitted display of all pulses corresponding to gamma-ray energies greater than 285 keV, and the time resolution achieved to date is 8 ns. It should be emphasized that the system is still being developed, with the hope of achieving improved performance. The output pulses of an ORTEC model 118A preamplifier are fed to two circuits in parallel. One input is that of a conventional linear amplifier-pulse height analyzer system and the other input is that of a 1 ns rise amplifier[20] with a voltage gain of 100. The output of this is then fed to conventional EGG timing circuitry.

Fig. 13 shows a spectrum obtained at 2.5 MeV neutron energy and with the system of Fig. 11, using pulsed beam techniques. Approximately 35 transitions in the two isotopes of Ga are identified, and approximately 20 of them are shown to be ground state transitions by excitation functions similar to that of Fig. 1. Since excitation functions are observed in 50 keV steps from 0.8 MeV to 2.5 MeV, the identification of all lines rests on many observations of them. Angular distributions have been measured for transitions corresponding to a cross section of ≈3mb/sr with relative uncertainties < 4-5% at a neutron energy of 1.5 MeV.

The spectrum of Fig. 14 illustrates data from a very simple system. For this spectrum the Ga sample is moved in to 6 cm from the neutron source and the detector is positioned 35 cm from the sample, but the detector is not shielded and the beam is not pulsed. The output of the preamplifier is fed to a pulse height analyzer with no gating of any kind. For purposes of intensity estimates, the 319 keV line corresponds to a cross section of roughly 10 mb/sr. The unlabeled lines are background transitions from neutron interactions in the Ge.

A 13cc Ge (Li) detector has been used as the central detector of an anti-Compton spectrometer by G. H. Williams and I. L. Morgan[31]. Their system is shown in Fig. 15, arranged for excitation functions at 55°. The sample is approximately 3.5 cm from the source and the detector is 56.7 cm from the sample. The performance of the spectrometer is illustrated for a single line in Fig. 16. Anti-coincidence gating of the Ge (Li) crystal with pulses from the annulus eliminates 80% of the Compton events. By coincidence gating with a narrow pulse height window set around 1 MeV, the 2-escape peak is selectively enhanced. This is a very effective way of identifying lines in a complex spectrum. The spectrum of Fig. 17 was obtained in a 90 min run with a 3.5 mole sample of Fe. This shows very clearly the sensitivity of the techniques as well as the practical energy limit for work with the gamma rays. To work with lines whose energies are $\gtrsim$ 3 MeV much larger detectors will be needed.

ACCURACY AND PRECISION

The major problem in measurements of the $(n,n'\gamma)$ reactions is the reduction of the yields to absolute cross sections. For this purpose measurements of the incident neutron flux at the sample and the gamma-ray detection efficiency must be made. Efficiencies for the "System I" detector at Kentucky have been measured by R. C. Lamb[13] using standard sources mounted in the same detection geometry as that for the $(n,n'\gamma)$ measurements. Efficiencies of the shielded anti-Compton spectrometer are available in the work of Ashe, et al[16] who described the characteristics of the spectrometer in use at Texas Nuclear Corporation. Neutron flux measurements have been described by many authors and will be discussed in another talk at this symposium.

The cross sections in many $(n,n'\gamma)$ experiments are obtained by normalizing them to the known cross section for the production of the 0.845 MeV gamma ray from ^{56}Fe. This avoids the necessity for the absolute efficiency and flux measurements mentioned above. Data for this reaction have been compiled[21] recently, but a casual glance at the compilation could create the impression that the cross sections are far from well known. This impression arises in part from the facts that cross sections were included per atom of element and atom of isotope, corrected and not corrected for angular anisotropy, and with small and large quoted uncertainties. For purposes of normalization, selected ^{56}Fe $(n,n'\gamma)$ and ^{56}Fe (n,n') measurements have been compiled by Davis B. Nichols[14].

Measurements included had quoted uncertainties <15% and an incident neutron energy spread $\geq$50 keV. Corrections to measurements which have appeared in authors subsequent publications were included; all are corrected for angular anisotropy using the distributions of Benjamin et al,[22] and all are listed per atom of isotope. The (n,n') data have been corrected to 90° differential gamma-ray production cross sections using angular distribution data and cascade contributions which have been published.[22] The compilation[23] is shown in Fig. 18. The dashed curve is an excitation function extracted from the data of Montague and Paul.[24] Except for one set of (n,n') data the cross sections are grouped within a spread of ±8%. The points with error flags are calculated weighted averages, which have been assigned an uncertainty of ±8%.

RESULTS AND ANALYSIS

The comparison[5] of statistical model or Hauser-Feshbach formalism calculations with measurements of gamma-ray angular distributions have been remarkably successful. The results of work recently reported for several odd A nuclei[4,14,25] all support the validity of the model. Fig. 19 shows a typical set of angular distributions[25] for $^{39,41}K$. The solid curve is a model calculation for the 3.603 MeV line, and the long-dash curve for the 2.817 MeV line is both a least squares fit to the measurements and a model calculation. Similar agreement between measured and calculated angular distributions was obtained[14] for transitions in $^{35,37}Cl$. To make the model calculations a neutron-nucleus potential is needed to generate transmission coefficients. The potential was obtained[14] by fitting total and differential elastic scattering cross sections in Ca. An analysis of neutron inelastic scattering cross sections and gamma-ray angular distributions in ^{51}V and ^{55}Mn has also been completed.[4] Neutron-nucleus potentials were obtained by finding ones which fit differential elastic scattering and total cross sections in ^{51}V and ^{56}Fe.

The gamma-ray angular distributions depend very weakly upon the potential used to calculate the transmission coefficients. For example, three independent potentials were determined by different groups to fit neutron total and differential elastic scattering cross sections in K. The gamma-ray anisotropies obtained with all of them agreed to within 5%. The Hauser-Feshbach formalism[1,5] also provides calculated neutron inelastic scattering cross sections for comparison with measurements. The calculated cross sections for the chlorine isotopes agreed with measurements[14] to within 25%. Table I shows a comparison of calculations and measurements for ^{51}V and ^{55}Mn, illustrating the success of the formalism when the neutron-nucleus potential has been carefully determined to fit neutron total and elastic scattering cross sections for the nucleus being studied and in the incident energy range employed for the inelastic scattering measurements.

Fluctuations Corrections

The study[25] of reactions in K suggested that the Hauser-Feshbach (HF) formalism will not fit the neutron inelastic scattering cross sections. Three independent determinations [14,26,27] of a potential to fit neutron cross sections in K have been made. All lead to inelastic scattering cross sections which are from 20-50% high. This fact and problems associated with representing inelastic scattering cross sections near threshold suggested a need for a modified statistical model. A model has been introduced by Moldauer from which fluctuation corrections[28] were derived for the transmission coefficients used in the HF formalism, and they have been employed[29] with some success to fit neutron inelastic scattering cross sections near threshold. It is important to see in what way these corrections affect the use of $(n,n'\gamma)$ in nuclear spectroscopy. Calculations[25,30] of them have been made for seven nuclei, including both odd and even A. The model calculations of interest are those of gamma-ray anisotropies and ratios of inelastic scattering cross sections to different levels. The ratios and anisotropies were both altered <9% in the cases tested.

The author is grateful to I. L. Morgan and others of Texas Nuclear Corporation and to J. C. Hopkins of Los Alamos Scientific Laboratory who graciously consented to the presentation of portions of their work.

REFERENCES

1. E. Sheldon, Rev. Mod. Phys. 35, 795 (1963).
2. D. E. Velkley, M. T. McEllistrem, and J. D. Brandenberger, BAPS 12, 492 (1967).
3. P. N. Tandon and H. G. Devare, Nuovo Cimento 32, 388 (1964). A. C. Li and Sergio Monaro, Nucl. Phys. A91, 353 (1967) and refs cited therein.
4. A. W. Barrows, R. C. Lamb, D. Velkley, and M. T. McEllistrem, submitted to Nuclear Physics.
5. E. Sheldon and D. M. Van Patter, Rev. Mod. Phys. 38, 143 (1966).
6. R. B. Day, Phys. Rev. 102, 767 (1956); Progress in Fast Neutron Physics, edited by G. C. Phillips, J. B. Marion, and J. R. Risser (University of Chicago Press, Chicago, 1963).
7. D. M. Van Patter, N. Nath, S. M. Shafroth, S. S. Malik, and M. A. Rothmann, Phys. Rev. 128, 1246 (1962).
8. D. A. Lind and R. B. Day, Ann. of Phys. 12, 485 (1961).
9. R. B. Day and M. Walt, Phys. Rev. 117, 1330 (1960).
10. K. Nishimura, K. Okano, and S. Kikuchi, Nucl. Phys. 70, 421 (1965).
11. Nuclear Spectroscopy Tables, A. H. Wapstra, G. J. Nijgh, R. Van Lieshout (North-Holland Publishing Company, Amsterdam, 1959).
12. Joan M. Freeman, International Conference on Neutron Interactions, Report TID-7547, 1957 (unpublished), p. 176, reports pulsed-beam work by R. B. Day undertaken at the suggestion of L. Cranberg.
13. R. C. Lamb, Ph.D. thesis, University of Kentucky, 1963 (unpublished).
14. Davis B. Nichols, B. D. Kern, and M. T. McEllistrem, Phys. Rev. 151, 879 (1966).
15. C. C. Trail and S. Raboy, Rev. Sci. Instr. 30, 425 (1959).
16. J. B. Ashe, J. D. Hall and I. L. Morgan, Rev. Sci. Instr. 37, 1559 (1966).
17. J. H. Neiler and W. M. Good, Fast Neutron Physics, Part I, edited by J. B. Marion and J. L. Fowler (Interscience, New York, 1960) ch. IV.A.
18. Henri Conde, Darrell M. Drake, and John C. Hopkins, LA-DC-7612, Los Alamos Scientific Laboratory, Los Alamos, New Mexico.

19. C. Chasman, K. W. Jones, and R. A. Ristenin, Nucl. Instr. and Methods 37, 1 (1965).
20. James S. Lunsford, Rev. Sci. Instr. 35, 1483 (1964).
21. Brookhaven National Laboratory Report BNL 325, IIA, (Office of Technical Services, Department of Commerce, Washington, D. C., 1966).
22. R. W. Benjamin, P. S. Buchanan, and I. L. Morgan, Nucl. Phys. 79, 241 (1966).
23. (n,n'γ) refs. are: R. B. Day, Phys. Rev. 102, 767 (1956); M. Hosoe and S. Suzuki, J. of Phys. Soc. of Japan 14, 699 (1959); D. M. Van Patter and R. W. Jackiw, Proc. Int. Conf. on Nuclear Structure, Kingston Canada (North-Holland Publishing Co., Amsterdam, 1960), p. 244; K. Nishimura, K. Okano, and S. Kikuchi, Nucl. Phys. 70, 421 (1965); and the (n,n') refs. are: J. C. Hopkins and L. Silbert, Nucl. Sci. Engr. 19, 431 (1964); W. B. Gilboy and J. H. Towle, Nucl. Phys. 64, 130 (1965); A. Jacquot and C. R. Rosseau, Nucl. Phys. 84, 239 (1966).
24. J. H. Montague and E. B. Paul, Nucl. Phys. 30, 93 (1962).
25. Davis B. Nichols and M. T. McEllistrem, to be published in The Physical Review.
26. J. D. Reber and J. D. Brandenberger, submitted to The Physical Review.
27. J. H. Towle and W. B. Gilboy, Nucl. Phys. 72, 515 (1965).
28. P. A. Moldauer, Phys. Rev. 135, B642 (1964).
29. P. A. Moldauer, Rev. Mod. Phys. 36, 1079 (1964).
30. S. C. Mathur, P. S. Buchanan, and I. L. Morgan, to be published in The Physical Review.
31. G. H. Williams and I. L. Morgan, Nucl. Instr. and Methods 45, 313 (1966).

TABLE I

Measured and calculated neutron inelastic scattering cross sections. E_x denotes the excitation energy of the level, J^π its spin and parity, and E_n the incident neutron energy. Columns headed σ_n are the measured cross sections and σ_T denotes the HF formalism calculations. All energies are in MeV; all cross sections are in mb.

			E_n=1.83		2.21		2.43		3.10	
	E_x	J^π	σ_n	σ_T	σ_n	σ_T	σ_n	σ_T	σ_n	σ_T
^{51}V	0.320	$5/2^-$	463	522	484	457	350	427	--	335
	0.930	$3/2^-$	176	135	195	164	207	172	200	165
	1.609	$11/2^-$	186	215	268	238	240	260	320	165
	1.813	$9/2^-$			233	170	203	193	274	270
	2.409	$(3/2)^-$							29	40
^{55}Mn	0.126	$7/2^-$	--	580	550	480				
	0.983	$9/2^-$	220	173	246	205				
	1.289	$11/2^-$	38	50	69	75				
	1.527	$3/2^-$	80	78	92	72				

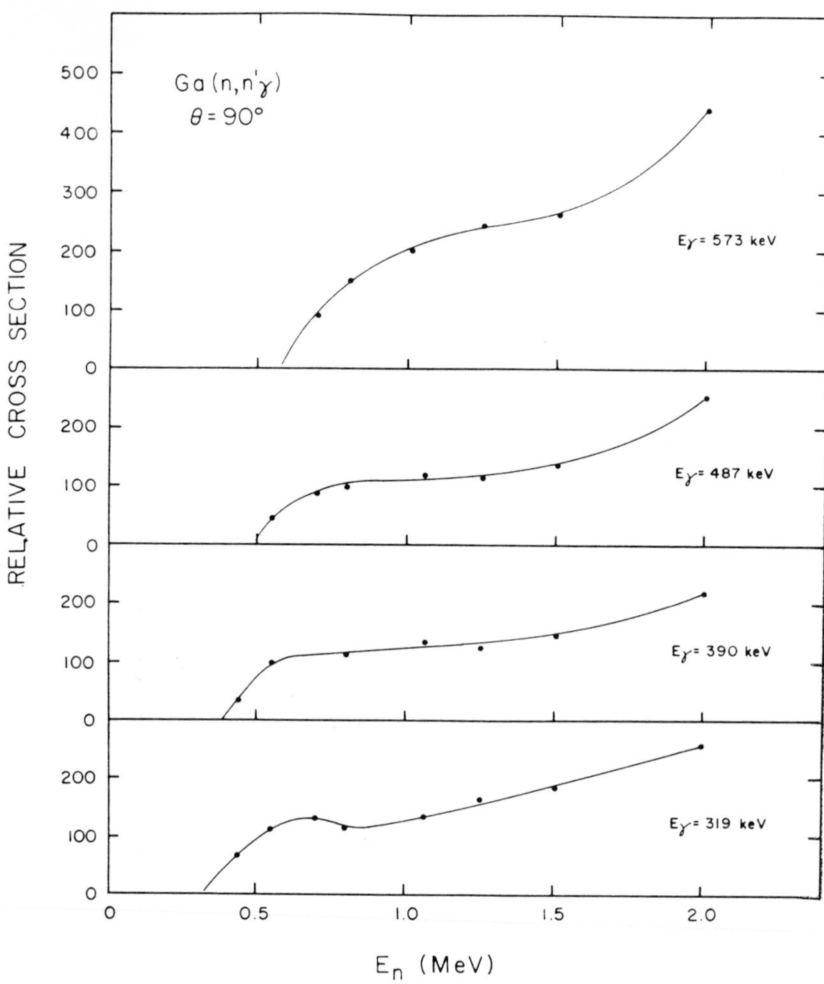

Fig. 1. Excitation functions observed with a 15 cc Ge(Li) detector and a 2 mole sample of Ga. (Ref. 2).

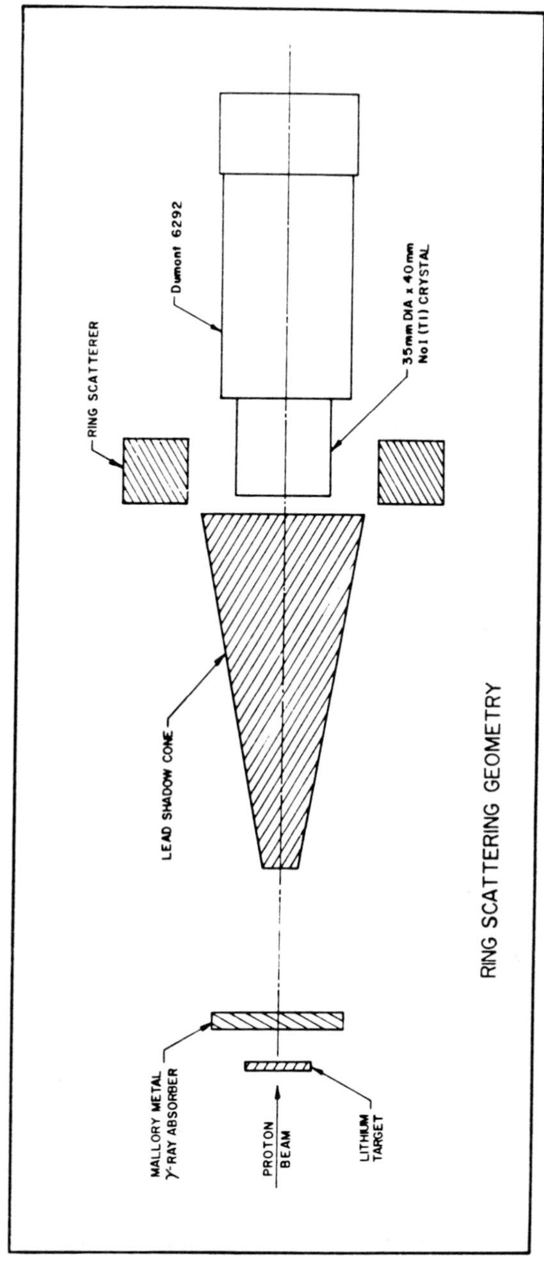

Fig. 2. Ring detection geometry showing shadow cone to shield detector. Source to detector distance was ~22cm and I.D. of the ring was ~7cm. (Ref. 7).

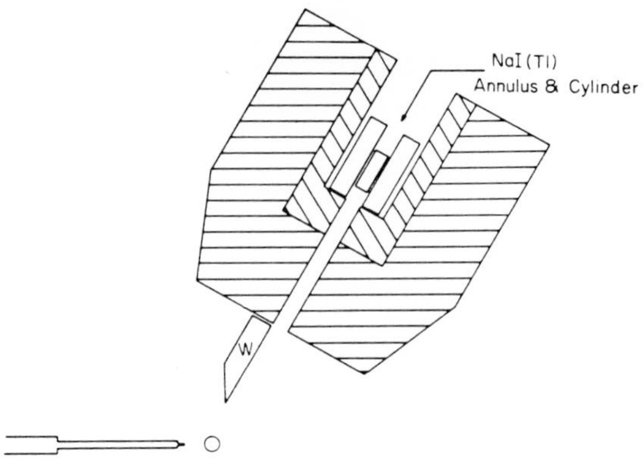

Fig. 3. Shielded anti-Compton spectrometer showing central detector mounted inside an annulus of NaI(Tl). The inner shield is Pb, and the outer is Li_2CO_3 + paraffin. (Ref. 14).

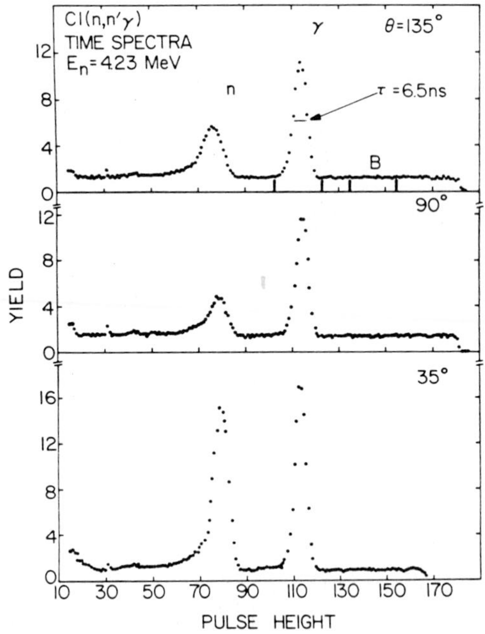

Fig. 4. Time spectra at several angles. The heavy marks under the γ-peak and under the displaced region of the time spectrum indicate the two regions used to gate pulse-height analysis.

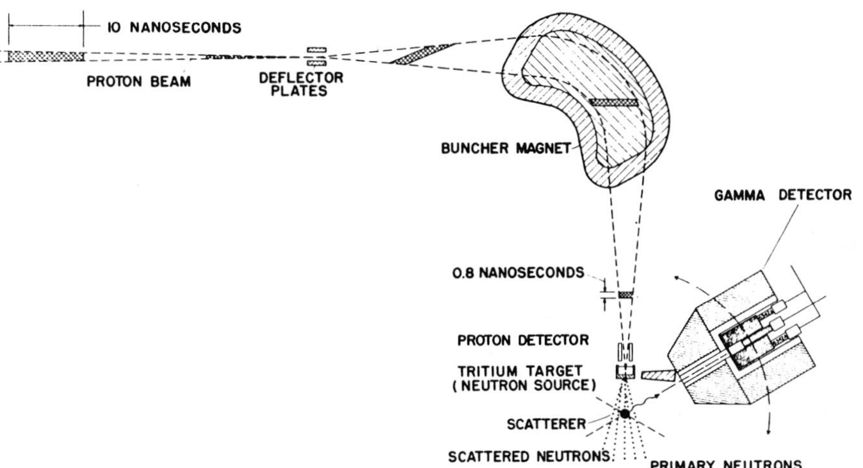

Fig. 5. Detection system in use at Los Alamos Scientific Laboratory. The shielded detector has an inner shield of Pb, and an outer shield of paraffin + Li_2CO_3. (Ref. 18).

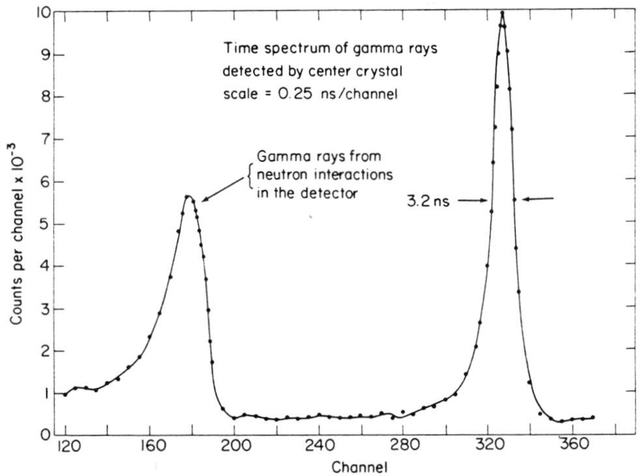

Fig. 6. Time spectrum obtained with the system of Fig. 5 and an Al sample.

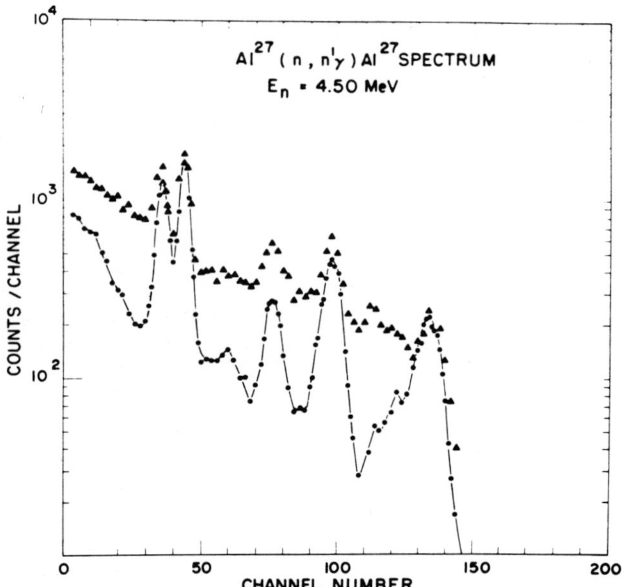

Fig. 7. Logarithmic display of time-gated pulse-height spectra obtained with system of Fig. 5. Triangles denote the spectrum of the central crystal alone. The dots show the spectrum obtained with anti-coincidence gating of the central crystal by the annulus.

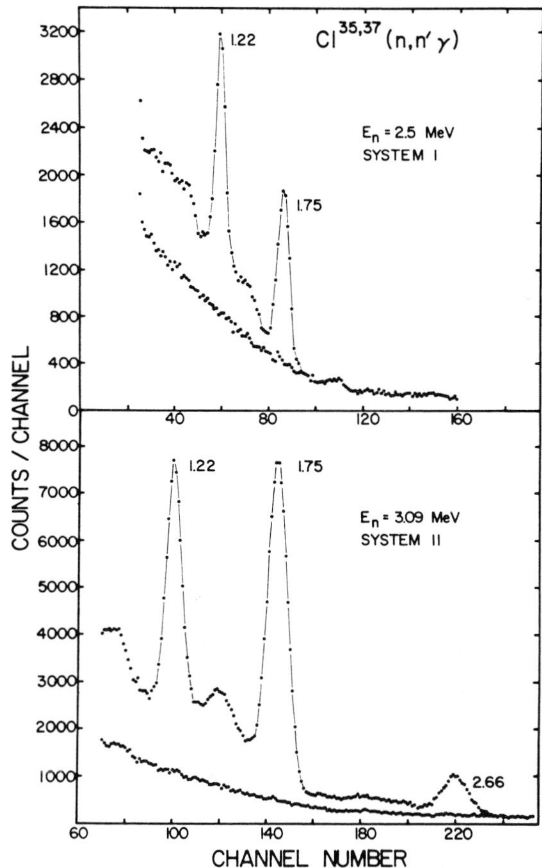

Fig. 8. Comparison of single crystal (System I) and anti-Compton detector (System II) spectra obtained under similar conditions.

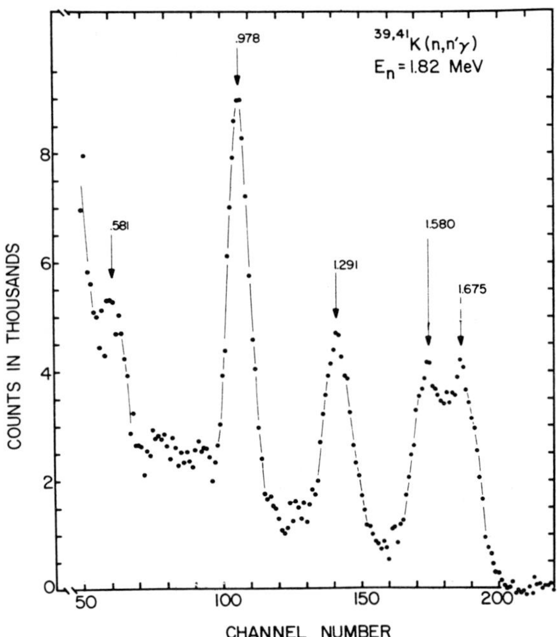

Fig. 9. Time-gated pulse height spectrum obtained with system of Fig. 3 and a 3.5-mole KOH sample. The incident neutron energy is below the threshold for the first excited level of ^{39}K.

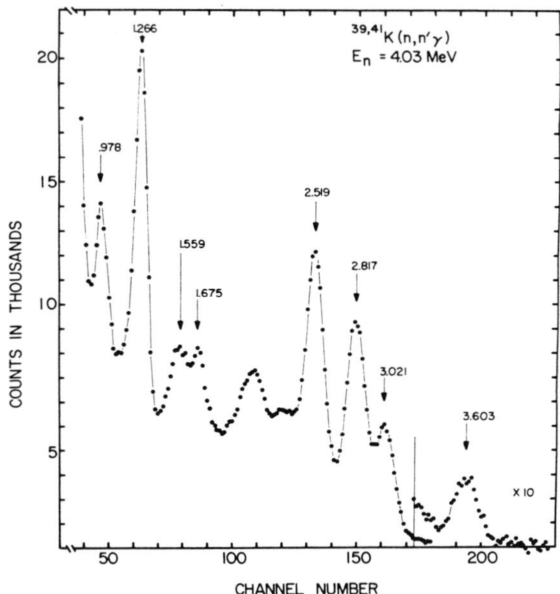

Fig. 10. Time-gated pulse height spectrum obtained with the system of Fig. 3.

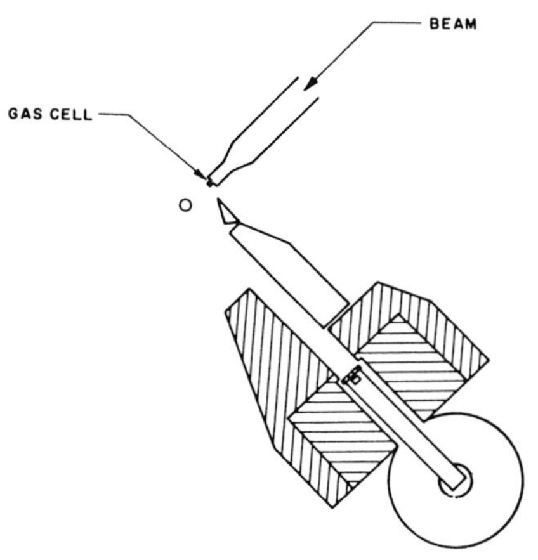

Fig. 11. Shielded Ge(Li) detector. A cylindrical Pb shield 6.5 cm thick is encased in Li_2CO_3 and paraffin.

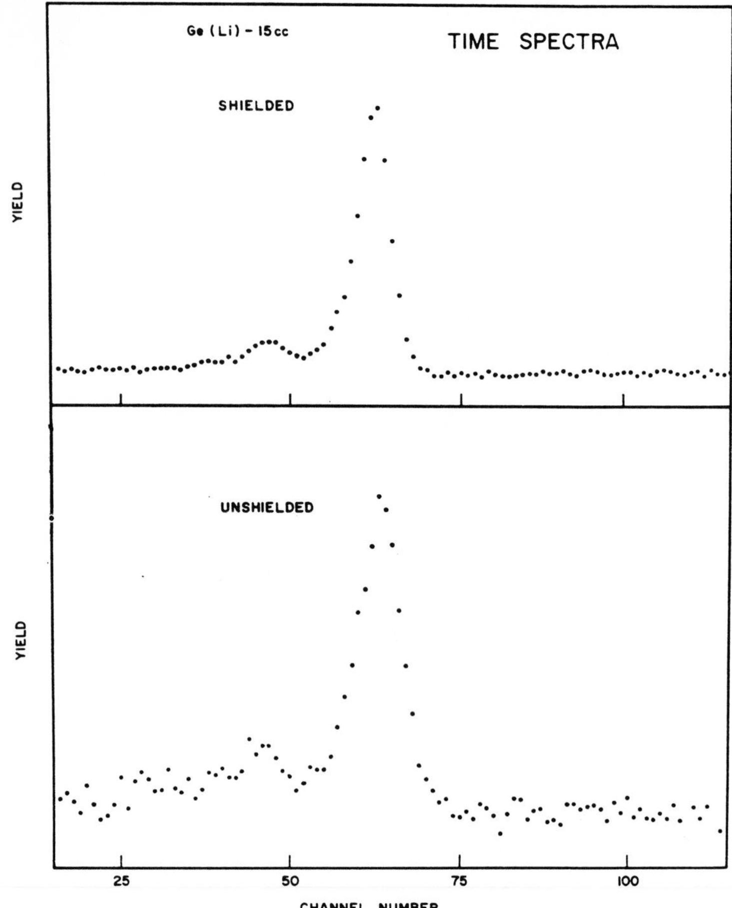

Fig. 12. Time spectra obtained with and without the shield of Fig. 11. The time resolution is 8 ns.

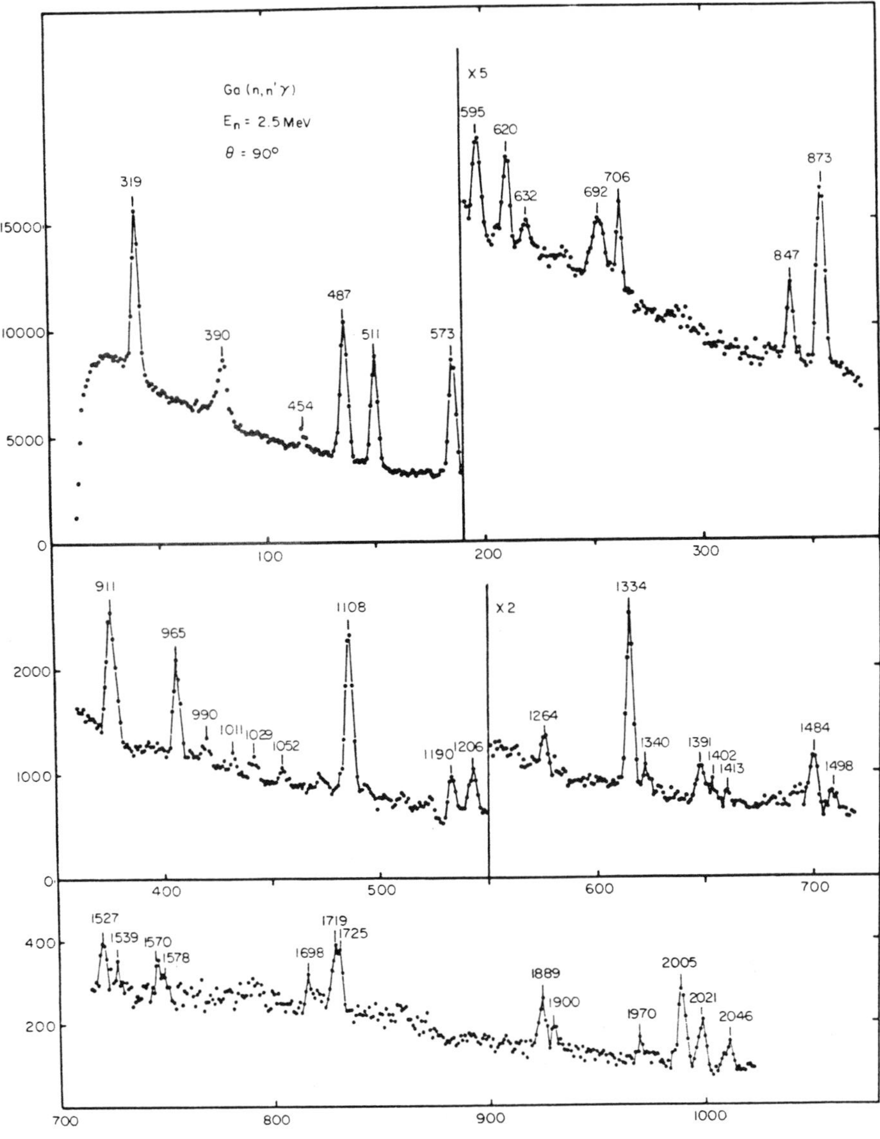

Fig. 13. Spectrum obtained with detector of Fig. 11 gated by the γ-ray peak of Fig. 12. Lines at 511, 692, and 847 keV are background lines.

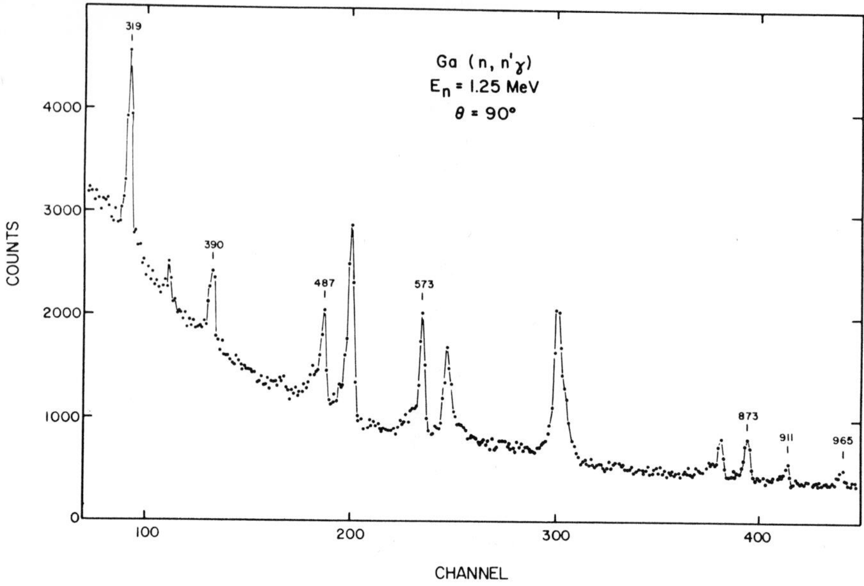

Fig. 14. Spectrum obtained with unshielded Ge(Li) detector and without time gating.

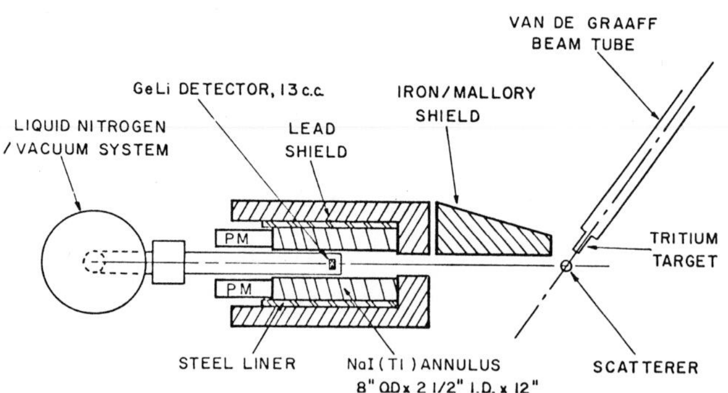

Fig. 15. Anti-Compton spectrometer with Ge(Li) central detector. (Ref. 31).

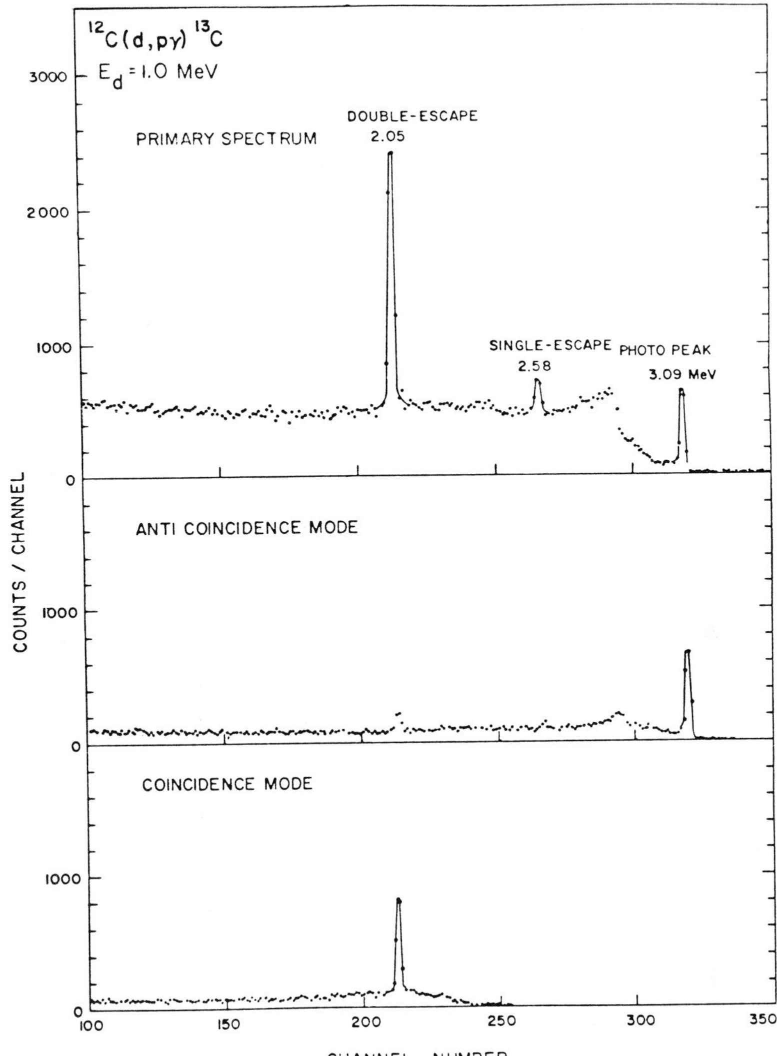

Fig. 16. Performance of detector of Fig. 15 with a single 3.09 MeV line. 83% of Compton events are rejected in AC mode. 88% are rejected in C mode.

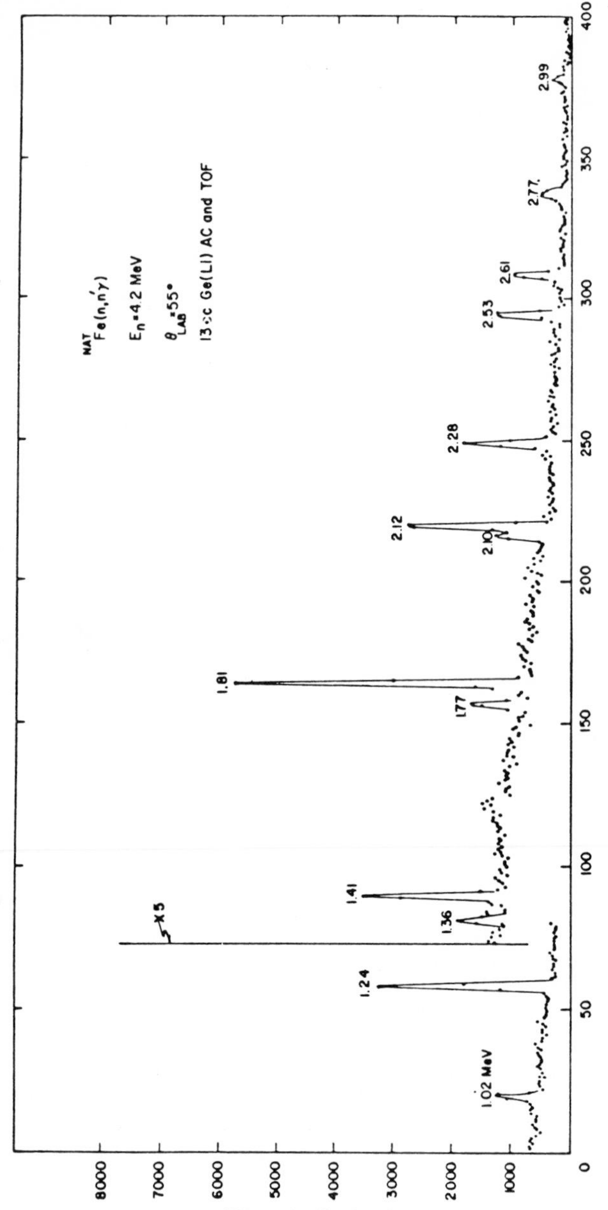

Fig. 17. Time-gated spectrum obtained with system of Fig. 15 and a 3.5 mole Fe sample located ~3.5 cm from the neutron source.

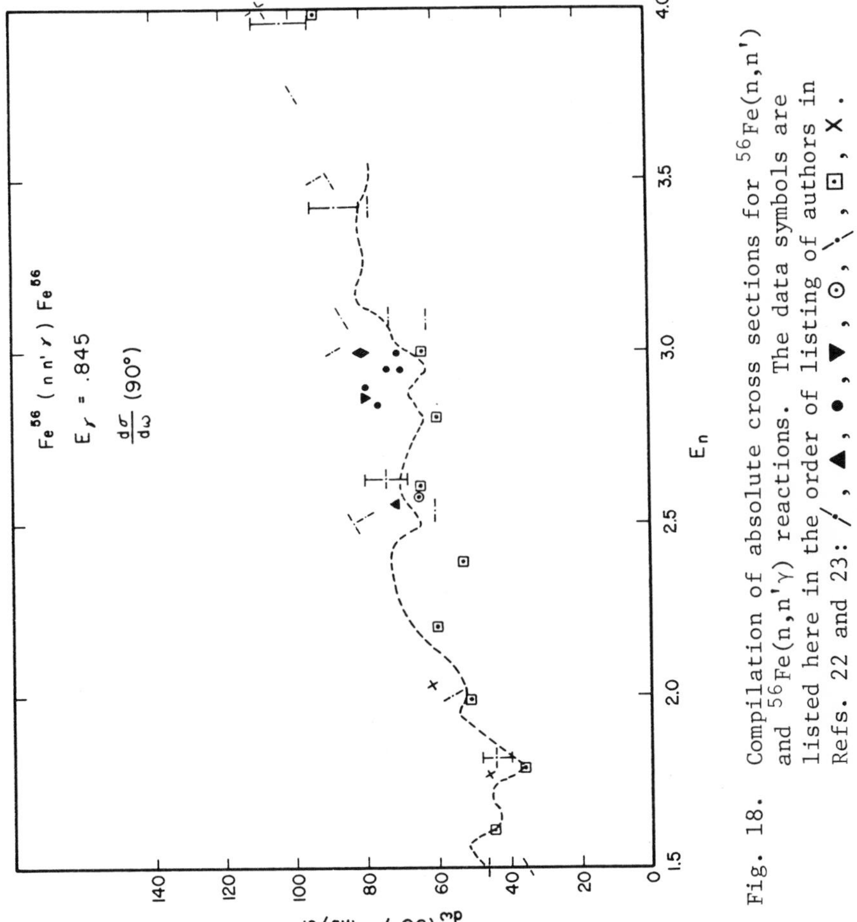

Fig. 18. Compilation of absolute cross sections for ^{56}Fe(n,n') and ^{56}Fe(n,n'γ) reactions. The data symbols are listed here in the order of listing of authors in Refs. 22 and 23: ⁄, ▲, ●, ▼, ⊙, ⁄, ⊡, X.

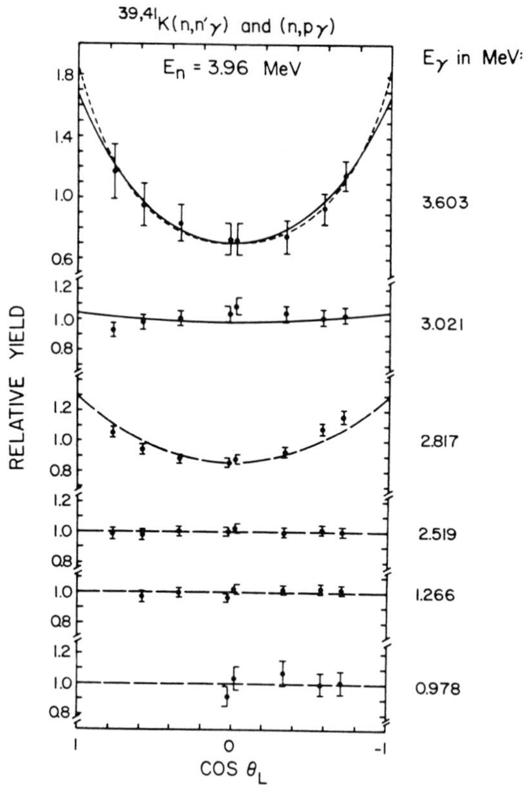

Fig. 19. Measured and calculated angular distributions for ^{39,41}K (n,n'γ). (Ref. 25). The dashed curve is a Hauser-Feshbach formalism calculation. The long-dash curves are both calculations and least-squares fits to the measurements. The solid curves are least-squares fits to the measurements.

ASTROPHYSICAL PROBLEMS

T. A. Tombrello

California Institute of Technology
Pasadena, California

Introduction

The title given to this talk by the organizing committee of the Symposium is broad enough to include anything I might care to say, since the universe has sufficient variety to guarantee that somewhere a particular nuclear reaction can be possible in an astrophysical process. One could easily devote the remainder of the conference to nuclear reactions that are of astrophysical interest -- assuming, of course, that you find a more knowledgeable speaker. I shall, therefore, limit my topic to a discussion of just the proton-proton chain, which ties in nicely with my own interest in the structure of the few-nucleon nuclei.

Although the importance of this reaction chain has been recognized since it was proposed by Bethe in 1939,[1] only in the past six months has the last of the important cross sections been obtained that permit accurate calculation of stellar reaction rates. At present, we think this set of reactions is well understood; however, we thought so five years ago and since that time one cross section value has changed by a factor of four, and another by a factor of two. Most of what I will say will be directed toward our attempts to understand these nuclear reactions in sufficient detail that we can in turn use them to understand the stellar fusion process. It should be emphasized at this point that what is required are not merely experimental measurements plus theoretical models of stars but a utilization of the techniques of both experimental and theoretical nuclear physics together with those of astrophysics. In the larger sense, if we were to become concerned with other problems, such as that of elemental abundances, then the fields of planetary geology and chemistry also become firmly intermeshed. This is what is exciting about astrophysical problems, they tend to create bridges between specialities that have become divergent and thereby generate new ideas and concomitant problems from the fresh viewpoints obtained.

So, in the next few minutes I hope to take this simple process as an example of the use of ideas and techniques of experimental and theoretical nuclear physics in understanding one stellar mechanism. The reactions of the p-p chain have sufficient diversity that in discussing them we shall see many of the problems that pertain to other astrophysical processes.

What are the problems that confront us in calculating the role of the p-p chain in the stellar interior? First we need to know the cross sections for the reactions involved -- this is easy, we can measure them. But here is where the most basic problem appears, we need to know the cross sections at energies corresponding to stellar temperatures, in this case in the few keV region. Since we are mainly talking about charged-particle reactions, this means that because of the Coulomb barrier we can't make measurements at such low energies and we need to be able to extrapolate the cross section -- necessitating some theoretical understanding of the reaction itself. Another problem that can occur is the existence of reactions that cannot be studied because of our unfortunate experimental shortcomings; for example, in the helium burning process, one needs the cross section for the capture of alpha particles by Be^8 and in the p-p chain the beta decay rate of two free protons. In cases such as these we need to find either indirect experimental techniques such as those used by Alburger[2] or Seegar and Kavanagh[3] in $Be^8(\alpha,\gamma)C^{12}$ or theoretical techniques that can be checked by reference to related reactions such as those used by Bethe and Critchfield[4] or Salpeter[5] for the positron decay of the diproton.

Survey of the Proton-Proton Chain Reactions

The dominant reactions of the p-p chain are summarized in Table 1 together with related information that we shall discuss a bit later. As you see, there are three paths given that are equivalent in that four protons are eventually converted to an alpha particle, two positrons, and two neutrinos with a total energy release of 26.7 MeV. The relative importance of each path is, of course, determined by the reaction cross sections, the stellar temperature and the relative abundances of hydrogen and helium in the star being considered. For the sake of brevity, we shall ignore reactions such as $H^2(d,n)He^3$, $H^2(d,p)H^3$, and $He^3(d,p)He^4$ because though they have large cross sections they have been shown to have a negligible effect on the p-p chain at the interior temperature of the sun, approximately 15×10^6 °K.[6] The major difference between the paths shown is in the amount of energy carried off by the neutrinos. This is especially large in the third ending and, as we shall see later, the presence of these high-energy neutrinos may be used to check on our detailed understanding of stellar processes.

Since all the nuclear reactions are initiated by charged particles the dominant part of the energy dependence at stellar temperatures is determined by the Coulomb field. In an attempt to remove this effect so that cross sections at energies within our range of measurement can be extrapolated to very low energy, the S-factor is defined:

$$\sigma(E_{c.m.}) = \frac{S(E_{c.m.})}{E_{c.m.}} e^{-2\pi\eta}$$

where $\eta = Z_1 Z_2 e^2/\hbar v$, v is the relative velocity of the particles involved, $Z_1 e$ and $Z_2 e$ are their charges and $E_{c.m.}$ is the center-of-mass energy.

One hopes that the S(E) extracted from measurements of the cross section will be well-behaved and in the best of all possible worlds will be a constant. As we shall find in the examples to be discussed, S(E) frequently has some energy dependence and may cause some consternation concerning the behavior of the cross section at those inaccessibly low energies.

$H^1(p,\beta^+\nu)H^2$

The first and most important reaction in the proton-proton chain is also one that is unlikely to ever be studied experimentally, since the strength of the continuum beta decay of two protons into a deuteron is determined by the size of the weak interaction Hamiltonian. It has been estimated that if you bombard a thick hydrogen target with protons, then you can expect only one event for every ten megawatt-years of bombardment.[7] The decay proceeds through the singlet state of the diproton to the deuteron ground state, a superallowed Gamow-Teller transition. The accuracy of the theoretical calculation can therefore be readily checked by comparing the matrix element obtained to that for the magnetic dipole transition in n-p capture, which involves the same operator, $\vec{\sigma}$, and the mirror continuum state of the deuteron. The uncertainty in the final answer has been estimated by Salpeter[5] to be about ± 12%.

This is our first example of how we need both theoretical and experimental results to accomplish our ends. Though the reaction rate can only be calculated theoretically, it would have a far larger uncertainty if it were not for our extensive knowledge of low-energy p-p and p-n scattering and p-n capture. But the coin is two sided; we must also rely heavily on the ideas of charge independence and beta decay theory.

$H^2(p,\gamma)He^3$

The results I'd like to discuss now are an example of not what you can do with a low-energy accelerator but rather what you can do without one. The experiment of Griffiths, Lal, and Scarfe[8] was performed using an R-F ion source and a 50 KV transformer rectifier set. This allowed them to investigate the capture of protons by deuterons for bombarding energies between 24 and 48 keV -- barely above energies corresponding to stellar temperatures. Thick heavy ice targets were used and the gamma rays were detected with a NaI crystal. Before discussing their results, I'd first like to summarize briefly what is known about this reaction at higher energies; this being necessary to understand why measurements were needed at such low energies.

For measurements above 1 MeV the angular distribution of gamma rays is almost pure $\sin^2\theta$; this is typical of a direct capture reaction where the P-wave phase shifts are not split strongly for states of different total angular momentum.[9] In addition to this dominant electric dipole contribution, there is also a small isotropic component of a few percent in magnitude. This could come from either the E-1 transition because of small splittings in the p-wave phase shifts or from s-wave magnetic dipole capture. If it is due to the latter, then at stellar temperatures it might well dominate the extrapolated effect of the p-wave E-1 process. Thus, measurements were required at very low energies to measure the energy dependence of the $\sin^2\theta$ versus isotropic components (in order to separate the two effects and allow them to be extrapolated individually). The $\sin^2\theta$ cross sections are found to vary between 0.1 μb and 0.03 μb, while the isotropic cross section varies between 0.03 and 0.01 μb. The energy dependence of the extracted values of S(E) are shown in Figure 1; the solid lines give the extrapolations expected assuming the $\ell = 0$ S-factor to be constant and the $\ell = 1$ S-factor to be linear -- these being the simplest assumptions possible. (The dashed lines give the estimated uncertainty from this extrapolation.) As you notice, even at stellar temperatures the E-1 capture is slightly the larger, but the contribution from the M-1 decay is certainly comparable. However, one might question the validity of such an extrapolation and its associated uncertainty. The problem is resolved by the dash-dot curves; these are based on extensive theoretical calculations for this capture reaction by Donnelly.[10] The few free parameters available are fixed using capture and photodisintegration data at higher energies -- not the data plotted here. You will notice that this independent extraction of the S-factors agrees excellently with both the data and the original extrapolation, though it does not reproduce the solid lines exactly.

$He^3(He^3,2p)He^4$

The significance of this reaction as one way of terminating the proton-proton chain was first recognized by C. C. Lauritsen[11] and E. Shatzman[12] in 1951. Recent experimental results, primarily from the Kellogg Radiation Laboratory at Caltech, have shown that the S-factor for this reaction is substantially different from that previously used[13] and have caused some important changes in our understanding of the completion of the proton-proton chain in stars. The experimental work at Caltech is in two parts: data obtained at relatively high energies (2-20 MeV) using the ONR-CIT tandem accelerator[14] and low-energy data obtained by two different experimental methods.[15,16] We need first to consider the results at the higher energies since they show some of the problems of the extrapolation procedure. For bombarding energies above about 2 MeV the reaction is dominated by a sequential process in which a high-energy proton is emitted leaving a Li^5 nucleus in its ground state, which subsequently decays into a relatively low-energy proton and an alpha particle. For the energy range between 2 and 12 MeV, this mode accounts for greater than 80% of the reactions,[17] though a small contribution from the decay into an alpha plus a diproton has been observed.[18] The reaction mechanism for the Li^5 process must be quite complicated since it requires the transfer of two nucleons into different orbits (a neutron with $\ell = 0$ and a proton with $\ell = 1$), so one might expect either an involved stripping process or perhaps some sort of non-resonant compound nucleus reaction.

At low energies, it might be expected that this would change, since the effect of the Coulomb potential necessarily makes it harder to move two particles through the barrier than for a reaction mode that involves only the transfer of a single nucleon. We thus might have anticipated (in retrospect, of course) that as the bombarding energy was progressively lowered, the relative sizes of the $p + Li^5$ and $He^4 + 2p$ channels would shift in favor of the latter. This effect is clearly visible in Figure 2, where proton spectra at 4, 2, and 0.8 MeV show the change in the relative contributions to the peak (the $Li^5 + p$ decay mode) and to the mid-spectrum continuum (which may be from the $He^4 + 2p$ decay). These data and the alpha particle spectra[15,18] (not shown) do not in themselves entirely justify the statements concerning which channels predominate and low-energy coincidence measurements are being planned to specify the decay modes more precisely. However, it is abundantly clear that the character of the reaction does indeed change as the energy is reduced, making extrapolation from higher energies uncertain.

The low-energy experimental work that I want to discuss first has been done during the past year by Winkler and Dwarakanath.[15] The experimental apparatus is quite novel and shows both ingenuity and careful attention to the limiting features of previous measurements. A schematic drawing of this equipment is shown in Figure 3. The target chamber is run at pressures near 15 mm of Hg and the He^3 gas is allowed to escape through a restricted beam entrance canal into the first volume which is pumped by a two-stage Roots pump. Another canal, less restricted than the first, connects to a second volume to which is attached a diffusion pump. The backing pressure for this diffusion pump is supplied by the first volume; thus, all the gas passing into the first and second volumes outside the target chamber is cycled through the Roots pump. Only a very tiny fraction of the gas (less than 1% in 24 hours) escapes through the canal connecting the second volume with the vacuum system of the accelerator.

After passing through the Roots pump contaminants in the He^3 are removed by passing the gas through a liquid nitrogen cooled adsorption trap. Since this cools the gas, the He^3 must then be run through a heat exchanger before being reintroduced into the target. I think that you can now appreciate the advantages of this system, because while allowing a windowless target (a necessity if one is to go to very low bombarding energies) it nevertheless is quite economical in He^3 consumption.

In the target chamber protons and alpha particles are identified using a dE/dx - E telescope composed of a proportional counter and a thick silicon surface-barrier detector. Since no exit foil is possible for beams of the energies involved, the beam power is measured in a low mass calorimeter. The two cups shown in the calorimeter allow the power introduced by the beam to be balanced against power from a heater coil in the second cup. The current to the heater is automatically fed in pulses until the temperature of the cups is balanced; thus, scaling the number of pulses gives a measure of the beam power. This quantity together with the beam energy give the number of particles passing through the target. Another virtue of this method is that it is independent of the number of neutral ions in the beam, which is not a negligible problem at these energies.

Figure 4 gives the resulting values of the S-factor versus the center-of-mass energy. The data of Good, *et al*.[13]

has previously been used for astrophysical calculations; the more recent values are seen to be rather different.[15,18,19] The data by Bacher and myself were obtained to confirm the results of Winkler and Dwarakanath. Because so much solar model computing time was dependent on the outcome, it was felt that an independent check should be performed, especially in view of the rather strong energy dependence of S(E) observed. We used a small gas cell with a thin entrance window; the beam was stopped within the cell and we provided a rather elaborate electron suppression scheme to insure that the beam current was integrated accurately. A counter telescope composed of 26 μ and 2 mm thick silicon surface-barrier detectors was used to identify the protons. At low energies, the cross section is very sensitive to the beam energy because of the Coulomb penetrability; thus, since we had a much higher energy loss than the differentially-pumped target, we had to make very precise measurements of the thickness of the entrance foil. The energy loss in this window was measured with a magnetic spectrometer for a He^3 beam at closely spaced points over the entire energy range covered by the experiment. The success of our precautions is demonstrated by the excellent agreement with our previous points at the higher energies[14] (these points are shown with error bars) and the good agreement with the data of Winkler and Dwarakanath. The precision of either experiment in this energy range is approximately ±10%, so the small discrepancy between our results is probably not significant. (At this point I must confess that the data of Bacher and myself were not obtained with a low-energy accelerator but with the ONR-CIT tandem -- probably a record for low-energy attained with an EN accelerator.)

The S-factor obtained has considerable energy dependence and makes an accurate extrapolation difficult. Measurements by Dwarakanath and Winkler at center-of-mass energies down to 100 keV are in progress but even these will not provide a complete answer to the problem. What is really needed is a theoretical model of the reaction that fits all the data and will permit a more confident extrapolation. May and Clayton at Caltech have made a calculation based on the neutron tunneling ideas of Breit for the single-neutron transfer process.[20] This calculation has only a single energy-independent free parameter and because it so appeals to one's intuition it was hoped that it might provide a straightforward solution to the problem of extrapolation. However, the results obtained do not show such a pronounced increase of S(E) at the low energies. There are several possible explanations for this:

(1) There is an appreciable contribution from not only the tail of the bound neutron wave function but also from the

region within the He^3 nuclei, eliminating the simplicity of the present calculation while at the same time increasing the number of free parameters.

(2) The two (or more) decay modes may interfere, thus introducing another energy dependence. Taking this interference into account would not only increase the difficulty of the calculation but also lower one's confidence in the validity of the final results.

In any event, this looks like a good place for a new idea, though the importance of the exact value of S(E) here may be such that it is not really necessary to have the most accurate of all possible extrapolations. This is because even with the old value of S(E), which was a factor of four or five smaller, this path would have accounted for over half of the endings of the p-p chain -- at least in stars like the sun. Now with the new higher value this path represents the only significant way to terminate the chain so that small additional changes in S(E) really will not affect greatly stellar energy production. Such changes will, however, modify the small fraction of times the p-p chain terminates through the other two paths, a point which is of particular importance in estimating the solar neutrino flux.[21]

$He^3(\alpha,\gamma)Be^7$

We progress now to the discussion of the weak paths through which the p-p chain can terminate. If a star has evolved sufficiently that there is already He^4 present, then it is possible that the radiative capture of He^3 by He^4 to form Be^7 can provide an alternate route in the stellar fusion process. As we have just indicated, this is now thought to be relatively unimportant for stellar energy generation, but it is the only way one can eventually produce a high-energy neutrino from B^8 decay. Since the neutrino is the only particle that can get out of the interior of a star, it may well provide the only direct way of checking experimentally our models of stellar processes.

The study of the reaction $He^3(\alpha,\gamma)Be^7$ gives us another good example of the combination of experimental and theoretical techniques that may be necessary in extracting the information needed in astrophysical calculations. In addition to the excellent total cross section and branching ratio data of Parker and Kavanagh for this reaction,[22] the data of Griffiths, *et al*.,[23] for $H^3(\alpha,\gamma)Li^7$ allowed the theoretical predictions to be checked in a much more stringent manner.

The model used was basically phenomenological. The analysis of He^3 plus He^4 elastic scattering had shown that s- and d-partial waves that contributed to the dominant E-1 transition were well described by hard-sphere phase shifts.[24]

This indicated that for these partial waves the wave function was small within the nucleus. In addition, both the intermediate coupling shell model and the cluster model predicted that the bound ground state and first excited state of Be^7 could be reasonably described as the two-body relative motion of a He^3 and an alpha particle. Taking these two properties of the Be^7 nucleus, we made a two-body model and neglected the contribution to the matrix element from inside the compound nucleus. The calculations were done for E-1, M-1, and E-2 capture from all partial waves up to and including $\ell = 3$, but only the E-1 capture from the s- and d-waves was found to be appreciable.[25] The only free parameters in the calculation were the reduced widths of the ground and first excited states for the $He^3 + He^4$ configuration which were fixed by normalization to the total cross section and the branching ratio -- since these parameters were energy independent, we could not use them to vary the shape of the resulting yield curve. The total cross section and the fit are shown in Figure 5; the solid line is the theoretical curve. Figure 6 gives the S-factor. It is important to point out that at the highest points shown, the s- and d-wave contributions are equal -- something that cannot be seen from the data alone. It is also to be emphasized that it is only the detailed agreement of theory and experiment over a large range of energy that allows a relatively precise extrapolation to be obtained; the data themselves could permit a quite large spread of values. These results are nice but the model required further checking. Now that we had fixed the reduced widths of the bound states, we no longer had any free parameters, so the total cross section, the branching ratio, and the angular distributions were calculated for the $H^3(\alpha,\gamma)Li^7$ reaction and in each case the agreement was virtually perfect.

$Be^7(p,\gamma)B^8$

Because of certain limitations on speaking time, publication space, and the attention span of the audience, I should like to skip several intervening reactions and consider the last step in the production of B^8. Since this path for the termination of the p-p chain is so small, the neutrino production rate is directly proportional to the cross section for $Be^7(p,\gamma)B^8$.[26] The most recent experiment is by P. D. Parker[27] using Be^7 targets prepared by R. Davis.

The Be^7 target on a thick platinum backing was bombarded with low-energy protons from the Brookhaven Van de Graaff. The target was swung out of the beam approximately once every second and was viewed by a surface-barrier detector for about an equal period of time. The decay of B^8 proceeds mainly to the 2^+ first excited state of Be^8 which then breaks up into two alpha particles. The detector thickness of 18 μ was thick enough to stop most of the alpha particles from the decay but gave only very small pulses from the B^8 positrons.

Figure 7 shows the S-factor obtained from the cross section data. The high point near 700 keV corresponds to the narrow 1^+ first excited state of B^8 which decays to the 2^+ ground state by M-1 radiation. The other points show the smooth behavior of the E-1 direct capture process that must be extrapolated to thermal energies. The smooth curve is a calculation I made using only the known data for the mirror reaction $Li^7(n,\gamma)Li^8$.[28] The agreement has only one "small" defect -- the calculated curve has been arbitrarily multiplied by a factor of about three to match the data. Thus, we again have a theoretical point that could use some attention.

The p-p Chain and Neutrino Astronomy

As I mentioned earlier, the only possible way we have to find out if any of this is correct is to find a probe that can escape from deep in the interior of the sun. The only choice is the neutrinos liberated in the stellar fusion processes. The solar models indicate that for our sun (the only high intensity source we have) the p-p chain is dominant, with only a negligible contribution from the carbon-nitrogen-oxygen cycle. Thus, we might expect that a measurement of the flux of neutrinos would give us some information about the validity of the p-p chain. An experiment underway now is being carried out by Ray Davis of Brookhaven in the Homestake Mine in South Dakota.[29] The detector is a 10^5 gallon tank of perchlorethylene (C_2Cl_4). The reaction used is

$$\nu + Cl^{37} \rightarrow e^+ + Ar^{37} ,$$

the inverse reaction to the usual electron capture decay of Ar^{37} (35 day half-life). The argon is swept from the tank with helium, the cleaning fluid vapors are condensed and finally the argon is collected on activated charcoal to remove the helium. This argon is introduced into a small proportional counter and the 2.8 keV Auger electron following the Ar^{37} decay is counted.

Because the detector reaction is endothermic by about 800 keV, "efficient" detection of the neutrinos from only a few of the reactions is possible. In addition, Bahcall has found that because of a superallowed matrix element connecting the lowest T = 3/2 excited state of Ar^{37} to the Cl^{37} ground state, the neutrino capture reaction in the detector proceeds mainly by the transition to this excited state.[26] This effectively raises the threshold for the reaction so that only the solar neutrinos from the B^8 decay have sufficient energy. In detail, there are expected to be six captures per day, of which most will come from B^8 and only about 6% from the Be^7 decay which is the next largest contributor.

Conclusion

It may, therefore, be hoped that within the next year we may have some confirmation that this one small section of all the astrophysical processes is really valid; however, we are just at the beginning of understanding many of the other processes that can occur. What other kinds of nuclear reactions come into play when a wider variety of stars and conditions are permitted? You can probably find nearly anything you like, for example:

1) Are you interested in neutron induced reactions? Then you may wish to look into the slow neutron capture (s) process[30] or some of the reactions of the Big or Little Bangs.[31]
2) Do you like heavy ion reactions? Try the carbon or oxygen burning processes.[32]
3) Perhaps you enjoy alpha capture or photodisintegration reactions -- consider helium burning,[32] silicon burning,[32] or the equilibrium (e) process.[33]
4) What about all the recent work on proton or neutron rich nuclei far from the line of beta stability -- perfect for the rapid neutron capture (r) process[30] or the infrequent proton capture (p) process.[32]
5) And finally, if you're interested in intermediate energy or even high energy interactions, there is the study of the spallation reactions that form the light (ℓ) process through which the elements lithium, beryllium, and boron were probably formed.[32,34,35]

To summarize, there are many types of astrophysical processes that involve nuclear reactions and there remain a nearly unlimited number of problems for both theory and experiment to solve together.

Acknowledgments

I wish to thank A. D. Bacher, M. R. Dwarakanath, and H. C. Winkler for their kind permission to refer to their unpublished results and for their help and advice in preparing this manuscript. Support for this work was by the Office of Naval Research [Nonr-220(47)].

References

1. H. A. Bethe, Phys. Rev. 55, 434 (1939).

2. D. E. Alburger, Phys. Rev. 124, 193 (1961).
3. P. A. Seeger and R. W. Kavanagh, Nucl. Phys. 46, 577 (1963).
4. H. A. Bethe and C. L. Critchfield, Phys. Rev. 54, 248 (1938).
5. E. E. Salpeter, Phys. Rev. 88, 547 (1952).
6. P. D. Parker, J. N. Bahcall, and W. A. Fowler, Astrophys. J. 139, 602 (1964).
7. W. A. Fowler, Modern Physics for the Engineer, ed. Ridenour and Nierenberg, McGraw-Hill, New York, 1961, p. 203.
8. G. M. Griffiths, M. Lal, and C. D. Scarfe, Can. J. Phys. 41, 724 (1963).
9. G. M. Griffiths and J. B. Warren, Proc. Phys. Soc. A68, 781 (1955).
10. T. W. Donnelly, Ph.D. thesis, University of British Columbia (1967).
11. As quoted by W. A. Fowler, Phys. Rev. 81, 655 (1951).
12. E. Shatzman, Compt. rend. 232, 1740 (1951).
13. W. M. Good, W. E. Kunz, and C. D. Moak, Phys. Rev. 94, 87 (1954).
14. A. D. Bacher and T. A. Tombrello, Rev. Mod. Phys. 37, 433 (1965).
15. H. C. Winkler and M. R. Dwarakanath, Bull. Amer. Phys. Soc. 12, 16 (1967).
16. A. D. Bacher and T. A. Tombrello, to be published.
17. A. D. Bacher, Ph.D. thesis, California Institute of Technology (1966).
18. T. A. Tombrello and A. D. Bacher, Physics Letters 17, 37 (1965).
19. W. Neng-ming, V. N. Novatskii, G. M. Osetinskii, and C. Nao-kung, Sov. J. Nucl. Phys. 3, 777 (1966).
20. R. M. May and D. D. Clayton, to be submitted to Phys. Rev.
21. G. Shaviv, J. N. Bahcall, and W. A. Fowler, submitted to Astrophys. J.
22. P. D. Parker and R. W. Kavanagh, Phys. Rev. 131, 2578 (1963).
23. G. M. Griffiths, R. A. Morrow, P. J. Riley, and J. B. Warren, Can. J. Phys. 39, 1397 (1961).
24. T. A. Tombrello and P. D. Parker, Phys. Rev. 130, 1112 (1963).
25. T. A. Tombrello and P. D. Parker, Phys. Rev. 131, 2582 (1963).
26. J. N. Bahcall, Phys. Rev. Letters 17, 398 (1966).
27. P. D. Parker, Phys. Rev. 150, 851 (1966).
28. T. A. Tombrello, Nucl. Phys. 71, 459 (1965).
29. R. Davis, Jr., Phys. Rev. Letters 12, 303 (1964).

30. P. A. Seeger, W. A. Fowler, and D. D. Clayton, Astrophys. J. Suppl. No. 97, 11, 121 (1965).
31. R. V. Waggoner, Science 155, 1369 (1967).
32. E. M. Burbidge, G. R. Burbidge, W. A. Fowler, and F. Hoyle, Rev. Mod. Phys. 29, 547 (1957).
33. F. Hoyle and W. A. Fowler, Astrophys. J. Suppl. No. 91, 9, 201 (1964).
34. D. S. Burnett, W. A. Fowler, and F. Hoyle, Geochim. et Cosmochim. Acta 29, 1209 (1965).
35. W. A. Fowler, E. M. Burbidge, G. R. Burbidge, and F. Hoyle, Astrophys. J. 142, 423 (1965).

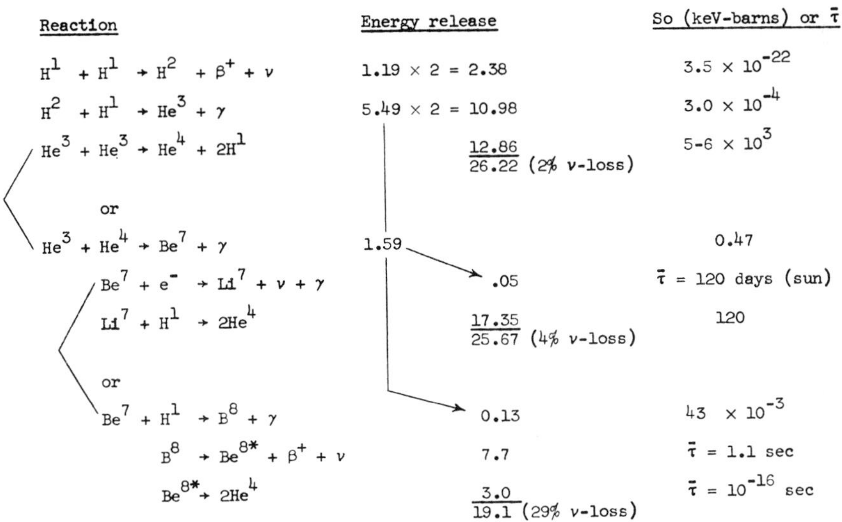

TABLE 1

Reactions of the proton-proton chain

Reaction	Energy release	So (keV-barns) or $\bar{\tau}$
$H^1 + H^1 \rightarrow H^2 + \beta^+ + \nu$	$1.19 \times 2 = 2.38$	3.5×10^{-22}
$H^2 + H^1 \rightarrow He^3 + \gamma$	$5.49 \times 2 = 10.98$	3.0×10^{-4}
$He^3 + He^3 \rightarrow He^4 + 2H^1$	12.86 / 26.22 (2% ν-loss)	$5\text{-}6 \times 10^3$
or		
$He^3 + He^4 \rightarrow Be^7 + \gamma$	1.59	0.47
$Be^7 + e^- \rightarrow Li^7 + \nu + \gamma$	.05	$\bar{\tau}$ = 120 days (sun)
$Li^7 + H^1 \rightarrow 2He^4$	17.35 / 25.67 (4% ν-loss)	120
or		
$Be^7 + H^1 \rightarrow B^8 + \gamma$	0.13	43×10^{-3}
$B^8 \rightarrow Be^{8*} + \beta^+ + \nu$	7.7	$\bar{\tau}$ = 1.1 sec
$Be^{8*} \rightarrow 2He^4$	3.0 / 19.1 (29% ν-loss)	$\bar{\tau} = 10^{-16}$ sec

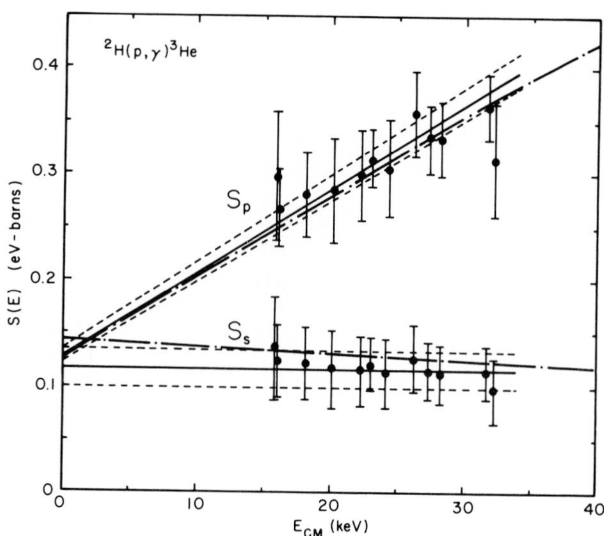

Fig. 1 The S-factors for the reaction $H^2(p,\gamma)He^3$ corresponding to S- and P-wave capture. The data and the solid and dashed lines are taken from Ref. 8 (the solid lines are the extrapolations; the dashed lines are the estimated uncertainties in the extrapolation). The dash-dot curves are taken from Ref. 10.

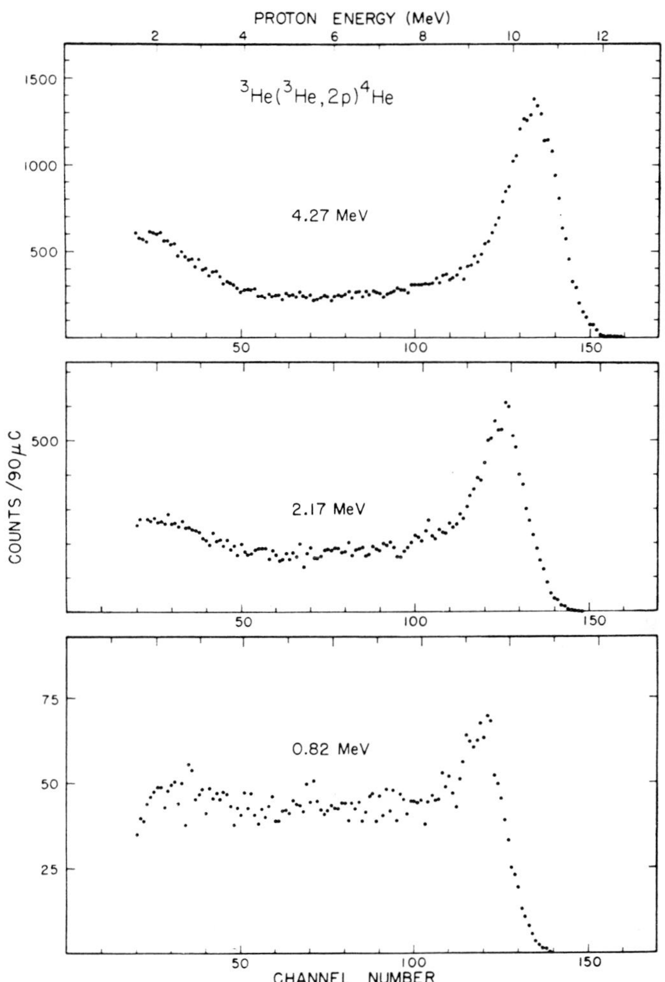

Fig. 2 Proton spectra from the reaction $He^3(He^3,2p)He^4$ at bombarding energies of 4.27, 2.17, and 0.82 MeV. These data are taken from Ref. 16.

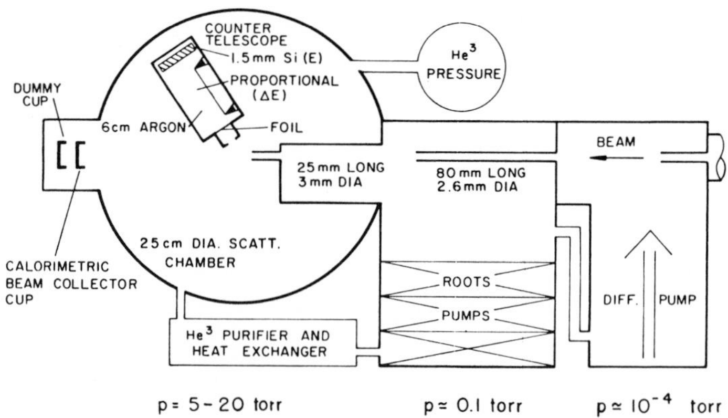

Fig. 3 A schematic drawing of the differentially-pumped, recirculating He^3 target chamber. (Taken from Ref. 15.)

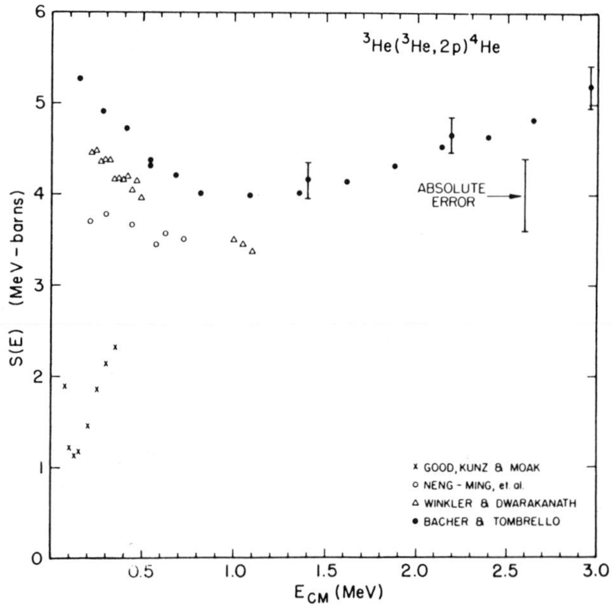

Fig. 4 The S-factor for the reaction $He^3(He^3,2p)He^4$. The data shown are taken from Refs. 13, 14, 15, 16, and 19. The data of Ref. 14 are shown with error bars; the points from Refs. 15 and 16 have a precision given by the sample error bar shown to one side of the figure.

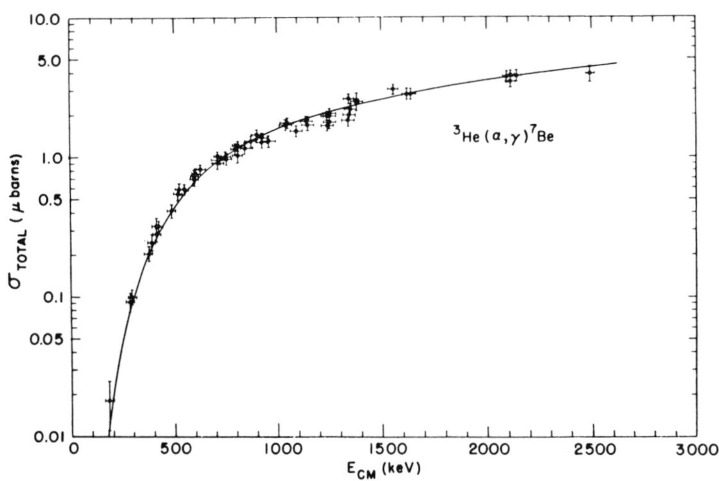

Fig. 5 The total cross section for $He^3(\alpha,\gamma)Be^7$. The data were taken from Ref. 22; the theoretical curve is from Ref. 25.

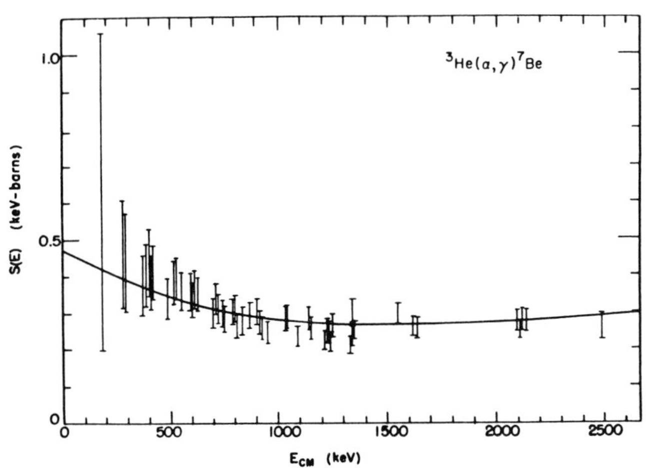

Fig. 6 The S-factor for $He^3(\alpha,\gamma)Be^7$. The data were taken from Ref. 22; the theoretical curve is from Ref. 25.

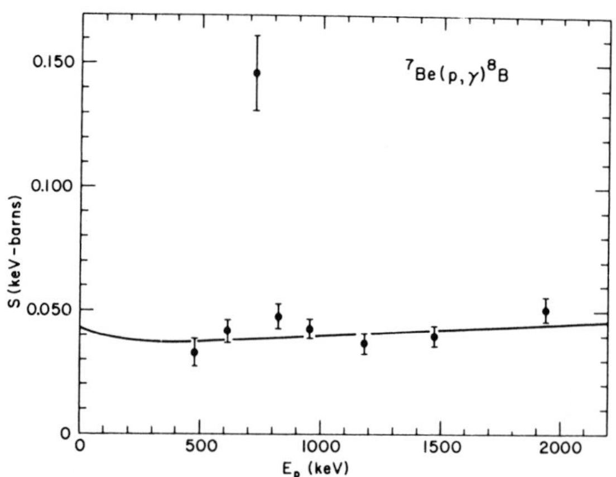

Fig. 7 The S-factor for $Be^7(p,\gamma)B^8$. The data are from Ref. 27; the theoretical curve is from Ref. 28, but has been arbitrarily normalized to the experimental points.

MULTIPARTICLE NUCLEAR REACTIONS

H. D. Holmgren

University of Maryland
College Park, Maryland

Abstract

The processes by which various multiparticle final state nuclear reactions can take place are discussed. Calculations of the kinematic behavior of three and four-body final state reactions are illustrated using the velocity vector diagram method. Experimental procedures employing relatively simple apparatus are considered. Angular correlation and branching ratio measurements are discussed and procedures for obtaining spectroscopic information from such measurements are considered.

I. Introduction

Nuclear reactions which lead to final states consisting of more than two heavy particles have been of interest for some time, but only relatively few such reactions had been studied in any detail at low bombarding energies prior to 1964. The increasing popularity of He^3 particles and tritons as projectiles in the study of nuclear reactions has stimulated the interest in studying the nature of such reactions, as the large Q values available in He^3 and triton induced reactions frequently lead to multibody final state systems. Such studies are especially interesting on light nuclei where generally only the first few levels are bound for heavy particle emission and the level spacing is such that many sharp, discrete levels often exist well above the threshhold for heavy particle emission.

Various groups have attempted to study multiparticle final state reactions by detailed analysis of the single particle spectra for such reactions. These studies, except in a few special cases, have often led to ambiguous results. Frequently peaks in the single particle spectra can result from a resonance or a state in another channel. In most cases it is necessary to measure simultaneously the energies of two of the particles emitted at specified angles in order to obtain definitive information concerning the nature of the interaction. As such coincidence measurements naturally require more time than the measurement of single-particle spectra and the display and interpretations of resulting information is more complex, many experimenters have avoided such studies in favor of simpler experiments.

The objective of the present paper is to attempt to provide a summary of the techniques by which multibody final state reactions can be studied. I will use examples with which I am familiar, and I beg the pardon of the numerous authors who have made significant contributions to this field, but to whom I will not attempt to refer. This paper is not intended to be a comprehensive review of the subject of multibody reactions. Furthermore, the comments will also be restricted to nuclear structure studies on light nuclei.

Many of the initial studies of multiparticle final state reactions at low bombarding energies were directed towards trying to understand the origin of the large continuum which is frequently observed in single particle spectrum of such reactions. Figure 1 illustrates such a spectrum in the case of $Be^9(He^3,\alpha)Be^8$ reaction. In this case the continuum can arise either from the reaction proceeding directly to the three α-particle final state with the shape of the spectrum being determined primarily by the available phase space, or by sequential processes in which recoiling Be^8 nuclei in various excited states breakup into two α particles in flight. Detailed studies of the $Be^9(He^3,3\alpha)$ reaction by Moazed et al.[1] have shown that the reaction proceeds to the 3α-particle final state primarily by sequential processes (an upper limit of about 5% can be placed on the direct decay which results in the phase space type of distribution). At the time of the 1964 Gatlinburg Conference on Correlations of Particles Emitted in Nuclear Reactions,[2] it became clear that most of the multibody final state nuclear reactions induced by low energy projectiles proceed to the final state by various "sequential" processes. The direct decay plays a significant role only in unusual circumstances at low bombarding energies.

The term "sequential," as used in this paper, must be carefully defined as many of the "states" of light nuclei have extremely short lifetimes and may be more appropriately described as resonances in the interaction between two of the components of the final state (e.g. the $\frac{1}{2}^-$ first excited state of Li^5 and the 4^+ second excited state of Be^8). In the case of very short-lived systems it may be more meaningful to consider the term "sequential" as implying only that the distribution of events within the available phase space is not random, but is modulated by the interactions among the components of the final state. We will illustrate this point by considering the reaction

$$a + b \rightarrow c + (d+e) \rightarrow d + e$$

where the system (d+e) is short-lived. The reaction will generally proceed in such a manner that the system (d+e) is left with a relative internal energy which corresponds to a resonance in the amplitude for the scattering of d on e. From a very elementary point of view the system (c+d+e) is formed at an arbitrary energy determined by the bombarding energy, so that it is not in general possible for all components of the system to have relative energies corresponding to resonance in their interactions. Hence one component must separate from the others with an energy not characteristic of a resonance in the system. On the other hand, at low bombarding energies it is highly improbable for all components to separate in this manner and, the most probable events are those in which as many of the components are left with relative energies, so that they are strongly interacting. This general point of view is similar to that discussed more formally in the 1952 paper of Watson[3].

If the system d+e is sufficiently long-lived that the probability of decay during the time that c and (d+e) are separated by distance comparable to the range of nuclear forces is small, then the decay of the system (d+e) will be essentially independent of c and the decay process in the recoiling system will depend entirely by the properties of the intermediate state[4]; i.e. the angular distribution of the decay will be determined by the angular momentum of the state and the branching ratio for the decay to the various internal states of d or e will depend upon the internal structure of the recoiling system. Hence the study of multiparticle reactions provides a tool for obtaining spectroscopic information about the states of relatively long-lived intermediate systems. In the case of short-lived systems where the decay occurs while the third particle c is close enough to interact with the components of the breakup of (d+e), the picture may become considerably more complex. As of yet very little experimental information has been obtained for such systems, except in the case of the few nucleon problem. The extent to which the third particle influences the breakup of the intermediate system is not well understood, but the experimental evidence often indicates that the effect may be less than one might have expected[5]. As a result the study of multibody reactions may also be useful in obtaining spectroscopic information about relatively short-lived intermediate systems. The detailed study of the decay of short-lived intermediate systems is of considerable interest in order to try to obtain a better understanding of the affects of the third particle on the decay process. Such studies are not only of interest from the point of view of nuclear physics, but also elementary particle physics where the same quantum mechanical principles should apply, but the problem of obtaining significant experimental data is much more difficult.

The study of multiparticle final state reactions induced by low energy projectiles is an exceedingly fruitful field in that it may yield

1. spectroscopic information about unstable nuclear systems,
2. information about the mechanism of nuclear interactions,
3. an insight into the basic quantum mechanical concepts of the interactions in systems consisting of more than two particles.

I shall restrict most of the remaining discussion, however, to the first point. Multiparticle nuclear reactions are especially useful in obtaining spectroscopic information about intermediate systems, because they frequently allow one to study simultaneously the formation process of a particular system as well as all of its possible decay modes. In addition, angular correlation measurements for various decay modes can often provide additional information about the angular momentum of the system as well as the mechanism of the initial interactions leading to the intermediate system.

II. Kinematics of Multiparticle Final State Reactions

I will consider here only the kinematical relationships for reactions which proceed to the multiparticle final state via sequential processes or by a series of such processes. These calculations can be generalized to non-sequential processes by permitting the Q values and the corresponding energies of excitation to take on continuous ranges of values. All expressions will be developed in the non-relativistic approximation.

1. Three-Body Final States

In the case of nuclear reactions which proceed to a three-particle final state via a sequential process, analytical expressions can easily be derived from which the kinematical relationships can be calculated given the bombarding energy and the energy of the intermediate states and internal state of excitation of the components of the final system. As the solutions are frequently multivalued such an approach often tends to obscure much of the physical insight into the nature of the problem. The use of velocity vector diagrams on the other hand permits the researcher to obtain readily an understanding of the kinematical behavior of the system. Furthermore, such an approach can easily be generalized with more complex reactions. The method of velocity vector diagram approach is also easily adapted to programming for computer calculation.

In the case of three-body final state reactions, the conservation of energy and momentum equations for reactions restricted to a plane lead to three equations with six unknown quantities

$$\tfrac{1}{2}M_1V_1^2 + Q = \tfrac{1}{2}M_3V_3^2 + \tfrac{1}{2}M_4V_4^2 + \tfrac{1}{2}M_5V_5^2$$

$$M_1V_1 = M_3V_3\cos\theta_3 + M_4V_4\cos\theta_4 + M_5V_5\cos\theta_5$$

$$0 = M_3V_3\sin\theta_3 + M_4V_4\sin\theta_4 + M_5V_5\sin\theta_5$$

(Reactions not confined to a plane lead to four equations with nine unknown quantities, but do not introduce any additional conceptual difficulties. The additional computational difficulties of considering non-coplanar reaction, however, adds nothing to the understanding of the three-body problem.) The measurement of the energies of two of the particles at specified angles, θ_A and θ_B, determines four of the unknowns and leaves us with three equations and two unknowns. Hence the system is over determined; nevertheless, the measurement of the extra quantities is often very helpful in interpreting the results. In many cases the solutions are often double-valued and the experimental determination of only three quantities could lead to ambiguous data. Furthermore, some reactions result in final state systems in which one or more of the particles can be left in an internal excited state. In such cases four quantities must be measured in order to determine which of the excited states the events correspond to. Finally, under most practical experimental conditions one is plagued with large backgrounds arising from accidental events which can frequently be eliminated by performing the complete measurement.

Figure 2 illustrates a velocity vector diagram for a

typical three-particle final state reaction when the first particle emitted in the sequence and one of the breakup particles are observed. The example involves the

$$Be^9 + He^3 \rightarrow \alpha_3 + Be^8(16.92) \rightarrow \alpha_4 + \alpha_5$$

reaction where α_3 and α_4 are observed. The subscripts 1, 2, 3, 4, and 5 refer to the bombarding particle, the target, the initial particle emitted in the final state, and the two breakup particles from the recoiling intermediate system, respectively. Quantities without subscripts refer to the recoiling intermediate system. Primes indicate velocities relative to the total center of mass; double primes, the center of mass of the recoiling system; and no primes, the laboratory system The initial steps are identical to the velocity vector diagram approach used in solving the two-body reaction in which the V_c, the velocity of the center of mass, is laid out from the origin of the laboratory system in the direction of the incident particle. The end point of the vector V_c becomes the origin of the overall center of mass system. The expressions for calculating the required velocities are given in the Appendix. An arc of radius V_3' is constructed about the center of mass origin and the intersection of this arc with the counter axis, θ_A, determines the V_3 and θ_3', thus completely specifying the kinematical quantities for the initial particle emitted, 3. The intermediate system of mass $M(\approx M_4 + M_5)$ recoils in the opposite direction to V_3' in the center of mass system with a velocity V'. The velocities of the breakup particles in the recoiling system, V_4'' and V_5'', can be calculated. If particle 4 is observed one can determine its kinematical behavior by constructing a circle of radius V_4'' with its center at the end point of V'. At the intersection of this circle with the axis of the second counter, θ_B, determines V_4 as well as θ_4'' and θ_4'. In the example chosen V_4'' is sufficiently large compared to V_c and V' that particle 4 can be observed at all angles. In this case the solution is single-valued. It should, however, be remembered that in some cases particle 4 might be observed at the angle θ_A and particle 3 at θ_B leading to a second solution. If particles 3 and 4 are experimentally distinguishable, these two solutions can be separated.

The example of the

$$Be^9 + He^3 \rightarrow \alpha_3 + Be^8(g.s.) \rightarrow \alpha_4 + \alpha_5$$

reaction illustrated in Fig. 3 demonstrates the situation when V_4'' is small compared to V'. In this case the observation particle 4 is restricted to a small range of values of θ_B for any specified θ_A (or cone in the case of non-coplanar events). Furthermore, it is apparent from the diagram that for any angle θ_B lying within the cone of observation there are two possible values of V_4 leading to double-valued solutions. Again it may also be possible to observe particle 3 at θ_B and particle 4 at θ_A leading in this case to four possible solutions.

The determination of the kinematical variables for the cases in which two of the breakup particles from the recoiling system are observed and the initial particle emitted in the sequence remains unobserved, is somewhat more difficult. As the initial particle is not observed, the direction of the recoiling system is not specified. However, we know the magnitude of the velocity of the recoiling system in the center of mass system, V'. The end point of this velocity can lie at any point on a circle of radius V' constructed about the end point of V_c (in the non-coplanar events, a sphere of radius V') The velocities of breakup particles in the recoiling system, V_4'' and V_5'', can be calculated. Furthermore, conservation of momentum requires that they lie in opposite directions. This fact can be taken into account by marking off from the center of a straight edge V_4'' in one direction and V_5'' in the opposite direction. If particle 4 is observed at θ_A and particle 5 at θ_B, then the end point of the velocity V_4'' on the straight edge must lie on the axis θ_A and the end of V_5'' on θ_B, but the center point must also lie on the circle V'. The graphical solution can be found by simply sliding the end point of V_4'' along the axis θ_A and moving the center point of the straight edge about the circle V' until the end point of V_5'' intersects the axis θ_B. Again it is generally possible to find two solutions and as before it may also be possible to observe particle 5 at θ_A leading to a total of four solutions. The above procedure s illustrated in Fig. 4 for the

$$Be^8 + He^3 \rightarrow \alpha_3 + Be^8(16.92) \rightarrow \alpha_4 + \alpha_5;$$

but in this case, as particles 4 and 5 are indistinguishable, only two solutions are possible. The above procedure is also relatively straight forward to program for computer calculations.

The kinematic solution for three-body final state reactions of the type a + b → c + (d+e) → d + e which proceed through various intermediate states of the system (d+e) corresponding to the observation of c at θ_A and d at θ_B lie on a smooth "kinematic curve" in the $E_A E_B$ plane representing the restriction of the conservation of energy and momentum. Events corresponding to reactions of the type

$$a + b \rightarrow d + (c+e) \rightarrow c + e \quad \text{and} \quad a + b \rightarrow e + (d+c) \rightarrow d + c$$

where again c and d are observed at angles θ_A and θ_B, respectively, also lie on the same kinematic curve regardless of the intermediate system involved. Such kinematic curves can be closed curves in the $E_A E_B$ plane in the case of endoergic reactions on very light nuclei (the few nucleon problem) or more generally curves which intersect the axes E_A and E_B. The kinematic curve can be generated by simply taking any one of the above three sequences of reactions and calculating the energies of E_c and E_d at angles θ_A and θ_B, respectively, for the range of possible energies of excitations of the intermediate system (not necessarily energies corresponding to actual levels).

If all particles of the final state are identical, as in the $Be^9(He^3,3\alpha)$ reaction, only one kinematic curve is possible. On the other hand, if all three particles of the final state (c, d and e) are distinguishable, then in principle six kinematic curves are possible in the $E_A E_B$ plane corresponding to observations of the type (θ_A θ_B): (cd), (ce), (dc), (de), (ec), and (ed).

If the components of the three-particle final state can be left in an excited state, each such state (corresponding to different amounts of kinetic energy available for the components of the final state) results in a different kinematic curve.

Figure 5 illustrates an example of the two-dimensional energy spectrum for the $Be^9(He^3,3\alpha)$ reaction at $\theta_A = +60^\circ$ and $\theta_B = -100^\circ$. The kinematic curve is clearly visible and the regions corresponding to the observation of the first α-particle leaving $Be^8(16.92)$ are seen at the positions indicated by a and d. The two regions corresponding to the observation of the breakup α-particles from the $Be^8(16.92)$ system occur at the positions indicated by b and c. The regions h and i correspond to the observation of the first α-particle emitted at θ_A and θ_B, respectively, for reactions proceeding through the first excited 2^+ state of Be^8. This combination of angles lies within the region where events corresponding to reactions proceeding through the ground state of Be^8 could be observed, but the conditions of the experiment are such that the four possible regions on the kinematic curve corresponding to events due to the ground state accidentally overlap with the four regions corresponding to the 16.92 MeV state of Be^8. Other states of Be^8 which undergo α decay, such as the very broad 4^+ state at 11.4 MeV and the 2^+ state at 16.62 MeV, are weakly excited in this reaction and are not apparent in the spectrum shown in Fig. 5. Figure 6 shows the projections of the above two-dimensional spectrum upon the E_A and E_B axis, as well as a graphical reconstruction of the kinematic curve. The lengths of the segments on the kinematic curve represent the known widths of the respective levels. The peaks corresponding to the various states of Be^8 are clearly visible; some indication of events due to the broad 4^+ state is evident. At other angles where events due to the 4^+ state are better isolated from events due to other states, more definitive evidence for the contributions from the 4^+ level to the $Be^9(He^3,3\alpha)$ reaction have been seen[1]. The regions e and f result because the angles chosen are near to the angles corresponding to the laboratory recoil direction of the Be^8 ground state system, and the solid angles of the detectors are sufficiently large so that it is possible to observe both of the breakup α-particles from the recoiling Be^8 ground (g.s.) system. Such events, of course, do not lie on the kinematic curve as the total kinetic energy of the system has been released in the detectors.

The $Li^6(He^3,p\alpha\alpha)$ reaction is another example of a three-body final state reaction which has been studied[6]. Three kinematic curves are possible for this reaction: $p\alpha$, αp and $\alpha\alpha$. The calculated kinematic curves are shown in Fig. 7 for $\theta_A = +60^o$, $\theta_B = -70^o$. This reaction may proceed by two possible sequential processes:

$$Li^6 + He^3 \longrightarrow \begin{cases} p + Be^8 \rightarrow \alpha + \alpha \\ \alpha + Li^5 \rightarrow p + \alpha \end{cases}$$

The expected positions of contributions from the various intermediate states of Be^8 and Li^5 corresponding to both sequences are indicated on each of the kinematic curves. By employing suitable experimental techniques, it is often possible to select only one of the kinematic curves. Figure 8 illustrates the two-dimensional spectrum for the $\alpha\alpha$ kinematic curve under the same conditions as the calculations shown in Fig. 7. Strong contributions can be seen in the region corresponding to the reaction proceeding through the Li^5(g.s.) system. Other processes are difficult to identify at this combination of angles because of the overlap of the various regions. However, by appropriate selection of angles it is generally possible to isolate effects due to a particular level on one of the kinematic curves.

A number of three-particle final state reactions have been observed, however, relatively few have been studied extensively and many others are as yet unexplored.

2. Kinematics of Four-Body Final State Reactions

In the study of four-body final state reactions one must in general take into account non-coplanar events in order to understand fully the kinematic properties of such systems. Conservation of energy and momentum in the nonrelativistic, three-dimensional problem provide us with four equations and 12 unknown quantities for each specified experimental condition, i.e. a given reaction with known overall four-body Q values and bombarding energy. The measurement of the energies of two of the final state particles at specified angles determines six of the unknown quantities, leaving us with six undetermined and only four equations. Hence, the four-body reaction cannot be completely determined by such measurements.

The additional degrees of freedom in the four-body problem lead to a kinematic region defined by the conservation of energy and momentum instead of a kinematic curve in the E_AE_B two-dimensional energy spectrum. In general more limited kinematic regions, which lie within the overall kinematic region, corresponding to the various possible four-body sequential processes occur in place of segments of a curve. Frequently the region for a particular decay sequence covers an extensive region of the allowable four-body kinematic region. Furthermore, the regions for various modes of decay often overlap. However, by appropriate selection of the angles θ_A and θ_B and combinations of particles studied, it is often possible to isolate a particular region of interest or at least to localize the contributions from a given process and enhance its effect relative to the general background due to other modes of decay, so that significant measurements can be made. By careful analysis of the kinematic behavior of such systems and judicious choice of the angles and bombarding energy, it is often possible to obtain a great deal of useful spectroscopic information about the intermediate system.

The procedure for calculating the kinematic behavior of the four-body system is an extension of that used for the three-body system. We will assume first that particle 5 is unstable and undergoes decay into particles 6 and 7 with velocities V_6''' and V_7''' in the frame of rest of particle 5. It is also possible that both components of the initial decay, leading to the intermediate two-body system, are unstable and decay each into two components. In this latter case we assume that particle 3 decays into particles 6 and 7 and that V_6''' and V_7''' are the velocities of particles 6 and 7 relative to the rest frame of particle 3.

We will illustrate some of the kinematic properties of the four-body system by considering a specific example: the $B^{10}(He^3, p\alpha\alpha\alpha)$ reaction in which the following four-body decay modes are possible for low energy He^3 particles

$$B^{10} + He^3 \to p + C^{12} \to \alpha_1 + Be^8 \to \alpha_2 + \alpha_3 \qquad \text{I}$$

$$\to \alpha_1 + B^9 \to p + Be^8 \to \alpha_2 + \alpha_3 \qquad \text{II}$$

$$B^9 \to \alpha_2 + Li^5 \to p + \alpha_3 \qquad \text{III}$$

$$\to Li^5 + Be^8 \to \alpha_2 + \alpha_3 \qquad \text{IV}$$

$$Li^5 \to p + \alpha_1$$

We will consider only the case where the energy of proton is measured at θ_p and the energy of an α-particle at θ_α, as such consideration will illustrate most of the significant features of the four-body reaction without leading to unnecessary confusion. Furthermore, we will consider that the axes of the detectors θ_p and θ_α lie in the plane containing the beam axis. Moazed[7R] has shown that the restriction of the entire decay to the plane of the detectors allows one to determine the extremes of the kinematic regions in the two-dimensional energy spectrum E_p-E_α associated with each mode of decay.

Events corresponding to sequence I or II of the type where the proton and initial α-particle emitted in the sequence are considered can be treated as effective three body reactions, even though the unobserved system is unstable and ultimately decays into two α-particles.

Events corresponding to sequence I in which the proton and α_2 are observed are illustrated by the velocity vector diagram of Fig. 9. Since the proton is restricted by the limitations of two-body kinematics its energy is discrete. The decay of C^{12} into $\alpha + Be^8$ is not restricted to the plane of the counters. Hence, the energy of $E_{\alpha 2}$ can take on a continuous range of values between the limits indicated by the two values of V_α shown in Fig. 9. Thus, such processes lead to straight lines perpendicular to the E_p axis in the two-dimensional energy spectrum E_p-E_α corresponding to the various states of C^{12}. Similarly sequence III in which the initial α particle, α_1, is observed leads to straight lines perpendicular to the E_α axis corresponding to the various states of B^9.

In the case of events corresponding to sequences II, III or IV where the proton is observed in coincidence with α_2, kinematic regions with finite areas result in the E_p-E_α plane.

The extent of these areas can in general be determined by rather straightforward extensions of the graphical procedures discussed above. An example of sequence IV in which $p\alpha_2$ events are observed is illustrated in Fig. 10.

Figure 11 illustrates the various possible kinematic regions of $p\alpha$ two-dimensional energy spectrum from the $B^{10}(He^3,p\alpha\alpha\alpha)$ reactions involving all of the known intermediate states found in the decay modes of the type II, III, IV. The decay modes of the type I would contribute along vertical lines at positions of the arrows indicating the known levels of C^{12}. The various regions are identified in Table I. Figure 12 illustrates the two-dimensional E_p-E_α spectrum for the same conditions as Fig. 11. The vertical and horizontal lines corresponding to the various states of C^{12} and B^9, respectively, are apparent, as well as the kinematic curves corresponding to the effective three-body reactions resulting in the ground and first excited states of Be^8. Detailed analysis of these and other similar data by Waggoner et al.[6] has shown the existence of contributions from many of the possible decay modes, and has yielded considerable spectroscopic information about many of the intermediate systems.

Again the logic of the velocity vector diagram approach, even in the case of the four-body reactions, lends itself to programming the calculations for computers. Programs which will calculate all of the possible decay sequences and any combination of observed particles have been developed by Moazed.

III. Experimental Procedures

The experimental procedures which have been employed at the University of Maryland in the study of multiparticle final state nuclear reactions are relatively straightforward and make use of rather simple apparatus. The scattering chamber used in these studies permits two detectors to be moved independently in a horizontal plane. A special device can also be installed which allows one of the detectors to be located at any angle above the horizontal plane. This latter angle, however, cannot be changed without letting the scattering chamber up to atmospheric pressure. The chamber has the usual collimating aperture arrangement, Faraday cup, and target support which permits the external selection of both the target and the angle of incidence.

Surface barrier solid state detectors have been used for the measurement of the energies of the particles. The thicknesses of these detectors are chosen to correspond approximately to the range of the highest energy particle of interest. Detectors which are used to observe α-particles are thus relatively thin, so that the maximum proton energy lost in such detectors is small compared to that of the highest energy α-particles. A thin aluminum foil, sufficiently thick to stop the maximum energy α-particles, is generally inserted in front of detectors used to observe protons. Most of the studies carried out to date have not required more elaborate means of particle identification. The display of kinematic curves in the two-dimensional E_AE_B spectrum for three-body final state reactions often helps to identify the various regions of interest. In special cases, however, the University of Maryland magnetic spectrometer or ΔE-E counter telescopes have been used where the problem of particle identification was more critical. Some laboratories have also used time-of-flight techniques in order to identify particles. This procedure usually requires the availability of an on-line computer.

One of the major considerations in the design of any two-particle coincidence experiment is the choice of the solid angles of the detectors. Under realistic experimental restrictions the ratio of the number of real-to-accidental events is generally proportional to the product of the solid angles of the detectors. As many measurements are time consuming, it is extremely important to use the largest possible solid angles consistent with the other limitations of the experiment. In the case of γ-ray angular correlations the solid angle is limited only by the desired angular resolution; but in the case of particle-particle correlations the use of large solid angles often leads to excessive kinematic energy broadening of the groups of interest. Hence, the energy resolution necessary to define groups of interest, rather than the desired angular resolution, generally limits the solid angles of the detectors. In many cases it is possible to use rectangular shaped apertures in order to obtain the largest possible solid angle with the least possible kinematic broadening. In other cases it may be possible to obtain a more favorable condition by using different solid angles for the two different detectors. For example, the observation of events corresponding to certain decay modes may not require the same energy resolution along both axes, or in cases where different types of particles are observed in the two detectors, the angular kinematic broadening for one type of particle may be greater than for the other. In any case compromises between energy resolution and the rate of accumulation of data with an acceptable real-to-accidental ratio must be carefully considered for each measurement.

Thin self-supporting targets have been used in a number

of the experiments. However, many targets were prepared by evaporating the target material onto thin carbon foils. Carbon foils form an excellent backing as most of the reactions induced by the commonly used projectiles on C^{12} do not lead to multiparticle final states. Furthermore, very thin foils of carbon which produce a minimum of elastically scattered particles are readily available and easy to use.

Figure 13 illustrates a typical circuit block diagram used in many of the two-particle coincidence measurements. If a two-dimensional pulse-height analyzer is available, however, all of the circuit below the dotted line can in general be replaced by such a device and the measurements greatly simplified. As such devices are not always available in smaller laboratories, we will consider only measurements made with the system shown in Fig. 13.

Fast coincidence between the pulses from the two detectors is achieved by using the signals derived from the zero crossover point of the doubly differentiated pulses provide to the timing-single-channel analyzers as the start and stop pulses for a time-to-pulse-height converter. The signal E_B is normally delayed by about 100 ns in order to allow the coincidence peak to occur in the mid-range of the time spectrum. The time spectrum can be observed with one of the multichannel pulse-height analyzers during the set up and a time window Δt_R set about the coincidence peak. A similar window can be set on the region corresponding to accidental events in order to provide a means of observing the effect of such events. The use of the TPC as a coincidence circuit has the advantage of allowing one to obtain the equivalent of the entire delay curve with points very closely spaced for a normal coincidence circuit in a single measurement. Furthermore, such an arrangement enables the experimenter to determine easily the minimum resolving time which can be used in a particular experiment and to select quickly the appropriate delay and resolving time. If an additional pulse-height analyzer is available, he can also monitor the time spectrum along with the real-to-accidental ratio during the course of the experiment. It should be pointed out that in experiments in which wide ranges of energies for each E_A and E_B are observed, the variation in the flight times of the particles to the detectors in any practical experimental arrangement normally limits the minimum resolving time to about 15 to 20 ns.

The oscilloscope, shown in Fig. 13, allows one to obtain a pictorial display of the two-dimensional $E_A E_B$ energy spectrum of coincidence events by taking a time exposure photograph of the oscilloscope screen. Figures 5, 8 and 12 were obtained in this manner. Such displays not only provide a means of qualitatively studying the contributions from various decay modes, but also enables the experimenter to determine the location of various discriminator windows set within the two-dimensional energy array.

The discriminator window ΔE_A imposes an energy requirement on the coincidence circuit C_1 so that the fourth section of analyzer II will display coincidence events within the energy window ΔE_A projected upon the E_B axis (see Fig. 14). The discriminator window ΔE_B imposes a similar requirement on C_2 such that the fourth section of analyzer I will display the projection of coincidence events within ΔE_B on the axis E_A. The adding circuit provides a signal, $E_S = xE_A+(1-x)E_B$, to the ΔE_S discriminator. The adding circuit is designed so that the value of x can be changed continuously from 0 to 1. The discriminator window on ΔE_S allows a diagonal window to be placed in the two-dimensional energy spectrum of Fig. 14 at any angle from 0° to -90° by varying x from 0 to 1: x = 0 corresponds to a horizontal window; $x = \frac{1}{2}$, a -45° window; and x = 1, a vertical window. The projection of events within such windows can be taken upon either axis and will appear in the third section of each analyzer for circuit shown in Fig. 13. The accidental events within the same sum window projected upon the E_A and E_B axes will appear within the second section of the respective analyzers. In some applications it is also useful to study the projections of various ΔE_A or ΔE_B windows upon the sum axis E_S. This can be done by providing the signal E_S to the input of one of the analyzers instead of E_A or E_B.

Many of the accidental events were eliminated in the projections shown in Fig. 6 by imposing the requirement of a broad diagonal window ΔE_S about the kinematic curve of Fig. 5. In the case of the two-dimensional spectrum for the $B^{10}(He^3,p\alpha\alpha\alpha)$ reaction shown in Fig. 12, it is possible to study the projections of effective three-body events leading to the ground state of Be^8 by imposing narrow sum windows about various regions of interest of Be^8(g.s.) kinematic curve. The use of various windows ΔE_A, ΔE_B and ΔE_S allow quantitative information to be obtained for any region of the two-dimensional energy spectrum $E_A E_B$. Waggoner et al.[8] have used such techniques to study various processes involved in the $B^{10}(He^3,p\alpha\alpha\alpha)$ reaction.

IV. Angular Correlation Studies

The measurement of the angular correlation function for

the sequential reactions of the form

$$a + b \rightarrow c + (d{+}e) \rightarrow d{+}e$$

where the particle c is observed at a fixed angle θ_c and particle d over a range of angles θ_d yields information concerning the spin and parity of intermediate system (d+e). The angular correlation of course depends upon the nature of the initial interaction leading to the intermediate system, as this interaction determines the population of the various m-substates of the recoiling intermediate system. In general, the population of the m-substates for different reaction mechanism will have different dependences upon the angle of emission of the initial particle; hence, the study of the behavior of the angular correlation as a function of the angle θ_c can also yield information about the nature of the initial interaction.

If (d+e) is a well defined intermediate system with definite spin and parity as well as a sufficiently long lifetime so that the decay can be treated as a true sequential process, the angular correlation measured in the frame of reference of the recoiling system will exhibit a periodicity of 180° in the plane of the initial reaction and reflectional symmetry about this plane[9]. The existence of such symmetry behaviors in an observed angular correlation function can be used as a test of the sequential nature of a particular decay. If, on the other hand, the intermediate system is long-lived so that it is known to be sequential, these symmetry conditions can be used to facilitate the accumulation of experimental data.

The experimental angular correlation functions must be transformed to the frame of reference of the recoiling system by appropriate transformations of angles and solid angles. Computer codes required to perform such transformations using an extension of the velocity vector diagram method have been developed by Moazed[7,10]. A coordinate system is chosen such that z-axis lies along the direction $\bar{k}_a \times \bar{k}_c$ and the x-axis lies along the recoil direction. We will define the angle α as the angle measured from the z-axis and β, the angle in the x-y plane measured from the x-axis. In this coordinate system the reaction plane corresponds to $\alpha = \frac{\pi}{2}$ and the recoil direction, $\beta = 0^{\circ}$. The experimental data is then fitted with an expression of the form

$$W(\alpha,\beta) = \sum_{n,i} A_i^n \, P_i^n(\cos\alpha) \cos n(\beta-\beta_n).$$

The 180° periodicity requirement in the reaction plane restricts n to be even and the reflectional symmetry with respect to this plane also limits i to even values.

The theoretical angular correlation function in the recoiling system can be expressed as

$$W(\alpha,\beta,\bar{k}_c,\bar{k}_d) = \sum_{KQ} \sqrt{\frac{4\pi}{2K+1}} \quad \rho_{KQ}(J,J)F_K \, Y_{KQ} \, (\alpha,\beta)$$

where

$$F_K = \sum_{LL'} C_L \, C_{L'} \, F_K(LL'J_dJ) \, b_K(LL'),$$

$Y_{KQ}(\alpha,\beta)$ is the ordinary spherical harmonic, J is the spin of the recoiling system and J_d is the spin of particle d. ρ_{KQ} is the usual density matrix, and C_L denotes the reduced matrix element which selects the contributions of the various angular components of radiation. The factor $F_K(LL'J_dJ)$ is the normal γ-ray angular correlation coefficient and the parameter b_K converts the expression from γ decay to particle emission. The separation of W into the product of ρ_{KQ} and $F_K \, Y_{KQ}$ allows one to separate the expression into the properties of the initial interaction which determine primarily the population of the m-substates of the intermediate system, as represented by ρ_{KQ}; and the properties of the decay of the intermediate system, as represented by $F_K \, Y_{KQ}$. A general discussion of the theoretical angular correlation function and the references to more detailed work is provided in the paper by Moazed[10].

The initial step in many of the He^3 and triton induced reactions which lead to multiparticle final state systems have been found to proceed largely by simple stripping or pickup interactions, even at rather low bombarding energies. In such cases the DWBA theory can be used to predict the theoretical angular correlations, given the appropriate optical model parameters and the wave function describing the transfer nucleon or cluster of nucleons.

In the event that the initial step is a pickup or stripping interaction the order of the angular correlation function W is limited by $K \leq$ minimum of $[2\ell, j+j', L+L', \text{ or } 2J]$ where ℓ and j are the appropriate orbital and total angular momenta transfer associated with the initial interaction. Furthermore, regardless of initial interaction mechanism $K \leq 2J$; hence by simply determining the order of the angular correlation function, it is always possible to set a lower limit on the spin of the intermediate state.

Fig. 15 illustrates the experimental angular correlations for the $Be^9(He^3,\alpha)Be^8(16.92) \rightarrow \alpha + \alpha$ reaction measured at a bombarding energy of 3.0 MeV for the initial α-particle emitted at 0° and 20° in the laboratory system. The curves are the theoretical fit to the data using the DWBA pickup theory where the optical model parameters have been previously chosen in order to fit the differential cross section measurements. Contributions for the picked up neutron in both the $p_{\frac{1}{2}}$ and $p_{3/2}$ states of Be^9 have been included. The 0° results are particularly interesting in that the theoretical angular correlation function at this angle is independent of the choice of the optical model parameters and provides a measure of the relative contribution of the $p_{\frac{1}{2}}$ and $p_{3/2}$ states. The data at larger angles, away from the pickup peak, require $k_{max} = 4$ contributions indicating the presence of other reaction mechanisms. The results are discussed in detail by Moazed[10].

V. Branching Ratios

The precise determination of the branching ratios for various decay modes of a particular intermediate system is in principle a rather difficult measurement in that it requires the determination of the complete angular correlation function for each decay mode. In many cases, however, adequate information can be obtained by measuring the coincidence yields at several appropriately chosen angles.

In the case of three-body final state reactions the branching ratio measurement requires that the contributions from the various decay modes be determined on each of the appropriate kinematic curves. As these curves may correspond to the emission of different types of particles the experimental conditions often have to be changed during the course of the measurement. In the case of four-body final state reactions, it is sometimes possible to observe the effect of different decay modes by studying only the two-dimensional spectra for a single combination of emitted particles.

The study of the $B^{10}(He^3,p\alpha\alpha\alpha)$ reaction by Waggoner et al.[8] illustrates several types of branching ratio measurements, as well as their application in obtaining spectroscopic information. A particularly simple example of such studies is the search in the $p\alpha$ spectra for contributions from the various levels of C^{12} to the Be^8(g.s.) kinematic curve (sequence I): any level of C^{12} which α decays to the 0^+ Be^8 (g.s.) must have a natural parity. A second example is the study of the decay modes for the 2.34 and 2.8 MeV levels of B^9. Observations of the projections of several ΔE_p and ΔE_s windows unto the E_α axis have shown that the $B^9(2.34)$ system decays almost entirely by α emission to Li^5(g.s.) whereas, the $B^9(2.8)$ system decays primarily by proton emission to Be^8(g.s.). Such limitations on the decay modes provide a severe test for any model of the internal structure of these two levels of B^9.

A number of three-body final state reactions on light nuclei have been observed at low bombarding energies, but except for the few nucleon problem relatively few such reactions have been studied in any detail.

Many interesting three-body reactions are as yet unexplored and very few studies have been carried out on four-body reactions. Much spectroscopic information about the intermediate systems is only accessible by means of such studies and remains to be obtained. Furthermore, a great deal of work is needed in the study of the behavior of decays involving short-lived intermediate system before the basic nature of the process involved in such decays can be understood.

References

1. C. Moazed, J. E. Etter, H. D. Holmgren, M. A. Waggoner, Rev. Mod. Phys. 37, 354 (1965).
2. Proceedings of the Conference on Correlations of Particles Emitted in Nuclear Reactions, Rev. Mod. Phys. 37, 327 (1965).
3. K. M. Watson, Phys. Rev. 88, 1163 (1952).
4. Č. Zupančič, Rev. Mod. Phys. 37, 330 (1965).
5. T. S. Bhatia, K. S. Jayaraman, L. S. Rodberg, D. W. Detenbeck, H. D. Holmgren, Bull. Am. Phys. Soc. 12, (1967).
6. F. C. Young, K. S. Jayaraman, J. E. Etter, H. D. Holmgren, M. A. Waggoner, Rev. Mod. Phys. 37, 362 (1965).
7. C. Moazed, private communication.
8. M. A. Waggoner, J. E. Etter, H. D. Holmgren, C. Moazed, Nucl.Phys. 88, 81 (1966).
9. A. Bohr, Nucl.Phys. 10, 486 (1959)
10. C. Moazed, Thesis, University of Maryland (1966) and C. Moazed and H. D. Holmgren, to be published.

Appendix

The following expressions can be used to calculate the various velocities required in the vector diagram kinematic calculations:

$$V_c = \frac{M_1}{M_1 + M_2}\sqrt{\frac{2E_1}{M_1}}$$

$$V_3' = \left[\frac{2M}{M_3(M_3 + M)}\left(\frac{M_2}{M_1 + M_2} E_1 + Q^n\right)\right]^{\frac{1}{2}}$$

$$V' = \left[\frac{2M_3}{M(M_3 + M)}\left(\frac{M_2}{M_1 + M_2} E_1 + Q^n\right)\right]^{\frac{1}{2}} = \frac{M_3}{M} V_3'$$

$$V_4'' = \left[\frac{2M_5}{M_4 M}(Q^m - Q^n)\right]^{\frac{1}{2}}$$

$$V_5'' = \left[\frac{2M_4}{M_5 M}(Q^m - Q^n)\right]^{\frac{1}{2}} = \frac{M_4}{M_5} V_4''$$

$$V_6''' = \left[\frac{2M_7}{M_5 M_6}\epsilon^m\right]^{\frac{1}{2}}$$

$$V_7''' = \frac{M_6}{M_7} V_6'''$$

where particle 1 is the incident projectile; 2, the target; 3, the first particle emitted in the sequence; 4 and 5 are the break up particles from the recoiling system; and 6 and 7 are the break up particles in a four body reaction resulting for the decay of particle 3, 4 or 5. The variables without subscripts refer to the initial recoiling system, (4 + 5).

$$Q^m = [M_1 + M_2 - M_3 - M_4 - M_5]c^2$$

where the superscript m refers to a specific combination of internal states of particles 3, 4 and 5.

$$Q^n = [M_1 + M_2 - M_3 - M^n]c^2$$

where n refers to a particular combination of internal states of the recoiling system and particle 3.

$$\epsilon^m = (M_5^m - M_6 - M_7)c^2$$

when particle 5 undergoes break up into 6 and 7. In the event that either particle 3 or 4 undergoes break up M_5^m is replaced with the appropriate mass.

Table I

	Reaction	Particles	B^9	Be^8	Li^5
a	II	$p\alpha_1$	2.34	g.s.	--
b	II	$p\alpha_2$	2.34	g.s.	--
c	II	$p\alpha_1$	11.62	g.s.	--
d	II	$p\alpha_1$	11.62	2.9	--
e	II	$p\alpha_2$	11.62	g.s.	--
f	II	$p\alpha_2$	11.62	2.9	--
g	III	$p\alpha_1$	2.34	--	g.s.
h	III	$p\alpha_2$	2.34	--	g.s.
i	III	$p\alpha_3$	(2.34, 11.62)	--	g.s.
j	III	$p\alpha_1$	11.62	--	g.s.
k	III	$p\alpha_2$	11.62	--	g.s.
l	IV	$p\alpha_1$	--	g.s.	g.s.
m	IV	$p\alpha_1$	--	2.9	g.s.
n	IV	$p\alpha_1$	--	g.s.	$\frac{1}{2}^-$
o	IV	$p\alpha_1$	--	2.9	$\frac{1}{2}^-$
p	IV	$p\alpha_2$	--	g.s.	g.s.
q	IV	$p\alpha_2$	--	2.9	g.s.
r	IV	$p\alpha_2$	--	g.s.	$\frac{1}{2}^-$

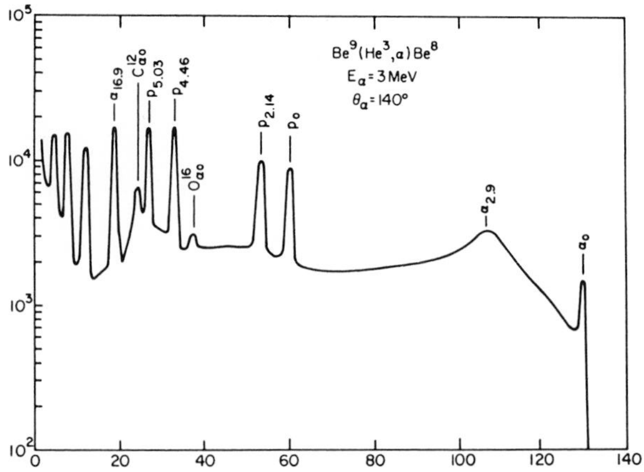

Fig. 1 Spectrum of α-particles from the $Be^9(He^3,\alpha)Be^8$ reaction at a bombarding energy of 3.0 MeV for θ_α = 140°.

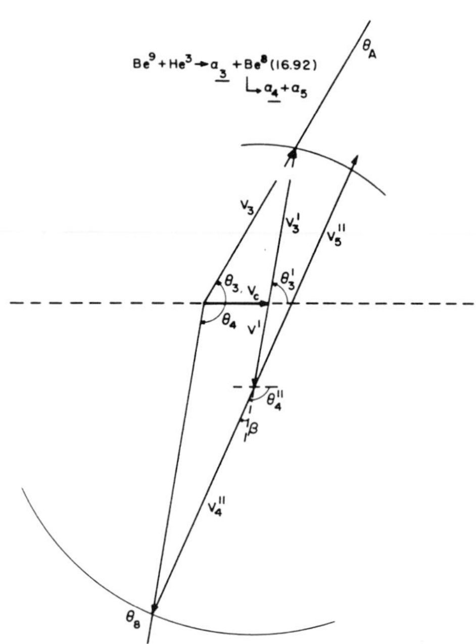

Fig. 2 Velocity vector diagram for the $Be^9(He^3 \rightarrow \alpha_3 + Be^8(16.92) \rightarrow \alpha_4 + \alpha_5$ reaction.

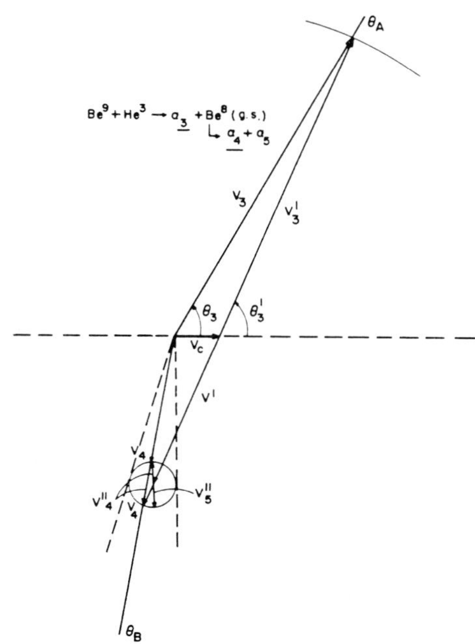

Fig. 3 Velocity vector diagram for the $Be^9 + He^3 \rightarrow \alpha_3 + Be^8(g.s.) \rightarrow \alpha_4 + \alpha_5$ reaction.

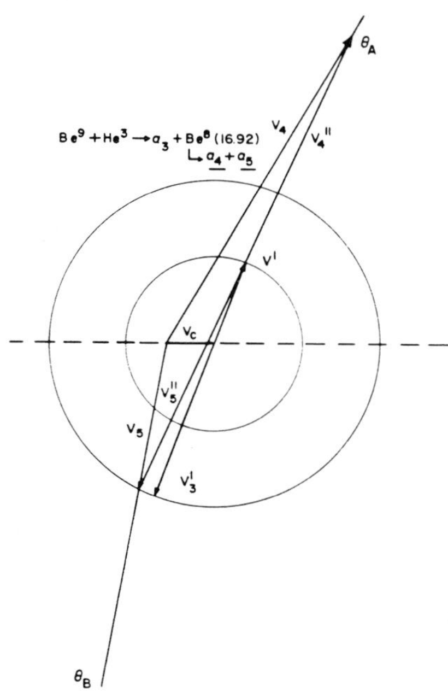

Fig. 4 Velocity vector diagram for the $Be^9 + He^3 \rightarrow \alpha_3 + Be^8(16.92) \rightarrow \alpha_4 + \alpha_5$ reaction.

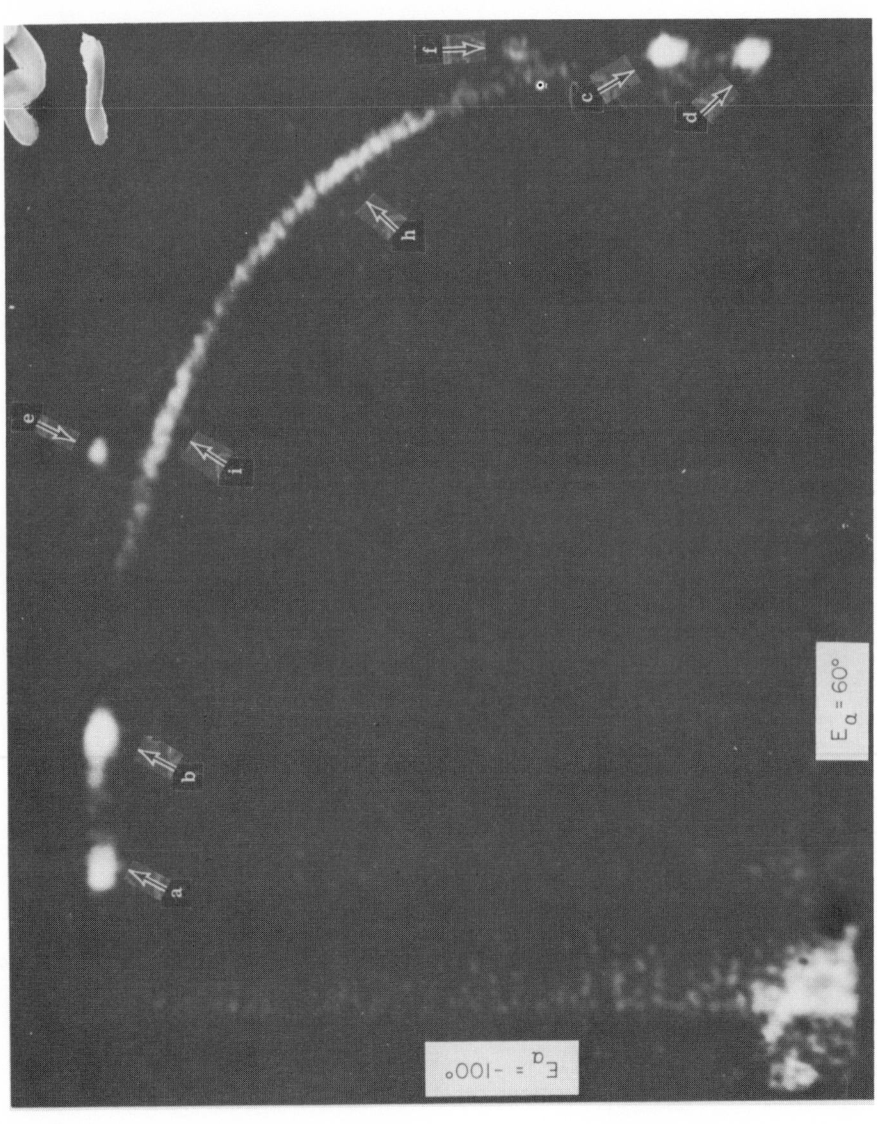

Fig. 5. The two-dimensional energy spectrum for the $Be^9(He^3,\alpha)2He^4$ reaction at $\theta A = +60°$ and

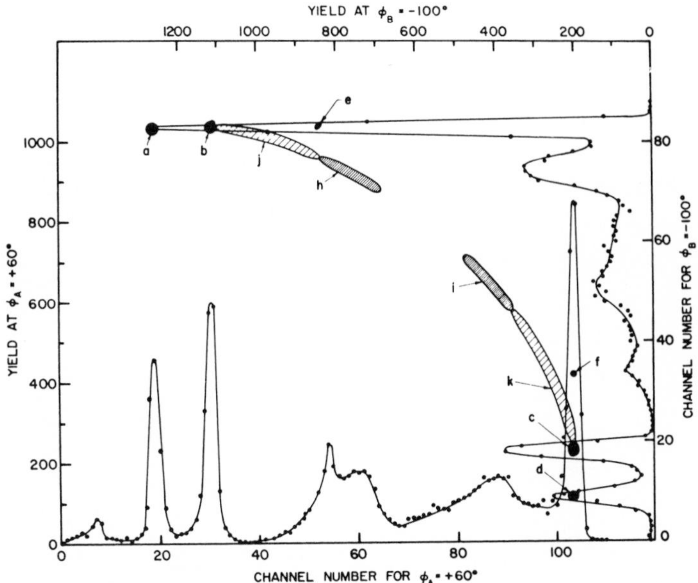

Fig. 6 The projections of the two-dimensional energy spectrum onto the E_A and E_B axes and the reconstructed kinematic curve at $\theta_A = +60^o$ and $\theta_B = -100^o$ for a bombarding energy of 3.0MeV. The positions of the points and segments corresponding to the various levels of Be^8, as well as resonances in the α-α system, are indicated.

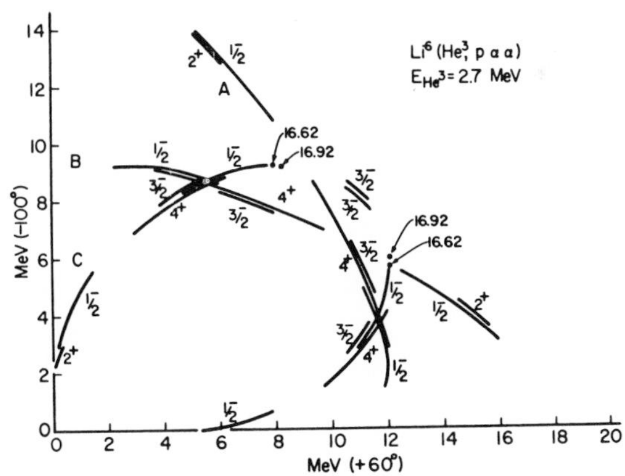

Fig. 7 The calculated two-dimensional energy spectrum for $\theta_A = +60^o$ and $\theta_B = -100^o$. The locations of various intermediate states of Be^8 and Li^5 are indicated.

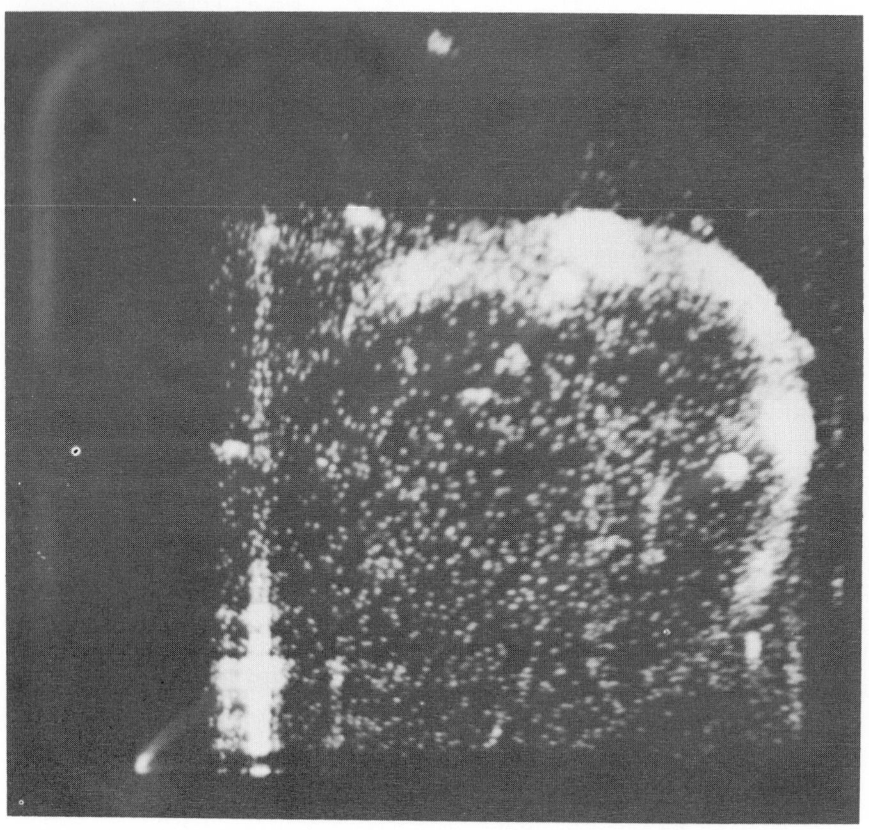

Fig. 8 The two-dimensional energy spectrum for the Li^6 $(He^3, p\alpha\alpha\alpha)$ reaction at $\theta_A = +60^o$ and $\theta_B = -100^o$ for a bombarding energy of 2.7 MeV.

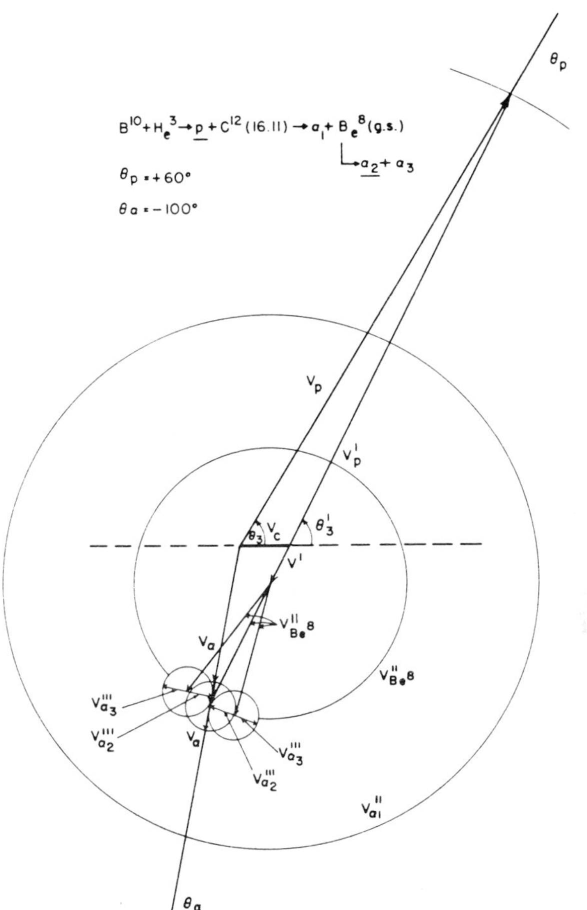

Fig. 9 Velocity vector diagram for the B^{10} + He^3 → p + C^{12}(16.11) → α_1 + Be^8(g.s.) → α_2 + α_3 reaction.

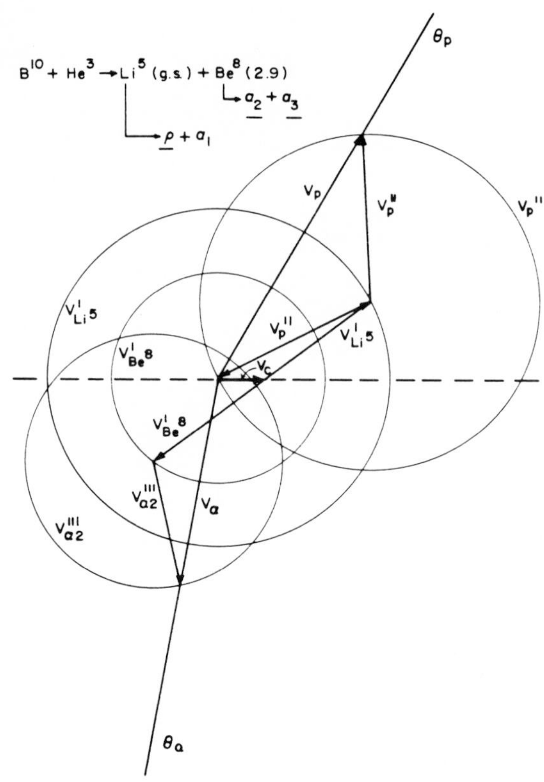

Fig. 10 Velocity vector diagram for the $B^{10} + He^3 \rightarrow$ Li^5(g.s.) + Be^8(g.s.) $\rightarrow \alpha_2 + \alpha_3$ reaction.
$\hookrightarrow$ $\underline{p} + \alpha_1$

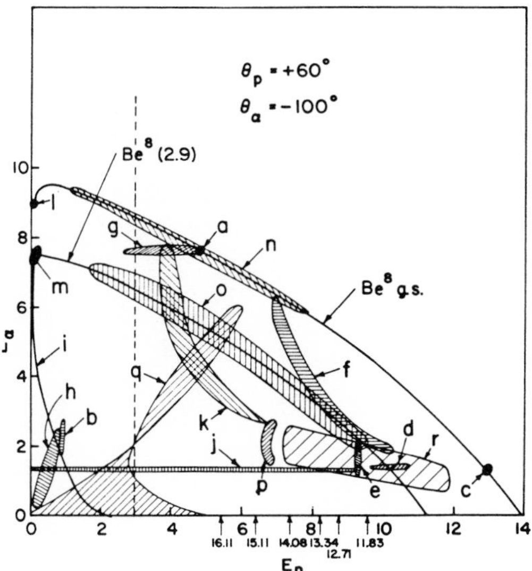

Fig. 11 The calculated kinematic regions for the reaction $B^{10}(He^3,p\alpha)\alpha\alpha$ plotted as a two-dimensional energy spectrum of coincident proton and alpha particle for $\theta_p = +60^o$, $\theta_\alpha = -100^o$ and $E_{He^3} = 2.45$ MeV. The process, observed particles and states associated with each kinematic region is indicated by a letter explained in table 1. The positions of the discrete energy proton groups produced by processes of type (I) are labelled with the excitation energy of the appropriate state of C^{12}.

Fig. 12 Two-dimensional energy spectrum for the $B^{10}(He^3, p\alpha)\alpha\alpha$ reaction for $\theta_p = +60^o$, $\theta_\alpha = -100^o$, $E_{He^3} = 2.45$ MeV.

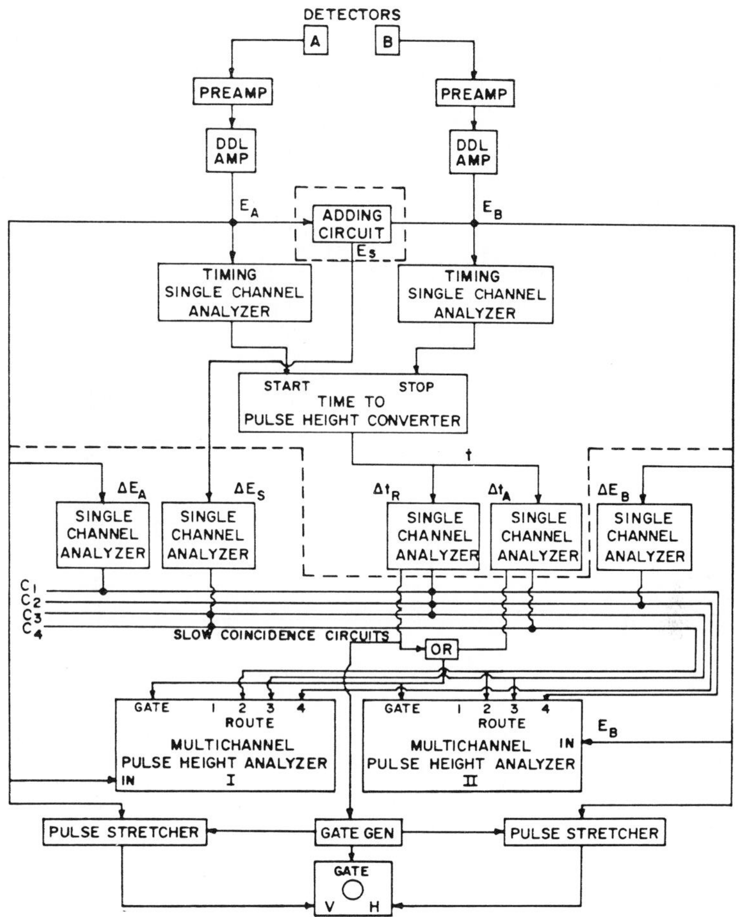

Fig. 13 Circuit block diagram for two-particle coincidence measurements.

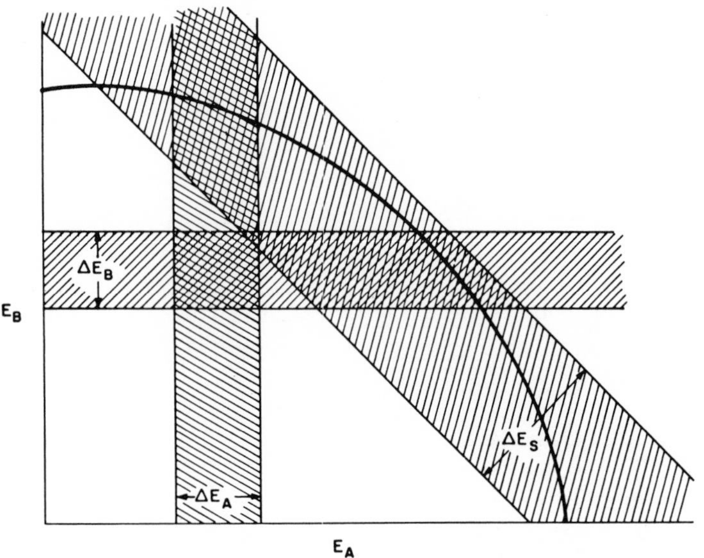

Fig. 14 Example ΔE_A, ΔE_B and ΔE_S imposed upon a two-dimensional spectrum.

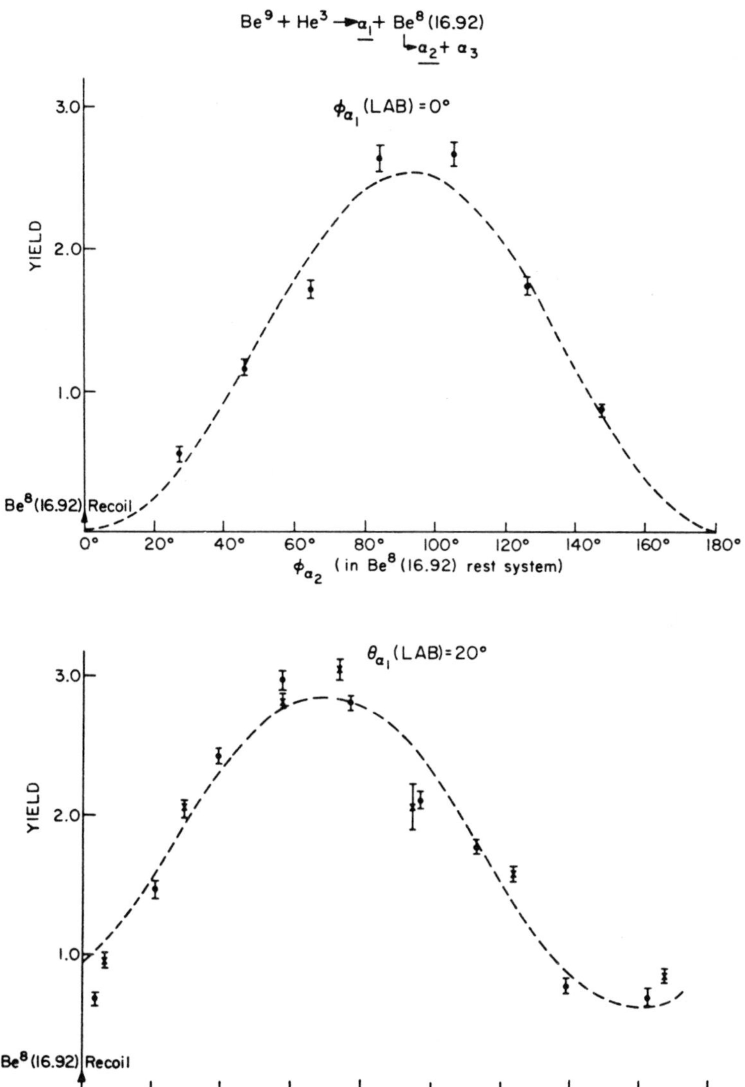

Fig. 15 Angular correlation measurements for the Be^9 + $He^3 \rightarrow \alpha_1 + Be^8(16.92) \rightarrow \alpha_2 + \alpha_3$ reaction at $E_{He^3} = 3.0$ plotted in the recoil system. The x's represent data at $\varphi_{\alpha 2} + 180^o$ and the dots, at $\varphi_{\alpha 2}$. The curve is the DWBA fit to the data.

PRECISION ELASTIC SCATTERING EXPERIMENTS

J. C. Armstrong

Institute for Defense Analyses
Arlington, Virginia

Introduction

In spite of the fact that the title of this presentation would imply a rather broad scope, I have chosen to drastically narrow the subject matter and to talk only about proton elastic scattering below 3 MeV. Further, I will do this by simply discussing a limited number of specific experiments. I hope that by doing so, a clear idea of what is involved in these experiments may be presented.

It is legitimate first to question what is meant by the word "precision" in the title. Obviously there is the implication that these experiments are somehow better in quality than those previously performed and this is the interpretation of "precision" which I will use. There are, of course, several methods of improving the quality of previous elastic scattering results and I have chosen only a few specific examples to illustrate this point. The experiments I will discuss are not necessarily the best examples, but they are the ones with which I am most familiar.

Maryland Experiments with Carbon Isotopes

I would like to first discuss a series of (p, p) experiments in which I have been involved and which were performed at the University of Maryland in collaboration with a number of graduate students.[1-3] We have studied, in turn, elastic proton scattering from C^{12}, C^{13}, and C^{14}. The C^{14} study is not quite complete, but tentative results were reported at the Washington APS meeting this spring.[4] It is the subject of the doctoral thesis of W. R. Harris.

All of these experiments with carbon were performed in a similar fashion and the only important differences result from variations in the methods of analysis. I would like briefly to describe the experimental equipment and procedures. The setup is shown in outline in Figure 1. It is I think, typical of a great many laboratories. The H^+ beam from the University of Maryland 3-MV vertical machine is deflected into the horizontal plane by a 90° magnetic analyzer. This analyzer can be used to determine beam energy to an accuracy of 1 keV. Through adjustment of the analyzer entrance and exit slits, the energy spread within the beam emerging from the analyzer can be held to less than 300 eV. The analyzed beam is focused with a magnetic quadrupole pair located approximately six feet from the exit of the 90° analyzer. The target chamber is located about 20 feet beyone this quadrupole pair. Just in front of the scattering chamber is a multiple slits box which is used to define the beam spot size on target and to reduce the number of secondary electrons which enter the scattering chamber. The scattering chamber is made from a hollow 8-inch OD aluminum tube which has a 1-inch wall thickness. A horizontal slot 3 inches high is machined around the side of the chamber over a 160° arc. The scattering chamber is coupled to a 180° magnetic spectrometer through use of a sliding seat covering this slot. The seal is made of 0.012-inch Be-Cu foil and when properly installed, is capable of holding a vacuum of better than 10^{-5} TORR while the spectrometer is being rotated. Under static conditions, the seal is good to at least 10^{-6} TORR. After numerous flexings, the foil tends to buckle easily and since this can cause vacuum leaks during rotation of the spectrometer, the foil must be periodically replaced. The spectrometer can be rotated from approximately 125° on one side of the beam to 30° on the other.

The characteristics of the spectrometer itself have been described before.[5] It is an n=1/2, double focusing spectrometer having a mean radius of curvature of 20 inches. The momentum resolution varies from about 0.001 to 0.002 as the solid angle is increased up to the maximum of 0.022 steradians. A set of micrometer-driven slits at the entrance permits the acceptance solid angle of the spectrometer to be varied continuously. Adjustable slits and apertures are also located in the focal plane of the spectrometer and a large-area solid-state detector is placed just behind these image slits so as to intercept everything which passes through them. There are three oil diffusion pumps in the system apart from the 1500 1/sec pump at the base of the Van de Graaff. One is located between the 90° magnetic analyzer and the qualrupole focusing magnet, one between the quadrupole and the scattering chamber, and one is attached directly to the spectrometer. A liquid N cold trap is mounted with each diffusion pump. We have found that the contaminant build-up on targets is noticeably reduced by the use of an additional cold surface within the scattering chamber, directly under the targets. Under optimum conditions the system vacuum is about 10^{-6} TORR.

The self-supporting targets used in the carbon experiments were all prepared in a similar fashion. Of course, the C^{13} and C^{14} targets are considerably more expensive than the C^{12} and, consequently, a great deal of effort was expended in order to maximize the efficiency of the process in preparing C^{13} and C^{14} foils. The fact that the C^{14} is radioactive further complicates the procedure. The method of preparation is described in detail elsewhere.[5] Essentially, methyl iodide is cracked onto a thin nickel foil by electrically heating the foil in the presence of a low pressure (∿10cm Hg) methyl iodide vapor. The carbon film can then be floated off the nickel onto a water surface and subsequently lifted from the water on a thin aluminum frame which supports the target during the experiments. The targets prepared in this fashion are usually transparent to some degree and vary in areal density from 20 μg/cm² to 70 μg/cm², determined simply by measuring the width of the $C^{13}(p,\gamma)N^{14}$ resonance at 1746.5 ± 0.5 keV. The foil thickness varies, somewhat unpredictably, but very thick and very thin foils can be prepared, when desired, with a fair degree of confidence. Contaminants on the targets consist of the undesired carbon isotope (s), oxygen, silicon, nickel, and iodine. An analysis of the target foil composition is easily made with the spectrometer by stepping the field through the appropriate region of magnetic rigidity and observing the size and location of each elastically scattered proton peak. Such a "target profile" is shown in Figure 2 for one of the C^{13} foils. These data were taken at a laboratory scattering angle of 90° with an incident proton energy of 2 MeV. Under these conditions the C^{12} and C^{13} peaks are clearly separated. At very large scattering angles, where there is good separation, we frequently do not need the spectrometer and can obtain satisfactory data by using a solid-state detector within the scattering chamber. At smaller scattering angles and lower energy the separation decreases and the spectrometer is required. There are, of course, lower limits in both energy and scattering angle beyond which separation is impossible. The method by which the spectrometer is used to obtain data depends upon how well the desired peak is separated from neighboring peaks. When the peaks are well separated, the image slits may be opened to accept the entire peak at a single spectrometer field setting. When the peak separation is not sufficient to do this, it is necessary to narrow the slits in front of the detector and trace out the profile of the peak in a series of runs, stepping the spectrometer field through the appropriate region. Figure 2 was obtained in this manner. Using either procedure, it is usually possible in a reasonable amount of time to obtain sufficient counting statistics to make this an acceptably small contribution to the total experimental error. The largest single contributor to this error is the value of the target thickness.

With only minor modifications in the apparatus which I have described we have measured the differential cross section for proton elastic scattering from C^{12} in the vicinity of the 1.7-MeV resonance, from C^{13} between 1.0 and 2.6 MeV, and from C^{14} between 1.0 and 2.7 MeV. In all cases the measured differential cross section is compared with a theoretical expression involving quantities (level parameters) which are varied in order to obtain the best possible agreement with the experiment. As usual, the theoretical cross section is written in terms of elements of the collision matrix, U. An element of U is simply the amplitude of the outgoing waves of the final state pair resulting from unit initial state flux. The cross section for production of a nuclear pair, c', by bombarding together a pair, c, is proportional to $|U_{c'c}|^2$. In order to write the elements of U in terms of the desired level parameters, it is of course necessary to formulate a description of the reaction proceeding through the compound nucleus, that is, a description of the reaction involving the internal region of the nucleus. For this purpose we have used the well-known R matrix theory.[6] There are some fundamental problems associated with the R-matrix, particularly when a two-level formula is required. I will mention some of these problems as they arise in the following examples but will avoid a lengthy discussion of the details of the R-matrix formalism.

The $C^{12}(p, p)C^{12}$ experiment was undertaken as an extension of earlier (p,γ) work[7] and was intended to provide more accurate values for the level parameters of the two often-studied states at 3.5 MeV excitation in N^{13}. The width of each of these levels is greater than their separation and our $C^{12}(p,\gamma)N^{13}$ work indicated that the level parameters should be more accurately determined. The previous measurements from elastic proton scattering had been made by the Wisconsin group[8] and analysed by Jackson and Galonsky in 1953.[9] Their measurements were made at four scattering angles the lowest of which was 106°. Our measurements were made at eight scattering angles between 25° and 125° over the energy range from E_p = 1.5 MeV to E_p = 3.0 MeV. In the analysis of this experiment a one-level approximation is all that is required for the theoretical fits. In order to accurately reproduce the measured absolute cross section in the vicinity of the 1.7 MeV anomaly it is necessary that the theoretically computed cross section include a term for the broad $J^{\pi} = 1/2^{+}$ resonance at E_p = 0.461 MeV. We did not observe this resonance but used parameners measured by previous investigators. With the previously reported resonance parameter values as a starting point we searched by trial and error for the best-fit. The theoretical computations were performed on the University of Maryland IBM 7094 which was programmed to plot the calculated cross section for three different inputs together with the experimentally measured value. It was therefore easy to select by visual inspection the best of the three fits on a particular run at a given angle. During the initial stages of the search there were ambiguities in selecting the overall best fit because the best set at one angle might be the worst at some other angle. However, as the fits were improved, the improvement occurred at all angles. Over the entire range of the experiment, our final fit was well within the 7% total error which we assign to our experimental values. A comparison of the level parameters obtained in the two analyses are shown in Table 1. The energy measurement differences are not particularly significant--there appears to be a shift of about 10 keV in the calibration curves of the two experiments. It is interesting to note that the measured resonance energy separations of the two levels differ by 2 keV in the two analyses. Our fit indicates a separation of 48 keV, while the Jackson and Galonsky fit is for a 50 keV separation. Although a difference of 2 keV in the separation of two levels only 50 keV apart does not seem at first consideration to be easily observed, the effect of changing this separation is quite apparent in the theoretically calculated cross section. With sufficiently accurate experimental data, one can make use of rather subtle variations in the shape of the anomaly which occur for relatively small changes in the level parameters. We have quoted a conservative ± 2 keV for our measurement of this energy difference. Examples of the data used in this experiment are shown in Figures 3 and 4. These data were taken at center-of-mass scattering angles of 54.7° and 90°, zeros of P_2 and P_{odd} respectively. The solid curve is the theoretical fit obtained with our level parameters, the dotted line is the fit using the Jackson and Galonsky parameters. It should be noted that neither theoretical curve has been normalized to the experiment in any way. The theoretical cross section is computed from the input resonance parameters without fiddling with the hard-sphere phase shifts, interaction radius, etc. Their fit has not been shifted to match our energy calibration. It might have been better to have done so in order to compare the two fits, particularly since the combined energy error in both experiments could almost account for the difference. It should be obvious, however, that shifting the data is not sufficient to account entirely for the difference in the two fits.

The C^{13} experiment was undertaken in order to fill a gap in elastic scattering data just below E_p = 2 MeV and to reinvestigate the adjacent energy regions with the hope of either correcting or verifying the conclusions of previous investigators.[10-13] We were also looking for some new levels which had been reported from (p,γ) work--this proved to be a pipedream.

Because of the close proximity of levels with the same J^π value, a two-level formula was used in the analysis. This was programmed for the 7094 and the output format was much like the C^{12} single-level program. In addition to an order of magnitude increase in complication caused by the use of a two-level formula instead of a single-level, the extended energy range and multiple resonances resulted in a time-and paper-consuming computer project. Typical data with a near-final fit are shown in Figures 5 and 6. I should point out again that there is no arbitrary normalization between experiment and theory. The magnitude of the theoretical cross section is a result of level parameter choices.

The final results of this study were to confirm previous J^π

assignments for five of the observed resonances and to change the previous assigned J^{π} values for two resonances. The two changes occur for the E_p = 1.54 MeV resonance and the E_p = 1.98 MeV resonance. These correspond to excitation energies of 8.98 MeV and 9.39 MeV respectively.

Figure 7 shows the data for the 1.54-MeV resonance at $\theta = 125.3°$ with several theoretical curves. The previous J^{π} assignment for this state was 1^+. I think it is evident from the 1^+ fits that this assignment is in error. The 2^+ curve gives a good fit and analyses at other angles lead to a firm 2^+ assignment. As can be seen from the figure the addition of $\ell = 3$ results in a somewhat inferior fit at this angle. The data obtained at other angles were equally inconclusive on this point and we are unable to make any statement about the relative strength of $\ell = 1$ and $\ell = 3$ in forming this state.

A sample of the data for the 1.98-MeV resonance, taken at 90° is shown in Figure 8. The adjacent $J^{\pi} = 2^-$ 2.11-MeV resonance is also shown. The previous 1^- assignment for this state does not fit the data at any angle. The best fits to the data occur for either 2^- or 3^- formed by $\ell = 2$ protons. The strong interference with the 2.11-MeV resonance expected for the 2^- assignment is evident from the figure. Of particular note is difference in the $J^{\pi} = 2^-$ curves A, B, and C. Curve A results from a pure channel spin = 1 assumption. With a 50% admixture of S = 0, Curve B is obtained. Curve C is the result of simply changing the sign on one of channel spin reduced width amplitudes in the Curve B fit. The best fit occurs with a 40%-60% mixture of S = 0 and 1 which corresponds to pure $d_{3/2}$ capture if the 2^- assignment is correct. We were, however, unable to rule out the 3^- possibility.

Well, here again as with the C^{12} experiment, I hope I have been able to give some idea of what is involved in the analysis of these (p, p) experiments. It is apparent that with sufficiently accurate data, definite conclusions can be drawn even concerning details other than J^{π} values, energies, and widths.

The C^{14} experiment is now being completed. The targets have a lower enrichment than was the case with C^{12} and C^{13} and this has made the experimental work more difficult. The most important difference however is in the analysis of the data. As with the C^{13} analysis, it is necessary to use a two-level formula because of the close proximity of levels having the same spin and parity. In addition, the computer program which Mr. Harris has prepared can handle an open channel other than the proton channel and the R-matrix boundary condition parameter can be changed externally. The possibility of varying the boundary condition has proven to be quite useful in this particular analysis.

The need for investigating the boundary condition parameter arose when using our usual boundary condition choice $B_\ell = -\ell$. Mr. Harris found that it was difficult to reproduce the experimental cross section behavior near the weak (Γ_p = 8 keV, Γn = 33 keV) $J^\pi = 1/2^+$, s-wave resonance at E_p = 1.3 MeV which overlaps with the broad (Γ_p' = 470 keV, Γ_n' = 5 keV) $J^\pi = 1/2^+$, s-wave resonance at E_p = 1.5 MeV. To be more specific, with $B_\ell = -\ell$, the only fit which appeared to reasonably reproduce the experiment occurred for unrealistic values of the level widths (Γ_p = 214 keV, Γ_n = 65 keV and Γ_p' = 138 keV, Γ_n' = 3.6 keV). The choice of B was then investigated and found to have a marked effect on the ability to fit the data if one restricts the width values by requiring that they correspond (at least approximately) to previously reported (more-or-less single-level fit) values. The final choice of B which Mr. Harris has decided to use, and which does result in a fit for realistic Γ's is that B equals the shift factor evaluated midway between the characteristic energies of the two levels. With this choice of B, when the levels are close together, the level shifts approach zero and the boundary condition is similar to one commonly used in single-level analyses, namely, B is equal to the shift function evaluated at the resonance energy. With Mr. Harris' choice of B we think we have a good boundary condition for overlapping levels in the sense that the best fits will occur for widths which appear to agree with single-level analyses. For levels which are well separated the partial widths are less sensitive to the choice B and therefore we are not strongly motivated to re-analyze the C^{13} data.

DTM Polarization Experiments

I would now like to discuss briefly some data from an entirely different type of elastic scattering experiment--the scattering of polarized protons. The experiments with which I am most familiar (because of their relation to our C^{12} experiment) are those of Dr. Brown and co-workers at the

Department of Terrestrial Magnetism of the Carnegie Institution of Washington.

For those who are not familiar with the DTM laboratory, I would recommend a visit. Their vertical Van de Graaff, first operated in 1938, is unique in many respects. Because of its large size, sturdy construction, and electrical power capabilities, it was well suited to accept a large and complicated apparatus such as a polarized ion source. As part of the ion source installed at DTM there are three oil diffusion pumps (650 1/sec), a 500 1/sec booster pump, and two ion getter pumps. All of this, together with the necessary magnets etc. is located within the high-voltage terminal. With some rearrangement there would probably still be room for a good sized pickup truck.

The source installed at DTM was built at the University of Basel, Switzerland and has been used for deuterons [14] as well as protons.[15, 16] The polarization of the proton beam is 0.480±0.004. Beam currents of a few nanoamperes are used.

In the most recently reported experiments,[17] Trachslin and Brown have measured the left-right asymmetries for protons elastically scattered from C^{12} and O^{16}. The measurements were made for proton energies from 1.5 to 3.0 MeV at fourteen scattering angles between 30° and 140° . Using their measured polarizations and experimental values for the differential cross section measured previously by other investigators, they have performed a phase shift analysis by searching for the sets of phases which best satisfy both the polarization and cross section data. This is done by locating for each energy the minima in an error function which takes into account both types of data. As part of this study they have investigated the number of minima in this function and find that there are 18 sets which satisfy to some degree the $C^{12}(p, p)C^{12}$ cross section data alone, and 3 sets which satisfy to the same degree the polarization data alone. There is, however, only one set which satisfies both types of data. Similar results are reported for the $O^{16}(p, p)O^{16}$ phase shift search and again only one set survives the selection process.

Figure 9 shows the measured polarizations in the $C^{12}(p, p)C^{12}$ reaction together with the polarizations calculated from the best set of phases. These phases are shown in Figure 10 together with the phases calculated from the resonance parameters measured in the Maryland C^{12}+p experiment just discussed. We consider the two experiments to be in excellent agreement.

I consider these polarization experiments, and as a matter of fact, most polarization experiments, to be "precision" experiments simply because a great deal of experimental finesse is required to obtain these data and, in addition, when analyzed, they usually prove to be quite sensitive to input parameter assumptions. In the present C^{12} and O^{16} experiments I should mention that the uncertainty in the polarization measurements vary from about 1% to several hundred percent depending upon scattering angle and measured polarization. The energy uncertainty in the polarized beam is ± 7 keV.

Duke Homogenizer and Cryogenic Target Chamber

Although I attempted in the introduction to make it clear that I was in no sense surveying the field of elastic scattering, I cannot get away without making at least some reference to the Duke Homogenizer and "Cryogenic Target Chamber"--particularly with Professor Bilpuch as a Session Chairman. Both of these systems have been thoroughly described in the literature, the Homogenizer having been reported in 1958 and the target chamber in 1964,[18, 19] and I would only like briefly to outline their function and then refer all questions to our chairman. I will not comment on the elastic scattering experimental results since they fall more properly within Dr. Morrison's talk which follows.

Briefly, then, the purpose of the Homogenizer is to remove the time-dependent energy fluctuations from the Van de Graaff beam. This is accomplished by putting a correlated time-dependent correction voltage on the target. The layout for the apparatus is shown in Figure 11. The HH^+ beam serves as a monitor for the H^+ energy. After separation of the two beams in the analyzing magnet, the HH^+ beam is deflected 90° by the electrostatic analyzer. A displacement of the beam at the exit of the analyzer resulting from an energy fluctuation is picked up as an imbalance at the image slits. The image slits signal difference is amplified and this drives a triode whose plate, operating at about +3.5 kV, is directly tied to the scattering chamber. A fraction of the plate voltage is picked off with a voltage divider and fed back to the outer analyzer plate--removing the need for a constant gain dc amplifier. Note that the fluctuations in H^+ beam are compensated for without any loss in intensity--by using the HH^+ beam. Usuable H^+ beams of 30 to 50 μA have been reported.

Of course, the Homogenizer is not the final solution for all energy resolution problems. There remains incoherent energy spread from the ion source, straggling of the beam in the vacuum system and target, and a Doppler spread due to motion of the target atoms. Typically, the incoherent ion source spread is 50 to 100 eV and the system straggling is less. The target thickness and Doppler spread however, are quite large and they usually limit the overall experimental resolution.

The Duke group has been able to beat this rap by constructing a Cryogenic Target Chamber. This is a windowless gas target chamber which operates down to 4° K, the operating temperature depending upon the target gas liquification point. The target thicknesses produced are uniform and on the order of 100 eV. The low counting rates one would ordinarily associate with such a thin target are obviated by the use of large currents, which are possible (at least partially) because of the Homogenizer and permissible because of very small energy loss and lack of any target backing. As an example of Duke data taken with the Homogenizer and Cryogenic Target Chamber, I had originally intended to show some $A^{40}(p, p)A^{40}$ data from their paper on isobaric analogue resonances in K^{41}.[20] However, Dr. Bilpuch has brought some more recent data to the symposium and has graciously consented to allow me to use them in this paper. I believe that Dr. Morrison will discuss the $A^{40}(p, p)^{40}$ data in the following talk.

Figure 12 shows the data for elastic scattering of protons from Ne^{22} in the energy range from near 1.0 MeV to just over 1.95 MeV.[21] The discontinuities at several points result from the fact that the runs have not yet been normalized. I understand that the experiment is still underway. Figure 13 shows on an expanded scale several regions of the excitation curve together with a theoretical single-level fit for four of the anomalies. The experimental resolution is 200 to 250 eV.

Finally, Figure 14 shows what I think is the current world record for the smallest experimentally measured width for an anomaly in a proton elastic scattering experiment.[22] The full width at half maximum is 120 eV. This width is essentially all attributable to the ion source incoherent energy spread (about 100 eV) together with target Doppler spread, target thickness, and natural width. Even though these results demonstrate remarkabl resolution, the Duke group will soon push it even further with the installation of a duoplasmatron ion source. The incoherent energy spread will then be reduced to 25 eV or less. Major increases in resolution beyond that point will become somewhat more difficult and will require the use of new techniques. If the requirement arises, however, it appears that experimental resolutions on the order of $\sim$10 eV could eventually be obtained in this type of experiment.

SUMMARY

I intended in this short talk to present some idea of what is involved in several types of elastic proton scattering experiments. There is no particular central theme or important point that I want to convey unless it is that there are numerous ways in which the data and analysis of elastic scattering experiments can be improved. There are, of course, many experiments which would serve to illustrate this point. I have simply selected several with which I am familiar.

Table 1

Resonance parameters for the 2nd and 3rd excited states of N^{13} as determined by C^{12} proton elastic scattering.

	$J^{\pi} = 3/2^{-}$ level		$J^{\pi} = 5/2^{+}$ level	
	Ref. 9	Ref. 1	Ref. 9	Ref. 1
Resonance Energy, Ep(MeV)	1.698	1.686	1.748	1.734
N^{13} Excitation Energy (MeV)	3,511	3,501	3.558	3.546
γ^2 (MeV cm x 10^{-13})	0.440	0.515	2.92	3.55
Γ (keV)	55	63	61	74

References

1. J. C. Armstrong, M. J. Baggett, W. R. Harris, and V. A. Latorre, Phys. Rev. 144, 823 (1966).

2. V. A. Latorre and J. C. Armstrong, Bull. Am. Phys. Soc. 9, 418 (1964).

3. V. A. Latorre and J. C. Armstrong, Phys. Rev. 144, 891 (1966).

4. W. R. Harris and J. C. Armstrong, Bull. Am. Phys. Soc. 12, 516 (1967).

5. V. A. Latorre, PhD thesis, University of Maryland, 1965 (unpublished).

6. A. M. Lane and R. G. Thomas, Rev. Mod. Phys. 30, 257 (1958)

7. F. C. Young, J. C. Armstrong, and J. B. Marion, Nucl. Phys. 44, 486 (1963).

8. H. L. Jackson, A. I. Galonsky, F. J. Eppling, R. W. Hill, E. Goldberg, and J. R. Cameron, Phys. Rev. 89, 365 (1953).

9. H. L. Jackson and A. I. Galonsky, Phys. Rev. 89, 370 (1953).

10. E. A. Milne, Phys. Rev. 93, 762 (1954).

11

11. D. Zipoy, G. Freier, and K. Famularo, Phys. Rev. 106, 93 (1957).

12. D. M. Zipoy, Phys. Rev. 110, 995 (1958).

13. E. Kashy, R. R. Perry, R. L. Steele, and J. R. Risser, Phys. Rev. 122, 884 (1961).

14. L. Brown, H. A. Christ, and H. Rudin, Nucl. Phys. 79, 459 (1966).

15. L. Brown and W. Trachslin, Nucl. Phys. A90, 334 (1967).

16. L. Brown, W. Haeberli, and W. Trachslin, Nucl. Phys. A90, 339 (1967).

17. W. Trachslin and L. Brown, to be published ("Polarization and Phase Shifts in $C^{12}(p, p)C^{12}$ and $O^{16}(p, p)O^{16}$ from 1.5 to 3 MeV").

18. P. B. Parks, H. W. Newson, and R. M. Williamson, Rev. Sci. Instr. 29, 834 (1958).

19. P. B. Parks, P. M. Beard, E. G. Bilpuch, and H. W. Newson, Rev. Sci. Instr. 35, 549, (1964).

20. G. A. Keyworth, G. C. Kyker, Jr., E. G. Bilpuch, and H. W. Newson, Phys. Letters 20, 281 (1966).

21. G. A. Keyworth, G. C. Kyker, H. W. Newson, E. G. Bilpuch, and P. Wilhjelm, Bull. Am. Phys. Soc. 12, 585 (1967).

22. E. G. Bilpuch, private communication.

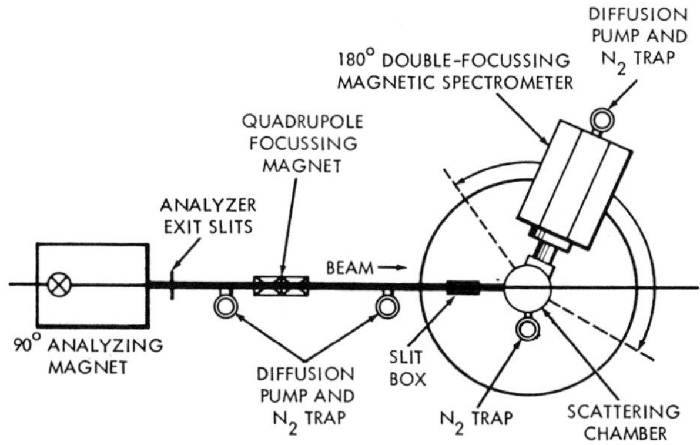

Fig. 1 - Schematic floor plan for University of Maryland proton elastic scattering experiments.

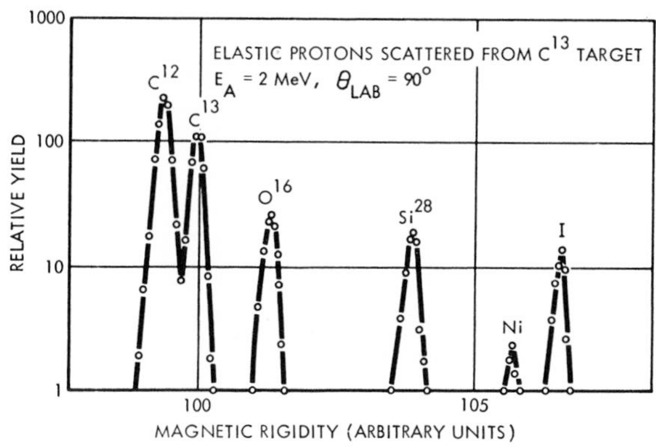

Fig. 2 - C^{13} target 'profile' showing the elastically scattered proton peaks from target contaminants.

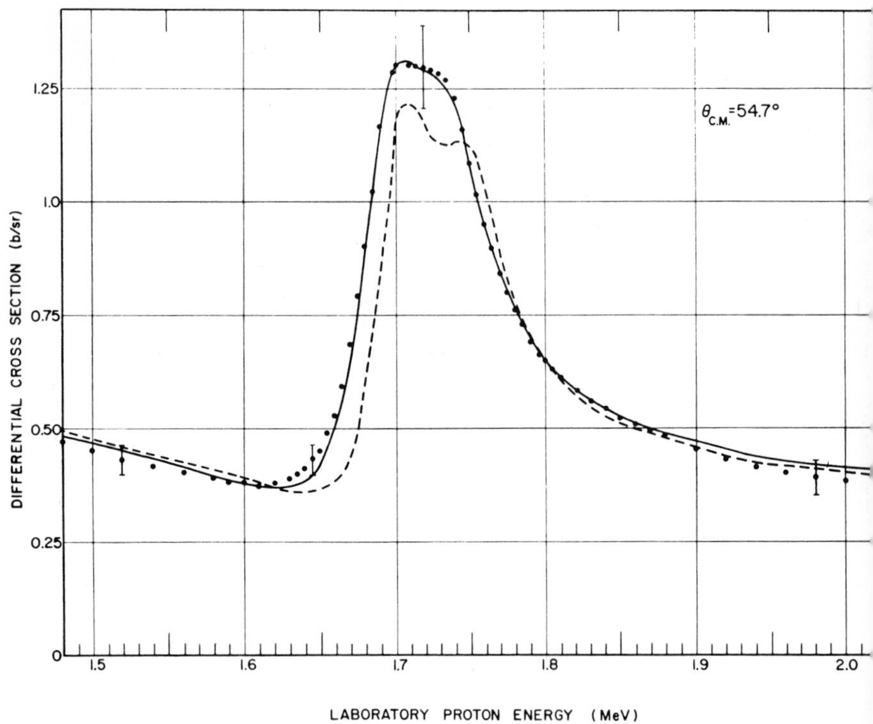

Fig. 3 - Representative data obtained at θ (c.m.) = 54.7° from the $C^{12}(p, p)C^{12}$ experiment at University of Maryland. Experimental data points are displayed as closed circles. Several representative error bars are shown. The solid curve is the Maryland fit (ref. 1). The dashed curve is the Wisconsin fit (ref. 9).

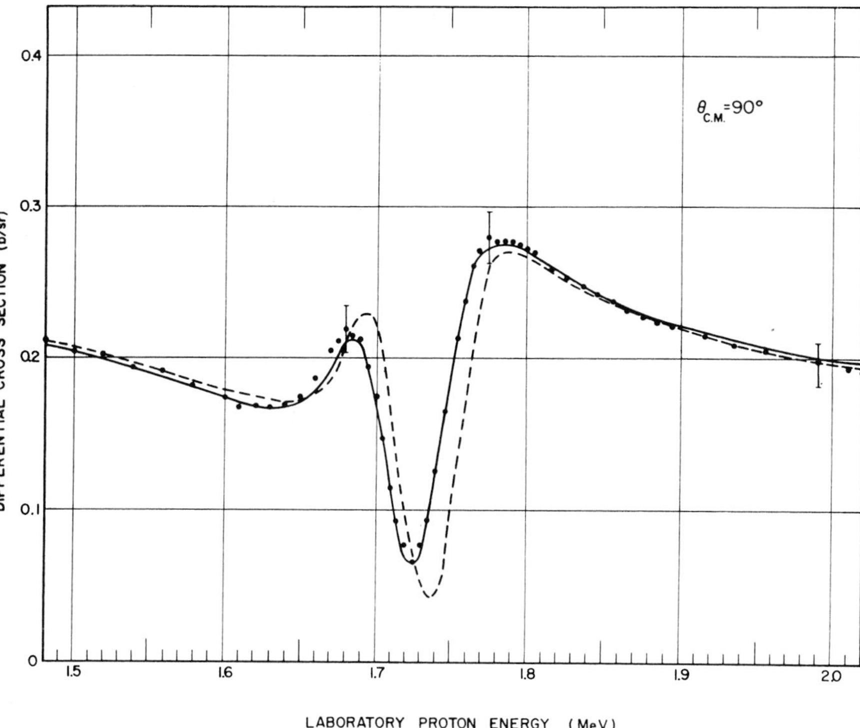

Fig. 4 - Representative data obtained at θ (c.m.) = 90° from the $C^{12}(p, p)C^{12}$ experiment at University of Maryland. Experimental data points are displayed as closed circles. Several representative error bars are shown. The solid curve is the Maryland theoretical fit (ref. 1). The dashed curve is the Wisconsin fit (ref. 9).

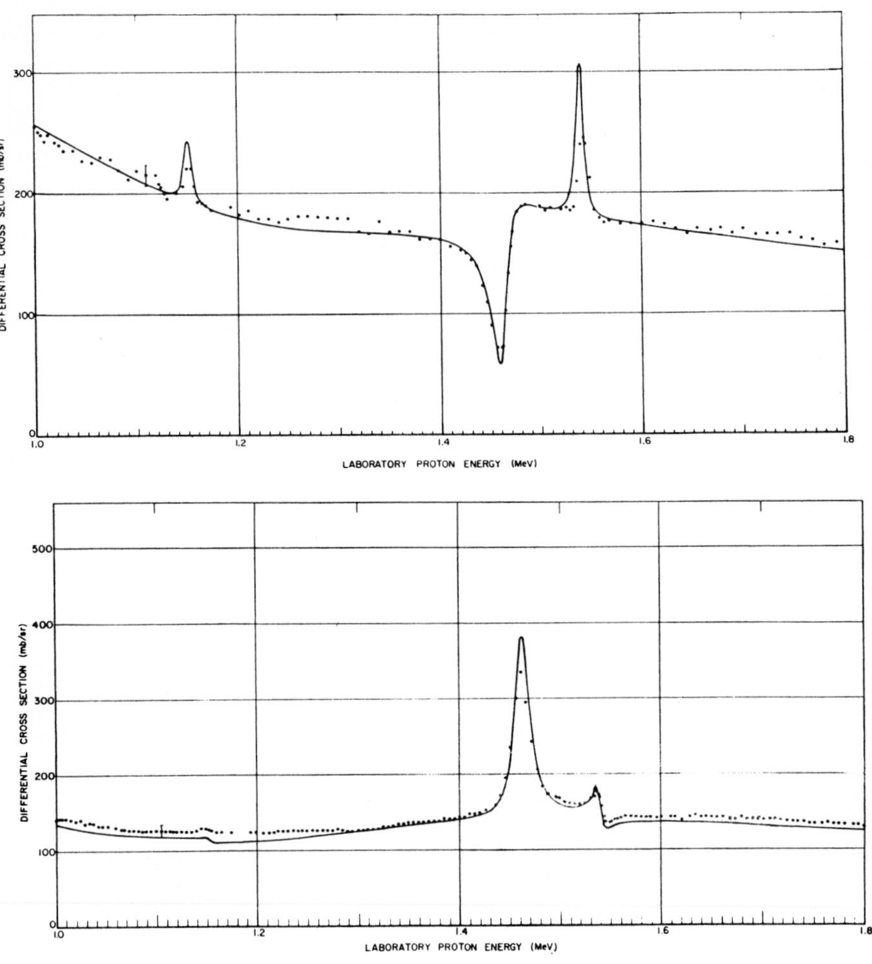

Fig. 5 - Representative data from the $C^{13}(p, p)C^{13}$ experiment at University of Maryland from E_p = 1.0 MeV to 1.8 MeV. Data in the top half of the figure were taken at θ (c.m.) = 90° while those in the bottom half are for θ (c.m.) = 125.3°. The solid curve in the "near-final" theoretical two-level fit. (From ref. 3.)

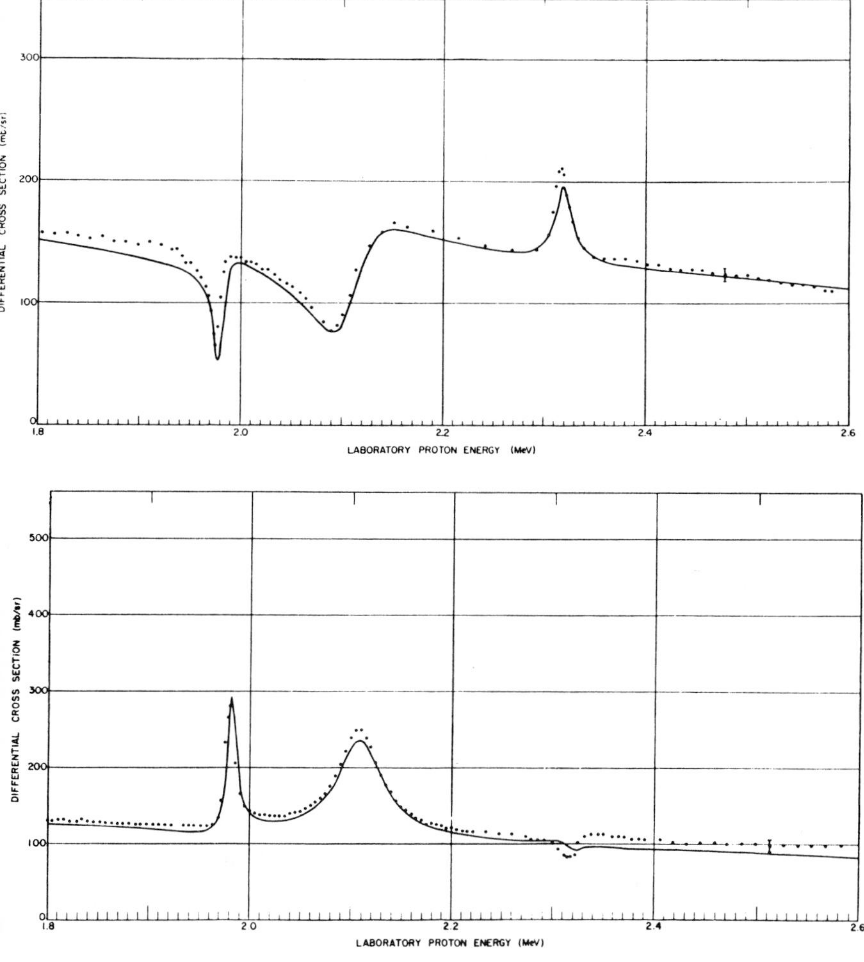

Fig. 6 - This is a continuation of the data shown in Figure 5.

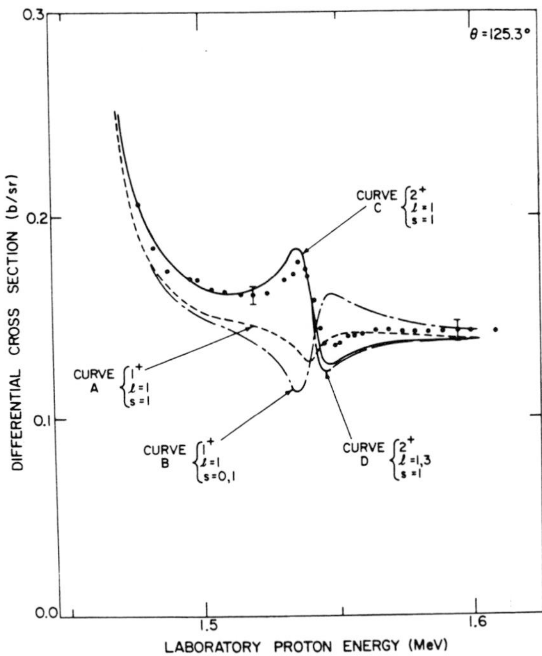

Fig. 7 - Differential cross section for elastic scattering of protons from C^{13} at the 1.54-MeV resonance. θ (c.m.) = 125.3° . The experimental data points are shown as closed circles. The four curves are the theoretical fits obtained for different assumptions concerning the formation of the level. The symbol ℓ denotes the angular momentum of the proton and s is the channel spin. The channel spin mixing indicated for curve B is 50-50 (that is, the assumed reduced widths for S=0 and 1 are equal), as is the ℓ -mixin in Curve D. (From ref. 3.)

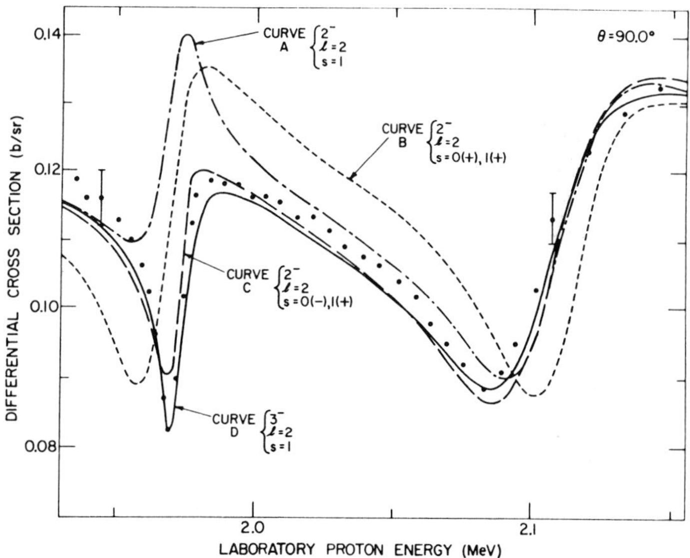

Fig. 8 - Differential cross section at θ (c.m.) = 90° for elastic scattering of protons from C^{13} near the 1.98- and 2.11-MeV resonances. The 2.11-MeV resonance has $J\pi=2^-$. The four curves are the theoretical fits obtained for different assumptions concerning the formation of the level. The reduced width mixtures in curves B and C are 50-50, the only difference in the parameters for these two curves is a sign change in the reduced width amplitude (denoted by + and - in the figure). (From ref. 3.)

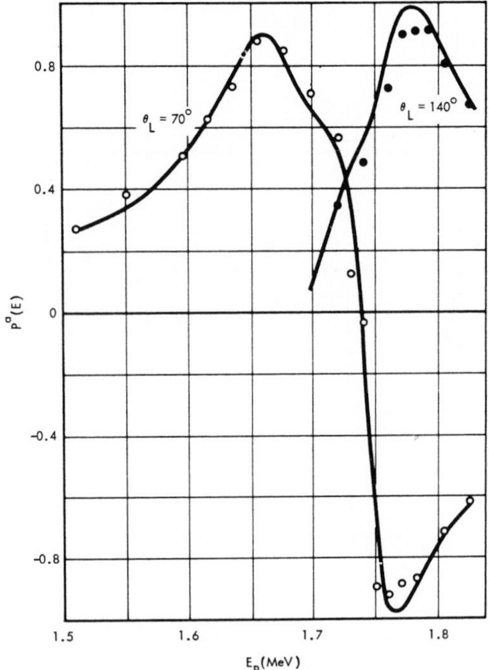

Fig. 9 - Measured (circles) and calculated (solid line) polarization excitation functions for the $C^{12}(p, p)C^{12}$ reaction. (From ref. 17.)

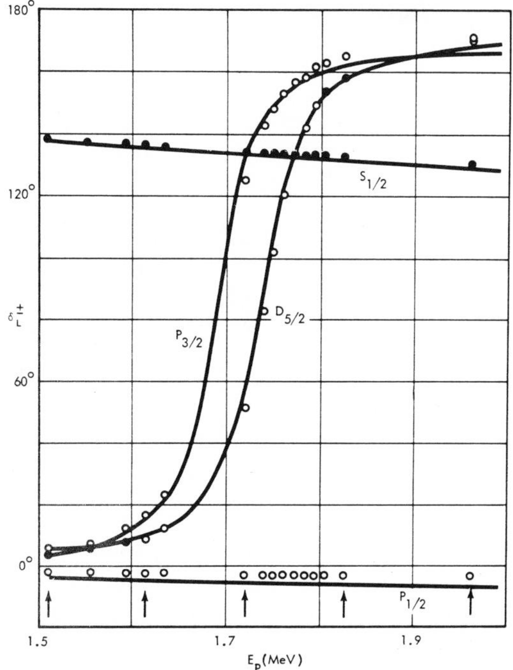

Fig. 10 - Phase shifts as a function of energy for the $C^{12}(p, p)C^{12}$ reaction. The solid line is based on resonance parameters obtained in ref. 1. The circles indicate the values for phases obtained from polarization and cross section data by searching for the best $p_{3/2}$ and $d_{5/2}$ phases while setting all others at values averaged with smooth curves from previous searches. Polarization is not used in the search between E_p = 1.74 and 1.78 MeV. (From ref. 17.)

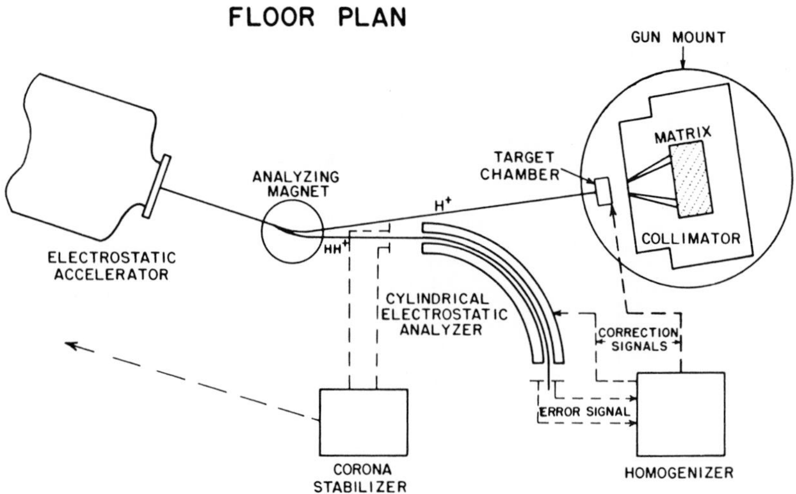

Fig. 11 - Floor plan of the Duke Ne experiments. The HH^+ beam is used for energy control and calibration and as the source of an error signal which is fed back to the target to cancel fluctuations in the machine energy.

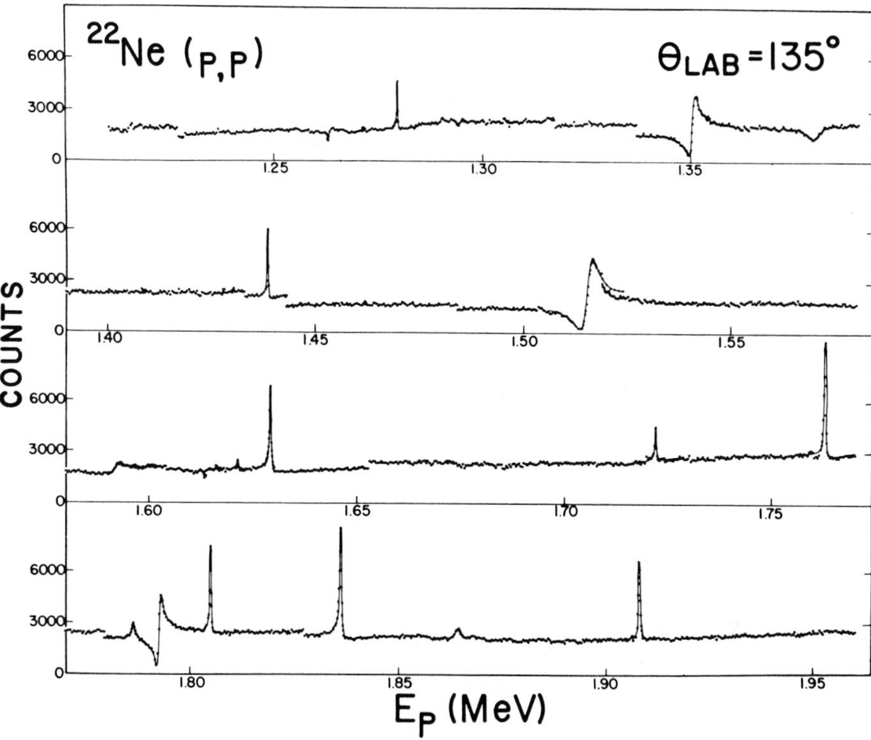

Fig. 12 - The Ne^{22}(p, p) data in the neighborhood of the expected analogue of the fourth excited state of Ne^{23}. The data are unnormalized. The total span is composed of many runs, each of which has a different relative yield due to variations in integrated beam current, target thickness, and geometry.

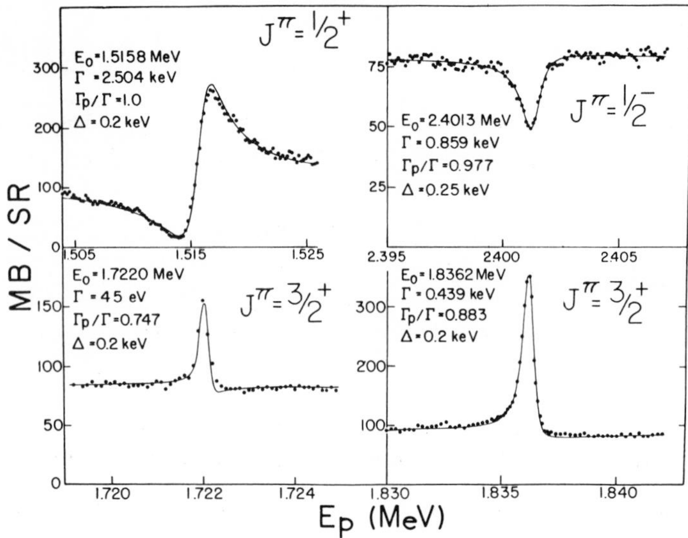

Fig. 13 - Some tentative computer-generated single-level fits for the Duke Ne data. The solid curves are theoretical fits using the indicated parameters. The experimental resolution is indicated by the symbol Δ. A value for R_0 of 1.4 fm was used in calculating the hard sphere phase shifts. These measurements were all made at a laboratory angle of 135°.

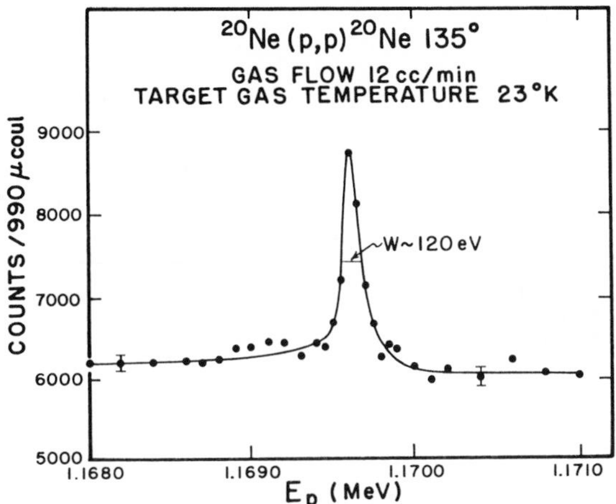

Fig. 14 - A narrow resonance at E* = 3.56 MeV in Na^{21} previously unobserved in the elastic scattering of protons by Ne^{20}. The total effective resolution available in the Duke measurements is demonstrated. This effective energy spread is due primarily to the incoherent energy spread in the proton beam but there are smaller contributions from target thickness, Doppler broadening and the natural width of the resonance.

ANALOG-STATE EXPERIMENTS

George C. Morrison

Argonne National Laboratory
Argonne, Illinois

Introduction

The occurrence of isobaric analog states in light nuclei has been known for a long time. However, I am sure you are all aware of the impact of their discovery[1] in heavy nuclei. It may have been thought that incident energies higher than those considered at this symposium would be necessary for their excitation in the heavier nuclei. This paper will attempt to show that this is not so, although some limitations are obviously imposed by the energy restrictions. In particular, these limitations preclude a comprehensive review; instead the approach will be to present specific examples that illustrate (a) the relevance of the study of analog states to low-energy experiments and (b) the information that can be obtained therefrom. The majority of these experiments will involve their observation in proton-induced reactions in which unbound analog states are excited as states in the compound nucleus and show up as resonances in the various reactions. Their observation in transfer reactions will be limited to a discussion of the (d,n) reaction. Charge-exchange reactions such as the (p,n) reaction (in which they were first observed in heavy nuclei) do not occur at low energies.

Before beginning detailed consideration of experiments involving isobaric analog states, some general comments concerning the importance of such states may be appropriate. In the first place, the Coulomb energy

---

*Work performed under the auspices of the U.S. Atomic Energy Commission.

difference (which arises from changing a neutron into a proton to form the analog state) can be computed from the observed position of the analog state. Such information is important for attempts to explain the systematic behavior of the Coulomb energy difference in terms of the configurations of the levels.[2] In the second place, their observation in nuclear reactions has proved important in stimulating and extending theories of nuclear reactions. However, we shall discover that their greatest importance is in nuclear spectroscopy. Being high-energy states whose structures are nearly identical to those of clearly identified low-lying states of the isobaric nucleus, they escape the general complexity usually associated with high-energy states. Particle widths of low-lying states can be directly inferred from the decay properties of their analog states. In addition, the existence of such simple states at high excitation energy is a great convenience in the study of lower lying states in the residual nucleus to which they decay.

Excitation of Analog States in the Compound Nucleus

Before discussing specific reactions, I would like to discuss first some general features of isobaric analog resonances. Figure 1 is a schematic diagram showing excitation of isobaric analog states in the compound nucleus. These states are formed by adding a proton to the target nucleus A and are the analogs (having the same isobaric spin) of the low-lying states in the nucleus formed by adding a neutron to the target [e.g., in a (d, p) reaction]. It is found that for all but the lightest nuclei, excitation energies of the analog states above the analog ground state are closely comparable to those of the corresponding low-lying levels in the analog nucleus. This feature, which is a consequence of the neutron excess in nuclei, is an obvious aid in the identification of corresponding analog states.

The analog states are shown as occurring at an excitation energy corresponding to a continuum of densely spaced and overlapping levels of lower T. This is the case for heavy nuclei. In lighter nuclei the analog states occur at progressively lower energy. At these low excitations the background states are less densely spaced and more narrow, so that for $A \lesssim 40$ the analog states can often be resolved experimentally. That they are observed as sharp resonances in the continuum is due to two reasons: (1) neutron decay of these states is T-forbidden, involving a change of isobaric spin $\Delta T = \frac{3}{2}$, as can be seen from the figure, and (2) states of similar configuration but lower T with which mixing might occur are much lower in energy—particularly for heavy nuclei.

The energy relations pertaining to the excitation of the ground-state analog resonance are shown schematically in Fig. 2. It is clear that the relation $E_p^{c.m.} = E_c - S_n$ holds, where E_c is the Coulomb energy difference and S_n is the neutron separation energy in the analog nucleus. It has been found[3] that E_c increases with A in good agreement with the empirical relation $E_c = 1.448(\overline{Z}/A^{1/3}) - 1.032$. The separation energy S_n is known to vary over the periodic table, exhibiting the effects of shell closure, of odd or even neutron number, and of varying neutron number in the same isotope. However, the general trend in S_n is a gradual decrease with increasing A. The requirement for a resonance experiment to be possible is that $E_p^{c.m.}$ be positive. For light elements $E_c < S_n$, so that the analogs of low-lying states cannot be excited in resonance reactions. Around $A \approx 40$—60, $E_c \approx S_n$ and resonance experiments involving low-lying analogs become energetically possible. Higher lying analog states may still be observed as resonances in lighter nuclei.

The observation of analog resonances also depends on penetration of the Coulomb barrier. Since C.B. $\approx Z/A^{1/3}$ and S_n decreases with A, the proton bombarding energy increases more rapidly than the barrier height. For heavy nuclei with $A \gtrsim 140$, $E_p^{c.m.}$ becomes greater than the Coulomb barrier. However, for the energies that are the concern of the symposium, $E_p \lesssim 5$ MeV, observation of resonances is limited to nuclei with $A \lesssim 100$; and for these nuclei, analog resonances are excited below the Coulomb barrier.

1. Elastic Proton Scattering

a. Gross Structure. Since analog states were first observed in proton elastic scattering,[4] nuclei investigated by this means are now very numerous and range over most of the periodic table. A typical excitation function taken at high energies is shown in Fig. 3 for scattering on Te^{130} at different angles.[5] Several analog resonances can be observed. The shape of an analog resonance is mainly due to interference between the potential-scattering amplitude (pure Coulomb at low energies) and a Breit-Wigner resonance amplitude. At low energies, at which the neutron channel is closed, compound elastic scattering may also contribute. A recent analysis[6] of resonances observed in low-energy proton scattering on Ca^{46} attempts to take the latter effect explicitly into account.

It was soon realized that the analysis of such resonances should give information similar to that from the (d, p) stripping reaction. Because of the term $P_\ell(\cos\theta)$ in the resonance amplitude, the ℓ value of the captured proton can be assigned from the vanishing of the resonance at particular angles (on the assumption that the spin-flip contribution is negligible), just as the ℓ value of the captured neutron in a stripping reaction can be obtained from the shape of the angular distribution. The elastic proton width is proportional to, and can be quantitatively related to, the reduced width, or to the spectroscopic factor S, of a level excited in the (d, p) reaction. The spectroscopic factor to be compared with that from stripping analysis is given[7] by

$$S_{pp} = (2T + 1)\, \frac{\Gamma_p^{\ell j}}{\Gamma_{SP}^{\ell j}}\,. \qquad (1)$$

That part of the expression that involves the ratio of widths derives from the definition of a spectroscopic factor. The theoretical single-particle width $\Gamma_{SP}^{\ell j}$ may be calculated from proton scattering on a real Woods-Saxon potential. The factor 2T + 1 takes account of the fact that the weight for forming a $T_>$ state by the addition of a proton is less than that by the addition of neutron.

It has been pointed out[8] that expression (1) is strictly valid only if the analog state is truly isolated. Problems arise because the analog state mixes with the surrounding states. In particular, for heavy nuclei the expression underestimates the spectroscopic factor. However, even for heavy nuclei the expression leads to ratios of spectroscopic factors in good agreement with those obtained from the (d, p) reaction. Thus a state strongly excited in the (d, p) reaction should have its analog strongly excited in the (p, p) reaction. Such a correspondence has now been demonstrated in many experiments.[9]

A comparison of spectroscopic factors from the (d, p) and (p, p) reactions on Ca^{46} is shown in Table 1.[6] Good agreement is observed. In extracting spectroscopic factors by use of Eq. (1), some advantages accrue for light nuclei. The calculated values of Γ_{SP} are sufficiently small that some of the ambiguities that arise for heavy nuclei from variation of the penetrability across a wide single-particle resonance do not occur.

An important extension to the study of resonant elastic scattering has followed from the realization that a measurement of the polarization of the elastically scattered proton can determine the J value of the resonance.[10]

b. Fine Structure. It is apparent that the analysis of an analog resonance discussed here ignores the question of the spreading of the resonance into the background state and treats only the gross-structure phenomena. Some mixing with the $T_<$ fine-structure background must exist in consequence of the observation of resonances in the (p, n) reaction. That analog resonances are complicated multilevel phenomena was first explicitly shown in a high-resolution experiment on elastic scattering on Mo^{92} below the neutron threshold.[11] Although individual levels were not resolved, it becomes apparent, as shown in Fig. 4, that the gross-structure resonance observed at 5.3 MeV in poor resolution is simply the envelope of the complicated structure observed in high resolution.

However, the most dramatic evidence of the spreading comes from the ultra-high-resolution experiments,[12] carried out at Duke University, in which the individual fine-structure states are actually resolved in proton scattering on Ar^{40}. This is shown in Fig. 5. The thick-target data (upper curve), taken previously over this region,[13] shows two resonance anomalies at 1.87 and 2.45 MeV. These can be identified as the analogs of the 1.35- and 1.87-MeV excited states in A^{41}, respectively. The two lower curves show the high-resolution data over the 1.87-MeV resonance for successively expanded regions of energy.

Simple Breit-Wigner analysis of the isolated resonances usually gives unambiguous assignments of spin, parity, and natural widths for the strong resonances. Multilevel fitting was used for the more closely spaced resonances. It was observed that the large majority of resonances in the region of 1.87 MeV (all of the resonances shown in the bottom of Fig. 5) were best fitted with $J^{\pi} = \frac{3}{2}^{-}$, and those in the region of 2.45 MeV with $J^{\pi} = \frac{1}{2}^{+}$. These values agree with the (d,p) stripping experiments[14] which assign $\ell = 1$ and 0, respectively, to the 1.35- and 1.87-MeV states in Ar^{41}.

The experiment provides more than a demonstration of the dissolution of the analog states into the background states. It also gives important information on the character of this spreading and permits theories of the spreading to be tested. Reduced widths for the proton resonances can be computed from the measured $\Gamma_p (= 2P\gamma_p^2)$. Their distributions over the resonances are shown in Fig. 6, where the differential proton strength functions of $\frac{3}{2}^{-}$ and $\frac{1}{2}^{+}$ analog resonances are plotted. By comparison, the strength of $\frac{1}{2}^{-}$ levels (not shown) is found to be distributed uniformly throughout the entire energy region. It is apparent that there is asymmetry in the enhancement of the fine structure at both resonances, the low-energy side showing increased strength.

Theoretical treatments of the problem predict this phenomenon as a natural consequence of coherent interference between the contribution to the fine-structure width from the analog state and the width of the fine-structure state in the absence of mixing.[15,16] The enhancement factor that multiplies the intrinsic width of the fine-structure state is given by an expression of the general form

$$|f|^2 = \left| \frac{E_A - E - \Delta}{E_A - E - \frac{1}{2} i\Gamma} \right|^2 . \qquad (2)$$

Good agreement with the experimental data can be obtained with such an expression (smooth curves), but the width Γ and resonance shift Δ which are deduced have different theoretical interpretations.[15,16]

The experimental results also appeared to suggest an apparent enhancement of level density in the region of an analog resonance but more detailed analysis showed the effect could be ascribed to weak levels missed off-resonance. Thus the analog resonance is seen to serve as a magnifier for the fine-structure levels in the neighborhood of the resonance, and suggests the possibility that new information on the interaction of levels and related problems may be obtained from such studies.

Finally, it should be emphasized that since the spreading is related to the entrance channel, it may be expected that the distribution of widths will be important for analog-state resonances in other proton-induced reactions.

2. Decay of Analog States

It has been stressed earlier that since an analog state is a basically simple state occurring at high excitation energies, important spectroscopic information can be obtained from the study of its decay properties. Such information may relate to the analog state (and hence to the low-lying states of which it is the analog) or to the final states in the decay. However, decay by a T-forbidden channel (such as neutron or α-particle emission) is not likely to prove an important spectroscopic tool since it arises only via isospin impurities.

a. Proton Decay (Inelastic Proton Scattering). At high energies much recent work has dealt with resonant inelastic scattering.[17] Some of the information that can be obtained is unique to such studies since excited states of the analog nucleus can be related to excited states of the target nucleus via the decay of the corresponding analog resonance as is shown in Fig. 7. In this way, the experimental equivalent of stripping or pickup reactions can be achieved for excited states.

At the low energies that are our concern here, a severe limitation on the observation of inelastic protons is imposed because of the greatly reduced penetration factors. In only a few cases have inelastic protons been studied by direct observation. In these cases, however, the low energy leads to some simplifications. The inelastic cross section has a simple Breit-Wigner shape. The value of $\Gamma_{p'}$ can readily be extracted by use of values of Γ and Γ_p derived from the corresponding elastic-scattering data. In addition, the proton decay usually involves only one ℓ value (the lowest allowed) so that the spectroscopic factor $S_{pp'}$ for that ℓ value can be obtained directly from $\Gamma_{p'}$. Inelastic scattering to the 2^+ states in Ca^{46} has been observed[6] at the two highest resonances shown in Table 1 and has been analyzed to obtain values of $S_{pp'}$.

<u>b. Neutron Decay</u>. Although analog-state resonances were first observed in the (p,n) reaction,[4] neutron decay arises only from the mixing of the analog state with the fine-structure states of lower T. In consequence, the shape of the (p,n) resonance should reflect the distribution of proton strength of the background states over the resonance. Thus the asymmetry which characterized the distribution of proton strength should again be in evidence in both the differential and integrated neutron yield over the resonance.[18] Furthermore, since the neutrons are emitted in the statistical decay of the fine-structure states, the ratio of relative intensities of the emitted neutrons should not change as the energy varies over the resonance. (Subtraction of the nonresonant background is assumed in both cases.)

The excitation function of the $Zn^{70}(p,n)Ga^{70}$ reaction[19] is shown in Fig. 8. The several prominent resonances correspond to the Ga^{71} analogs of the states in

Zn^{71}, whose relative positions are shown at the top of the figure. Each resonance shows an asymmetrical shape having a low-energy tail. Figure 9 shows the 3.80-MeV resonance in detail. The theoretical fit provides a good value of Γ but is insensitive to Δ. In addition to providing information of importance for the theory of nuclear reactions, the (p,n) reaction serves as a simple and fast way to locate analog states.

Recent experiments have also measured the spectra of emitted neutrons.[20,21] In addition to being a test of the variation of intensity of specific neutron groups over the resonance, it has been suggested[21] that the study of the neutron decay on and off resonance can lead to spin and parity assignments of the final states. The method derives from the selective enhancement of the transitions to particular final states in consequence of the unique spin of the analog resonance. It has been discussed by a previous speaker (Stelson).

As a final example of neutron decay, Fig. 10 shows the fine structure of the isobaric-analog resonance in $V^{51}(p,n)Cr^{51}$ at $E_p = 2.33$ MeV.[22] This case has been chosen since it shows an apparently asymmetrical shape reversed from the usual one, i.e., the tail is on the high-energy side. The same authors also observed a similar shape in the $V^{51}(p,\gamma)Cr^{52}$ reaction. It is not clear to the author whether this reversal is consistent with current theories—or indeed whether it is actually observed experimentally.

c. Alpha Decay. Alpha decay of an isobaric-analog state to the low-lying states of the residual nucleus is also T forbidden. Thus the situation is similar to that for neutron emission in that the emission again arises from isobaric-spin impurities. A mixing of the analog states with states of lower T should again be in evidence. Actually, however, few cases of analog resonances have been observed in the (p,α) reaction, since the effects of competition usually allow them to be observed only in light nuclei. Nevertheless, some interesting results come from such studies. For lighter nuclei the levels are narrower and more widely spaced and isospin mixing is less. Some analog states are almost pure; others may mix with only a small number of neighboring states.

One such case is the $Cl^{37}(p,\alpha)S^{34}$ reaction[23] in which a number of strong 3^- resonances in the excitation function are observed at an energy at which the analog of the second excited state in Cl^{38} should be expected to occur. [This state is the 3^- member of a $(d_{3/2})^{-3} f_{7/2}$ configuration.] The reduced strengths $\Gamma_p\Gamma_{\alpha_0}/(2\Gamma P_\ell)$, where P_ℓ is the proton penetrability, are plotted in Fig. 11. Since the Q value of the reaction is positive, Γ_p is small compared to Γ_α and the reduced strengths will be approximately equal to the proton reduced width $\Gamma_p/2P_\ell$ over most of the energy region shown. Since the proton width of an analog resonance should be much larger than those of neighboring resonances, the strong jump in the integrated reduced strength of the 3^- resonances at $E_p \approx 1.15$ MeV (lower plot) marks the occurrence of the analog state. The 2^+ resonances drawn for comparison show no such behavior. In addition, the sum of the reduced strengths over the resonance is in good agreement with the width expected from the spectroscopic factor of the second excited state as determined from the $Cl^{37}(d,p)Cl^{38}$ reaction.[24] The upper plot shows the distribution of reduced strength of the 3^- resonances and again gives evidence of an asymmetry in the distribution of proton widths.

As a final comment, it is obviously dangerous to apply the excitation of a resonance in a (p,α) reaction as a criterion for T assignments.

d. Gamma Decay. At the high energies necessary for the excitation of analog states in heavy nuclei, many particle channels are open. The heavy competition virtually eliminates the possibility of detecting any capture radiation from an analog state. However, in lighter nuclei the situation is different; the analog state occurs at lower incident energy and the competition is less. In this region they are indeed observed as resonances in the (p,γ) reaction and complement the study of these resonances in elastic proton scattering. For the case of the $f_{7/2}$ analog resonances in the 2s1d shell, the strength of the resonances in the (p,γ) reaction (large Γ_p and Γ_γ) and the simple nature of the γ decay (namely to the $f_{7/2}$ state of lower T) easily distinguish the analog state.[25,26] The wealth of spectroscopic information contained in these (and related) studies of the γ decay of the analog state has been demonstrated by a previous speaker (Harris) and will not be discussed further.

The γ-ray studies show further examples of the splitting of analog strength in lighter nuclei. An example is again found in Ar^{38}. The analog of the first excited state in Cl^{38} [the 5^- member of the $(d_{3/2})^{-3}f_{7/2}$ configuration previously mentioned] is split into two components,[27] as shown schematically in Fig. 12. The spins and parities of the 5^- and 4^- levels shown were determined by angular-correlation and polarization methods. The point of interest is that both states show an almost identical γ decay which proceeds by M1 emission entirely to the $J^\pi = 5^-$, T=1 bound states. The observation that the lower 5^- resonance is also weakly excited as a resonance in the $C^{37}(p,\alpha_0)S^{34}$ reaction[23] confirms that the resonances are indeed isospin mixed—a pure T=2 state should not decay by α-particle emission.

Another example of splitting in lighter nuclei is the analog in Sc^{49} of the $\frac{3}{2}^-$ ground state of Ca^{49} which was found to be split into two main components in elastic proton scattering.[2] In this case, γ decay of the two components of the states is completely different,[28] as shown in Fig. 13. (The experimental branching ratios are calculated on the basis of the observed γ rays only.) However, neither decay is simple and the M1 transitions do not dominate as they did in the 2s1d shell. It will be of interest, as other cases of mixing are found, to see which situation is the exception—or whether each is characteristic of its own mass region.

3. T-Forbidden Analog Resonances

A T-forbidden analog resonance is one in which the formation of the analog state in a proton-induced reaction is forbidden by isobaric-spin considerations. Figure 14 is a schematic diagram showing the restrictions applying to the excitation of $T=\frac{3}{2}$ and T=2 states. In both cases the ingoing channel is seen to be T-forbidden. In the case of the $T=\frac{3}{2}$ states, neutron emission (although T-allowed) is energetically forbidden. For the T=2 states, neutron decay may be energetically allowed but it is T-forbidden—as also is all charged-particle decay (except for the excitation of $T=\frac{3}{2}$ states with "4n+2"-type targets, which have low-lying T=1 states). Only γ decay is allowed. These factors are responsible for the extreme intrinsic sharpness of such states, their particle widths arising solely from isospin mixing. Thus their observation in resonance reactions, although difficult, can give information on isospin mixing.

These states were originally observed as states in the residual nucleus from allowed reactions, such as the (He^3, n) and (p, t) reactions,[29,30] and also from delayed proton emitters.[31] Such experiments serve to locate an approximate proton energy region at which the resonance should occur.

Since the gamma channel is the only T-allowed decay mode, the analog resonances are most likely to show up strongly in the (p, γ) reaction. The strength of the resonances, proportional to $\Gamma_{p_0}\Gamma_\gamma/\Gamma$, will usually be not much less than Γ_γ, since $\Gamma_{p_0} \lesssim \Gamma_\gamma$ would require an unreasonably high degree of isospin purity. Since the low-lying $T=\frac{3}{2}$ and T=2 states represent simple configurations, large radiation widths and strong (p, γ) resonances may be expected.

An excitation function of the $Mg^{24}(p,\gamma)Al^{25}$ reaction is shown in Fig. 15.[32] (In practice the gamma-ray yield was determined by measuring the positron activity of the residual Al^{25} nucleus between beam bursts.) Resonances corresponding to the analogs of the ground state and first excited state of Na^{25} ($T = \frac{3}{2}$) are clearly revealed. It is an advantage that a relatively thick target can be used in this work. The sharp rise in yield at the resonance energy reflects the narrow resonance width, while the magnitude of the step is proportional to the resonance strengths.

$T=\frac{3}{2}$ analog states have also been observed in proton scattering, which is twice-forbidden. Figure 16 shows[33] the same resonances as were seen above in proton scattering on Mg^{24}. Here they are extremely sharp and show up only with thin targets. Thus the (p,γ) and (p,p) reactions serve to complement each other: the (p,γ) reaction more easily locates the states and the (p,p) yields a value of Γ_p (the quantity directly related to the isospin impurity).

The γ decay of the $T=\frac{3}{2}$ states has also been observed directly[29] and useful spectroscopic information has been derived from it. Conversely, the expected characteristics of the gamma decay of the T=2 states has recently been used to locate the position of the analog resonances.[34] (Previous attempts to observe these levels as compound-nucleus resonances in proton scattering had not been successful.) Such T=2 states having $J^{\pi} = 0^+$ should preferentially cascade through the lowest $J^{\pi}=1^+$, T=1 states. The experimental results on the lowest T=2 states in Mg^{24} observed in the $Na^{23}+p$ reaction are included in Fig. 17. The upper half shows the singles gamma spectra observed in a large NaI(Tl) crystal at proton energies on and off resonance. Gamma rays of energy around 10 MeV, which are evident at the resonance energy, correspond to the decay of the T=1 states in Mg^{24} which are intermediate in the T=2 cascade. Coincidence spectra (lower half) taken at the resonance energy clearly reveal the primary gamma rays around 5 MeV in the T=2 cascade. The inset shows γ-γ correlation measurements which unambiguously define the J^{π} values of the states involved. Figure 18 summarizes the decay scheme.

Before concluding our discussion of resonances in proton-induced reactions, it is of interest to contrast the "forbidden" and "allowed" types of analog resonances. The difference is represented schematically in Fig. 19, which shows the distribution of proton reduced widths at the resonance for each case. Heavy lines represent the

$T_>$ component. In the allowed case, the $T_>$ width of the original analog state is spread out over the fine-structure states (which have only small $T_<$ widths to begin with). The result is an asymmetrical distribution of widths, as has been previously discussed. In the forbidden case, the analog state is one state whose width is derived entirely from the $T_<$ states. The form of the interaction matrix g_i which determines the mixing is the same in both cases, but clearly different effects are produced.

Excitation in the Residual Nucleus: (d,n) Reactions

This survey of the analog-state experiments that are possible within the energy domain of this symposium will be concluded by briefly considering the excitation of analog states in transfer reactions, and in particular in the (d,n) reaction (which was considered also in Session II-B:1). Since the (d,n) reaction adds a proton to the target, it can again form both $T_>$ and $T_<$ states in the final nucleus. It thus provides a convenient extension of proton-resonance experiments to the bound-state region. As before, there is a factor (2T + 1) between the spectroscopic factors derived from the (d,n) and (d,p) reactions to analog states. Such states will therefore be recognized in the (d,n) reaction by comparison with the low-lying states excited in the (d,p) reaction. [Of course, the above considerations apply also to other transfer or pickup reactions such as (He^3,d) and (He^3,α) reactions.]

Use of the (d,n) reaction has some advantage in the observation of analog states. The maximum energy dispersion of a time-of-flight system occurs at high excitation energies (which is the region of interest). The time spectrum of neutrons emitted at 0° in the $Al^{27}(d,n)Si^{28}$ reaction,[35] shown in Fig. 20, illustrates this feature. In addition, the variation of cross section with Q value is such as to considerably favor the excitation of highly excited states. This is most marked for $\ell=0$ proton transfer—as is the case for the majority of those neutron groups labeled by the corresponding excitation energy in Si^{28}. Thus weak or unobserved $\ell=0$ transfer in the (d,p) reaction may be clearly revealed in the (d,n) reaction to the analog state.

Table 2 compares the spectroscopic factors observed from the (d,n) and (d,p) reactions on Al^{27} for $\ell=0$ momentum transfer.[35] At such low incident energies, a compound-nucleus contribution $d\sigma_{CN}$ enters and was estimated by means of a Hauser-Feshbach calculation. Details of this calculation and of the DWBA analysis are given in Ref. 35. The spectroscopic factors of the analog states are found to be in good agreement. In addition, the distribution of strength to the T=0 and T=1 states in the (d,n) reaction is closely the same, as should be the case from the sum rules of MacFarlane and French[36] if the $2s_{1/2}$ orbitals are empty both for neutrons and for protons. Studies of such transfer reactions also lead conveniently to a value of the isobaric-spin splitting, from which the magnitude of the isospin potential may be obtained.[37]

Finally there would be considerable interest in a high-resolution examination of the spreading of an analog state formed in the (d,n) reaction—e.g., in the case of the ground-state analog of Ca^{49} which is observed to be split in the resonant proton scattering.

Conclusions

In this review an attempt has been made to show some of the ways in which analog states enter into nuclear reactions and some of the effects which they produce. Much of the presentation has been devoted to experiments pertinent to the theoretical understanding of these states and their effects. However, it should be stressed again that the greatest importance of the analog state to an experimentalist is in the nuclear spectroscopy which they make possible. This depends mainly on their existence and does not require a detailed theoretical description of their nature.

For the incident energy range with which this Symposium is concerned, the most fruitful source of spectroscopic information would appear to be the γ decay of the analog state. Another fruitful area of study would appear to be proton-induced reactions which are T-forbidden; in principle, these contain information directly related to isospin mixing. In practice, it is not yet clear how sensitive a test they provide.

It is also apparent that we have in a sense come full circle. Resonance theory was first developed to describe excitation functions of scattering and capture reactions at low energies. The resonances themselves were thought to have a complicated nature but such studies were justified as a means of obtaining information on the lower lying states fed by the resonance. The successful application of resonance theory in the description of the gross structure of analog states observed in heavy nuclei has served to emphasize the simple nature of the analog state. Finally, resonance physics in the lighter nuclei has been revitalized by the identification of analog states in these nuclei.

References

1. J. D. Anderson and C. Wong, Phys. Rev. Letters 7, 250 (1961).
2. K. W. Jones, J. P. Schiffer, L. L. Lee, Jr., A. Marinov, and J. L. Lerner, Phys. Rev. 145, 894 (1966).
3. D. D. Long, P. Richard, C. F. Moore, and J. D. Fox, Phys. Rev. 149, 906 (1966); J. D. Anderson, C. Wong, and J. W. McClure, ibid. 138, B615 (1965).
4. J. D. Fox, C. F. Moore, and D. Robson, Phys. Rev. Letters 12, 198 (1964).
5. J. L. Foster, Thesis, University of Texas, January 1967.
6. C. Gaarde, K. Kemp, and P. Wilhjelm, to be published.
7. L. L. Lee, Jr., A. Marinov, and J. P. Schiffer, Phys. Letters 8, 352 (1964).
8. D. Robson, in Proceedings of the Conference on Isobaric Spin in Nuclear Physics, Florida State University, Tallahassee, Florida, 17-19 March 1966, edited by J. D. Fox and D. Robson (Academic Press, New York, 1966), p. 411.

9. For example, P. Richard, C. F. Moore, J. A. Becker, and J. D. Fox, Phys. Rev. 145B, 971 (1966).
10. G. Terrell and C. F. Moore, Phys. Rev. Letters 16, 804 (1966).
11. P. Richard, C. F. Moore, J. D. Fox, and D. Robson, Phys. Rev. Letters 13, 343 (1964).
12. E. G. Bilpuch, in Ref. 8, p. 235; G. A. Keyworth, G. C. Kyker, Jr., E. G. Bilpuch, and H. W. Newson, Nucl. Phys. 89, 590 (1966).
13. A. C. L. Barnard and C. C. Kim, Nucl. Phys. 28, 428 (1961).
14. E. Kashy, A. M. Hoogenboom, and W. W. Buechner, Phys. Rev. 124, 1917 (1961).
15. D. Robson, Phys. Rev. 137, B535 (1965).
16. A. Mekjian and W. MacDonald, Phys. Rev. Letters 18, 706 (1967).
17. For example, D. L. Allan, G. A. Jones, G. C. Morrison, R. B. Taylor, and R. B. Weinberg, Phys. Letters 17, 56 (1965); S. A. A. Zaidi, P. v. Brentano, D. Riek, and J. P. Wurm, Phys. Letters 19, 46 (1965).
18. D. Robson, J. D. Fox, P. Richard, and C. F. Moore, Phys. Letters 18, 86 (1965).
19. G. P. Couchell, D. P. Balamuth, R. N. Horoshko, and G. E. Mitchell, to be published.
20. E. Finckh, U. Jahnke, and J. Wirsich, in Ref. 8, p. 713.
21. H. J. Kim, R. L. Kernell, R. L. Robinson, and C. H. Johnson, to be published.
22. E. Teranishi and B. Furubayashi, in Ref. 8, p. 641.
23. B. Bosnjakovic and C. van der Leun, Phys. Letters 23, 687 (1966).
24. J. Rapaport and W. W. Buechner, Nucl. Phys. 83, 80 (1966).
25. A. K. Hyder, Jr., and G. I. Harris, Phys. Letters 24B, 273 (1967).
26. J. Walinga and J. C. H. Oudemans, Physica, to be published.
27. F. C. Erné, W. A. M. Veltman, and J. A. J. M. Wintermans, Nucl. Phys. 88, 1 (1966).
28. C. Chasman, K. W. Jones, R. A. Ristenen, and J. T. Sample, Phys. Rev. Letters 18, 219 (1967).

29. G. T. Garvey, J. Cerny, and R. H. Pehl, Phys. Rev. Letters 12, 726 (1964).
30. E. Adelberger and A. B. McDonald, Phys. Letters 24B, 270 (1967).
31. J. C. Hardy and B. Margolis, Phys. Letters 15, 276 (1965); R. McPherson, in Ref. 8, p. 162.
32. G. C. Morrison, D. H. Youngblood, R. C. Bearse, and R. E. Segel, to be published.
33. G. M. Temmer and B. Teitelman, to be published.
34. S. Riess, W. J. O'Connell, D. W. Heikkinen, H. M. Kuan, and S. S. Hanna, to be published.
35. B. Lawergren, G. C. Morrison, and A. T. G. Ferguson, Nucl. Phys., to be published.
36. J. B. French and M. H. MacFarlane, Nucl. Phys. 26, 168 (1961).
37. A. M. Lane, Nucl. Phys. 35, 676 (1962).

TABLE 1

Comparison of Spectroscopic Factors from (p, p) and (d, p) Reactions on Ca^{46} (Ref. 6)

	Sc^{47}				Ca^{47}	
J^{π}	E_p^{lab} (MeV)	Γ (keV)	Γ_p (keV)	S_{pp}	Excitation (MeV)	S_{dp}
$\frac{3}{2}^-$	1.86	5.5	1.79	0.59	2.01	0.82
$\frac{1}{2}^-$	2.77	11.2	6.7	0.22	2.88	0.24
$\frac{1}{2}^-$	3.95	100	60	0.40	4.05	0.44

TABLE 2

Summary of Spectroscopic Information from (d, n) and (d, p) Reactions on Al^{27} for $\ell = 0$ Angular Momentum Transfer (Ref. 35)

Si^{28}					Al^{28}	
Excitation (MeV)	Excitation above g.s. analog (MeV)	$d\sigma/d\Omega$ at 0° (mb/sr)	$d\sigma_{CN}$ at 0° (mb/sr)	$(2J+1)S_{dn}$	Excitation (MeV)	$(2J+1)S_{dp}$
1.77		0.45	0.34	0.85 ± 0.2		
6.27		0.74	0.26	0.75 ± 0.1		
7.80 7.93		} 1.16	0.20	0.8 ± 0.1		
8.59		3.14	0.18	1.7 ± 0.2		
9.335 9.41	0 0.075	} 9.35	0.16	4.0 ± 0.4	0 0.031	} 5.1 ± 0.7
10.38 10.42	1.045 1.085	} 0.85	0.12	0.24 ± 0.1	1.017	0.36
11.42	2.085	1.07	0.08	0.6 ± 0.1	2.147	1.1 ± 0.2
higher states				~0.5		

$G_p(T_<) = 0.34 \pm 0.04$

$G_p(T_>) = 0.45 \pm 0.04$

$G_n = 1.2 \pm 0.2$

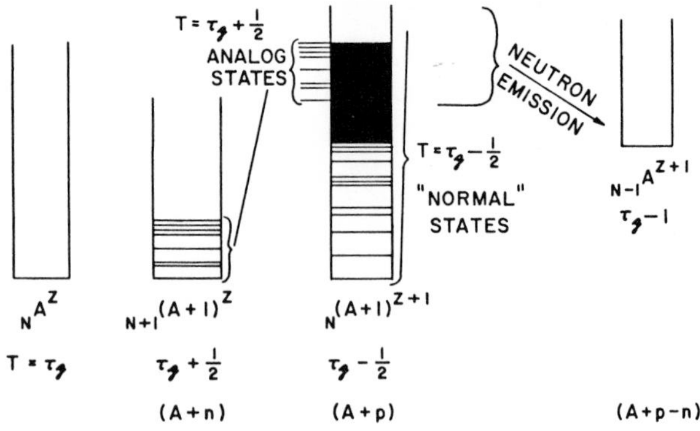

Fig. 1 Schematic diagram illustrating the relation between isobaric analog states in the nuclei A + p and A + n.

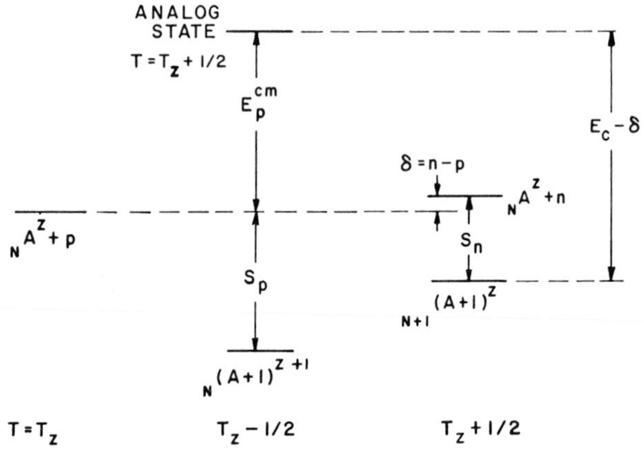

Fig. 2 Energy relations between isobaric analog states.

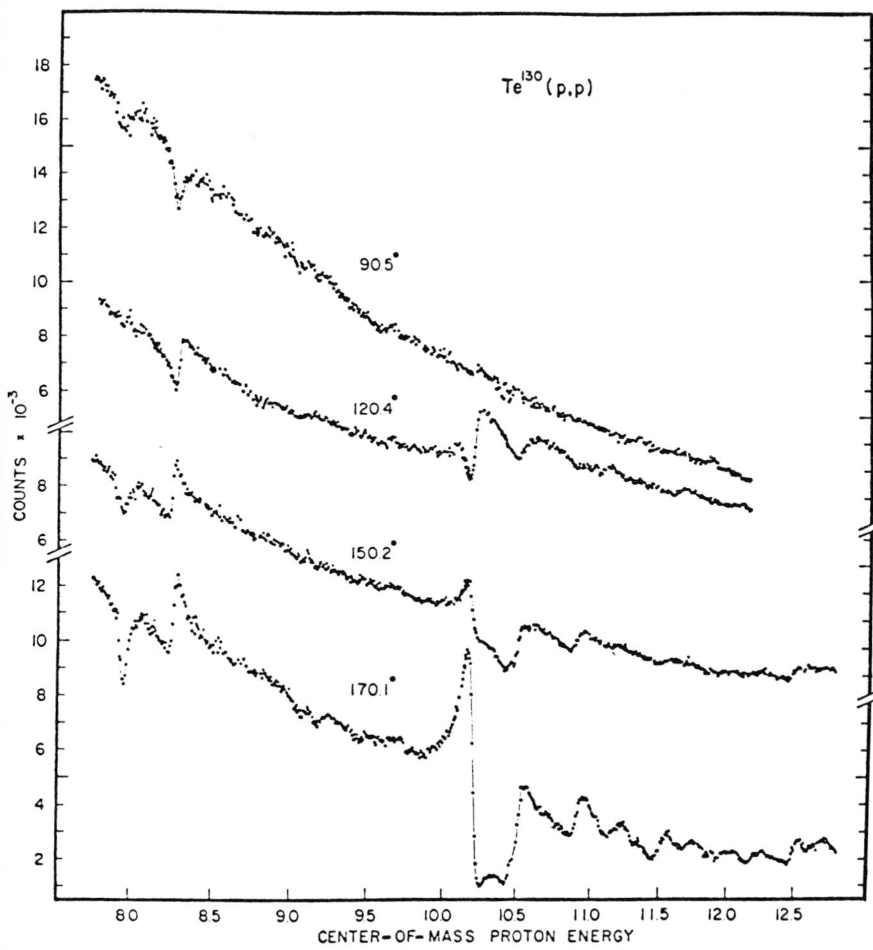

Fig. 3 Excitation functions of protons scattered elastically on Te^{130} (Ref. 5).

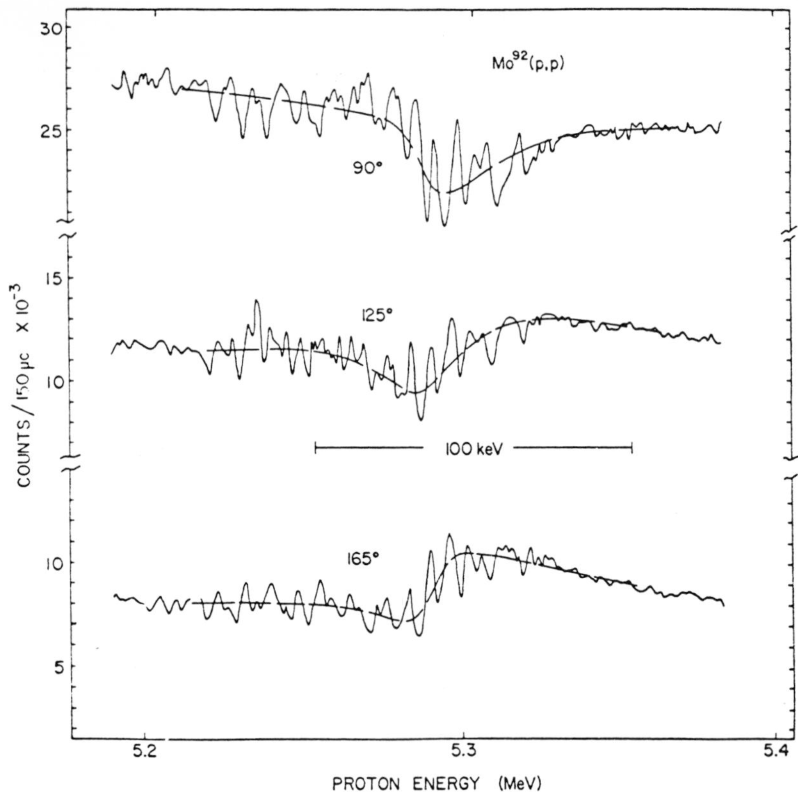

Fig. 4 Yield of protons scattered elastically from Mo^{92} in the neighborhood of the s-wave isobaric analog resonance at 5.3 MeV (Ref. 11). The dashed curve is a theoretical fit for an isolated level for which it is assumed that $\Gamma_p = 7$ keV, $\Gamma = 27$ keV.

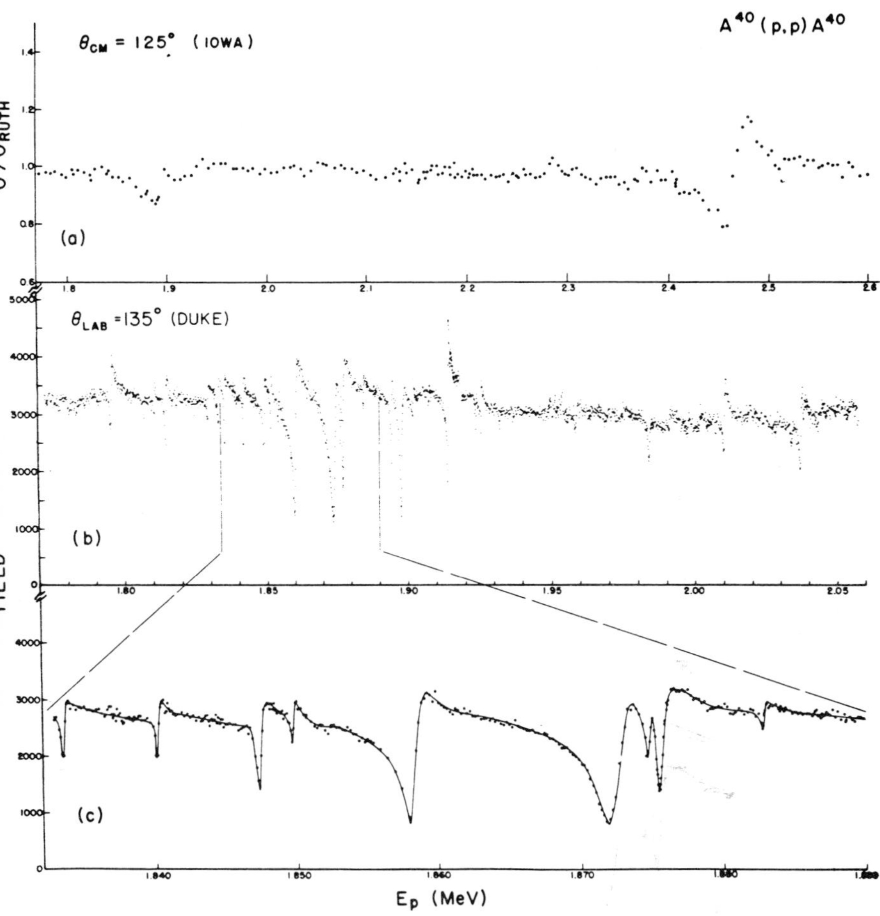

Fig. 5 Yield of protons scattered elastically from A^{40}. (a) Data taken with a 6-keV target (Ref. 13). (b) High-resolution data from 1.77 MeV to 2.05 MeV (Ref. 12). (c) Expansion of (b) near the 1.87-MeV analog resonance.

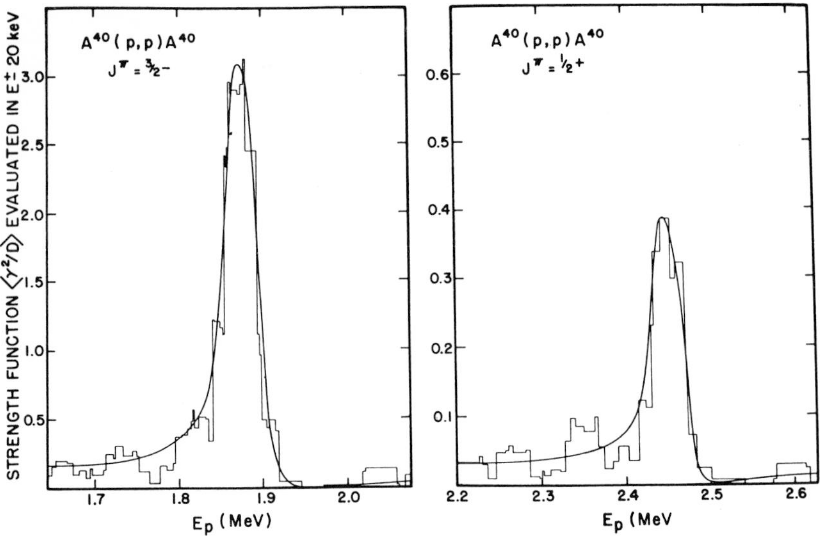

Fig. 6 Differential strength-function plots of the $\frac{3}{2}^-$ and $\frac{1}{2}^+$ analog resonances (Ref. 12). Curves are calculated from Eq. (2) with Γ = 20 keV, Δ = -74 keV, E_A = 1.878 for the $\frac{3}{2}^-$ plot and Γ = 16 keV, Δ = -45 keV, E_A = 2.455 for the $\frac{1}{2}^+$ plot.

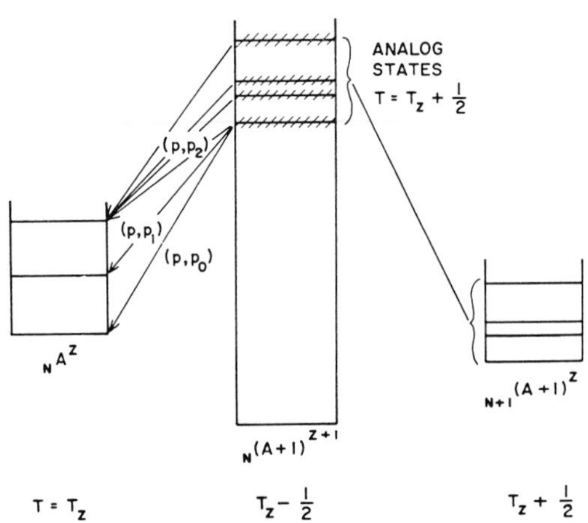

Fig. 7 Schematic diagram showing elastic and inelastic scattering at isobaric-analog-state resonances.

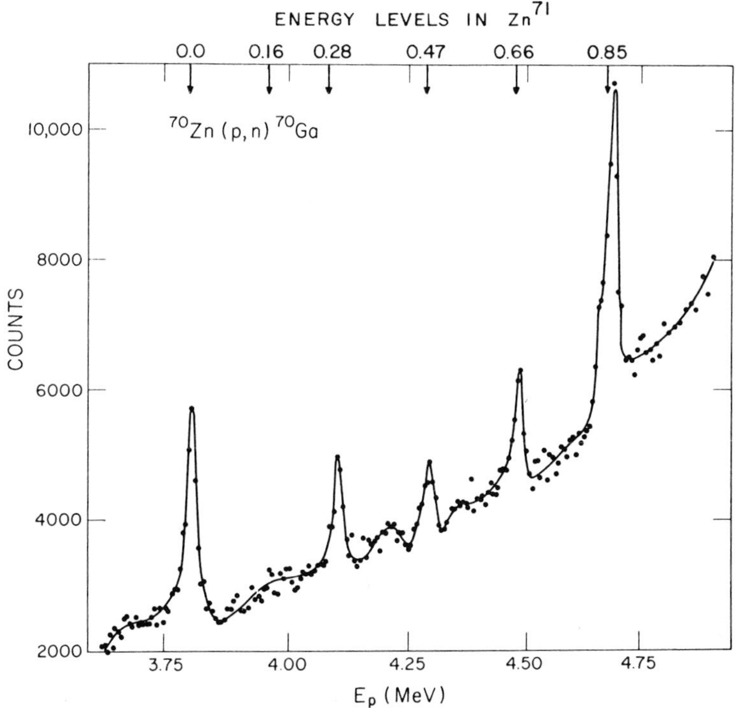

Fig. 8 Yield of neutrons from the Zn^{70}(p,n)Ga^{70} reaction (Ref. 19). Positions of the levels in Zn^{71} to which the analog resonances correspond are shown above.

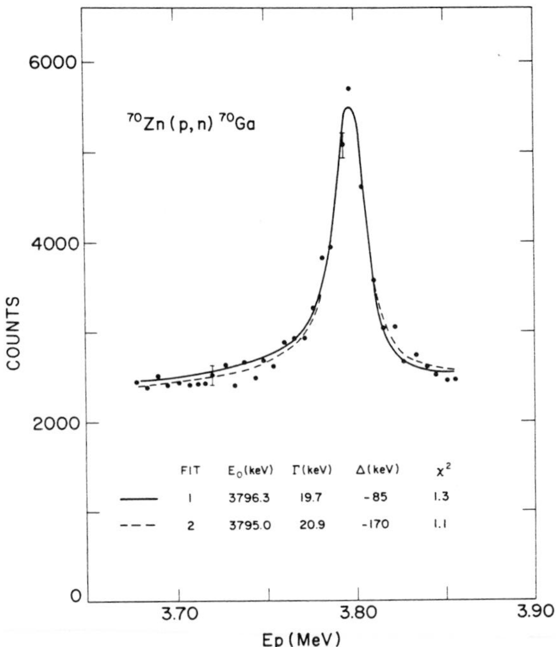

Fig. 9 Yield of neutrons from the Zn^{70}(p,n)Ga^{70} reaction in the neighborhood of the isobaric analog resonance at 3.997 MeV (Ref. 19). The theoretical curves are calculated from Eq. (2) with the parameters shown.

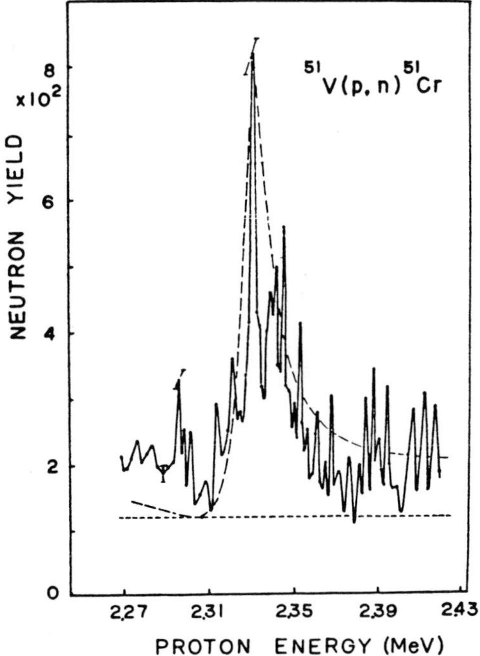

Fig. 10 Yield of neutrons from the $V^{51}(p,n)Cr^{51}$ reaction in the neighborhood of the isobaric analog resonance at 2.33 MeV (Ref. 22). The theoretical curve (dashed line) is calculated from Eq. (2) with Γ = 14 keV, Δ = 25 keV, E_A = 2.331 MeV. The dotted line is the estimated yield of background neutrons.

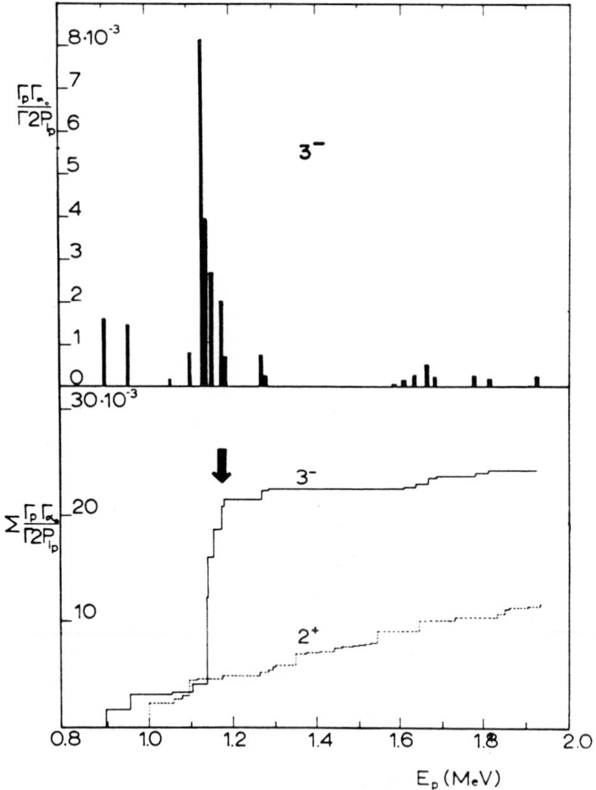

Fig. 11 Strengths (Wigner-limit units) of resonances in the $Cl^{37}(p, \alpha_0)S^{34}$ reaction (Ref. 23). (a) Reduced strengths of 3^- resonances. (b) Integrated reduced strengths of 3^- and 2^+ resonances.

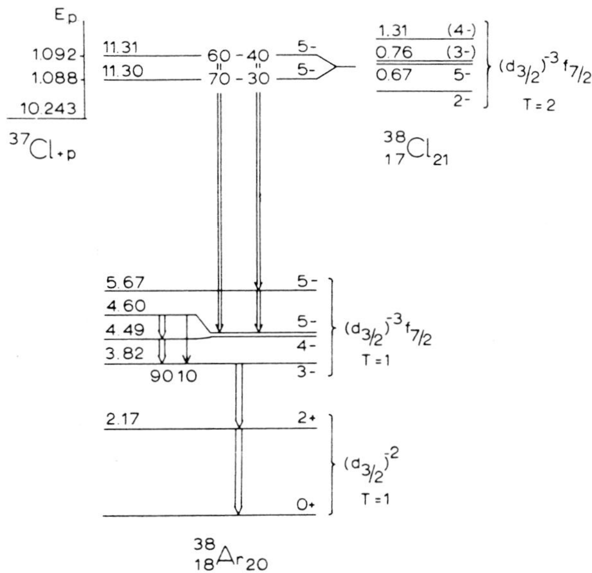

Fig. 12 Principal γ decay of the resonances in Cl^{37} + p at E_p = 1.088 and 1.092 MeV (Ref. 27).

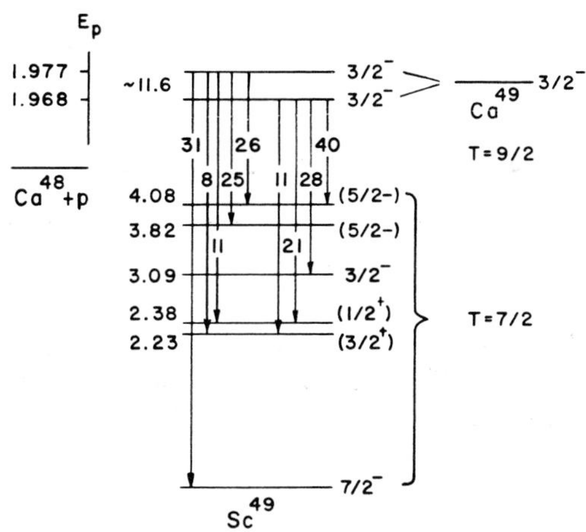

Fig. 13 Principal γ decay of the resonances in Ca^{48} + p at E_p = 1.968 and 1.977 MeV (Ref. 28).

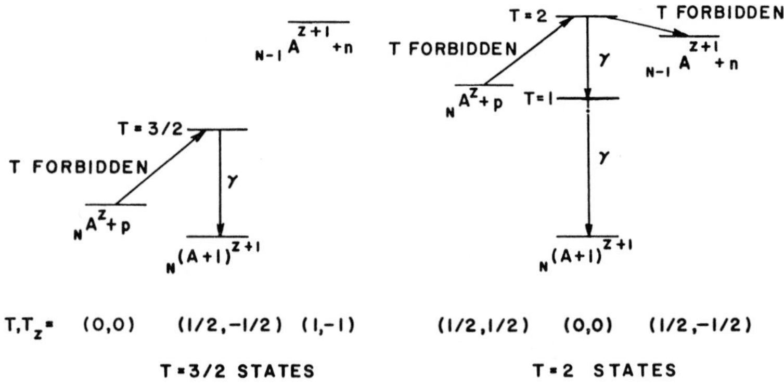

Fig. 14 Schematic diagram illustrating the excitation of $T=\frac{3}{2}$ and T=2 states in T-forbidden proton-induced reactions.

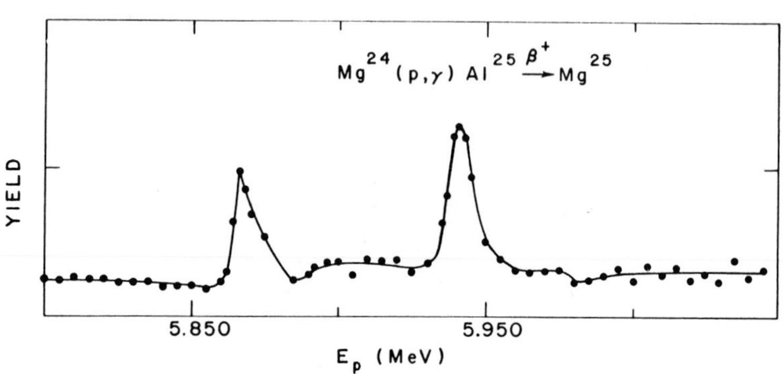

Fig. 15 Yield curve for the $Mg^{24}(p,\gamma)Al^{25}$ reaction (Ref. 32). The resonances correspond to the two lowest $T=\frac{3}{2}$ states in Al^{25}.

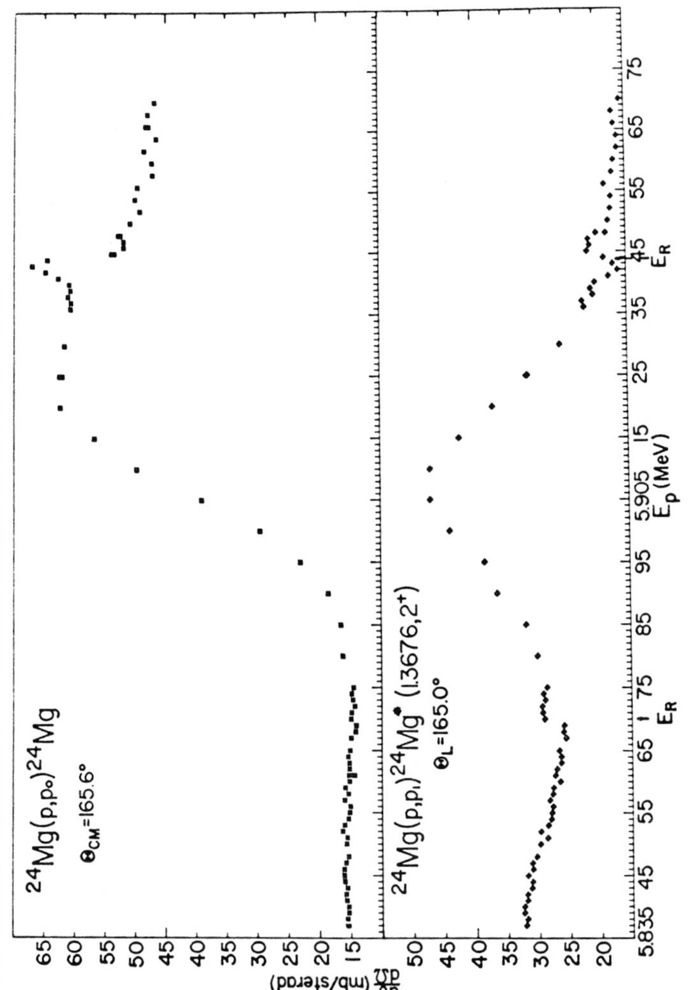

Fig. 16 Excitation functions of protons scattered elastically and inelastically on Mg^{24} (Ref. 33). The resonance energies E_R correspond to the two lowest $T=\frac{3}{2}$ states in Al^{25}.

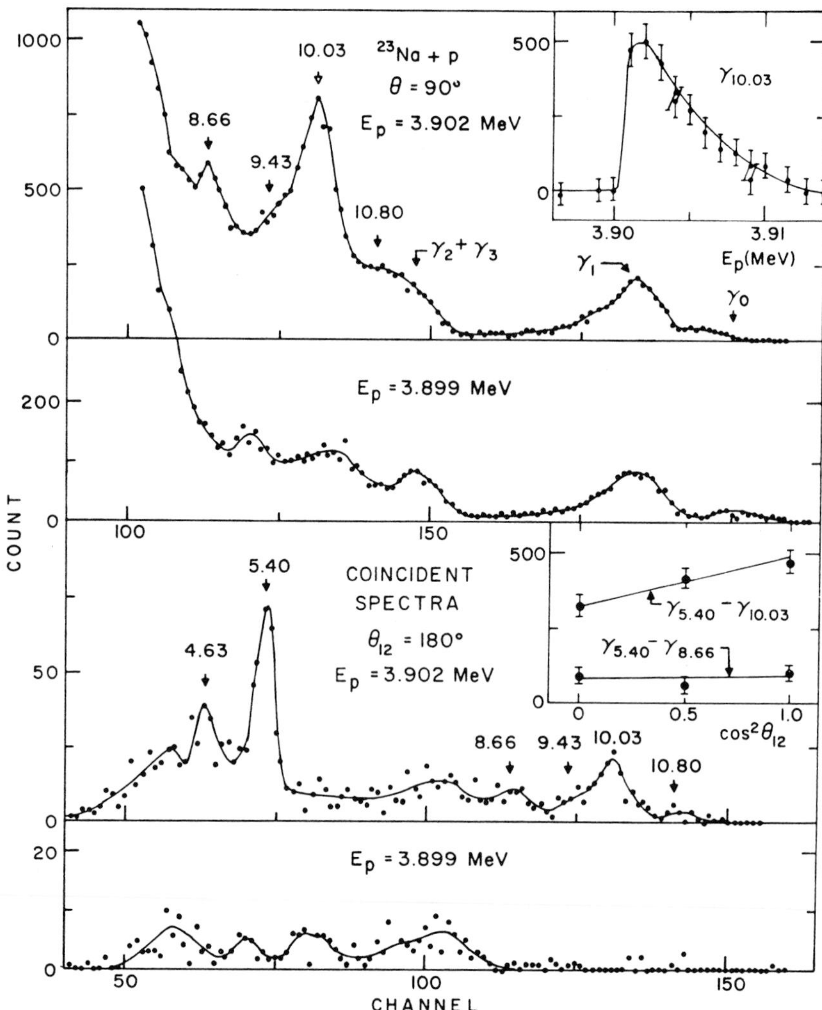

Fig. 17 Spectra of γ rays from the $Na^{23}(p,\gamma)Mg^{24}$ reaction at proton energies on and off the T=2 resonance at 3.902 MeV (Ref. 34). The upper half shows the singles spectra; the lower half shows coincidence spectra. The upper inset shows the yield of the 10.03-MeV gamma ray; the lower shows the results of angular-correlation measurements.

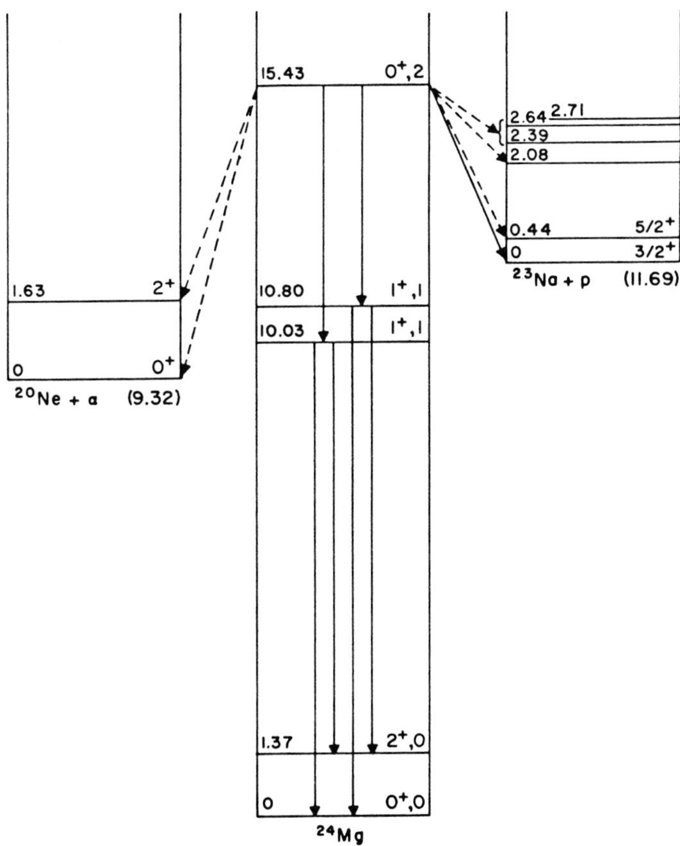

Fig. 18 Decay of the T=2 state in Mg^{24} (Ref. 34).

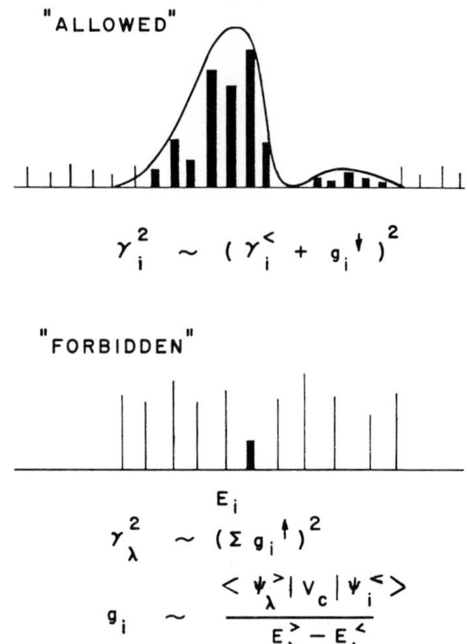

Fig. 19 Schematic representation of proton reduced widths for allowed and forbidden isobaric analog resonances. In the allowed case V_C is an effective interaction defined in Refs. 15 and 16.

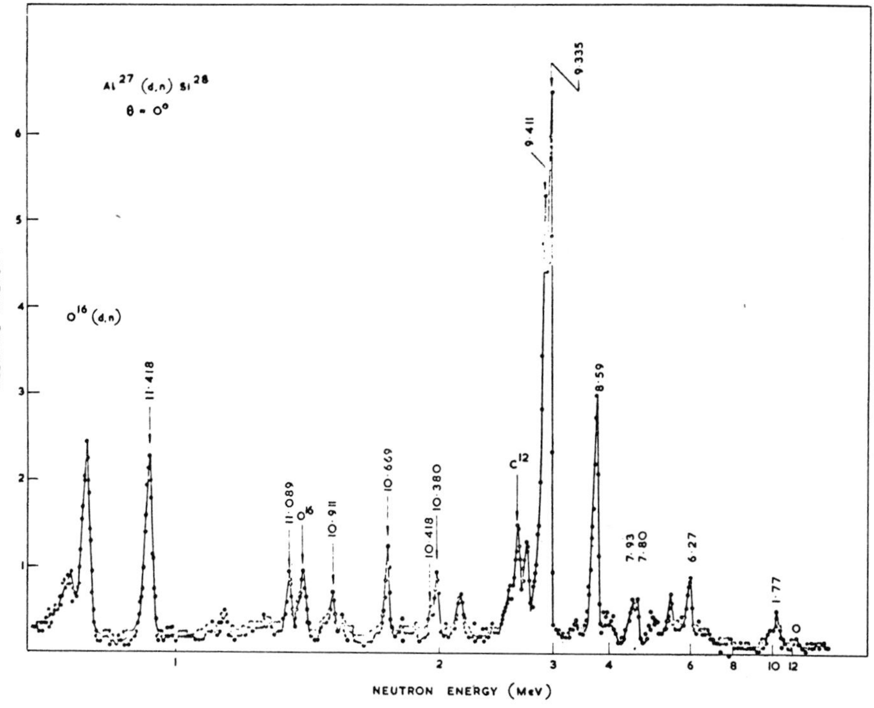

Fig. 20 Spectrum of neutrons at 0° from the reaction $Al^{27}(d,n)Si^{28}$ (Ref. 35). Most of the groups labeled with the excitation energy in Si^{28} are $\ell=0$ transitions.

NEUTRON POLARIZATION STUDIES

Roger W. Finlay

Ohio University
Athens, Ohio

INTRODUCTION

The field of neutron polarization measurements has recently grown into a profitable area of research at many nuclear physics laboratories. Recent improvements in experimental technique have reduced some of the hazards which once characterized this type of experiment. Reliable neutron polarization data can be extremely helpful in the analysis of three classic problems in nuclear physics, namely the reaction mechanism of neutron production reactions such as (d,n), (p,n), (He^3,n), etc., the determination of spin-parity assignments for compound nuclear states, and the effect of spin-orbit forces in the scattering of fast neutrons by other nuclei. Most neutron polarization experiments have been performed in conjunction with low energy accelerators, and, with suitable improvements in technique, many other experiments remain to be done in this energy region.

An excellent review article by Haeberli[1)] in Fast Neutron Physics cites most of the important references up to 1962, while the proceedings of the Karlsruhe Conference[2)] in the summer of 1965 is an important source of information concerning more recent developments.

Since conventional neutron detectors are not sensitive to the neutron spin direction, the measurement of neutron polarization generally involves a double scattering process. Fig. 1 shows a typical geometry for fast-neutron polarization measurements.

The magnitude of the neutron polarization is defined as

$$P(\theta_1, E_1) = \frac{N^+ - N^-}{N^+ + N^-} \tag{1}$$

where N^+ and N^- are the numbers of neutrons with spin parallel and antiparallel to a direction $\vec{n}_1$ perpendicular to the scattering plane. By convention, the sense of $\vec{n}_1$ is defined by

$$\vec{n}_1 = \frac{\vec{k}_1 \times \vec{k}_1'}{|\vec{k}_1 \times \vec{k}_1'|} \tag{2}$$

The second reaction, or analyzing reaction, is usually an elastic scattering of the partially polarized neutrons from a spin-zero target nucleus. The analyzing power of the second scattering is written

$$\vec{P}_2 = \vec{n}_2 \; P_2 \; (\theta_2, E_n) \tag{3}$$

where

$$\vec{n}_2 = \frac{\vec{k}_1 \times \vec{k}_2'}{|\vec{k}_1' \times \vec{k}_2'|} \tag{4}$$

and is equal to the polarization which would be produced by the scattering (at θ_2) of an incident beam of unpolarized neutrons of energy E_n.

If neutron detectors are then placed at a fixed scattering angle θ_2 but with azimuthal angles $\phi_2 = 0$ and π, the intensities measured by these counters (called I_R and I_L, respectively) can be simply related to the polarization product P_1P_2 by the fundamental expression for the asymmetry ε,

$$\varepsilon = P_1P_2 = \frac{I_R - I_L}{I_R + I_L} \; . \tag{5}$$

It follows then that a direct measurement of either P_1 or P_2 is not possible. If, however, the analyzing power P_2 can be calculated for some nucleus, it is then possible to measure P_1 for a great variety of source reactions. The current procedure is to choose a light nucleus (usually He^4 or C^{12}) as a standard analyzer for these experiments. For these cases, total cross sections and angular distributions for neutron scattering are known rather well over a wide range in energy so that a value of $P_2(\theta_2,E_n)$ can be calculated directly from the phase shifts. Of course, the phase shift analysis and consequent calculation of P_2 is constantly undergoing revision as better n - He^4 and n - C^{12} experiments are performed, but at least in principle a standard polarization analyzer exists.

MEASUREMENT OF SOURCE POLARIZATION
THE $D(d,n)He^3$ REACTION

Before going into the details of experimental technique, it might serve to underline some of the problems associated with neutron polarization measurements by examining one case in which the previously outlined procedure was followed, i.e. the analyzing power of C^{12} or He^4 was calculated, and asymmetry measurements were made using several different techniques. The $D(d,n)He^3$ reaction has probably received more attention than any other nuclear polarization reaction. Fig. 2 shows a compilation of 15 different experiments for deuteron energies between 0.08 and 20 MeV.* Haeberli[3)] and Barschall[4)] have discussed this confused situation at previous conferences. At this time it appears that for deuteron

* The author wishes to acknowledge R. L. Walter for the use of this figure.

energies above 2 MeV four sets of measurements at four different laboratories fall on the lower curve while seven or eight measurements (including the five most recent experiments) fall on the upper curve. One must agree with Barschall's conclusion[4)] that "these discrepancies show the difficulties of neutron polarization measurements".

If one examines the low energy region of this curve one finds less dramatic but still serious discrepancies there also. Fig. 3 illustrates the available data until about 1964 for deuteron energies below 400 keV. The solid curve is the theoretical prediction of Blin-Stoyle[19)] arbitrarily normalized to the polarization measurement of Pasma.[7)] The data above 200 keV are by Pasma and by Boersma _et al._[16)] Both of these experiments used helium as an analyzer. The experiments below 200 keV (Kane,[20)] and Rogers and Bond[21)]) were both done with C^{12} analyzers. In this case one has a choice between the phase shift analysis of Meier[5)] _et al._ and Wills _et al._ [22)] In order to facilitate comparison, these data are all plotted relative to the phase shift analysis of Wills _et al._ The striking feature of these low energy data is the remarkably high value of the polarization at deuteron energy as low as 67.5 keV. Even if the theoretical calculation were renormalized to the data of Boersma _et al._ at higher energies, the data near 100 keV would still lie considerably above the line. Two points of caution must be mentioned in regard to the very low energy data. First, the deuterium targets which were used in these experiments were thick enough to stop the incident deuteron beam. Consequently, many investigators[20,21,23)] do not simply quote the dome voltage of the accelerator as the deuteron energy. Rather, they calculate some average deuteron energy in terms of the stopping power of the target material and the energy dependence of the $D(d,n)He^3$ cross section. Second, this average is made ambiguous by the presence of an unknown fraction of molecular deuterium ions in the beam. The horizontal error bars on the data of Rogers and Bond emphasize this problem.

Since 1964, two experiments have been performed and one other is in progress in which the molecular deuterium component of the accelerator beam is discarded by magnetic analysis. The data of Hänsgen *et al.*[23)] were obtained with a C^{12} analyzer while Behof *et al.*[24)] used a He^4 analyzer. Results are shown in Fig. 4. Unlike the previous figure, incident deuteron kinetic energy is now plotted on the horizontal axis. The data appear to agree in the region of 100 keV, and the Behof data also agree with the result of Boersma[16)] and the recent cloud chamber experiment of Mulder[25)] near 350 keV. Again, as with the data in Fig. 3, the polarization near 100 keV is large compared to the theoretical prediction. Even more striking is the fact that the large peak near 100 keV reported by Hänsgen is not observed by Behof.

A peak in the neutron polarization in this reaction would have interesting consequences. Hänsgen has suggested an explanation in terms of a virtual level in the He^4 compound nucleus. Such a level, if present, would be at nearly 24 MeV excitation and would be extremely narrow compared to previously observed excited states in He^4. Another confusing aspect of this problem is that recent measurements[26)] of angular distributions for the $D(d,n)He^3$ reaction and the $D(d,p)H^3$ reaction do not exhibit resonance structure in this energy region. Another polarization experiment in this energy region is now in progress. Hopefully, some definite statements about this highly interesting question will be possible in the near future.

EXPERIMENTAL TECHNIQUES

Two basic experimental techniques have been employed in all of the polarization measurements mentioned in the previous section. If C^{12} is used as the analyzer, then all methods involve the detection of scattered neutrons. However, if He^4 is used as the analyzer, one has the option of measuring either the scattered neutrons or the recoil α-particles. In fact, many current experiments involve the measurement of both the scattered neutrons and the recoil α-particles.

Fig. 5 shows a typical arrangement for the measurement of scattered neutrons. Neutrons from the source reaction are allowed to emerge at a specified angle θ_1 by means of suitable collimators. Elastically scattered neutrons are detected in a plastic scintillator located at an angle θ_2 with respect to the neutron beam. No coincidence requirements are involved. The neutron detector is moved from the "right" to the "left" position periodically--the counting time in each position being determined by some appropriate neutron monitor. Counting times can be reduced by a factor of two if two scintillation counters are used simultaneously. In this method, the "left" and "right" counters must be interchanged periodically so that individual differences in the efficiencies of the counters will cancel out. The interchange of detectors is accomplished in either of two different ways. The common method is to simply switch the two phototube assemblies. In this case one can define a "right-left ratio" as

$$r = \left[\frac{I_{R1}}{I_{L1}} \times \frac{I_{R2}}{I_{L2}}\right]^{1/2} \qquad (6)$$

where the I's again refer to intensities, the subscripts 1 and 2 identify the particular detector, and R and L again refer to their positions. The asymmetry is then given by

$$\varepsilon = P_1 P_2 = \frac{r - 1}{r + 1} \quad . \qquad (7)$$

Alternatively, the two detectors may be interchanged indirectly, i.e. by reversing the direction of incident polarization vector. This is accomplished by rotating the entire apparatus--shield, scatterer, and detectors--about a vertical axis through the neutron-producing target. In both cases, great care must be taken to guarantee that the interchange of detectors does not introduce false or systematic asymmetries into the experiment. The importance of false asymmetries has been emphasized by many authors and probably represents a first-order problem in the measurement of neutron polarization, especially when either P_1 or P_2 is small as is the case for much of the work in the present discussion.

Another problem associated with this type of measurement is the relatively high background counting rates in the neutron detectors. Room-scattered neutrons and gamma rays will also be counted by the detectors. Rogers and Bond reported a background or sample-out counting rate which was approximately 80% of the sample-in counting rate. Hänsgen added pulse shape discrimination in his experiment but still had a background counting rate of 50% of the sample-in rate.

Background counting rates were greatly reduced in the experiment of Behof _et al._ These authors employed gaseous helium as an analyzer, and observed the scintillation pulses from the recoil α-particles with another scintillation counter. A fast coincidence (approximately 10 nsec) was required between the recoil α-particle and the scattered neutron. Background counting rates were less than 10% of the total counting rates. Furthermore, prompt gamma rays produced in the vicinity of the source were completely eliminated because of their different times-of-flight. High pressure gas scintillation cells have been described by Shamu[27)] and are now in use in many laboratories.

A major improvement in the elimination of false asymmetries was first employed by Hillman _et al._[28)] This method, which has also been successfully used by several other groups, utilized the Larmour precession of the polarization vector $\vec{P}_1$ through 90° about the neutron beam axis in the magnetic field of a solenoid inserted between the neutron-producing target and the analyzing scatterer. Fig. 6 shows a typical arrangement. The current in the solenoid is chosen so that the integrated field will have the proper value to cause the desired rotation of the polarization vector. By simply reversing the sense of the solenoid current, the polarization vector may be rotated through ±90°. The analyzing plane determined by the neutron beam axis and the scattered neutron direction ($\vec{k}_2'$ in Fig. 1) is now vertical and is perpendicular to the plane of the neutron-producing reaction. Measurement of neutron intensity with the solenoid current in one direction followed by a measurement with the solenoid current reversed is completely equivalent to the interchange of detectors in the standard right-left experiment. The solenoid has several important advantages over the methods previously described. First, the detectors are never moved during a particular asymmetry measurement so that all efficiencies, geometrical effects and background effects tend to cancel out in the right-left ratio. Second, the effective interchange of detectors is accomplished quickly and remotely. Third, fast coincidence techniques such as helium scintillation or time-of-flight are easily employed for the reduction of background. Finally, a massive solenoid placed between the neutron source and the detector does provide some useful neutron shielding.

One problem connected with the use of a solenoid is the effect of the fringing magnetic field. This effect can appear in three different forms. First, the fringing field can change the gain of the photomultiplier systematically every time the magnetic field is reversed. Magnetic shielding of the solenoid can be used to reduce the field in the vicinity of the photomultipliers to less than 5 gauss so that careful shielding of the photomultipliers can effectively eliminate this possible source of error. Second, the fringing field can also deflect the incident charged particle beam in the region of the target. Again, if the fringing field is kept small, a simple calculation shows that this effect can easily be neglected. Finally, some depolarization of the neutron beam itself can be caused by the radial component of the magnetic field. This effect is absent in an infinitely long solenoid, and has been accurately calculated in the practical case. Atkinson and Sherwood[29)] have shown that for a ratio of solenoid length to beam radius of 20:1, the fractional depolarization of the neutron beam is less than 1%.

Before leaving the subject of magnetic spin precession, it should be pointed out that some of the best neutron polarization experiments have been performed using the transverse magnetic field of an iron magnet rather than the longitudinal field of a solenoid. With this method, which has been used extensively at the Argonne National Laboratory,[30)] the magnetic field strength must be sufficient to rotate the incident polarization vector through a full 180°. Measurements are taken with the magnet field on then off to effect the reversal of $\vec{P}_1$ with respect to $\vec{P}_2$. The use of iron pole faces makes possible much higher field strengths than are currently used in solenoids so that the overall length of the magnet is not greater than a typical solenoid. One major advantage of the 180° spin precession technique is that the second scattering plane is parallel with the first plane so that large, permanent detector shielding arrangements can be mounted on the floor in the usual manner.

THE ASSOCIATED-PARTICLE TECHNIQUE

An alternative method for the measurement of neutron polarization which also allows for the reduction of background by the requirement of fast coincidence is the associated-particle time-of-flight technique. Such a system is currently being used at Ohio University in a preliminary measurement of polarization in the $D(d,n)He^3$ reaction. This method, which has become widespread in the study of scattering and reactions induced by 14 MeV neutrons from the $T(d,n)He^4$ reaction, can also be employed with some difficulty with the $D(d,n)He^3$ reaction. The use of associated-particles is well known and will be only briefly reviewed. Basically, the detection of an α particle from the $T(d,n)He^4$ reaction in a given solid angle means that an associated neutron was produced with a known momentum vector. Scattering experiments can then be performed by placing a sample in the path of the associated neutron. An accurate "start" signal is provided by the pulse from the α-particle detector and a "stop" signal is obtained when a scattered neutron is subsequently detected. These pulses are then sent to a time-to-amplitude converter. Several such systems are now in operation, and overall time resolution of 1 to 2 nsec is commonly achieved.[31)]

The simplifying feature of the $T(d,n)He^4$ reaction is, of course, the large positive Q value of the reaction (17.6 MeV). Elastically scattered deuterons are easily absorbed by foils before they reach the α-detector. The ultimate limitation of systems of this type seems to be the counting rate capability of the α-particle detector, but the method does have the very important advantage that nanosecond time-of-flight experiments can be performed using the smallest Cockcroft-Walton accelerator without resorting to expensive beam-pulsing and bunching apparatus.

The application of associated-particle time-of-flight techniques to the $D(d,n)He^3$ reaction has been successfully developed by Kahne and Vergezac[32)] and by Bell *et al.*[33)] The present experiment is an extension of these techniques to the particular case of neutron polarization measurements. Fig. 7 shows the beam analyzing magnet, the deuterium target, scattering chamber, and spin-precession solenoid.

The spin-precession solenoid consists of three separate aluminum tape coils 5¾ in. long and bound on each end by iron plates. The overall length of the solenoid is 20 in. and the diameter of the bore is 2.12 in. The coils are connected in parallel and are energized by a 100 kilowatt motor-generator. A current of 70 amps.

per coil produces a field of 5.1 kilogauss along the bore of the solenoid, and this is sufficient to precess the neutron spin through 90.0 ± 0.3°. The measured asymmetry is quite insensitive to the angle (near 90°) through which the neutron spin is precessed. Therefore, a slight error in the measurement of the magnetic field does not significantly effect the results. Nevertheless, the magnetic field is measured by an axial Hall probe with absolute accuracy of 0.25% while the solenoid current is regulated to at least 0.5%. During actual operation, the solenoid dissipates 19 kilowatts and is water cooled.

Since the specific purpose of this experiment was to re-examine the neutron polarization in the energy region reported by Hänsgen _et al._, only neutrons which are emitted at θ(Lab) = 50° are of interest. Consequently, as the incident deuteron energy is changed, the emission angle of the associated He^3 changes over a few degrees range. Provision is made in the scattering chamber for the rotation of the He^3 detector. However, for the purpose of this discussion, this detector will be placed at 115.1° with respect to the incident deuterons. This angle turns out to be correct for deuteron energy of about 110 keV. A heavy ion surface barrier detector was chosen for the He^3 counter because of its high electric field strength and fast charge collection times.

The principal problem with this method is that the He^3 detector is bombarded by several other radiations, the most troublesome of which are the elastically scattered deuterons which arrive at the detector in overwhelming numbers. Either an additional magnetic (or electric) field analysis or else an absorbing foil is needed to prevent the deuterons from reaching the detector. The foil is certainly the simpler of the two methods, and is employed in the present experiment. However, as other experimenters have observed, the choice of this foil is not trivial as the foil which is thick enough to positively stop the undesired deuterons is very nearly the correct thickness to stop the associated He^3 beam. This difficulty is made worse in the present experiment because at the required backward angles, the He^3 energy is considerably lower than that reported by other experimenters. The effect of this absorbing foil on the four important radiations is shown in the table.

Incident Deuteron Energy	110 keV
Scattering Angle	115.1° (Lab)
Nickel Foil Thickness	0.6 mg/cm^2

Particle	Energy before Foil* (keV)	Energy after Foil (keV)
p	2880	2840
H^3	820	730
d	97	0
He^3	650	180

* Calculated from reaction kinematics
Measured with a mercury pulse generator

Pulses from the solid state detector are sent to a charge-sensitive preamplifier, main amplifier, and biased post amplifier. A typical pulse height spectrum is shown in Fig. 8. The horizontal axis is not a linear energy axis because the high energy proton pulses overload the main amplifier. The He^3 peak is safely separated from the noise in this figure, but as the terminal potential is raised above 150 keV, pulses from elastically scattered deuterons straggling through the foil become observable in the low channels.

Pulses from the He^3 particles are not large enough, before amplification, to trigger a fast discriminator.

Accordingly, a time pick-off system designed by Williams and Biggerstaff[34)] is placed between the preamplifier an the main amplifier as shown in Fig. 9. The fast amplifier in the time pick-off unit brings the He^3 pulse height up to the 150 to 200 mv level which is then an adequate amplitude for most commercially available fast discriminators; however, the slow rise time of the charg sensitive preamplifier output pulse results in increased variation in threshold crossing times at the fast discri minator.

The neutron detector is a standard plastic scintillator coupled to a 56AVP photomultiplier tube. The anod pulses are sent directly to another fast discriminator module. No effort is made in this experiment to use a zero-crossing discriminator because the timing uncertainty in the detection of the He^3 pulse is too large to justify this refinement.

Pulses from each discriminator are sent·to a time-to-amplitude converter the output of which is stored in multichannel analyzer after several subsidiary condition are met. First, the linear signals from each detector are analyzed, and a suitable region of interest is selected. Second, an auxiliary fast coincidence between the He^3 and neutron is required so that events characterized by the arrival of a signal at the neutron detector before the arrival of a He^3 pulse are excluded.

The overall performance of the system can be easily checked by removing the carbon analyzer and placing the neutron detector directly in the associated neutron beam The results of such a test are shown in Fig. 10, which shows the output of the time-to-amplitude converter gate as described above. The time scale is 1.0 nsec per chan nel, which means that the time resolution of the system is a rather disappointing 9 or 10 nsec. About 2 nsec of time spread can be attributed to geometry and kinematic factors, but the remainder is due to the difficulty of obtaining a good timing signal from the very low energy He^3 ion which gives an output pulse height only slightly above the detector noise. This high noise level means that the fast discriminator threshold must be set high enough that a 5 or 6 nsec timing error is unavoidable for pulses with rise times of about 40 nsec. A significant improvement would result if the time pick-off unit could be used in the manner originally suggested by Williams and Biggerstaff, namely, in front of the charge-sensitive preamplifier. Accurate timing pulses from the proton and triton groups have been obtained in this way, but the severe energy loss of the He^3 ion in passing through the nickel foil has thus far made this method unworkable. Several improvements are now being incorporated into the present arrangement which should bring about the desired time resolution, but these will be expensive and time-consuming. It is unfortunate that we can't simply change the Q value for the reaction.

The He scintillation cell has another advantage over the associated-particle time-of-flight scheme. The associated-particle method produces a start pulse for the time-of-flight circuit every time a neutron impinges on the scattering sample, whereas the He cell gives a pulse only when the neutron interacts with the scatterer. Consequently, the counting rate in the He^3 detector can be an order-of-magnitude higher in the present scheme, and a less favorable signal-to-background ratio will result. Current experience would indicate that in the present method background rates in the vicinity of the neutron time-of-flight peak can be reduced to 15-20% of total counting rates. If this should prove inadequate, other improvements such as detector shielding and pulse-shape discrimination might have to be incorporated.

In summary, then, the current experiment is an attempt to remeasure neutron polarization in the D(d,n) He^3 reaction near 100 keV. Background counting rates are kept low by the use of fast coincidence techniques, data are recorded in a time-of-flight format to facilitate the identification and subtraction of remaining background, and a spin-precession magnet is used to eliminate false asymmetries. It might be mentioned again here that a spin-precession magnet has never been used in the study of this reaction at deuteron energies below 200 keV.

In view of all the difficulties experienced with the associated-particle method, it might appear profitable to abandon it in favor of more familiar techniques. The justification for using the associated-particle method can be given in terms of the long-range research program of the Ohio University Cockcroft-Walton laboratory. Neutron polarization measurements yield information either about the source polarization $P_1(\theta)$ or about the polarization in the scattering reaction $P_2(\theta)$. By requiring a scintillation pulse from the analyzing reaction for timing purposes, the experimenter limits himself to the study of source polarization, $P_1(\theta)$ unless he can fabricate the nucleus used as an analyzer into a scintillator, or unless he has sufficient source intensity to perform triple scattering experiments. At Cockcroft-Walton energies, the number of interesting source reactions which might be studied is pitifully small. However, once the question of the source polarization of D(d,n)He neutrons is adequately understood, the time-of-flight spectrometer can be used for a systematic study of polarization effects in elastic scattering from a wide range of nuclei. Hopefully, such a study would contribute significantly to our understanding of spin-orbit effects in the neutron-nucleus interaction.

ACKNOWLEDGMENTS

The author wishes to acknowledge the many conversations with his colleague R. O. Lane, whose experience in the field of neutron polarization has helped the author to avoid many pitfalls. The generous cooperation of T. R. Donahue of Ohio State University and R. L. Walter of Duke University is also gratefully acknowledged.

REFERENCES

1) W. Haeberli, Fast Neutron Physics, ed. by J. B. Marion and J. L. Fowler (Interscience Publishers, New York, 1963) Part II, Chap. V. G.

2) Proceedings of the 2nd International Symposium on Polarization Phenomena of Nucleons (Birkhäuser Verlag, Basel and Stuttgart, 1966).

3) W. Haeberli, Progress in Fast Neutron Physics (University of Chicago Press, 1963), pp. 307-321.

4) H. H. Barschall, in Proceedings of the 2nd International Symposium on Polarization Phenomena of Nucleons (Birkhäuser Verlag, Basel and Stuttgart, 1966), pp. 393-409.

5) R. W. Meier, P. Scherrer and G. Trümpy, Helv. Phys. Acta 27, 577 (1954).

6) I. I. Levintov, A. V. Miller, E. Z. Tarumov and V. N. Shamshev, Nucl. Phys. 3, 237 (1957).

7) P. J. Pasma, Nucl. Phys. 6, 141 (1958).

8) W. W. Daehnick, Phys. Rev. 115, 1008 (1959).

9) J. A. Baicker and K. W. Jones, Nucl. Phys. 17, 424 (1960).

10) P. Avignon, Y. Deschamps and L. Rosier, J. Physique 22, 563 (1961).

11) P. S. Dubbeldam and R. L. Walter, Nucl. Phys. 28, 414 (1961).

12) T. H. May, R. L. Walter and H. H. Barschall, Nucl. Phys. 45, 17 (1963).

13) I. S. Trostin and V. A. Smotryaev, JETP 44, 1160 (1963).

14) H. Niewodniczanski, J. Szmider and J. Szymankowski, J. Physique 24, 871 (1963).

15) N. V. Alekseyev, U. R. Arifkhanov, N. A. Vlasov, V. V. Davydov and L. N. Samoilov, JETP 45, 1416 (1963).

16) H. J. Boersma, C. C. Jonker, J. G. Nijenhuis and P. J. Van Hall, Nucl. Phys. 46, 660 (1963).

17) I. I. Bondarenko and P. S. Otstavnov, JETP 47, 97 (1964).

18) N. P. Babenko, I. O. Konstantinov, A. P. Moskalev and Y. A. Nemilov, JETP 47, 767 (1964).

19) R. J. Blin-Stoyle, Proc. Phys. Soc. (London) A64, 700 (1951).
R. J. Blin-Stoyle, ibid. A65, 949 (1952).

20) P. P. Kane, Nucl. Phys. 10, 429 (1959).

21) J. T. Rogers and C. D. Bond, Nucl. Phys. 53, 297 (1964).

22) J. E. Wills, J. K. Bair, H. O. Cohn and H. B. Willard, Phys. Rev. 109, 891 (1958).

23) H. Hansgen, H. Pose, G. Schirmer and D. Seeliger, Nucl. Phys. 73, 417 (1965).

24) A. F. Behof, T. H. May and W. I. McGarry, Bull. Amer. Phys. Soc. 12, 87 (1967).

25) J. P. F. Mulder, Phys. Lett. 23, 589 (1966).

26) R. B. Theus, W. I. McGarry and L. A. Beach, Nucl. Phys. 80, 273 (1966).

27) R. E. Shamu, Nucl. Instr. Meth. 14, 297 (1962).

28) P. Hillman, G. H. Stafford and C. Whitehead, Nuovo Cimento 4, 67 (1956).

29) J. Atkinson and J. E. Sherwood, Nucl. Instr. Meth. 34, 137 (1965).

30) R. O. Lane, A. J. Elwyn and A. Langsdorf, Jr., Phys. Rev. 126, 1105 (1962), Phys. Rev. 136, 1710 (1964).
A. J. Elwyn, R. O. Lane and A. Langsdorf, Jr., Phys. Rev. 128, 779 (1962).

31) A. J. Frasca, R. W. Finlay, R. D. Koshel and R. L. Cassola, Phys. Rev. 144, 854 (1966).
P. L. Beach, R. W. Finlay, R. L. Cassola and R. D. Koshel, Phys. Rev. 156, 1201 (1967).

32) P. J. Kahne and P. Vergezac, J. Physique 24, 962 (1963).

33) R. A. I. Bell, N. G. Chapman and P. B. Johnson, Nucl. Instr. Meth. 33, 13 (1965).

34) C. W. Williams and J. A. Biggerstaff, Nucl. Instr. Meth. 25, 370 (1964).

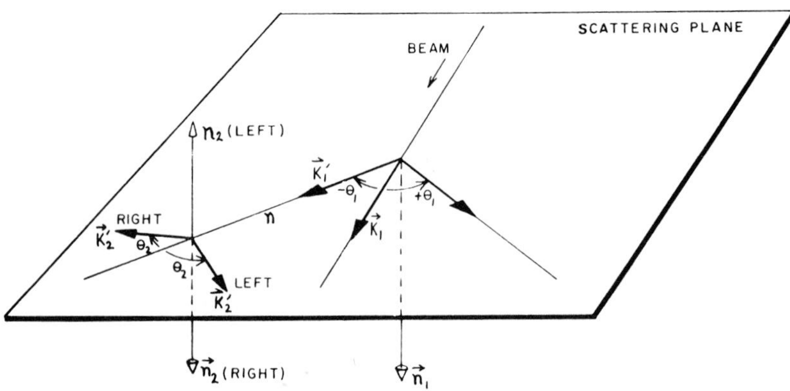

Fig. 1. Typical geometry for neutron polarization experiments showing the propagation vectors $\vec{k}_1$, $\vec{k}_1'$, and $\vec{k}_2'$ for the incident charged particle, emitted neutron, and scattered neutron, respecively. $\vec{n}_1$ and $\vec{n}_2$ are unit axial vectors.

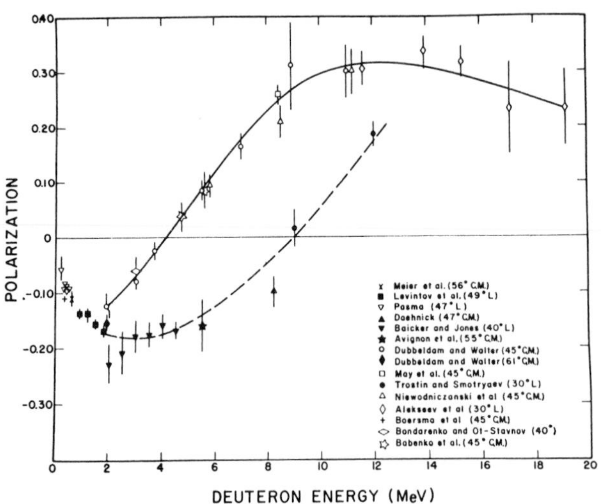

Fig. 2. $D(d,n)He^3$ neutron polarization measurements at reaction angles indicated. L = lab system; CM = c.m. system. The original experiments are described in Refs. 5) to 18).

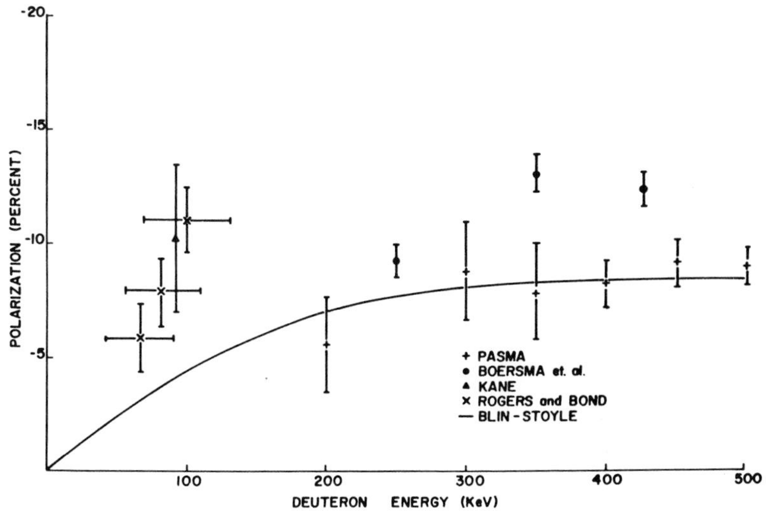

Fig. 3. Low energy $D(d,n)He^3$ neutron polarization experiments performed prior to 1964. The solid curve is based on the formula derived by Blin-Stoyle (ref. 19).

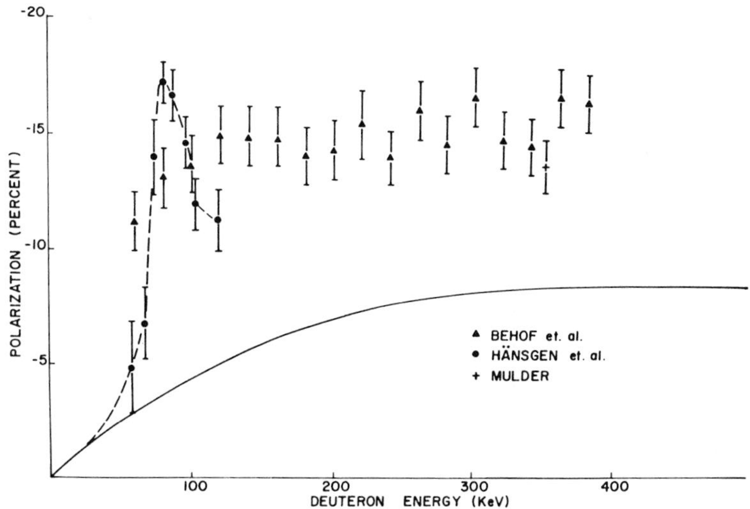

Fig. 4. Recent measurements of neutron polarization in the $D(d,n)He^3$ reaction for incident deuteron energy less than 0.5 MeV.

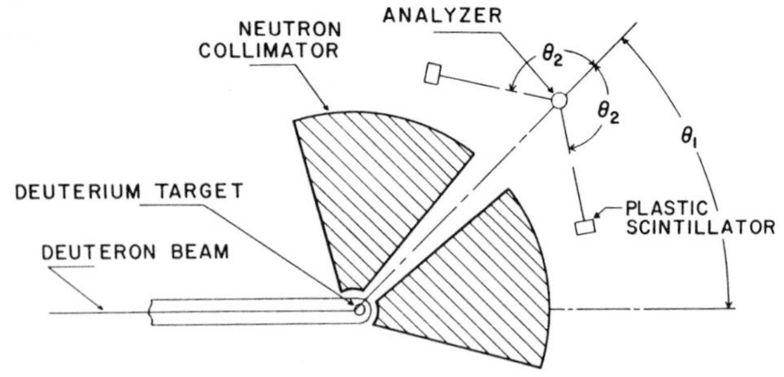

Fig. 5. Schematic diagram of apparatus used in a typical measurement of neutron polarization.

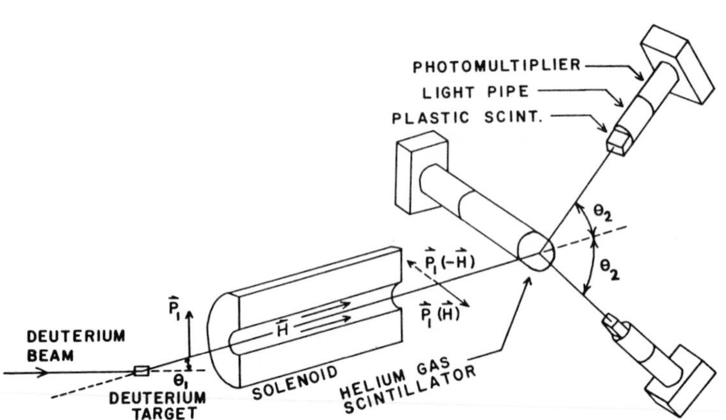

Fig. 6. Experimental arrangement used in a neutron scattering experiment involving a spin-precession solenoid. The polarization vector P_1 is turned through an angle of 90° by the magnetic field H.

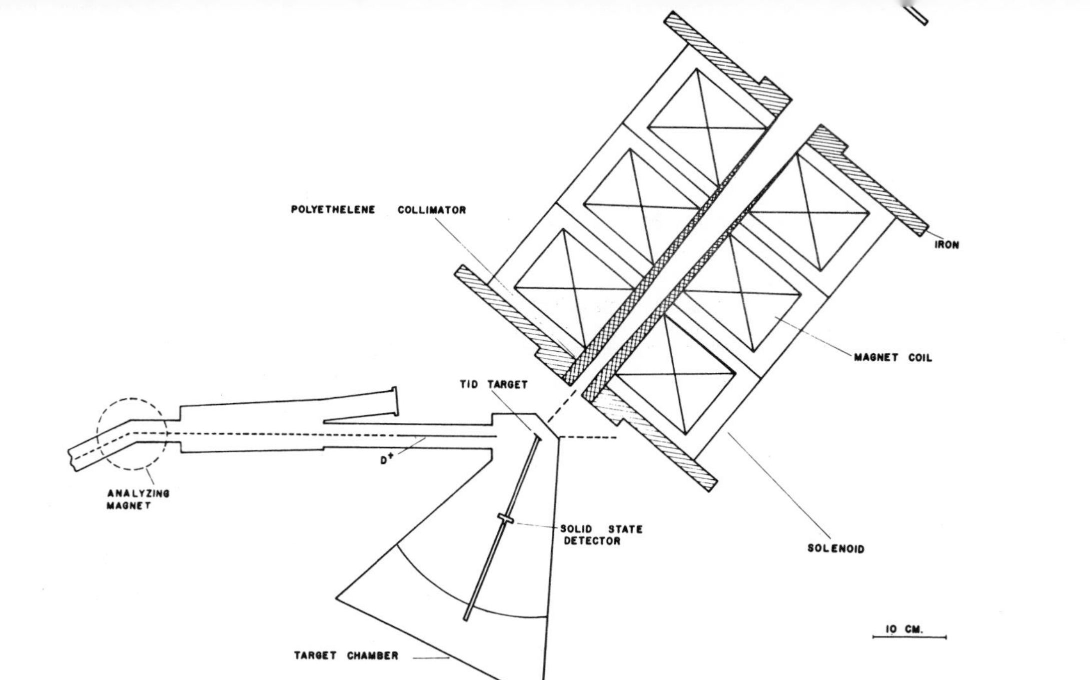

Fig. 7. An associated-particle time-of-rlight system adapted to polarization measurements. He^3 ions from the $D(d,n)He^3$ reaction are detected in a surface barrier detector. Coincident neutrons strike the carbon analyzer after passing through a tapered polyethylene collimator inside the solenoid bore. The neutron detector (not shown) is placed at $\theta_2 = 50°$ (lab system) above the plane of the diagram.

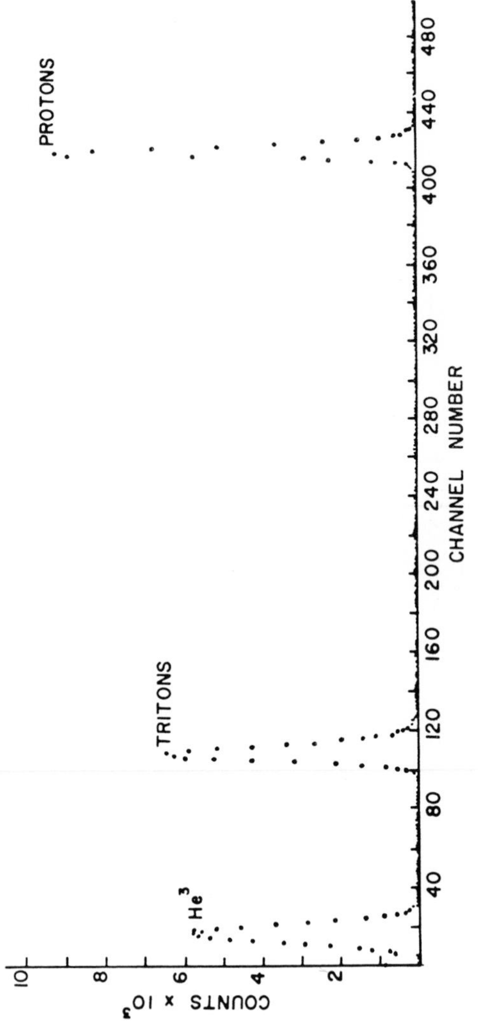

Fig. 8. Typical pulse height spectrum of charged particles from the D + D reaction.

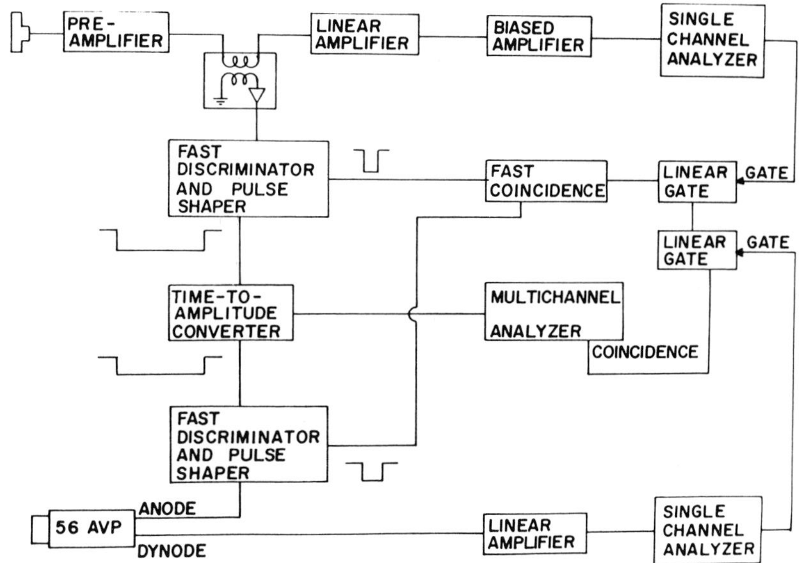

Fig. 9. Simplified block diagram of the electronics used in the present experiment.

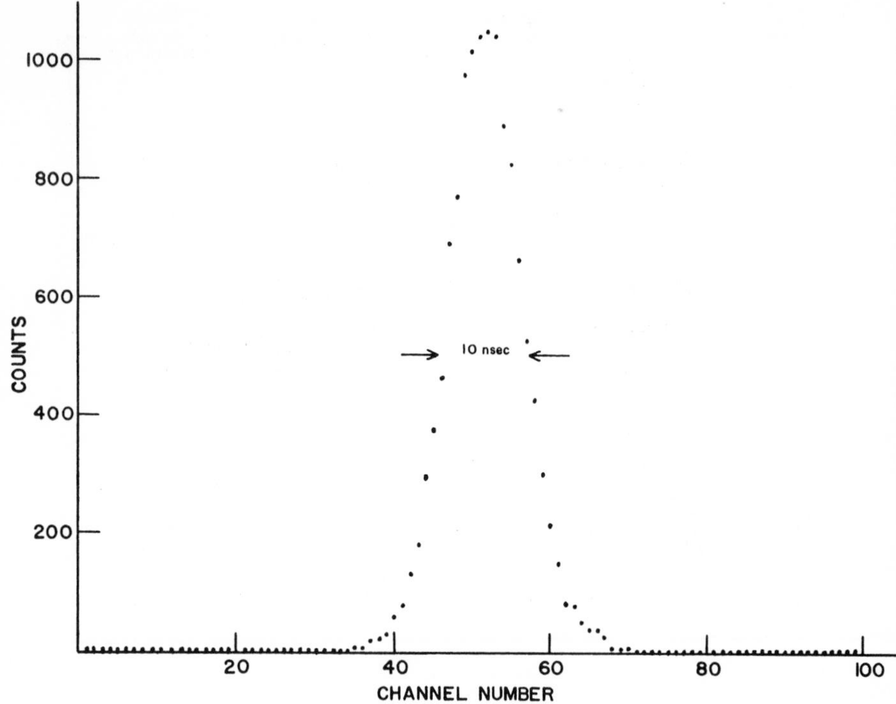

Fig. 10. Time-of-flight spectrum obtained with the neutron detector placed directly in the associated-neutron beam and the scattering sample removed. The time scale is 1.0 nsec per channel.

SURVEY OF (n,z) REACTIONS

R. A. Peck, Jr.

Brown University
Providence, Rhode Island

Within the time limit is it impossible to be simultaneously comprehensive, detailed and up to date. In choosing between a detailed report of recent work and a broad but cursory summary of the field I have chosen the survey as more appropriate to this Symposium. Therefore I claim the privilege of presenting generalities in place of details and representative results in place of the latest.

The subject is limited to reactions induced by neutrons of energy below about 20 MeV and resulting in the emission of a charged nuclear particle, (n,z) reactions. The emitted particle is limited to the three nuclei of hydrogen and two of helium, on the basis of Q-value and penetration through matter which decrease rapidly thereafter. Two particle emission will appear only incidentally, for its role in reaction studies so far has been that of an accountable deviation rather than a primary object of study.

Compilations of (n,z) data[1] have appeared at the rate of four per year in the last five years, and their information content has recently been comprehensively and critically reviewed[2]. My task therefore reduces to summarizing the picture of these processes and the nuclear information they have yielded so far, not substantially different from the picture projected in the reviews cited, and speculating on new information which may be obtained from future (n,z) reaction studies capitalizing on more advanced experimental techniques.

STATUS

Methods and Measurements

Analytical studies of (n,z) reactions are just over 10 years old. The prototype technique uses a counter telescope with two to four collinear detectors in coincidence, usually two gas counters and a solid detector. The coincidence requirement serves to define direction of travel and to reduce background response, an overriding necessity in the intense neutron fluxes required. Since about 1961 the differential pulse information has increasingly been used also for particle identification, the product E(dE/dx) being an approximate discriminant for the particle (mz^2), although the resolution in this parameter has heretofore not been very good; about 20% is typical. Angular definition is determined by the final detector's size and location, and is limited by the cross section and neutron flux. Energy measurement is by pulse height analysis of signals from the final detector, conventionally a scintillator but with a marked preference for solid state detectors since about 1963, because of their superior energy resolution and flexibility. The effective thickness of the junction detector, a primary factor in its resolution, is bias-controlled. The overall energy resolution is determined by that of the charged particle spectrometry. Neutron energy precision is determined only by target thickness and accelerator energy, and with a Van de Graaff a precision of 20 keV is not uncommon, with 1 keV available in principle. By application of target-correction voltages the accelerator energy can be stabilized one or two orders of magnitude more closely. The resolution usually obtained with alkali halide scintillators is of the order of 100 keV, though another order of magnitude is available in principle.

The second major class of conventional techniques is that employing wide-angle track recorders, i.e., emulsions and cloud chambers. Most commonly the reaction target is incorporated in or placed directly upon the detector, although good geometry is possible with emulsions in a radial multiplate camera. More common than the latter is the few-plate camera, in which the detector's solid angle is large but still small enough to simplify analysis by restricting recorded tracks to an angular range of interest. Spectrometry is by range measurement, and particle discrimination by selective development when practiced at all. Selective development is limited to discrimination in favor of the more densely ionizing particle, and is not practical for differentiation among the hydrogen isotopes. Most often emulsion measurements have been confined to spectral regions in which one particle type is isolated by virtue of the Q-values or cross sections governing its competitors.

The third major technique employed in (n,z) studies is activation, the chief source of excitation functions and the only source of information on many of the smaller cross sections. Nuclear product particles are not detected, but rather the beta or gamma emission of the product nucleus, discriminated with respect to half life or energy or both. The best technique now utilizes coincidence methods, energy discrimination and chemical separation to reduce the level of background (unwanted lifetimes) and to concentrate the subject activity.

Recent advances affecting the subtlety of information obtained from pulse data are the refinement of coincidence and correlation techniques, such as those entailed in polarization determinations and the measurement of excitation functions for isomeric ratios, and implementation of the superior resolution of the junction spectrometer. By this means particle-discrimination resolutions of 2%-3% have been achieved (in the pulse-product), and energy resolutions below 1%. Most (n,z) applications so far have entailed large collection angle with target in or on the detector, but this introductory phase is receding rapidly.

The following table, more or less complete to about the end of 1966, represents the extent to which various techniques (across) have been applied to various reactions (down). "Tracks" identifies emulsion and cloud chamber work, "pulses" the use of telescopes and some form of pulse height analysis. "Advanced" experiments are those involving either high precision, fairly elaborate particle discrimination or some unusual correlation feature. Table entries are the numbers of nuclei which have been subjected to the measurements indicated and, in parentheses, the highest A reached by the studies. (The lowest A involved is in every case below about 30 and in most cases below about 10.)

	Activation	Tracks	Pulses	
			Standard	Advanced
(n,α)	97 (238)	15 (90)	35 (209)	18 (209)
(n,p)	145 (239)	43 (197)	37 (197)	4 (39)
(n,d)	3 (80)	9 (120)	18 (107)	20 (130)
(n,t)	8 (54)	3 (10)	5 (64)	2 (14)
(n,He^3)	2 (133)			
(n,nz)	29 (186)	19 (130)	19 (90)	
All (n,z)	284	89	114	44

It is noteworthy that the more sophisticated studies are accelerating rapidly, at the rate of about 14 new nuclei per year, as compared with 6 per year from conventional pulse-analysis studies, 1 per year from emulsions and 12 per year by activation methods.

A functional review of these studies is tabulated below. Table entries are numbers of nuclei for which particular information (across) has been obtained, again with the maximum A reached in parentheses. The most obvious features of the picture are that (n,α) and (n,p) are well represented, reactions producing mass-3 particles little known, and (n,d), studied only since about five years ago, is rapidly crossing from the one class to the other under the combined stimuli of DWBA codes for their analysis and improved particle discrimination methods. It is of interest to point out the existence, in addition to the well-known comprehensive listing CINDA, of a tape library[3] including total cross sections and excitation functions for over 200 nuclei. Neutron energies up to 21 MeV are represented with several resonances for each.

	Some Cross Section	Excitation Function	Spectrum	Angular Distrib.
(n,α)	107 (238)	37 (209)	39 (209)	30 (209)
(n,p)	151 (239)	47 (197)	35 (197)	23 (197)
(n,d)	32 (130)		25 (130)	19 (120)
(n,t)	12 (64)	7 (40)	6 (14)	4 (14)
(n,He^3)	2 (133)			
(n,nz)	53 (186)	12 (186)		9 (103)

Reaction Mechnisms

We first consider the (n,z) process as an object of study rather than as a measuring device. The R-matrix formalism is the fundamental basis for ordering information about the reactions, but as usual the limited rate of acquisition of data has dictated an ordering instead on a framework of complementary models. This interim framework is a spectrum of interaction times, associated with progressive assimilation of the neutron into the nucleus. At its extremes are the promptly terminated surface direct reaction and the compound nucleus process terminated only after establishment of an equilibrium condition. Much current activity is associated with the identification and analysis of intermediate processes occurring between these extremes. The various modes are competitive, and the first order description of an (n,z) process is in terms of the model branching ratios in various nuclear domains.

The direct reaction occurs within roughly the nuclear transit time for the incident neutron, ~ (0.6 - 6) x 10^{-22} sec for $1 \leq E_n \leq 20$ Mev and $20 \leq A \leq 200$. It consists of the pickup or knock-on of a proton or cluster, generally from the nuclear surface, and is characterized by large cross sections, hard spectra (emphasis on low residual excitation) and angular distributions biassed toward small angles. Angular momentum and parity restrictions often impose a finite angular threshold generating a characteristic principal peak in the angular distribution and secondary oscillations reflecting the selection of a unique partial wave. When residual states are not resolved the latter effects disappear but forward peaking remains, as do the large cross sections and hard spectra. The direct cross section is given by a two-particle matrix element and with wave functions determined by the best available optical model parameters (in the DWBA analysis which is now standard) gives a generally adequate account of observations. In most situations it is thus known what the direct cross section is and how it behaves, so that confronted with data one can meaningfully ask if this is the operative process. The ratio of observed to correctly computed absolute cross section is the spectroscopic factor, whose principal component is the fraction of single particle configuration in the nuclear wave function.

The compound nucleus reaction occurs only after a relaxation time of $\hbar$ divided by the partial width of the compound nucleus state for emission into the incident neutron channel and a similar time lapse before formation of the outgoing channel. In the low excitation region of resolvable resonances, these times range from 10^{-19} sec for light nuclei to 10^{-16} for heavy. The incoherence implicit in the definition of a compound nucleus process is a sufficiently extreme simplification of the general situation that the R-matrix formalism generates cross section formulae which, while rigorous (given compound nucleus formation and incoherence) are relatively tractable. The cross sections are expressed in terms of transmission factors $T^J_{\alpha \ell j}$ directly related to the partial widths linking compound states to channels, J being the spin of the nuclear state and α, ℓ , j comprising all channel quantum numbers with orbital angular momentum and channel spin explicit. The differential cross section is

$$\frac{d\sigma_{\alpha\alpha'}}{d\Omega} = (4k_\alpha^2)^{-1} \sum_{J\ell j\ell' j'} gT^J_{\alpha\ell j}\, T^J_{\alpha'\ell' j'}\, [\Sigma_{\alpha''\ell'' j''}\, T^J_{\alpha''\ell'' j''}]^{-1}$$
$$X \sum_L f\rho_L(\cos\theta)$$

and the total cross section is obtained by replacing $\sum_L \cdots$ by 4π and factoring it from the remaining summation. Unprimed and singly primed indices are summed over the input and output channels actually populated, doubly primed indices over all those available. The quantity g is a simple statistical factor and f a combination of vector coupling coefficients involving all the angular momenta. L is an even index ranging upward from the least of 2ℓ, $2\ell'$ and $2J$, and J is summed over all states contributing to the cross section, providing the essential complexity to the expression. For unresolved final states, summation of the total cross section yields the Weisskopf-Ewing formula

$$\frac{d\sigma_{\alpha\alpha'}}{dE_{\alpha'}} \propto (2J_{\alpha'} + 1)E_{\alpha'} \cdot \sigma_c \cdot \rho$$

in which σ_c is the cross section for compound nucleus formation through the output channel and ρ the local density of final states. The proportionality constant is the summed and integrated total of the expressed function over all open channels.

Generally adequate values of σ_c are available from optical model calculations, and the crucial factor in the cross section is the nuclear level density ρ. Virtually all available expressions for the latter are based on the model of a Fermi gas of nucleons, for the excellent reason that nothing more is necessary to account for available data. Properties of the density function are chiefly determined by combinatorial effects and degneracies, and are quite insensitive to the single particle spacing generated by the underlying model. The resulting density function involves only the excitation energy and angular momentum parameters:

$$\rho(U,J) = Cu^{-2}\, e^{2\sqrt{aU}} \cdot (2J+1)\, e^{-\{J(J+1)/2\sigma^2\}}$$

C is a known constant. The exponent -2 is a product of the specific model used; if angular momentum is ignored it becomes -5/4. The parameter a corresponds to the spacing of single-particle levels and appears in the Fermi gas equation of state, $U = at^2 - t$, relating excitation to temperature. The value provided by the Fermi gas model, surprisingly close to that found to apply, is

$$a = A \left(\frac{r_o}{4.4} \right)^2$$

in which r_o is the constant $A^{-1/3}R$(fermis). The "spin cut-off parameter" σ, so called because of its obvious role in limiting the population of high-J states, represents an effective moment of inertia increasing with excitation,

$$\sigma = \frac{It}{\hbar^2}$$

Observed shell effects are plausibly incorporated by introducing the dependence of single particle level degeneracy on single particle angular momenta, using shell model values for the latter. Isotopic systematics enter through pairing-energy corrections to the excitation energy, an approach formalized by a superconducting model which translates the pairing energy into an energy gap (shift of the zero of excitation).

The 90° symmetry of angular distributions implicit in the differential cross section formula has been extensively employed as a discriminant for the compound nucleus process. When this condition obtains, a measure of the spin cutoff factor is available in the ratio of strengths of P_2 to isotropic components, which is given by $(\bar{J}\ \bar{\ell})^2/(12\ \sigma^4)^2$. The weakness of this criterion for compound nuclear processes has been widely publicized in recent years, however. On the one hand, direct processes involving exchange contributions can easily produce 90° symmetry; on the other, the compound process produces 90° symmetry only in the extreme cases of a single contributing state and incoherent contributions from many. When the resolution of levels begins to fail, input and output channels lose their independence, the angular distribution will generally become asymmetric and both it and the total cross section will show rapidly fluctuating energy dependence[4]. The observation of these "Ericson fluctuations" is generally regarded as the best evidence of a compound nucleus process; failing the resolution to observe them, consistency of the value of absolute cross section with the now well-established level density equation is probably the next best evidence.

Reaction mechanisms intermediate in degree of relaxation have been formulated near to both extremes. A step removed from the channel states of direct reactions are the particle-hole excitations[5] known as "doorway states". Such states channel progress in the direction of increasing complexity and are apparently sufficiently long-lived to impose on excitation functions a detectable fine structure of resonances roughly 50 - 200 keV wide, corresponding appropriately to 2-10 times the direct reaction time. Presumably an (n,z) reaction terminating from a doorway state represents the first disordering of a direct reaction. These "intermediate resonances" are of course quite distinct from the Ericson fluctuations whose widths are of the order of nuclear level widths. Slightly antecedent to the compound nucleus process is the partial equilibrium situation analyzed by Izumo[6]. A more sophisticated rendering of Bethe's early suggestion of "local heating" of the nucleus, this model envisions a reaction terminating after the establishment of equilibrium among a limited number of nucleons and hence not spatially localized, with a considerably reduced density of states resulting for a given excitation.

For (n,α) reactions, the validity of the compound nucleus model is quite well established in the mass range from $30 \lesssim A \lesssim 100$, statistical model cross sections agreeing well in absolute magnitude with those observed, as well as heavier neutron-magic nuclei in which evaporation of neutrons, the primary competitor with alpha emission, is suppressed by an anomalously low level density consequent on neutron shell closure. The direct reaction dominates both below $A \sim 20$ and above $A \sim 140$, in the former case because of shortage of nucleons and in the latter because of barrier inhibition of the low energy alphas favored by the statistical process. In heavy nuclei the dominance of direct events is signalled by rather slowly varying cross sections of order 1 mb two or three orders of magnitude greater than the compound nucleus values. In the transition regions the discrepancies are generally less than one order of magnitude, indicating that the two processes can be comparable, a conclusion further supported by occasional evidence of extreme sensitivity of angular distribution to neutron energy, as[7] in Ca^{40} and O^{16}.

Within the central mass range, spectra often show direct reaction contributions in the form of superfluities of high-energy alphas and (n,αn) contributions in similar low-energy excesses. The direct contributions are generally too weak for analysis beyond the observation that they are forward-peaked. The spectral mid-ranges show good linearity when rectified according to the Weisskopf-Ewing formula, 90° symmetric angular distributions and, most convincing of all, yield level density parameters of good consistency and with plausible dependences upon nuclear species. Energy resolution in most experiments has been insufficient to resolve compound nucleus states, though low residual states have sometimes been resolved.

The direct reaction, though frequently observed, has not been extensively studied in (n,α). The most detailed studies have been among the lightest nuclei (up to O^{16}), yielding spectra, angular distributions and excitation functions which are generally consistent and usually show a combination of pickup (or knock-out) and heavy-particle (exchange) stripping. The distinction between pickup and knockout from angular distributions is difficult, in the absence of appropriate DWBA codes; rarely, the differentiation has been effected through the measured ratio of spectroscopic factors for specific residual states[8]. Among heavy nuclei the direct reaction cross section, though dominant in (n,α), is absolutely small and no systematic analysis has been done. Interesting observations are gross structure peaks in the spectra[9], observed to be quite stable over the range $93 \leq A \leq 209$, and the persistence of forward peaking to high residual excitations[10] in Ag(n,α).

The measurement of (n,α) excitation functions with sufficiently high neutron energy resolution to observe intermediate resonances is a recent innovation gaining enormous popularity. Data on structures of order 100 keV wide and their correlation functions are rapidly accumulating, and though often analyzed in terms of Ericson fluctuations seem in fact more closely linked to doorway states.

Like (n,α), the (n,p) process is characterized by sizeable cross sections and in the middle mass range is dominated by the compound nucleus process, as evidenced by good absolute agreement of observed excitation functions with those computed from the consistent statistical parameters evolved from (n,α) studies. The statistical nature of (n,p) in the mass mid-range has also been attested by study of the ratio of the total cross section to that for neutron scattering. Above A ~100 the direct process dominates; e.g., for I^{127} the direct/compound ratio is below 1/10.

In heavy nuclei the direct process dominates but with small absolute cross section, and is practically known only in its total cross sections. Some direct reaction studies of light nuclei have been made, but not as yet to well resolved final states, and model analyses have been limited[11].

Marked systematic variations of (n,p) total cross section, consisting of both shell effects and isotopic variations, are reflected in a sensitive dependence of this cross section on the reaction Q-value[12] and are embodied in present representations of the level density.

The (n,d) reaction is apparently dominated by the direct pickup process for all nuclei, at least at 14 Mev and fairly low residual excitations, and is the subject of most analytical work so far done on direct reactions of (n,z) type. Angular distributions of transitions to resolved final states in roughly 20 nuclei (to mass 60) have been measured with sufficient precision to fit theoretical forms and, where previously unknown, to determine J^{π} data, but spectroscopic factors have as yet been extracted in only a few cases. In general the backward peak marking heavy particle stripping is not seen.

Except among the lightest nuclei, study of (n,t) and (n,He^3) has been limited by their small cross sections, well below 1 mb for neutrons of 14-20 MeV. For (n,He^3), upper limits ranging from 20 to 300 μb have been set by activation scans, and this reaction has apparently only once been observed. Detailed (n,t) studies have been limited to the very lightest nuclei and their analysis confined to exploration of kinematics and transitory product systems.

Most abundant of the two-particle emission events are those emitting a neutron in company with α or p. Little work has been specifically directed to these processes, because they have generally been relatively minor contributions to one-particle distributions in the energy ranges chiefly studied, a concerted study requires a higher order of experimental sophistication, and in most cases a satisfactory account of the process seems to be rendered by the statistical evaporation model . A general threshold law equation[13] based on 3-body kinematics is available for (n,np) and (n,nα), and statistical model estimates of cross sections for (n,2p) and 3-particle emission processes[1].

Nuclear Parameters

The parameters describing nuclear states are of two classes quantum numbers, and coefficients in the wave function. As the complexity of the state rises, with excitation or number of nucleons, the latter increase in variety, but the former do not. These parameters are most simply visible in the tabulated resonance parameters determined from slow neutron work on individual levels, consisting of resonance energy (excitation), g-factor (J) and partial widths for gamma and (s-wave) neutron channels. At low energy the level width is the sum of Γ_n and $\Gamma\gamma$ only; as energy increases, new partial widths are added as new channels open, successively for higher ℓ values (and thus different channel spins), for protons, for alpha particles and for other nucleon clusters. The proliferating partial widths represent wave function information of increasing complexity, being directly related to coefficients of fractional parentage. These coefficients constitute the essence of the wave function, for they quantify the expansion of the true wave function on a basis of single particle states in the specific nucleus represented. Each cfp thus measures the fraction of the nuclear wave function which has the configuration of a particular single particle channel. If the nuclear wave function is known, the cfp is available from R-matrix theory as its overlap integral with the channel configuration; conversely, insofar as the cfp's are measured in reaction studies the wave function is determined. In direct reaction analysis the cfp appears within the directly measurable spectroscopic factor. In compound nucleus resonance analysis, it appears as the reduced width γ^2 , the partial width linking state to channel with the mechanical separation probability extracted. When levels are not resolved the same quantity emerges in statistical form as the strength function, explicitly $\langle\gamma^2\rangle/\langle D\rangle$ or the average reduced-width-density, measuring both the strength of the specified single particle configuration in an average nuclear state at the excitation specified and the strength of the residual interaction between particle and nucleus.

The chief advantage of the neutron in studying resolved states is access to low levels in the compound nucleus above the neutron binding energy; the same advantage does not apply to the decay channel in (n,z) processes so that most information on compound nucleus resonances has come from neutron scattering and capture. Nevertheless a substantial and growing number of resonance parameters rest on (n,z) excitation functions; in $O^{16}(n,\alpha)C^{13}$, 21 resonances have been observed between 5.0 and 8.8 MeV of neutron energy[14]. In general, however, (n,z) spectra have yielded very few new levels, and not all of those have survived further investigation. Of the many reduced widths now known for specific states[15], a substantial number are based upon analysis of direct angular distributions to resolved states; the number of these involving (n,z) reactions is small but now growing rapidly[16].

The level density function is the statistical representation of the quantum numbers of nuclear states, and work on (n,z) reactions has contributed much of the present understanding of it. The Fermi gas model has been an adequate framework within the precision so far available, and the functional form of $\rho(U,J)$ contains in effect five parameters to be extracted from experimental studies: the single-particle spacing parameter $\underline{a}$ which determines the average rate of convergence of levels, the effective single-nucleon angular momenta j_n and j_p which relate $\underline{a}$ to the shell model, the pairing energy δ(or energy gap Δ) and the effective moment of inertia parameter σ which de-populates high-spin states.

The variation of $\underline{a}$ with nuclear species is quite well established experimentally[17]. The plot of $\underline{a}(A)$ is remarkably consistent as determined from excitation function resonances, total cross sections and spectra, from reactions (n,n'), (n,α), (n,p) and (p,α), and a(A) may resonably be considered a known quantity within the scatter of these data. The dominant effect is an essential proportionality of a to A, the average slope of 0.14 being remarkably close to the absolute Fermi gas value $(r_o/4.4\ f)^2$. First-order correction effects are strong dips in a and hence in level density observed at closed proton shells in (n,α) and (n,p) and at closed neutron shells in (n,α). These shell effects involve both the pairing energy and the abruptly changing j_n and j_p. The latter dependence is well reproduced by the Fermi gas model using shell-model angular momenta[18]. The pairing energy both contributes to the shell effects and introduces isotopic systematics[19] such that, e.g., $\rho_{oo}(U) \cong 2\rho_{Eo}(U) \cong \rho_{EE}(U)$. Pairing energy, becoming inoperative above the ground state, contributes an artificial suppression of the ground state relative to the rest of the level spectrum and so enters $\rho(U)$ as an energy shift to be subtracted from the actual excitation before evaluating ρ. It has been phenomenologically interpreted as the energy gap of a superconducting model[20], which gives a remarkably good account of the observed $\Delta(A)$ with little residual isotopic variation. Deformation effects have still to be introduced into the superconducting model.

It has been noted that the spin cutoff factor σ can be deduced independently from angular anisotropy and from spectrally determined temperatures. The values thus obtained so far show general consistency, though experimental uncertainties are high and systematic variations of σ are submerged in experimental uncertainties. The systematic examination of this factor remains to be done.

The average reduced width density (strength function) is well known for neutron channels of relatively low energy, virtually none of the information deriving from (n,z) work. The s-wave neutron strength function is known in about 200 nuclei over $20 \lesssim A \lesssim 250$ and is characterized by giant resonances centered around A = 50 and 150 representing the 3s and 4s single particle resonances respectively, the latter deeply split by the large static deformation of the nuclei concerned. The optical model account of this function, while not perfect, reproduces the curve's features very well, the apparent energy-dependence of the requisite parameters being attributable to the operation of non-local potentials. The principal feature of the p-wave neutron strength function, known over $50 \lesssim A \lesssim 240$ principally from neutron capture work, is the 3p particle resonance around A = 100. This also is split, apparently not by the spin-orbit interaction as believed for some time but by deformation, although the latter has yet to be demonstrated quantitatively. The d-wave neutron strength function is known with much less accuracy and more limited range, and appears to display a broad plateau over $120 \lesssim A \lesssim 190$. Little is known about the proton strength function, though (n,p) data have been utilized to demonstrate the correlation between the ratio Γ_p/Γ_n and displacement from the most stable neutron-proton ratio.

Wave function parameters of higher order are represented by the intra-nuclear lifetimes of nucleon clusters. Values of the alpha particle lifetime estimated from direct reaction (n,α) cross sections[21] and spectra[22] show generally good consistency and are small fractions of the nuclear transit time.

Contributions of (n,z) studies to knowledge of the 2-body force have been restricted by the technological lag, although certain earlier few-body studies have been noted. Recent studies[23] include $H^2(n,p)2n$, $H^3(n,p)3n$ (sought but not found), $H^3(n,d)2n$ and $H^3(n,t)n$. The two-neutron interaction peak has been clearly seen (peak:valley $>$ 3:1) and the triton scattering angular distribution fitted by a resonating group structure with Serber exchange mixture.

PROSPECTS

Techniques

In 1960, (n,z) studies were at least ten years behind their charged-particle-induced counterparts in extent of coverage and in precision. The "coverage gap" has narrowed steadily since then but closure of the "precision gap" began only recently has far to go. (There is no "energy gap"; because of the availability of high-Q source reactions an experimental study of a neutron-induced process starts out ahead of its p- or d-induced counterpart by the equivalent of about one tandem stage.) Because the compound nucleus process is dominant over much of the mass range, (n,z) studies are largely subject to experimental difficulties inherent in compound nucleus work, in particular the need to discriminate among particles and measure their energy over a large energy range enhanced in its least tractable portion. Hence much of the early work either omits a large part of the spectrum or fails to discriminate among particles, or both, and the domain open to future work does not exclude that already studied.

Among new technical advances those most needed in (n,z) work are the ones relating to coincidence, correlation and polarization measurements and to the drastic improvement of resolution, both in charged particle spectrometry and particle identification. Of techniques implementing the latter, the junction detector has already introduced a discontinuous improvement in (n,z) data, though for few studies as yet and rarely in good geometry arrangements. The magnetic spectrograph and time-of-flight apparatus, achieving further gains in precision and versatility by freeing the detector of its role as energy transducer, have yet to be applied to neutron-induced transformation reactions.

Each of these advances is the subject of a paper in the Symposium, and it is unnecessary to attempt to elaborate on their potentialities. Their applicability to (n,z) work is primarily contingent on the availability of sufficient neutron flux, the omnipresent limit in this work. Recent and continuing advances in ion source technology are relieving one of the two basic flux-limiting factors, and it is not unreasonable to anticipate the availability of low-energy beam currents of order 1 ma in time. At such a current and with energy definition (target thickness) of 50 keV a 5 MeV accelerator will offer, in principle, fluxes or order 10^9 neutrons/steradian·sec from 0-8 Mev and 14-22 MeV and over 10^{10} at 0.5 MeV. Realization of such high, precision fluxes will depend on elaboration of methods for utilizing such currents in such thin targets. The dissipation of this 50 watts/cm^2 presents no problem when thick backings and coolants can be employed, and even with thin backings, or none, much can be gained by beam shaping and a judicious choice of material in terms of elastic and thermal properties. The utilization of high currents in thin targets is a prerequisite to major advances in (n,z) studies and deserves attention.

Multichannel analysis of data can offset intensity limitations to a considerable extent through the conservation of data, as in the simultaneous registration of spectra of several particle types or at many angles. The most effective multichannel installations are expensive and possibly disproportionate to low energy accelerators, but through tape-recording of multichannel data similar ends can be achieved through computer facilities not specifically attached to the nuclear project.

Mechanisms

The mechanics of genuine compound nucleus reactions seem to be well established and relatively few questions responsive to conventional (n,z) studies are apparent in that area. Such studies retain very significant value, however, for the determination of nuclear parameters through the compound nucleus mechanism (next section).

On the direct reaction mechanism, on the other hand, substantial information remains to be obtained from the (n,z) versions. Direct reaction analysis of (n,α) has been virtually confined to light nuclei, the contribution being generally dismissed as a plausible surplus in the mid-range of A and discouragingly small in heavy nuclei. The extent and nature of heavy particle stripping, in particular, needs clarification[24]. Direct (n,p) transitions to resolved states and (n,d) pickup to appreciably excited states have yet to be studied, the former presumably pertinent to the elucidation of particle-hole doorway configurations. No systematic survey of direct reaction cross sections has yet been reported, nor any extensive or precise studies for other than light nuclei. Pickup reactions involving the transfer of two nucleons, whose study has barely begun, are a natural vehicle for the study of i-spin selection rules since it seems established that the dominant process is a simultaneous pickup of the two nucleons. Closely related is the open question of the "spin-flip amplitude", the probability of conversion between S=0 and S=1 pairs in the course of pickup. In the (α,d) reaction, deuteron transfer shows gross resonances (peak:mean as high as 10:1) and monotonic forward-peaked angular distributions.

Advances in precision are already stimulating intensive searches for Ericson fluctuations and doorway state resonances, in excitation functions and spectra. Since the intermediate resonance widths correspond in effect to reaction time lapse, it might well be expected that they will flatten and broaden progressively as one moves to the domain of dominance of the direct mechanism from that of the compound nucleus. Fluctuation surveys taken across the transitional mass ranges for (n,α) and (n,p) seem to be in order.

Competition between direct and compound nucleus processes, in fact, is one of the most interesting problem areas of reaction mechanics. Because they present distinct dominions of each process and equally well defined transitional domains, (n,α) and (n,p) reactions are powerful tools for this study. In this competition one is attempting to observe the systematics of relaxation of the random phase approximation itself, in terms of nuclear species and especially of excitation. Hence information on the highly excited nucleus is the principal requisite, available in principle through the application of adequate correlation techniques to 2- and 3-body emission processes. The study of competition will be hampered by small compound nucleus cross sections but facilitated by the probability that <u>interference</u> between the modes will enhance the sensitivity of observed yields to small compound fractions[4]. Beside the broad transition zones of the periodic table, suitable loci for the study of competition are the neighborhoods of magic nuclei in which, due to neutron shell closure, the compound (n,z) cross section is locally enhanced.

The most conceptually appealing approach to analysis of competition among mechanisms, direct timing of the products of the intra-nuclear cascade, has been discussed for years but is still out of reach. The relevant sector of the delay spectrum is 10^{-16} to 10^{-21} sec, and coincidence techniques still do not reach below 10^{-11} sec, although recoil-Doppler methods have reduced the limit of measurable gamma emission lifetimes to 10^{-15} sec. The systematic study of intermediate resonances or doorway states is of course an equivalent approach through the time-conjugate energy variable, as is the search for evidence of nuclear time delay in the spectrum of bremsstrahlung accompanying nuclear reactions[25].

Parameters

The overriding fact about (n,z) studies to date is the enormous preponderance of data at 14 MeV; for future work, the difference between accelerators of low energy ($\lesssim$ 5 MeV) and "no energy" ($\lesssim$ 0.5 MeV) can scarcely be exaggerated. Many valid surveys remains to be done with neutron energy as a controlled variable, and the importance of isotopic range- of breadth of reach beyond the valley of maximum stability- has been stressed by many commentators. These processes have a unique applicability to the examination of particle penetration through the nuclear surface, to its shape and consitution. Studies of the transfer of clusters will be responsive to continuing advances in particle discrimination techniques.

In the study of specific states and their parameters, direct (n,z) reactions have barely begun to receive their just application. DWBA analysis of (n,d) distributions is now straightforward but little used except around A = 30, although spectroscopic factors for the proton-channel-linked states thus available are in fairly short supply. Correlated surveys of neutron stripping and pickup have traced many single-neutron levels across the A range, from above the dissociation energy to well below the Fermi level, but the corresponding data for single-proton states have not been taken. The examination of "conditional" quantum numbers (i-spin, collective and single-particle quantum numbers) can be, but has not been, materially advanced by (n,z) studies.

The two regions in which the nuclear level density is well known, by direct counting and from the energy dependences of cross sections respectively, are still well separated. Closure of the gap depends in part upon an upward extension of the excitation to which single-state measurements can be made, and is thus linked to advances in energy resolution, particle discrimination and correlation techniques. The accelerating study of Ericson fluctuations applies to this region. Also falling within this obscure zone is the missing phenomenon of a "phase transition" reflecting the relaxation of ground-state pairings[26]. Also related to pairing is the question of the significance of the superconducting model[27], requiring precision cross section measurements and to which (n,p) work seems particularly pertinent.

The spin-cutoff parameter of the level density function is still little known, and techniques for its measurement need to be sharpened. The study of intensity ratios of isomeric transitions, leading by the same process to states of similar excitation but differing spin, is one of the most direct methods but little applied with (n,z) as yet because of the energy resolution required. With low energy accelerators this work can best be done with incident neutrons because of the necessity for sufficient energy to form high-spin states. The study of σ through anisotropy in compound nucleus reactions may be advanced in correlation studies of two-particle emissions, in which the second emission may be expected to display the lower moment of inertia because of its reduced excitation, and a correspondingly enhanced anisotropy. It has been noted that the proton strength function is little known, as is the neutron strength function for $\ell > 1$. The proton channels are available to (n,d) work, and the more complex (n,z) reactions may be expected to have an increasing role in neutron strength function determinations at the higher energies at which scattering and capture lose their key roles.

Both the DWBA matrix element of direct reactions and the formation cross section in compound nucleus reactions are involved with the optical model, and insofar as (n,z) processes offer means for studying both they can in principle provide information on the nuclear parameters of the optical model. The study of polarization in the reactions offers a powerful means to this end, and can probe independently the shape of the potential and the strength of its spin-orbit component. Charge-exchange calculations exist for direct (n,p) reactions and predict fairly large polarizations, but with the exception of $Li^6(n,\alpha)H^3$, polarization studies of (n,z) reactions lie wholly in the future.

Finally, we should note the immediate technical value of accurate data on a number of (n,z) reactions. While Li^6(n,α) has been extensively studied there remains uncertainty as to its absolute cross section and excitation function below 1 Mev. Pertinent to the establishment of activation standards are absolute excitation functions of high precision for B^{10}(n,α) and B^{10}(n,αγ) up to 1 MeV and S^{32}(n,p) up to 14 MeV. For detector applications of importance to reaction investigations, flux monitoring and shielding evaluation, excitation functions up to around 10 Mev and with good accuracy at least relative to the standards are needed for isotopes of Mg, Al, Si, P, Ti, Fe, Ni, Co, Cu and Mo. A full study of He^3(n,p) is needed in the interests of neutron spectrometry, excitation functions to about 2 MeV of Cl and K isotopes for reactor calculations and O^{16}(n,α) in the neighborhood of 10 MeV for radiation damage calculations. All of these cross sections represented unsatisfied needs about a year ago.

REFERENCES

1. P. Jessen et al, Nuclear Data A 1, 103 (1966); H. Liskien and A. Paulsen, "Compilation of Cross Sections for Some Neutron Induced Threshold Reactions", EUR 119e (1966); A. Chatterjee, Nucleonics 22, #8, 108 (1964); 23, #8, 112 (1965); H. Neuert and H. Pollehn, "Tables of Neutron Cross Sections", EUR 122e (1963); E. T. Bramlitt and R. W. Fink, Phys. Rev. 131, 2649 (1963); M. D. Goldberg et al, "Angular Distributions in Neutron-Induced Reactions", BNL 400, Second Edition (1962).

2. N. Cindro, Revs. Modern Phys. 38, 391 (1966); L. Colli, in "Progress in Fast Neutron Physics" (U. of Chicago Press, 1963), p. 145; F. L. Ribe, in "Fast Neutron Physics" (Interscience Publishers, 1963), Vol. II, p. 1775.

3. D. A. Klopp, in "Proceedings of Conference on Neutron Cross Section Technology", Washington, D.C. (March 1966), CONF-660303, p. 309.

4. T. Ericson, in "Proceedings of the International School of Physics 'Enrico Fermi', Course 23", Varenna (Academic Press, 1963), p. 142.

5. H. Feshbach, Revs. Modern Phys. 36, 1076 (1964); K. J. Le Couteur, Phys. Letts. 11, 53 (1964).

6. K. Izumo, in "Direct Interactions and Nuclear Reaction Mechanisms" (Gordon and Breach, 1962), p. 312.

7. G. Calvi et al, Nucl. Phys. 39, 621 (1962); 48, 408 (1963); D. R. Maxson and R. D. Murphy, "Study of the $O^{16}(n,\alpha)$ Reaction" (in press).

8. R. A. Al Kital and R. A. Peck, Jr., Phys. Rev. 130, 1500 (1963).

9. P. Kulišić et al, Nucl. Phys. 73, 548 (1965).

10. K. Breuer and E. Rössle, Nucl. Phys. 69, 587 (1965).

11. N. Austern et al, Phys. Rev. 92, 350 (1963): G. Schiffrer, Phys. Letts. 17, 122 (1965). The latter introduces exchange terms.

12. N. K. Majumdar, Nucl. Phys. A 89, 329 (1966); V. Levkovskii, Soviet Physics-JETP 18, 213 (1964); D. G. Gardner, Nucl. Phys. 29, 373 (1962).

13. R. W. Hart et al, Phys. Rev. 108, 1512 (1957).

14. E. A. Davis et al, Nucl. Phys. 48, 196 (1963).

15. A. M. Lane, Revs. Modern Phys. 32, 519 (1960); M. H. Macfarlane and J. B. French, Revs. Modern Phys. 32, 567 (1960).

16. L. Colli, reference 2, pp. 146 - 148.

17. G. S. Mani and M. A. Melkanoff, in "Direct Interactions and Nuclear Reaction Mechanisms" (Gordon and Breach, 1962), p. 318; U. Facchini et al, Nucl. Phys. 51, 460 (1964); E. Erba et al, Nuovo Cimento 22, 1237 (1961).

18. K. K. Seth et al, Phys. Letts. 11, 308 (1954); D. B. Thomson, Phys. Rev. 129, 1649 (1963); T. D. Newton, Can. J. Phys. 34, 804 (1956).

19. D. L. Allan, Nucl. Phys. 24, 274 (1961); reference 12.

20. C. J. Thompson, Nucl. Phys. 77, 477 (1966); Phys. Letts. 14, 146 (1965).

21. H. Gauvin et al, Nucl. Phys. 39, 447 (1962); M. Arnold et al, Nucl. Phys. 19, 500 (1960); P. E. Hodgson, Nucl.

Phys. _8_, 1 (1958).

22. J. I. Sebrennikov, _Soviet Physics_-JETP _8_, 547 (1959); reference 9.

23. K. Debertin, _Nucl. Phys._ _81_, 220 (1966); J. M. Kootsey, "The Interaction of 14.1 Mev Neutrons with Tritons" (in press).

24. M. K. Banerjee, _Nucl. Phys._ _83_, 575 (1966).

25. R. M. Eisberg, _Revs. Modern Phys._ _36_, 1100 (1964); G. C. Phillips, _ibid_, p. 1085.

26. T. Ericson, _Nucl. Phys._ _6_, 62 (1958). See also "Direct Interactions and Nuclear Reaction Mechanisms" (Gordon and Breach, 1962), pp. 263 - 265.

27. H. K. Vonach, _Nucl. Phys._ _60_, 84 f (1964).

NEUTRON INELASTIC SCATTERING BY TIME-OF-FLIGHT

A. B. Smith

Argonne National Laboratory
Argonne, Illinois

Abstract

The status of inelastic neutron scattering studies using fast time-of-flight techniques is reviewed in the context of nuclear models and structure.

Introductory Remarks

The present technology provides precisely controled ion beams with energies well above the coulomb barrier and charged particle detection with good resolution and sensitivity. As a result, studies of primary charged particle reactions have provided a deep insight into nuclear structure with economy of time and funds. In contrast neutron scattering deals with a secondary reaction, is demanding of shielding and intensity and requires precise and difficult spectroscopic measurements with uncharged particles. Thus, it is not strange that during a period of rapid growth in charged particle physics, fast neutron scattering studies have been relatively limited.

In the present context a strong motivation for neutron scattering endeavors is the energy restriction of $\sim$ 5 MeV. Charged particles of that energy are limited in their ability to probe the nuclear surface and beyond. Often severe intensity and resolution requirements associated with charged particle studies can be relaxed through the use of neutron projectiles. Further, there are features of nuclear structure and forces that are intrinsically suitable for study by fast neutron scattering. There is a strong applied motivation for the study of neutron scattering and this has lead to the establishment and support of some specialized and complex facilities.

This paper will deal with fast neutron scattering from the point of view of nuclear structure. The intent is to delineate the current status and future potential of the field including; a) techniques, specifically the pulsed beam time-of-flight method, b) elastic scattering and its relation to the inelastic process, c) direct reactions (DR) and competition with compound processes and e) statistical and intermediate structure phenomena. Hopefully, the discussion will illuminate fertile areas of investigation.

Experimental Ways and Means

The strength of the time-of-flight method lies in the spacial, energy, and time definition of the source and the accuracy of the time detection of the neutron. In the present context of low energy accelerators, intense neutron sources are available for energies extending to $\sim$ 8 MeV and from $\sim$ 14 to 19 MeV. These sources can be made mono-energetic to within $\lesssim$ 20 keV. Scattering samples are $\sim$ 1/2 a mean free path in thickness and take forms ranging from rings to spheres. Detectors are most often proton recoil scintillators having low backgrounds (particularly with γ-ray suppression circuitry) and are sensitive to neutrons of $\lesssim$ 50 keV[1]. Attention must be given to the shielding of the detector from the primary source and to any collimating aperture defining the scattered neutron flight path[2]. The choice of flight path depends upon the particular experimental objective and may vary from tens of centimeters to many meters. Excellent timing circuitry is commercially available in both analog and digital forms. The former are more versatile and are in wider usage.

Associated particle techniques have been employed to establish a source time fudical mark[3]. The method can provide good time resolution and a degree of geometric collimation but is limited to the detection of light reaction products having relatively high energy (the d(t,n) reaction for example). More general use is made of the pulsed beam technique pioneered by Cranberg and the Los Alamos group[4]. This method achieves excellent sensitivity and resolution over a wide neutron energy range and it is the technique employed in all the work described in subsequent portions of this paper. The pulsed beam method is most productive when it includes an ion bunching system so as to increase the intensity of the source burst. Bunching has been achieved by use of a pre- or post-acceleration klystron cavity in the manner developed by Moak and his co-workers[5] or a post-acceleration magnetic time contraction as suggested by Mobley[6]. These bunching techniques can provide ion bursts of $\sim$ 1-10 ma intensity, for a duration of $\sim$ 1 nsec and with a beam energy modulation of 5-10 keV. The klystron method is not restricted in source location but may increase complexity in a difficult to service high voltage terminal. The magnetic technique is limited to a fixed target position but is simple in function.

The time equivalence of the source energy spread, the source time definition, the neutron transit time across the sample and the detector, the detector response time and electronic time resolution are each $\gtrsim$ 1 nsec resulting in a cumulative system time resolution of $\gtrsim$ 2.5 nsec. This is, in fact, what is practically observed corresponding to scattered neutron resolutions of $\gtrsim$ 15 keV.

An example of a system using the magnetic bunching principle is outlined in Fig. 1 [7]. The apparatus is unique in providing for the concurrent measurement of up to ten scattered neutron spectra with automated system function delegated to an on-line digital computer. The lower right of the figure shows ten time-of-flight spectra obtained by scattering 650 keV neutrons from W^{186} at varying angles. Each such spectrum was recorded in a two dimensional energy-time matrix as illustrated in Fig. 2 by the observed scattering from natural tungsten. To the left of this figure are 15 time spectra corresponding to progressively larger proton recoil energies within the neutron detector. The detector time response broadens and straggles to longer times as the recoil energy decreases to a minimum value of $\sim$ 60 keV. The computer system corrects for this "walk" effect and sums the differential spectra over selected biases to obtain spectra such as are indicated at the right of Fig. 2. The upper of these spectra reveals the 46 keV state in the low abundant isotope W^{183} despite the intense elastic contribution at the 60 deg. scattering angle. Structure is evident in the broad peak corresponding to the excitation of the 2+ collective states in the three even isotopes separated from one another by $\sim$ 10 keV. The FWHM of the elastic peak is 2.7 nsec corresponding to an energy resolution of $\sim$ 18 keV. Figure 3 shows several examples of spectra obtained by scattering relative low energy neutrons from Ta, Re, and Pt. A wealth of structure, some of it previously unobserved, is evident. At higher incident energies it becomes increasingly difficult to resolve detailed level structure. However, results obtained by McConnell et al. at the Oak Ridge Laboratory and elsewhere have achieved excellent detail as illustrated by the scattering $\sim$ 5 MeV neutrons from Fe shown in Fig. 4 [9]. Here the scattered neutron resolution is $\sim$ 100 keV at an energy of $\sim$ 2 MeV.

Future improvements in the fast time-of-flight technique will likely occur and be most productive in the area of intensity. It is reasonable to expect at least an order of magnitude improvement in peak source intensity, thereby achieving a factor of three better velocity resolution with improved sensitivity. Such improvements will make the method competitive with many of the best techniques employed in charged particle scattering. At present, some time-of-flight facilities are capable of providing vast quantities of multi-dimensional information. There is already a need for major improvements in data processing and analysis and the situation rapidly becomes more acute. This area must receive major attention and this probably means a further descent of the "ferrite curtain."

Elastic Scattering and the Nuclear Potential

Elastic scattering cannot be divorced from the inelastic processes. At low energies the two are coupled through the compound nucleus (CN) and at all energies elastic scattering guides the selection of the potential to be employed in the interpretation of the inelastic results. A profusion of optical potentials have been proposed. The non-local form of Perey and Buck (P + B) has been successful over extended energy intervals[10]. The surface absorption potential of Moldauer (PAM) well describes low energy scattering and strength functions in the spherical nuclei[11]. Typical comparisons of measured and calculated elastic scattering at 1.0 MeV are shown in Fig. 5. The description of experiment obtained with the PAM potential is good. The P + B potential provides good agreement with observed elastic scattering of 7.0 MeV neutrons from Bi^{209} as indicated in Fig. 6. As pointed out by Hooton and others, detailed comparisons of measured and calculated elastic scattering distributions at isolated energies can be deceptive and potentials should be established by comparison with experiment over an extended energy region[14]. The requisite experimental information is only now becoming available. For example, Fig. 7 compares calculated and measured elastic scattering from Sn over an energy interval of $\gtrsim$ 1.2 MeV. Such detailed measurements can be sensitive to variations in potential parameters, in this example the real potential V.

At low incident neutron energies compound nuclear processes are strongly influenced by only a few states and are as a result, highly individualistic. As the incident energy increases, a systematic behavior of both elastic and inelastic cross section emerges until $\sim$ 1.5 MeV where both experiment and calculation become unreliable due to uncertain knowledge of excited states. At much higher energies compound elastic processes are insignificant and calculation again becomes representative of experiment. The systematic behavior near 1.0 MeV is indicated in Fig. 8. Here are shown the elastic cross section, first two coefficients of the legendre expansions of the angular distributions, and the total inelastic cross section as a function of mass number, A. The solid points indicate the experimental values and the curves calculations carried out with the PAM potential using several imaginary well values, W. The calculated results obtained with W = 14 MeV are descriptive of measurements over a wide mass region despite the fact they pre-date the acquisition of ∿ 40% of the experimental information. Certain trends are immediately evident. As expected, the elastic and inelastic cross sections for deformed nuclei are not well described by the spherical potential employed. The results are strongly shell dependent. This is partly due to shell effects on level densities entering into compound nuclear processes. Beyond this, the potential itself is sensitive to proton and neutron shell closures. This is very evident in the elastic angular distributions shown in Fig. 9 [16]. As the double shell closure at A = 208 is approached, calculations based on the PAM potential remain in good agreement with experiment if the imaginary value W is reduced from the general value of 14 MeV to ∿ 5 MeV at A ∿ 209. Similar but less pronounced effects have been noted at P and N ∿ 50[12].

General potentials established from comprehensive elastic scattering information provide the basis for interpretations of inelastic scattering and for the assay of detailed structure effects. They are not always quantitatively successful particularly where spin-orbit forces and polarization are involved.

Inelastic Neutron Scattering and the Compound Nucleus

The observed compound nucleus (CN) inelastic scattering is dependent on the resolution of incident and emitted neutrons. The processes are governed by the incident neutron energy spread, ΔE, and the average resonance width, Γ, and spacing, D, of the compound nuclear states. Where $\Gamma \ll D$ and $\Delta E \ll D$ the excitation of individual compound states is described by the Briet-Wigner relation[17,18]. In the present context such processes are predominately in very light nuclei and will not be further discussed. As the energy and scattering mass increases the levels become broad and closely spaced and, finally overlap ($\Gamma \sim D$). When this occurres and $\Delta E \sim D$ a small number of compound states participate in the inelastic scattering process. The result is a rapidly varying cross section which may not be symmetric about 90°. Where $\Gamma \ll D$ and $D \ll \Delta E$ many compound states are excited resulting in average cross sections that are symmetric about 90° and relatively smooth functions of energy though small (Ericson[19]) fluctuations may remain. These average CN cross sections can be described in terms of Hauser-Feshbach (H-F) theory particularly when modified to correct for width fluctuation effects[20].

The cross sections for the CN excitation of a specific state rises rapidly from threshold to a broad maximum then decreases in a manner determined by the availability of exit channels. Structure insight requires experimental determination of the emitted neutron energies and the respective cross sections. Representative inelastic excitation cross sections extending over the periodic table are indicated by data points in Figs. 10 to 12 [21]. Cross sections pertaining to the excitation of the first few states are given together with the corresponding level structure. The results of H-F calculations using the indicated spins and parities and the general PAM spherical optical potential are noted by solid curves. The calculations are not descriptive of the excitation of collective states in deformed nuclei such as W^{182}. The dashed curves were obtained by correcting the H-F result for fluctuation effects in the manner of Moldauer[22]. The corrections are most pronounced near threshold where the available exit channels are limited, Fe, Nb, and Te, for example. The correction effect is particularly clear in Fig. 13 where the measured and calculated excitations of the 2+ (846 keV) state in Fe are compared. The corrected Hauser-Feshbach result (H-F') provides a reasonable agreement with experiment.

Many, but not all, of the above cross sections correspond to the excitation of well known states. The calculations thus illustrate the qualitative understanding of excited states that can be obtained from measured inelastic excitation functions. This can be considerable in cases where beta-gamma spectroscopy, Coulomb excitation, or other techniques provide little or no structure information. An example relating the inelastic measurement to a possible single particle configuration is given in Fig. 14 [8]. The unified model of Mottelson and Nilsson[23] predicts the single particle configurations in the odd A deformed nuclei Re^{185} and Re^{187}. The $\frac{5}{2}$ + ground state is the basis of a rotational band. The next single particle state is $\frac{9}{2}$ - [514] and has been clearly identified in Re^{187} and Re^{183} but not in Re^{185} as excitation by either decay or Coulomb excitation is unavailable. As evident in Fig. 14, the inelastic excitation of a state of the expected energy (∿ 380 keV) was observed. Further, calculations (solid curves) based upon the $\frac{9}{2}$ - configuration describe the measured results far better than other spin choices although the result is not sensitive to parity. This example is typical of the structure information that has been obtained through the measurement of inelastic excitation cross sections at relatively low energies.

The angular distribution of neutrons emitted in CN inelastic scattering is nearly isotropic at low bombarding energies and generally symmetric about 90°. As the incident neutron energy increases, the distributions become relatively anisotropic and can be sensitive to the spin of the final state. An example is the inelastic scattering from Pb^{206} shown in Fig. 15 [24]. At an incident energy of 2.5 MeV a number of angular distributions are observed each well described by calculations using specific spin assignments. The parity selection is not as unique.

The transition from discrete to continuum inelastic neutron distributions is not abrupt. An intermediate example is the inelastic scattering of 7.0 MeV neutrons from Fe shown in Fig. 16 [25]. The excitation of several states is evident followed by a continuum distribution having a simple maxwellian temperature of 0.96 MeV. The cross sections for inelastic scattering in the continuum region are dependent upon the CN formation cross section and the density of nuclear states. There have been extensive theoretical treatments of excited level densities extending from simple fermi gas models to complex considerations inclusive of spin cut-off factors, shell effects, and pairing energies. Many of these have been reviewed by Ericson[26]. Some of these complexities are evident in Fig. 17 where results of scattering 5 to 7 MeV neutrons from Ho, Ta, and Pr are plotted as a function of U, the excitation energy corrected for pairing[27]. The results for Ho and Ta agree with theory, but Pr, a closed neutron shell nucleus, deviates from a linear relation. Level density parameters, a, can be derived from the measurements and compared with theoretical predictions based upon low energy resonance data. Agreement is not always achieved, possibly due to theoretical uncertainties. The continuum measurements are deceptively simple, requiring well established sensitivity calibrations over large dynamic range. Perhaps for this reason,experimental results have been seriously discrepant and have not always agreed with those obtained in (p,n) and other studies. Both direct reaction (DR) and (n,2n) processes can further confuse the experimental measurements and their interpretation. In addition, an intriguing statistical concept, proposed by Moldauer, but not yet observed experimentally, is the $(n;\gamma,n')$ cascade process[28]. Calculation indicates that cross sections for the process can be appreciable.

Direct Inelastic Scattering, Channel Coupling, and Collective Excitation

As the incident neutron energy increases, direct inelastic scattering becomes more probable and the compound excitation of single states drops as the number of available exit channels increases. The transition can be abrupt as noted by Cranberg et al. in the excitation of 3- (2.6 MeV) state in Pb^{206} [29]. Over an incident interval of 4 to 6 MeV the excitation of this state by CN processes falls by an order of magnitude while the DR more than doubles and strongly dominates at 6 MeV.

Direct excitation of a number of individual states has been observed at incident energies of ∿ 14 MeV where the experimental conditions are particularly favorable. An excellent example is the inelastic scattering from Al reported by the Oak Ridge Group and others and shown in Fig. 18 [30]. The curves represent cross sections calculated using a DWBA approximation and an optical potential. The experimental resolution of ∿ 450 keV defines inelastic scattering to individual and/or composites of closely spaced levels. The calculated excitation of both quadrupole and octupole collective states and was obtained with an effective deformation in good agreement with that reported in Coulomb excitation and other work. Bonozzola et al.[31] have studied the same inelastic Al excitations assuming that the structure involved was due to a coupling of the 1d 5/2 proton hole to the 1.78 MeV 2+ core state in Si^{28}. The relative calculated (n,n') intensities closely correspond to those obtained in (d,n') experiments.

The elastic scattering and the inelastic excitation of the first rotational state in even-even nuclei can be strongly coupled and explicit calculation of the cross section is possible[32]. Experiment often does not resolve the inelastic contribution at incident energies sufficiently high to provide a large effect. However, at relatively low energies the DR can be present as indicated by the scattering of 0.6 MeV neutrons from W^{184} shown in Fig. 19[33]. The observed excitation of the rotational 2+ state (110 keV) is not symmetric about 90°. Results of coupled channel calculations by Dunford using a deformed potential (solid curves) nicely describe the elastic scattering and the shape (not magnitude) of the observed inelastic angular distribution[24]. The DR contribution here is not large (∿ 20% of the CN excitation) but rises steadily until it is the dominant factor at several MeV.

Observed Intermediate Structure

The experimental resolution may $\underset{\sim}{\sim}$ D in scattering from light and intermediate nuclei and an intermediate structure may be observed with a width, $\overline{\Gamma}_I$, and spacing, $\overline{D}_I$, such that $\overline{\Gamma}_{sp} >> \overline{\Gamma}_I >> \overline{\Gamma}$ and $D_{sp} >> \overline{D}_I >> \overline{D}$. It has been suggested that this intermediate structure is related to the dynamics of CN formation, shell structure and strength functions, and that it may be correlated between differing reaction channels[35]. Experimental results showing such an apparent intermediate structure in Fe are shown in Fig. 20. Detailed resonance structure characteristic of the CN is shown in the lower half of the figure. This is superimposed on much broader modulations. These general trends are also evident in the elastic scattering cross sections (upper portions of figure) observed with incident energy resolutions $\sim \times 20$ broader than used for the total cross section measurements. Both total cross section and scattering measurements were made using the same basic time-of-flight apparatus[7]. Figure 21 shows similar broad structure in the observed elastic and inelastic scattering cross sections of V. It is not clear that the observed structure is correlated between elastic and inelastic exit channels. From this type of evidence the dynamic characteristics of CN formation are not clear. Indeed, these particular results have been qualitatively outlined by Moldauer using only a statistical interpretation of the poles of the S-matrix[37].

A Summing Up

The time-of-flight technique has made possible the illumination of what was only a few years ago the virtually unknown area of inelastic neutron scattering. This knowledge has permitted the critical assay of a wide range of nuclear concepts and has had an appreciable impact on certain applied nuclear endeavors. The methods have now reached the maturity required for studies of nuclear structure particularly those facets not easily examined by other means. This does not imply that such studies are either simple, easy, or cheap. Entrance into the field of inelastic neutron scattering with a low energy and non-specialized accelerator should be on a highly selective basis emphasizing those problems and techniques not normally compatible with the programs of major facilities motivated by applied objectives.

References

1. Roland Gauggel, private communication.
2. A. Langsdorf, Jr., "Neutron Collimation and Shielding for Experimental Purposes," Fast Neutron Physics, Vol. 1, J. Marion and J. Fowler, editors, Interscience Pub. Inc. N.Y. (1960).
3. J. Neiler and W. Good, "Time-of-flight Techniques", Fast Neutron Physics, Vol. 1., J. Marion and J. Fowler, editors, Interscience Publ. Inc. N.Y. (1960).
4. L. Cranberg and J. Levin, Phys. Rev. 103, 343 (1956).
5. Moak et al., Rev. Sci. Inst. 35, 672 (1964).
6. R. C. Mobley, Phys. Rev. 88, 360 (1952).
7. Smith et al., "Multi-angle Fast Neutron Time-of-flight System", to be published in Nucl. Inst. and Methods.
8. Smith et al., "Scattering of Fast Neutrons from Ta, Re, and Pt", to be published (1967).
9. J. M. McConnell et al.,private communication.
10. F. Perey and B. Buck, Nucl. Phys. 32, 353 (1963).
11. P. A. Moldauer, Nucl. Phys. 47, 65 (1963).
12. A. Smith and R. Hayes, "Fast Neutron Scattering from Elemental Mo, Sn, Sb, and Te", ANL-7274 (1967), unpublishe
13. Zafiratos et al., Phys. Rev. Letters, 14, 913 (1965). Also Beyster et al., Phys. Rev. 104, 1319 (1956).
14. D. J. Hooton, Phys. Rev. 128, 1805 (1962).
15. A. Smith, private communication (1967), See also, "Nuclear Structure Study with Neutrons", p-89, North Holland Pub. Co., Amsterdam (1966).
16. W. G. Vonach, et al., Phys. Letters, 11, 331 (1964).
17. The present author referred to the work of Dr. P. Hodgson for much of the experimental interpretation; particularly to "The Optical Model of Elastic Scattering", Oxford, Univ. Press, London (1963), and "Theories of Neutron Inelastic Scattering", (private communication).
18. See M. A. Preston, "Physics of the Nucleus", Addison-Wesley Publishing Co., Reading, Massachusetts (1962).
19. T. Ericson, Phil Mag. 9, 425 (1960).
20. W. Hauser and H. Feshbach, Phys. Rev. 87, 366 (1952).
21. A. B. Smith, private communication (1967).
22. P. A. Moldauer, Rev. Mod. Phys., 36, 1079 (1964). See also, A. Lane and J. Lynn, Proc. Phys. Soc. A70, 557 (1957).
23. B. Mottelson and S. Nilsson, K. Danske Vidensk, Selsk. mat.-fys. Skr. 1, No. 8, (1959).
24. "Angular Distributions of Neutron-induced reactions", BNL-400, 2nd Ed. M. Goldberg, et al., (1962).
25. J. Towle and R. Owens, private communication (1966).

26. T. Ericson, Annals of Physics, 23, 390 (1963).
27. R. Owens and J. Towle, "Nuclear Structure Study with Neutrons", p-547, North Holland Publ. Co. Amsterdam, (1966).
28. P. A. Moldauer, Proc. Conf. on Neutron Cross Section Technology, Washington, D. C. (1967), CONF-660303.
29. Cranberg et al., Phys. Rev. Letters, 11, 341 (1963). See also P. Hodgson and Brandenberger et al., private communication (1967).
30. P. Stelson et al., Nucl. Phys. 68, 97 (1965).
31. Bonozzola et al., Phys. Rev. 140, B835 (1965).
32. T. Tamura, Rev. Mod. Phys. 37, 679 (1965).
33. D. Lister et al., "Fast Neutron Scattering from the 182, 184, and 186 isotopes of Tungsten", ANL-7288, unpublished.
34. C. Dunford, Private communication; also Proceedings of IAEA Conf. on Nuclear Data, Paris (1966); to be published.
35. H. Feshbach, "Nuclear Structure Study with Neutrons", p-257, North-Holland Publishing Company, Amsterdam, (1966).
36. A. Smith, private communication, (1967).
37. P. A. Moldauer, Phys. Rev. Letters, 18, 249 (1967).
38. Tucker et al., Phys. Rev. 137, B1181 (1965).
39. A. Smith, private communication (1967).

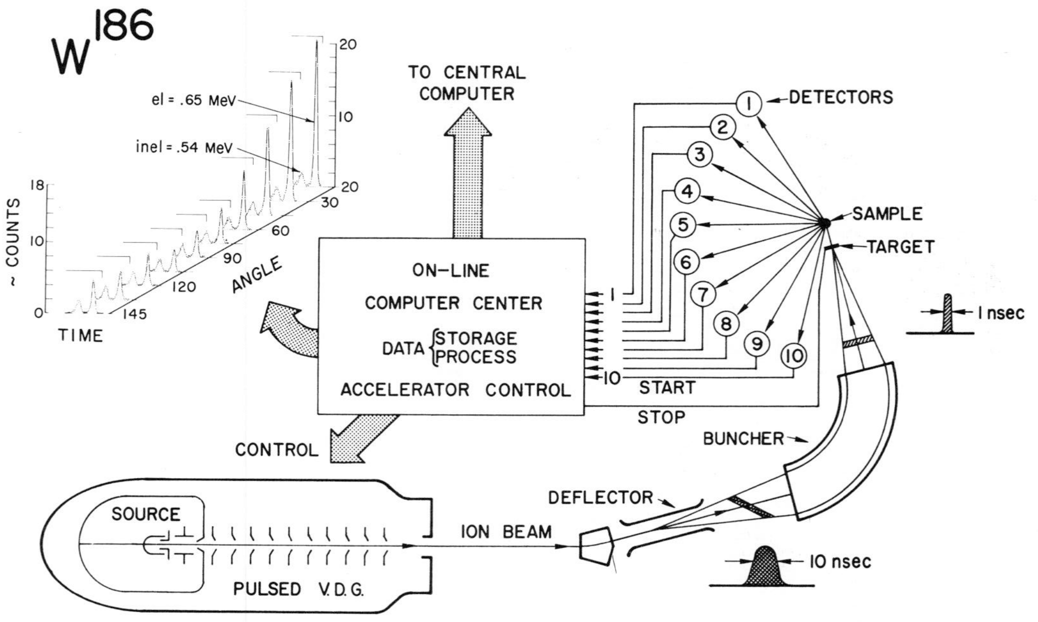

Fig. 1 Schematic diagram of an automated time-of-flight facility[7]. Ten concurrently measured time distributions obtain by scattering 650 keV neutrons from W^{186} are shown at the right.

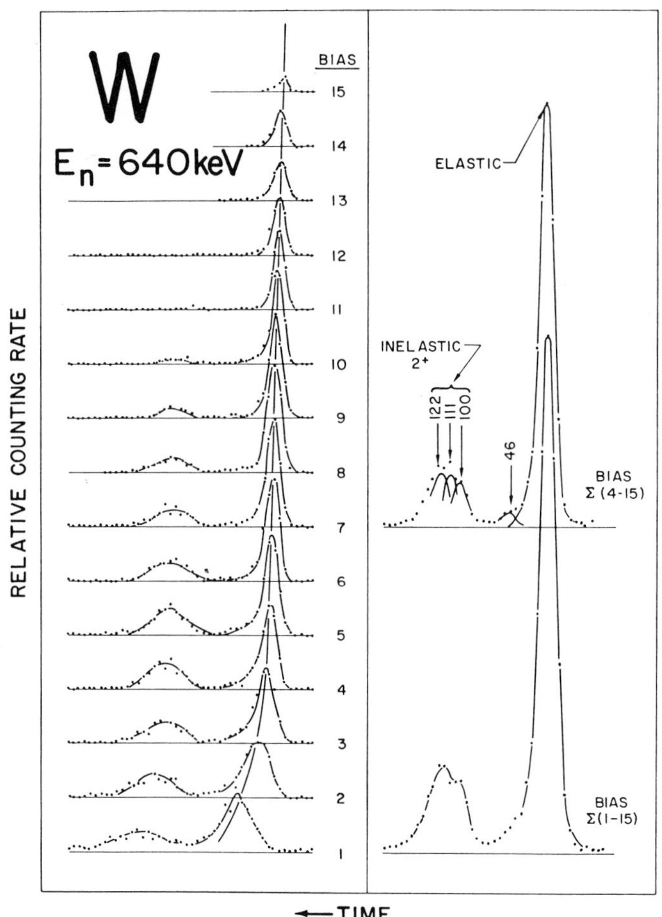

Fig. 2 Time spectra for scattering 640 keV neutrons from tungsten[7]. Left; differential spectra and the "walk" effect. Right; the spectra at left summed over indicated biases and "walk" corrected. Time resolution ∿ 2.7 nsec.

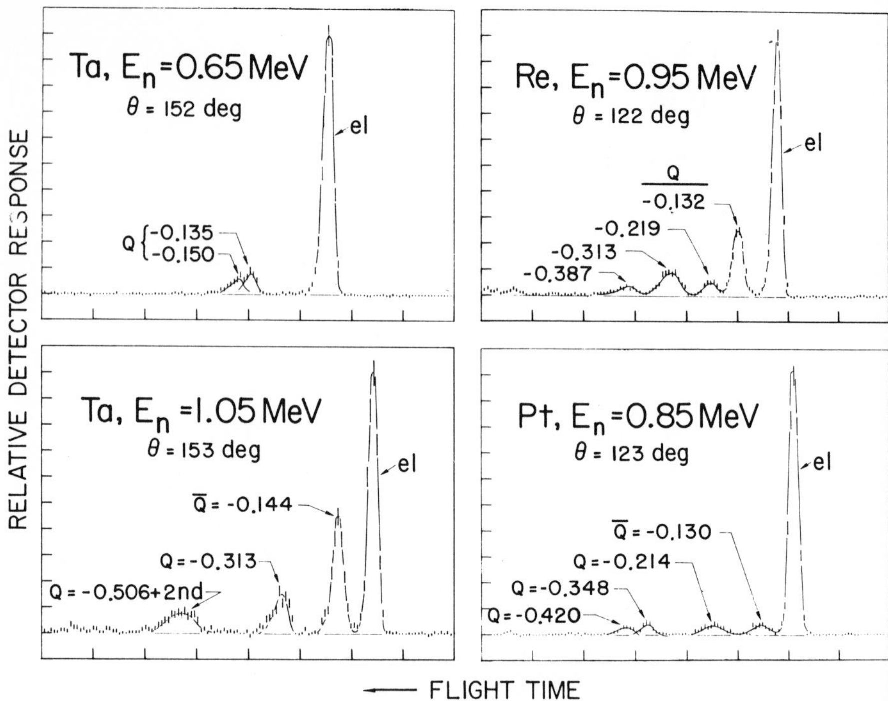

Fig. 3 Time spectra obtained by scattering neutrons from Ta, Re, and Pt[8]. Observed reaction Q values are indicated.

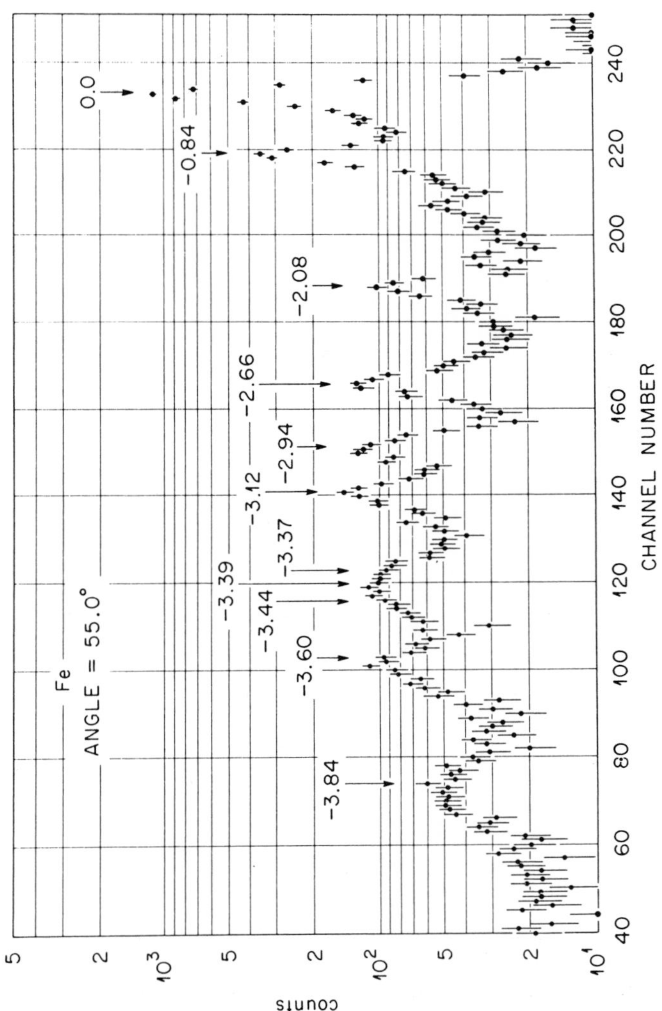

Fig. 4 Time spectrum resulting from the scattering of ~ 5 MeV neutrons from Fe^9. The measured structure is correlated with known reaction Q values.

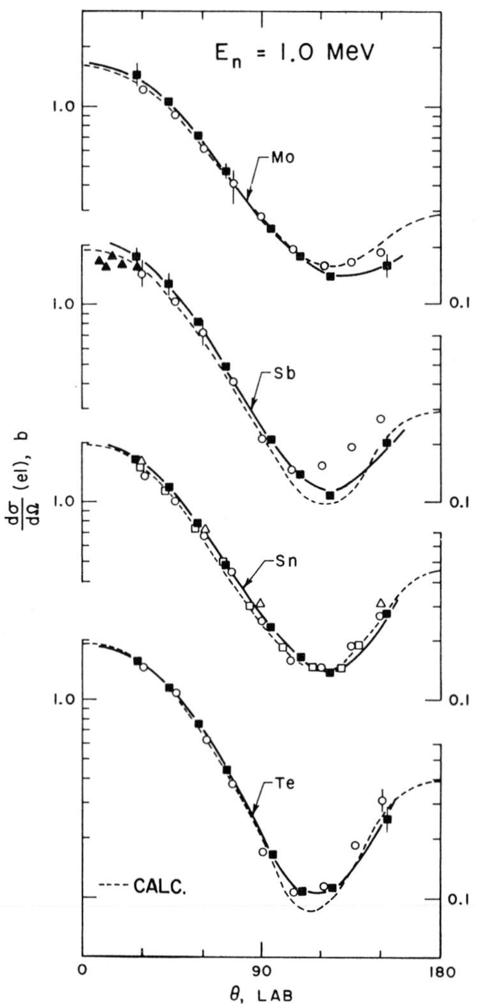

Fig. 5 The elastic scattering of 1.0 MeV neutrons from Mo, Sb, Sn, and Te. The dotted curves were calculated using a general optical potential[11,12,24].

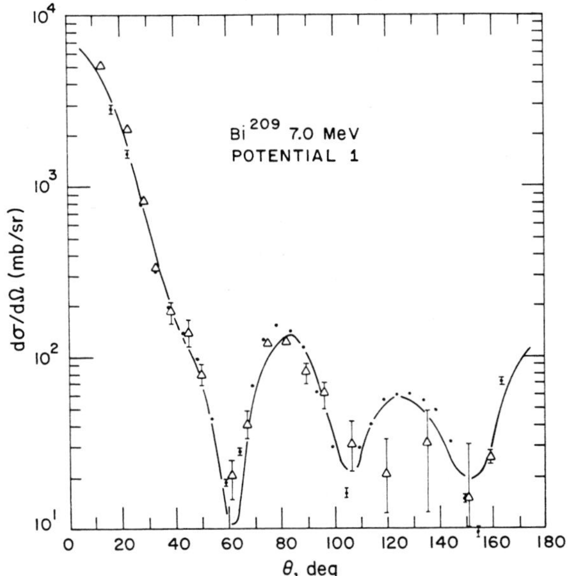

Fig. 6 Measured and calculated elastic scattering of 7 MeV neutrons from Bi^{209}. The agreement with experiment obtained with a non-local potential is excellent[10,13].

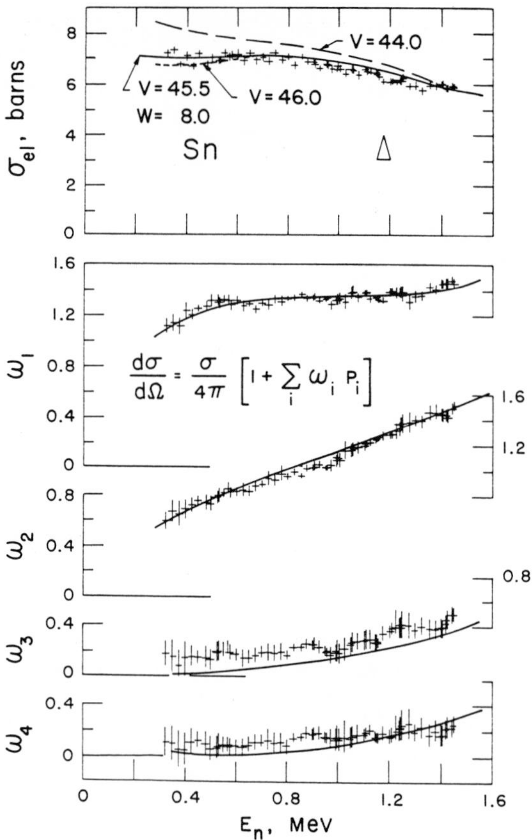

Fig. 7 Differential elastic scattering from Sn expressed as a legendre expansion[12]. The detailed energy dependence permits a precise selection of the real portion of the optical potential, V[12].

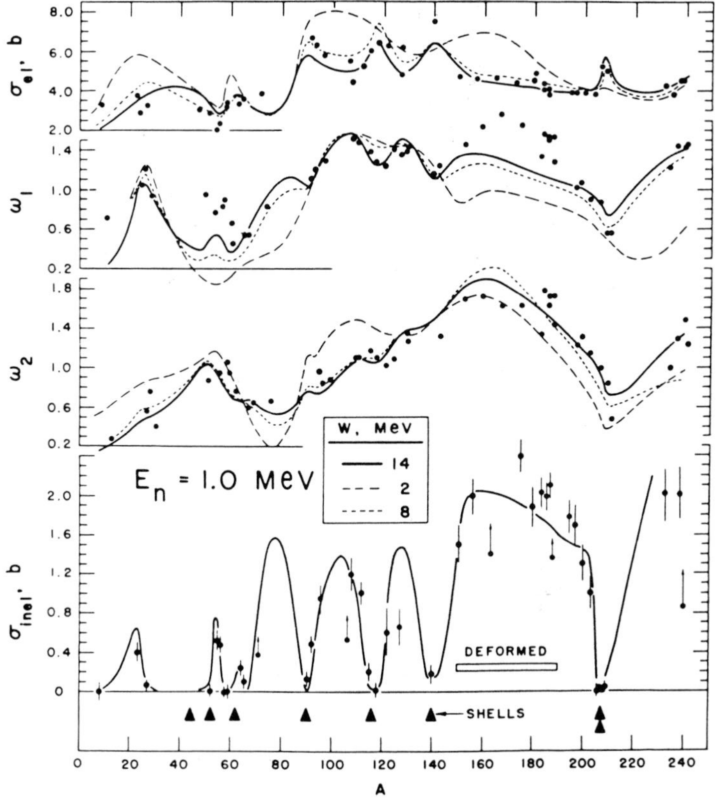

Fig. 8 The systematic behavior of measured and calculated differential elastic and total inelastic scattering cross sections at an incident neutron energy of 1.0 MeV[15].

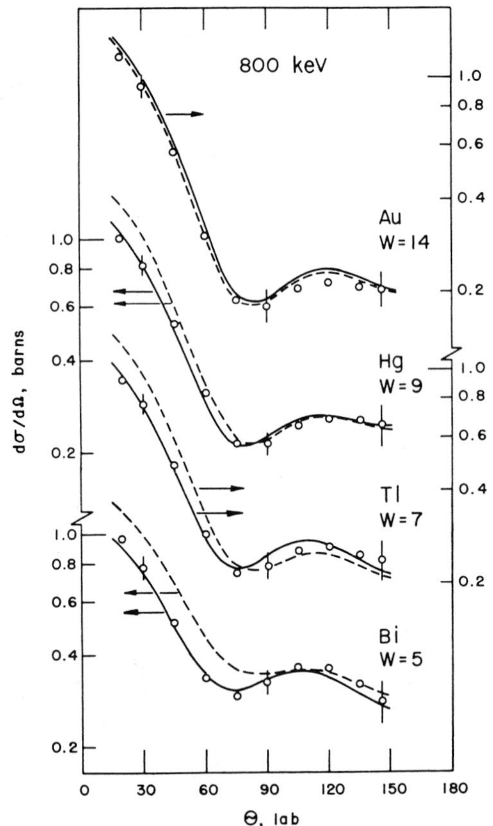

Fig. 9 Shell dependence of the optical potential at 800 keV. Good agreement with experiment is retained as A = 208 is approached if the imaginary potential, W (MeV), is reduced[16].

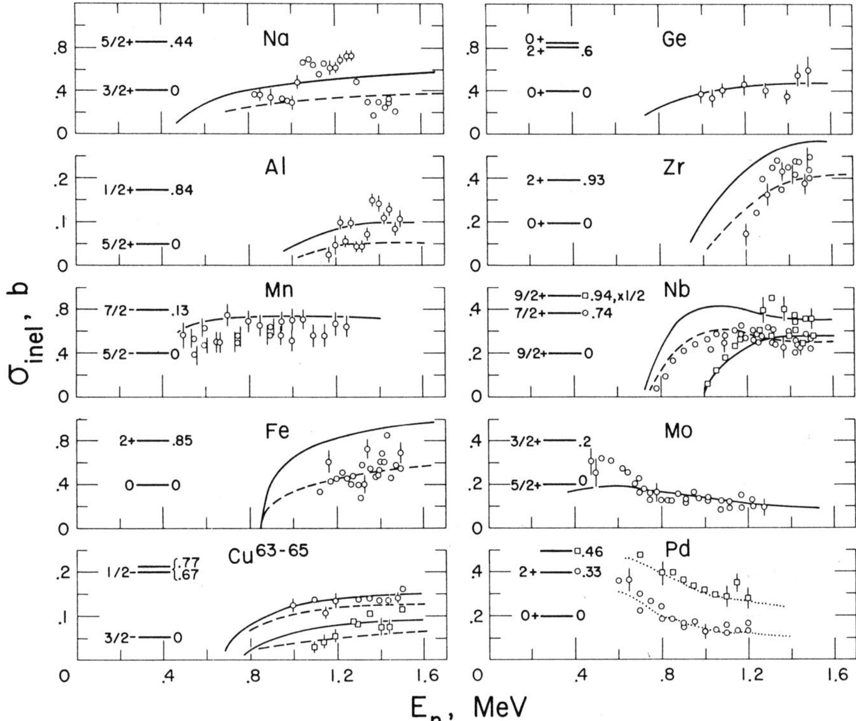

Fig. 10 Measured inelastic excitation cross sections in the interval Na to Pd[21]. Contributing level structure is indicated. Solid curves are the results of Hauser-Feshbach calculations[20] using the PAM potential[11], the dashed lines incorporate fluctuations corrections to the theory[22].

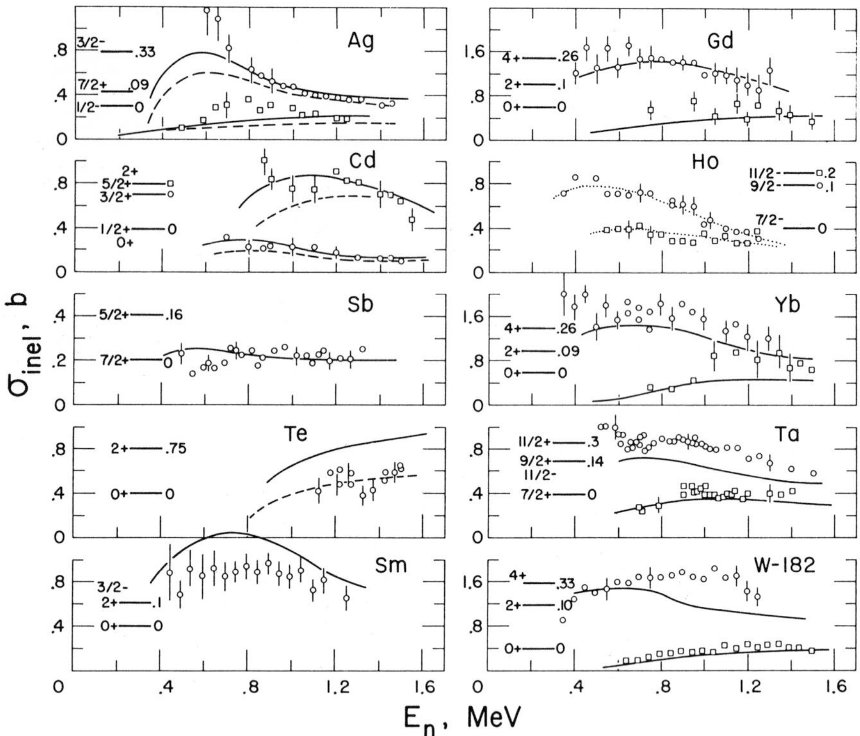

Fig. 11 Inelastic excitation cross sections in the region Ag to W^{182} [21]. The curves have the same significance as in Fig. 10.

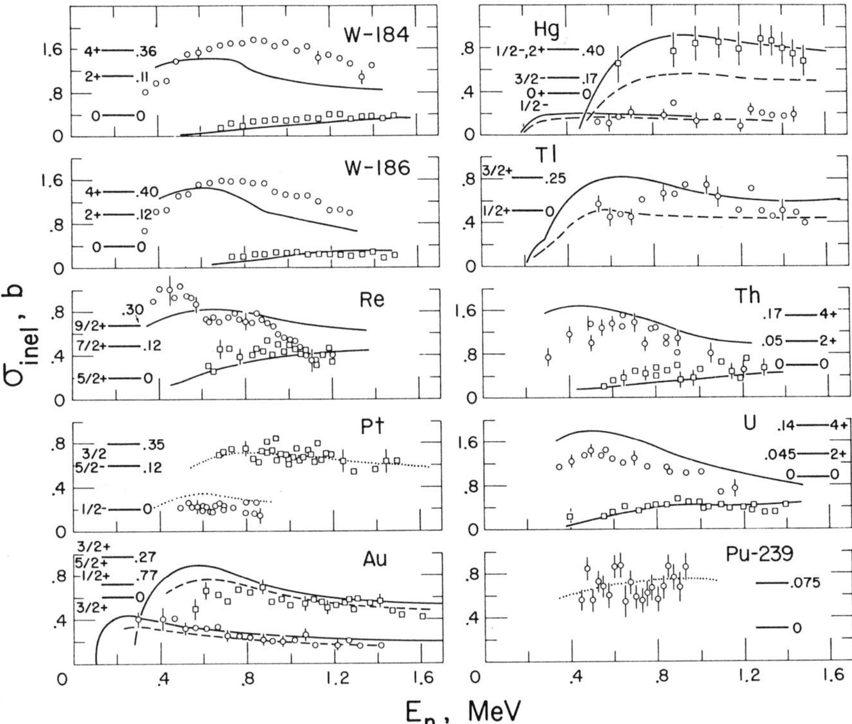

Fig. 12 Selected inelastic excitation cross sections in the deformed nuclei, W^{184} to Pu^{239} [21]. Calculations, indicated as per Fig. 10, are based upon a spherical potential[12].

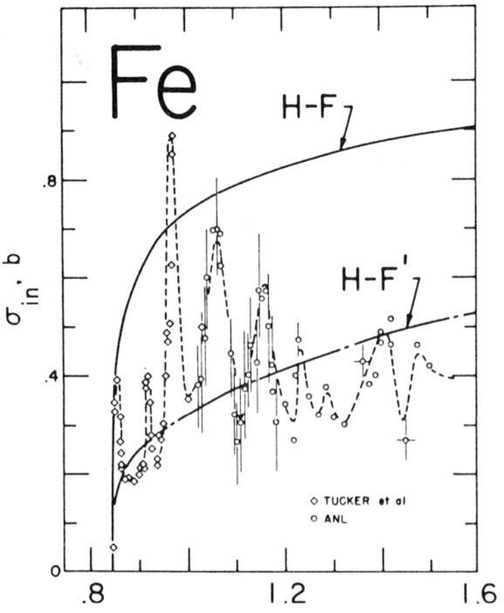

Fig. 13 Near threshold inelastic excitation of the 846 keV state[38,39,40] in Fe. Agreement with experiment requires fluctuation corrections (H-F') to the Hauser-Feshbach (H-F) result[20,22]. The PAM potential is employed[11].

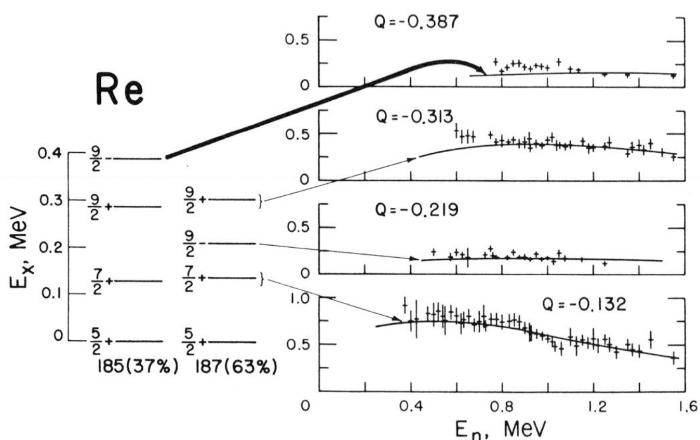

Fig. 14 Cross sections for the inelastic excitation of low lying states in Re[8]. Curves indicate the results of calculations based upon the premise that the 387 keV state is a $\frac{9}{2}$ - single particle configuration in Re^{185}.

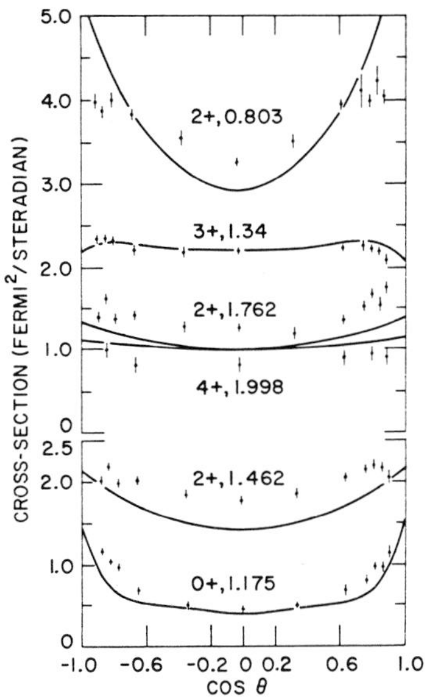

Fig. 15 Observed and calculated differential inelastic scattering of 2.5 MeV neutrons from Pb^{206} [29]. Calculation based upon an energy dependent potential and indicated spin assignments well describes experiment.

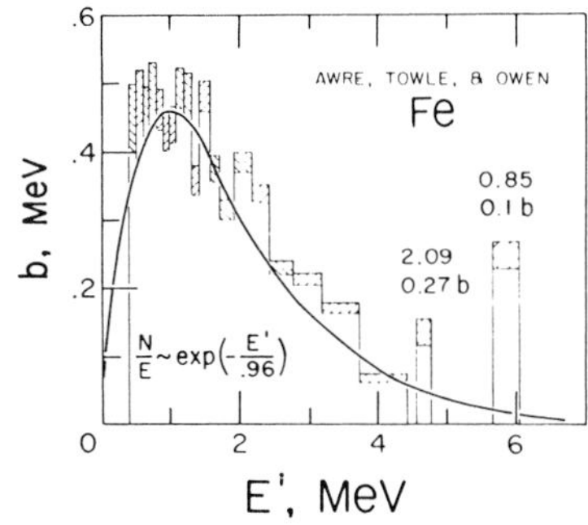

Fig. 16 Inelastic scattering of 7.0 MeV neutrons from Fe[25]. Direct states at 0.85 and 2.09 MeV are evident together with a continuum distribution having a simple temperature of 0.96 MeV.

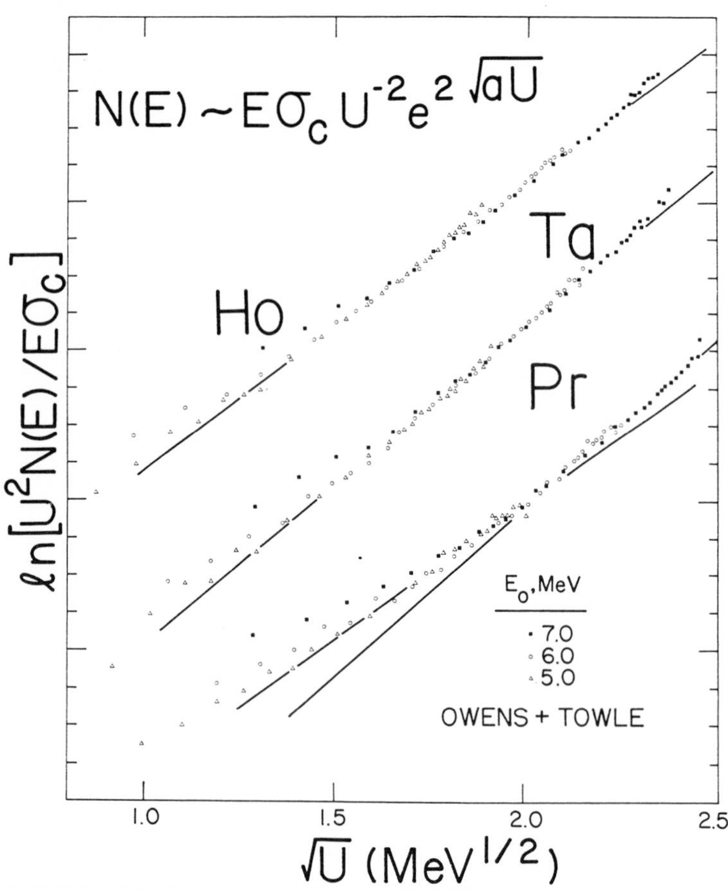

Fig. 17 Semi-log plots of measured temperature distributions for Ho, Ta, and Pr[27] as a function of $\sqrt{U}$, U = excitation energy corrected for pairing. The closed shell Pr does not give a linear plot.

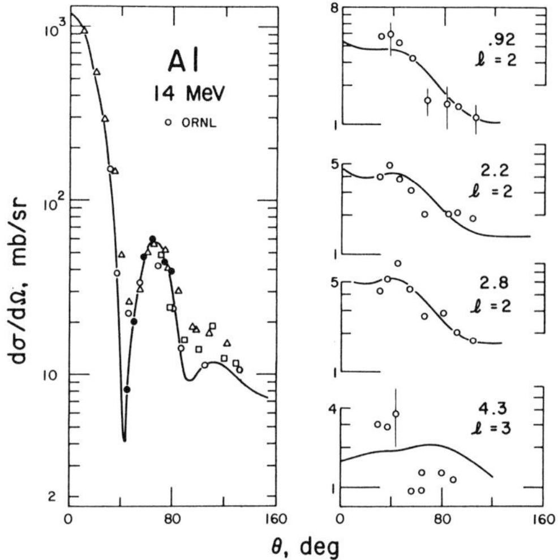

Fig. 18 Elastic and inelastic scattering of 14 MeV neutrons from Al[30,24]. Solid curves indicate calculations based upon a direct inelastic process.

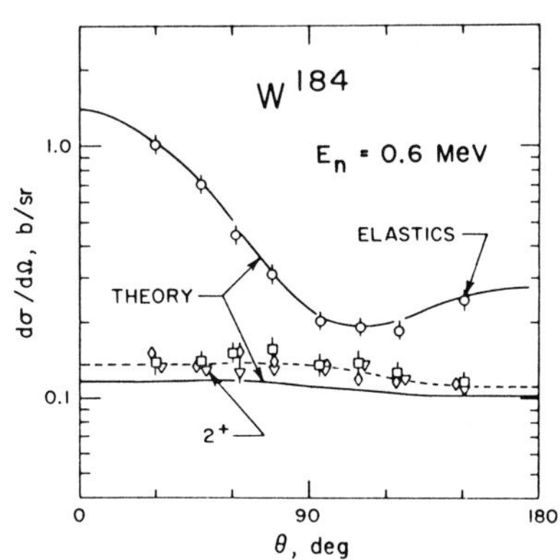

Fig. 19 Elastic and inelastic scattering of 0.6 MeV neutrons from deformed W^{184}. Solid curves were obtained using coupled channel theory and a deformed potential[32,33].

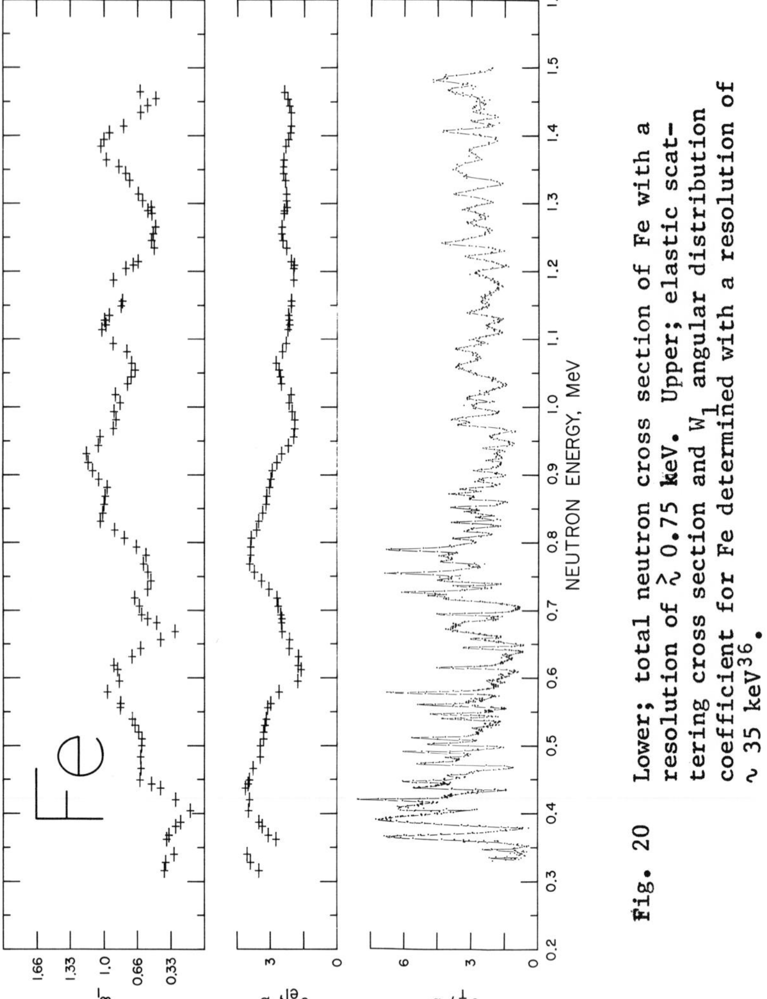

Fig. 20 Lower; total neutron cross section of Fe with a resolution of $\gtrsim$ 0.75 keV. Upper; elastic scattering cross section and W_1 angular distribution coefficient for Fe determined with a resolution of ~ 35 keV[36].

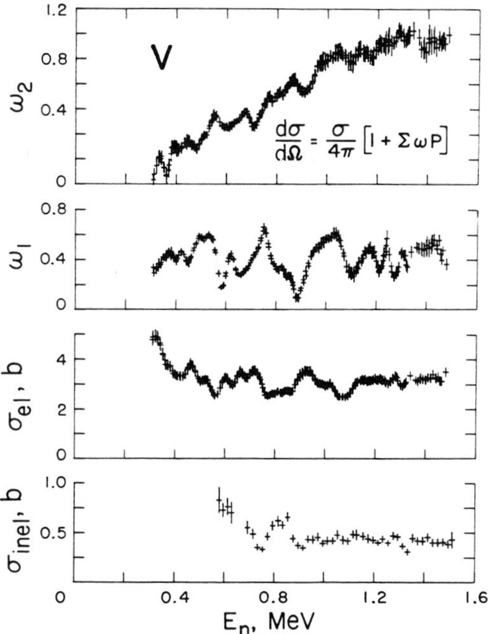

Fig. 21 Elastic and inelastic scattering cross sections of V determined with a resolution of ∿ 50 keV[36]. An intermediate structure is evident.

PARTICLE-GAMMA ANGULAR CORRELATION EXPERIMENTS

D. R. Tilley

North Carolina State University, Raleigh, North Carolina

and

Duke University Nuclear Structure Laboratory
Duke University, Durham, North Carolina

INTRODUCTION

This paper will be devoted primarily to $(d,p\gamma)$ and $(He^3,\alpha\gamma)$ reactions although much of the discussion could apply equally well to other reactions involving a particle in and a particle out followed by gamma emission. Prior to the last three or four years most of the $(d,p\gamma)$ and $(d,n\gamma)$ experiments were done as reaction mechanism studies rather than as spectroscopic measurements. They were primarily tests of plane wave and distorted wave Born approximation theories of stripping. More recently, by means of the axial symmetry techniques pointed out by Litherland and Ferguson[1], particle-gamma angular correlation experiments have become established as powerful methods for the rigorous determination of level spins and gamma-ray multipole parameters.

A majority of the experiments in both of these categories have been carried out with low energy ($\lesssim$ 5 MeV) accelerators. While low energies have limited the range of nuclei investigated, they have also minimized the difficulties associated with high neutron and gamma-ray backgrounds that occur with the large number of exit channels that are open at high bombarding energies.

Before discussing some of the experiments that have been done, let me remind you of the form of the theoretical expression that describes the angular distribution of gamma rays that follow the excitation of a level of spin $\underline{a}$ in the final nucleus. Equation (1),

$$W(\bar{k}_p,\bar{k}_d,\theta,\phi) \propto \sum_{L',L,k,q} \rho_{kq}(a,a)\left[(2k+1)^{-1/2} C_L C_{L'} F_k(L,L'ba)\right] Y_k^q(\theta,\phi) \quad (1)$$

gives the correlation function for the deuteron stripping reaction as expressed by Huby, Refai, and Satchler[2], in a form that is particularly suitable for this discussion.

In this expression, k_d and k_p represent the directions of the deuteron and proton, and θ and ϕ specify the direction of the emitted gamma ray. The quantities ρ_{kq} are statistical tensors which describe the population of the magnetic substates of the state a after it has been formed. The F_k's are the gamma emission coefficients as defined e.g. by Devons and Goldfarb[3], and the quantities C_L are the multipole amplitudes[4]. The index k takes on even values $\leq$ 2a, or $2L_{max}$. The reason for showing this expression is to emphasize the fact that the particle-gamma correlation function involves two parts, one of which depends on the reaction mechanism, the ρ_{kq}, and one of which depends on the spins of levels a and b and the multipole components of the gamma transition. The first half of this talk will concern experiments which seek to investigate the information contained in the ρ_{kq}. The second half will be devoted to the discussion of experiments designed to extract the information on spins and multipole mixtures contained in the other part.

REACTION MECHANISM STUDIES

In Fig. 1 the stripping process is pictured according to the assumptions of the plane-wave Born approximation. The plane-wave assumption corresponds to well defined deuteron and proton linear momenta and, therefore, to well defined transfer or recoil momenta. The process is equivalent to capture of neutrons incident along the recoil direction[2]. Consequently, the recoil axis is an axis of symmetry for the angular distribution of gamma ryas, and the distribution should be isotropic when measured by a gamma detector moving in a plane perpendicular to the recoil axis. The angular distribution of gamma rays about the recoil axis should be independent of bombarding energy and proton angle, since the g_k, defined by Satchler and Tobocman[5], do not depend on energy and proton angle. Fig. 2 shows some angular correlation measurements for the $C^{12}(d,p\gamma)C^{13}$ reaction involving the 3.68 and 3.85 MeV excited states of C^{13}. These data were obtained by N. R. Fletcher, R. M. Williamson and myself[6]. The state at 3.68 MeV has ℓ_n = 1,J=3/2, and the 3.85 MeV state has ℓ_n = 2,J=5/2. It is apparent that the p_2-γ distributions are very nearly symmetric about the recoil direction for protons detected on the stripping peak (20°), but the anisotropy does change some with energy. For larger proton angles the symmetry axis departs from the recoil axis, the anisotropy changes drastically and is very nearly washed out completely at θ_p = 150°. These data are similar to those from a number of other (d,pγ) and (d,nγ) experiments with light nuclei and low bombarding energies. A survey of the experiments done up to 1962 was made by

R.M. Williamson[7].

Now, in view of the well known limitations of plane-wave stripping theory the observed energy and angular dependence of (d,pγ) angular correlations is not surprising. Let us consider the predictions of the distorted wave Born approximation. The quantities ρ_{kq} of Eq.(1) can, in principle, be calculated by DWBA, and these calculations as well as the general features of the effects expected from distorted waves have been discussed by Huby, Refai, and Satchler[2] and by Satchler and Tobocman[5]. The predicted effects of distortions are that, in general, the simple symmetry about the recoil axis is destroyed, some azimuthal asymmetry about the recoil axis is introduced, and the degree of anisotropy is changed. For the $\ell_n = 1$ case to which we shall limit ourselves here, these authors have expressed the predictions in terms of parameters α, β, ϕ_o' and λ as shown in Fig. 3. Here the anisotropy parameter for the reaction plane is α, and that for tne plane perpendicular to the symmetry axis is β. The symmetry angle in the reaction plane is ϕ_o'. The geometry is defined in the drawing. A distortion parameter λ is defined which varies between 1 (the plane-wave limit) and 0 (complete distortion).

The $C^{12}(d,p\gamma)C^{13}$ 3.68 data previously shown was subjected to a DWBA analysis by D. G. Gerke _et al_[8]. The calculations were made at the Oak Ridge National Laboratories with the DWBA code SALLY of Bassel, Drisko, and Satchler[9]. These calculations were made with optical parameters which give the best fits to the C^{12} + d and C^{13} + p elastic scattering cross sections measured at the appropriate energies. The results are shown in Fig. 4. The fits to the (d,p) differential cross sections as well as the fits to the symmetry angle ϕ_o' and the distortion parameter are shown for a set of cut-off radii. It is interesting to note that the symmetry angle and the distortion parameter are not too far from the plane-wave values in the region in which the Butler curve fits the differential cross section; but at angles of 60° and beyond, both ϕ_o' and λ depart drastically from the plane wave values, qualitatively in the way predicted by DWBA. The 153° correlation is in clear disagreement with DWBA. These calculations are open to criticism in that C^{12} is certainly not a particularly suitable choice for DWBA calculations considering the resonance structure in the yield curves. Furthermore, the optical parameters used here are not consistent at the different energies investigated. Since these calculations were made, Satchler[10] has obtained a set of C^{12} + d parameters which vary smoothly over an energy range from 2.8 to 34 MeV. So far we have not repeated the calculations using Satchler's parameters.

An interesting investigation involving $B^{11}(d,p\,\gamma)B^{12}_{0.95}$ has been carried out recently at the University of Virginia by A. P. Borden and R. C. Ritter[11]. I am very grateful to Dr. Ritter for loaning me his slides. The dependence of the distortions on proton angle and bombarding energy were investigated, the angles and energies having been chosen to test systematically the polology predictions in regard to distortions in stripping reactions. D. H. Wilkinson suggested in a 1958 paper[12] that low Q-value stripping reactions carried out at low bombarding energies should tend to be relatively undistorted due to the fact that the small momentum components required by the proton at the time of stripping in such reaction can be acquired from the internal motion of the deuteron with the proton relatively far away from the residual nucleus. Tests of this prediction have been carried out by Warburton and Chase[13], Sellschop and Mingay[14] and others[15,16] in terms of Amado's and Shapiro's dispersion theory restatement of Wilkinson's predictions. These tests have generally been discussed in terms of the stripping denominator D defined as follows

$$\frac{d\sigma}{d\Omega} \sim \left[\frac{F_1 F_2}{D} + \text{Other terms}\right]^2 \qquad (2)$$

$$D=3.18E_d+1.85Q+ \varepsilon-2[2E_d(0.92Q+1.09E_d)]^{1/2}\cos\theta_{dp} \qquad (3)$$

The first term is taken to be the Butler, or plane-wave, amplitude. Thus plane-wave theory should be exact at the stripping pole (D = 0), but the pole occurs at unphysical values of cos θ as shown in Fig. 5, in which Borden and Ritter have plotted values of D for $B^{11}(d,p_1)B^{12}$ versus the cosine of the proton angle for various values of E_d. The experiments mentioned earlier tend to show that the fit of angular distributions to plane-wave theory extends to larger angles as the bombarding energy is lowered corresponding to decreasing D, the distance to the stripping pole. Fig. 5 also shows the position of the break between the experimental and PWBA curves as observed by Sellschop[14], as well as the positions of the proton counter that were used for the angular correlation measurements. Three of the eleven measured angular correlation curves are shown in Fig. 6. It is apparent that the anisotropy as well as the symmetry angle changes with angle and energy.

Since this is an $\ell_n = 1$ stripping process, the parameters λ and ϕ_o' defined earlier are still applicable. These quantities are plotted as functions of the quantity D and compared with the plane wave limit in Fig. 7. It has been assumed that $\lambda = 1$ is closely approximated in correlation No. 10 in which the largest anisotropy was observed. It is apparent that the symmetry axis positions* ϕ_o' do follow the predicted trend, up to D = 4.5 MeV. The predictions of the D concept do not appear to hold for the anisotropy or distortion parameter λ, however. The largest anisotropy does not occur for the smallest value of D.

These measured angular correlation parameters were also compared to the detailed predictions of DWBA as calculated by G. R. Satchler with the code SALLY. The deuteron optical potential used was from C^{12} + d, and the proton potential was consistent with those discussed by Perey. Fig. 8 shows the comparison between the experimental values of λ and the DWBA predictions. It is seen that the experimental values of λ are farthest from the plane-wave limit at the intermediate energy of 3 MeV in contrast to the DWBA predictions. In fact, the DWBA predictions are quite close to the PWBA curves. The experimental and theoretical symmetry axis positions ϕ_o' are compared in Fig. 9.

Bordon and Ritter point out that, on basis of these results, the anisotropy of the angular correlation does offer a sensitive test of the distortions, in that it shows distortions where angular distributions do not. They also conclude that the symmetry axis shifts can have ambiguous interpretations.

In a recent experiment at Columbia by Horoshko, Weinberg, Lidofsky, and Mitchell[17], angular correlations were measured for the $Mg^{25}(d,p\gamma)Mg^{26}$ reaction through the 1.13 and 1.18 MeV states. The experiment was done in order to determine whether a mixture of ℓ_n values would be required in the DWBA analysis of the differential cross section measurements. The results were in qualitatively good agreement with the mixture requirement although the calculated fits to the measured correlations were not very satisfactory.

An extensive study of the $Si^{28}(d,p\gamma)Si^{29}$ angular correlation measurements involving the 1.28 and 2.03 MeV states in Si^{29} was published last year by Hausman, Davis, Phillips, Sullivan, and Unrine[18] at Ohio State. Measurements in the reaction plane and in a plane perpendicular were made at five bombarding energies between 4 and 6 MeV. The 1.28 and 2.03 MeV states are populated by ℓ_n =2 stripping, and the DWBA formalism is too lengthy to present here. Briefly stated, the statistical tensors defined by Huby, Refai, and Satchler[2]

---

*ϕ_o' of Fig. 3 is written as ϕ_o in Fig. 5, 6, and 8.

were calculated from the reaction-plane measurements at each energy and compared with the measurements out of the plane and with DWBA calculations. General agreement between DWBA and experiment was obtained, but the effects of spin-dependent forces or compound nucleus processes were not ruled out and are being investigated further.

Several other interesting experiments along the same lines as those discussed above have been done in the past few years, but I hope this discussion has provided a representative sampling.

MEASUREMENTS OF SPINS AND MULTIPOLE RATIOS

While particle-gamma angular correlation experiments of the type just discussed seem to constitute sensitive tests of the reaction mechanism, it is apparent that the usefulness of these experimental techniques for the measurement of spins and gamma-ray multipole parameters is severely limited because of the fact that a knowledge of the quantities ρ_{kq} depends on an accurate description of the reaction mechanism. The techniques of axial symmetry pointed out by Litherland and Ferguson circumvent this difficulty. In the particle-gamma angular correlation technique referred to as Method II, the particles are detected by an axially symmetric counter either near 0° or 180°. The quantities ρ_{kq} then reduce to a weighted sum over the population parameters of the magnetic substates of a, with the beam direction as the quantization axis. Furthermore, the maximum number of magnetic substates that can be populated is limited by the sum of the spins of the incident particle, the outgoing particle and the target. The form of the correlation function is given in Fig. 10. The notation is that of Poletti and Warburton[19] from their $O^{16}(He^3,p\gamma)F^{18}$ paper in which they provide a highly useful description of the technique and tabulations of the quantities $\rho_k(a,\alpha)$, $F_k(L,L',b,a)$ and $U_k(Lab)$. The angular correlation equation is similar to the form of Eq. (1) except that it has been specialized to the condition of axial symmetry, and the attenuation coefficients Q_k for the gamma detector have been inserted. The statistical tensors $\rho_k(a)$ are now expressible explicitly in terms of the population parameters of the 2a + 1 magnetic substates. If the beam and target are unpolarized then the substates are symmetrically populated. The $F_k(ab)$ is given here for the case of a mixture of L and L + 1 multipole radiation. The quantity x is the multipole mixture parameter. In the sign convention of Litherland and Ferguson, $\sigma = 0$ for an ML, EL + 1 mixture and 1 for an EL, ML + 1 mixture. The expression can be easily modified, in the manner shown by Litherland and Ferguson and by Poletti and Warburton[19], to describe the angular distribution of the second gamma ray (first gamma ray unobserved) in a cascade $a \rightarrow b \rightarrow c$.

The number of unknown population ratios depends on the reaction, for example, the (d,p) reaction on a zero spin target involves one unknown population ratio P(3/2)/P(1/2), which together with the unknown multipole ratio x, can be determined from the experimental angular distribution provided the distribution contains terms up to $P_4(\cos\theta)$ or higher ($a > 5/2$). The reactions (He^3,α) or (α,α') on spin zero targets involve no unknown population ratios.

The analysis is carried out by making least-squares fits of the population parameters to the measured angular distribution for discrete values of x, the best fit corresponding to the lowest values of χ^2 where χ^2 is given by

$$\chi^2 = \frac{1}{n}\sum_i \left[\frac{Y(\theta_i)-W(\theta_i)}{\Delta\, Y(\theta_i)}\right]^2 \qquad (4)$$

The calculation is then repeated for other values of x, usually by choosing values of arctan x in 5° steps from -90° to +90°. A plot of χ^2 vs. arctan x then shows dips corresponding to possible solutions for a given choice of spins a and b.

I shall make no attempt here to survey, in any sense, the experiments that have been done with the use of this method. The literature of the past two or three years has many examples of the work of groups at Brookhaven, Chalk River Kansas, Yale, Freiburg, Strasbourg, and other laboratories. Instead, I think it might be useful for a conference of this type to describe in some detail, one experimental setup for such experiments with a low energy accelerator. In particular, I will describe the experiments on (s,d) - shell nuclei being done in the Duke Nuclear Structure Laboratory by N. R. Roberson, R. V. Poore, V. H. Webb, M. B. Lewis, L. C. Haun, and myself.

Some of the advantages of He^3 beams are evident from the preceding discussion. In addition to those mentioned, the high Q values of (He^3,α) and (He^3,p) reactions plus the possibility of doubling the beam energy by using the He^{++} component makes He^3 highly useful in low energy accelerators. Fig. 11 shows the He^{++} source[20] developed for use in the Duke 4 MV Van de Graaff accelerator. We wished to obtain the maximum intensity beam of He^{++} (normally about 1/2% of the total beam) without having to accelerate the unwanted singly charged component. The small angle (3.5°) magnetic deflection was N. R. Roberson's idea. It enables us to run under optimum conditions for He^{3++}, giving typical total He^{++} beams of 0.5μA while accelerating only 15 μA of He^+. We are thus able to control the accelerator on the He^+ component at the 17° beam port while focusing the maximum amount of He^{++} into the target chamber at the 25° beam port. This gives us up to about 0.30 μA of doubly charged He^3 at energies from 1 to 8 MeV. We seldom use over 0.15 μA for angular correlation experiments.

Fig. 12 shows the target chamber used for the angular correlation experiments. The beam first passed through a set of beam defining slits located approximately 8 ft. before the chamber. A set of magnetic quadrupole lenses and steerers was situated between these beam defining slits and the target chamber. The beam enters the chamber, which is essentially a 6 in. diameter brass cylinder with bakelite ends, through a pair of 1/16 in. collimators separated by 5 in. The first collimator was 9 in. from the target and was followed by a solid lead tube. A 3/16 in. diameter stainless steel tube passed through the center hole in the annular detector and served as the anti-scattering collimator. The annular surface barrier detector is mounted at 180° and collimated to admit particles between 173° and 177°. The collimator mounted on the front of the detector limits the amount of beam backscattered from points other than the target. The Faraday cup is located 54 inches from the chamber. The gamma rays were detected in a 3 x 3 in. NaI crystal mounted on an Amperex 58AVP photomultiplier tube.

Fig. 13 shows a block diagram of the electronic setup. Fast risetime signals were obtained from the surface barrier detector with a time pick-off circuit, and from the gamma-ray detector directly from the anode of the 58 AVP. These signals each operated Chronetics fast discriminators, the signals were clipped to 15 ns and fed to two parallel fast coincidence circuits, one in which the delay was set for real coincidence, and a second which the delay was set for randoms only. The resolving times were about 30 ns and gave a ratio of real to random coincidences for counts underlying the peaks of interest of between 6 to 1 and 10 to 1. The pulses from the two coincidence circuits were mixed such that either generated a gate pulse for the particle and gamma-ray analog-to-digital converters. The mixer circuit also generated a signal to indicate whether the event was associated with the randoms circuit. The digitized outputs of the analog-to-digital converters, along with the real-random flag, were processed by the Duke Nuclear Structure Laboratory on-line computer. The computer interface was designed by N. R. Roberson; the programming was done by Roberson, Poore, and Lewis. The computer was programmed to store and display the coincidences in a 128 x 64 channel matrix and simultaneously to record, event by event, both the real plus random and the random coincidences on magnetic tape.

The time pick-off circuit was determined to have a rather broad cut off resulting in a varying efficiency over part of the particle energy spectrum. The use of low resistivity (800 ohm-cm) surface barrier detectors reduced, but did not eliminate the problem. Thus, using a single-channel analyzer on any one particle peak led to errors of as much as 10%. This problem was circumvented by storing a 512-channel monitor spectrum by fanning out the linear signal from the particle amplifier to a separate ADC gated by the output of the fast discriminator. The number of counts in each particle group were later used to normalize the corresponding particle-gamma angular correlation point. This monitor spectrum was stored on magnetic tape along with the two parameter data.

To prevent double pulsing, the gamma-ray discriminator was modified to have a 1.5 μs dead time. Dead time correlations were made by decoding with the computer, after prescaling by 10^5, the total number of gamma discriminator pulses. The measured dead times were always less than 5%.

The computer program used for the data analysis was made available to us by E. K. Warburton and was modified to the extent necessary for running on the Nuclear Structure Laboratory DDP-224 computer by R. V. Poore.

I would like now to show a few examples of the angular correlation data which we have obtained recently for isotopes of Magnesium and Silicon. The phase convention of x in the following cases is that called Convention II by Poletti and Start[21].

Fig. 14 shows the angular correlation and the analysis for the 0.96 MeV level of Si^{27} populated by the $Si^{28}(He^3,\alpha)Si^{27}$ reaction. The experiment was done by M. B. Lewis. Plots of χ^2 versus arctan x are shown for spin assignments of 3/2, 5/2, 7/2, and 9/2. The validity numbers indicated on the right hand side give the probability that a solution with the corresponding value of χ^2 is the correct one. The experimental angular distributions and the caluculated distributions for the most probable mixing ratio x are shown in the upper part of the figure. In this case a spin of 9/2 is ruled out, but 3/2, 5/2 and 7/2 are allowed. Hinds and Middleton[22] have measured angular distributions for this reaction which indicate $\ell_n = 2$ pick up, ruling out the 7/2 possibility. From the remaining curves it is seen that J = 3/2 is more than 6 times as likely as J = 5/2. In addition, if J = 5/2, then the E2/M1 mixing ratio x for the 0.96 $\rightarrow$0 transition is greater than 1.4 which is more than 10^4 times the single-particle E2 Weisskopf estimate and quite large for nuclei in this mass region. Then

J = 3/2 with either $x = +(0.36 \pm 0.03)$ or $x > +6.0$ is the favored assignment. The finite size effect was checked by attempting a fit with P(3/2) = 0.02 P(1/2). In no case was the fit appreciably improved.

The two solutions for x corresponding to J = 3/2 indicated here represent a common situation, since the fitting procedure usually has double-valued solutions one of which gives a very large mixing ratio. Lifetime measurements are sometimes useful in determing the correct solution. These are not available for the levels of Si^{27}, but several are available for Al^{27}. These measurements together with the systematics of other nuclei in this mass region lead us to favor $x = +(0.36 \pm 0.03)$ as the most probable value.

Fig. 15 shows the results for the 2.65 MeV level of Si^{27} which decays with branching ratios ∿18% and 82% to the ground state and to the 0.96 MeV state respectively. The 2.65 →0 angular correlation did not restrict the spin of the level. The left side of the figure shows the χ^2 analysis of the 2.65 →0.96 gamma-ray distribution, while the right side shows the triple correlation analysis of the 0.96 MeV gamma distribution with the intermediate radiation unobserved. The distribution data for the first gamma ray rules out spins 1/2, 7/2, and 9/2. The 0.96 MeV transition, analyzed by taking $x_2 = 0.36$ as determined earlier, indicates that J = 5/2 is the correct spin choice because of the smaller value of χ^2 and because only the 5/2 choice gives a mixing ratio consistent with the analysis on the left.

An interesting case arose in the analysis of the angular correlations for $Mg^{24}(He^3,\alpha\gamma)Mg^{23}$. These are data of L. C. Haun. Fig. 16 shows the analysis of the $(\alpha_1,\gamma_{0.45})$ angular correlation. A spin of either 3/2 or 5/2 is indicated for the 0.45 MeV state. The distribution of the 2.04→0 transition had indicated a preferred assignment J = 7/2 for the 2.04 state. The angular distribution of the strong 2.04→0.45 gamma ray, the analysis of which appears at the left in the Fig. 17, led to an assignment of 5/2 for the 0.45 MeV level and a favored E2/M1 mixing ratio $x' = -0.14 \pm 0.09$. As a conformation of this assignment we carried out the triple correlation analysis of the 0.45 MeV gamma ray observed in the decay of the 2.04 MeV state. In this procedure the mixing ratio for the 2.04→0.45 transition was fixed at the value indicated in the analysis on the left, and the mixing ratio x for the second transition is varied. The results indicate a spin of 5/2 for the 0.45 MeV state consistent with the plot on the left, and a mixing ratio of approximately zero for the 0.45→0 transition in agreement with the value that was indicated by the J = 5/2 choice in the analysis of the $(\alpha_1,\gamma_{0.45})$ angular correlation.

Fig. 18 shows the angular correlation results and analysis for the 1.70 MeV level populated by the $Si^{30}(d,p)Si^{31}$ reaction. The spin is uniquely determined as 5/2 with possible values of arctan x at 26° and 76°. This result is in agreement with $\ell_n = 2$ stripping angular distributions that have been observed for this level. The finite size effect was calculated by taking P(5/2) = 0.05 P(3/2), and the effect is seen to be small. The χ^2 analysis indicates that by far the most probable value for the E2/M1 mixing ratio is $x = 4.70 \pm 1.00$. This is quite large, but the same result has been obtained in the triple correlation analysis of the 1.70 MeV gamma ray in coincidence with the α-particle group which populates the 3.14 MeV state.

Fig. 19 shows the analysis of the 2.79 MeV-ground state transition. The spin solutions for 1/2 and 7/2 are ruled out by the $\ell_n = 2$ stripping angular distributions observed for this state, but the analysis does not distinguish between 3/2 or 5/2. A spin of 5/2 has been indicated by J dependence for stripping to this level, however, and our results are consistent with this assignment. The values for the E2/M1 ratio indicated are either $x = + (0.20 \pm 0.10)$ or $x < -10$. The $Si^{30}(d,p)Si^{31}$ data discussed here are from an experiment by V. H. Webb.

In conclusion I would like to correct an impression that may have been created by the way in which I have divided reaction mechanism investigations and nuclear spectroscopic measurements into separate categories. I would like to stress the point that has been made by Poletti, Olness, and Warburton[23] and others, that the methods of axial symmetry not only give rigorous solutions for the spins and multiple parameters, but they also provide rigorous values for the population parameters of the magnetic substates. The population ratios contain the information concerning the reaction mechanism by which the level was formed. It is expected, therefore, that these alignment parameters from axial symmetry experiments should themselves be quite valuable for the study of reaction models.

REFERENCES

1. A. E. Litherland and A. J. Ferguson, Can. J. Phys. 39, 788 (1961).
2. R. Huby, M. Y. Refai, and G. R. Satchler, Nucl. Phys. 9, 94 (1958)
3. S. Devons and L. J. B. Goldfarb, in Handbuch der Physik, ed. by S. Flugge (Springer-Verlag, Berlin, 1957) Vol 42, p. 362.

4. L. C. Biedenharn and M. R. Rose, Revs. Mod. Phys. 25, 729 (1953).
5. G. R. Satchler and W. Tobocman, Phys. Rev. 118, 1566 (1960).
6. N. R. Fletcher, D. R. Tilley, and R. M. Williamson, Nucl. Phys. 38, 18 (1962).
7. R. M. Williamson, Proc. Conf. on Direct Reactions and Nuclear Reaction Mechanisms, ed. by E. Clementel and C. Villi (Gordon and Breach, New York, 1963) p. 695.
8. D. G. Gerke, D. R. Tilley, N. R. Fletcher and R. M. Williamson, Nucl. Phys. 75, 609 (1966).
9. R. H. Bassel, R. M. Drisko, and G. R. Satchler, Oak Ridge National Laboratory Report ORNL-3240 (1962) unpublished.
10. G. R. Satchler, Nucl. Phys. 85, 273 (1966).
11. A. P. Borden and R. C. Ritter, Phys. Rev. (to be published).
12. D. H. Wilkinson, Phil, Mag. 3, 1185 (1958).
13. E. K. Warburton and L. F. Chase, Jr., Phys. Rev. 120, 2095 (1960)
14. J. P. F. Sellschop and D. W. Mingay, in Proc. Conf. on Direct Interactions and Nuclear Reaction Mechanisms, ed. by E. Clementel and C. Villi (Gordon and Breach, New York, 1961) p. 425.
15. W. Schier, G. Michel, and R. E. Benenson, Nucl. Phys. 88, 373 (1966).
16. R. V. Poore, P. E. Shearin, D. R. Tilley, and R. M. Williamson, Nucl. Phys. A92, 30(1967).
17. R. N. Horoshko, R. B. Weinberg, L. J. Lidofsky, and G. E. Mitchell, Phys. Rev. 140, B1557 (1965).
18. H. J. Hausman, W. E. Davis, C. V. Phillips, R. P. Sullivan, and G. R. Unrine, Phys. Rev. 148, 1136 (1966).
19. A. R. Poletti and E. K. Warburton, Phys. Rev. 137, B595 (1965).
20. N. R. Roberson, D. R. Tilley, and E. R. Weller, Nucl. Instr. Methods 33. 84 (1965).
21. A. R. Poletti and D. F. H. Start, Phys. Rev. 147, 800 (1966).
22. S. Hinds and R. Middleton, Proc. Phys. Soc. 73, 727 (1959).
23. A. R. Poletti, J. W. Olness, and E. K. Warburton, Phys. Rev. 151, 812 (1966)

PLANE WAVE STRIPPING

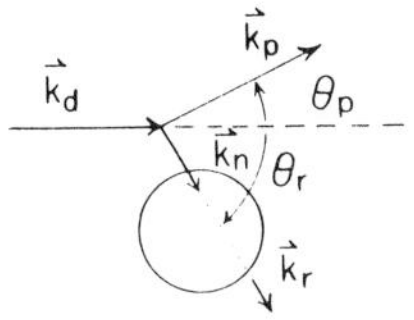

$$W(\theta_\gamma) = \Sigma_k g_k P_k \left[\cos(\theta_\gamma - \theta_R)\right]$$
$$g_k = \eta_k F_k$$
$$\eta_k = \sum_{jj'} \theta_{j\ell}\theta_{j'\ell}\, \eta_k(jj'J_T a)$$
$$F_k = \sum_{LL'} C_L C_{L'} F_k(LL'ba)$$

Fig. 1 Schematic picture of plane-wave deuteron stripping. The p-γ angular correlation formula is from reference 5. The coefficients η_k[5] and F_k[4] have been tabulated. The $\theta_{j\ell}$ are reduced widths for neutron capture with $j = \ell_n \pm 1/2$.

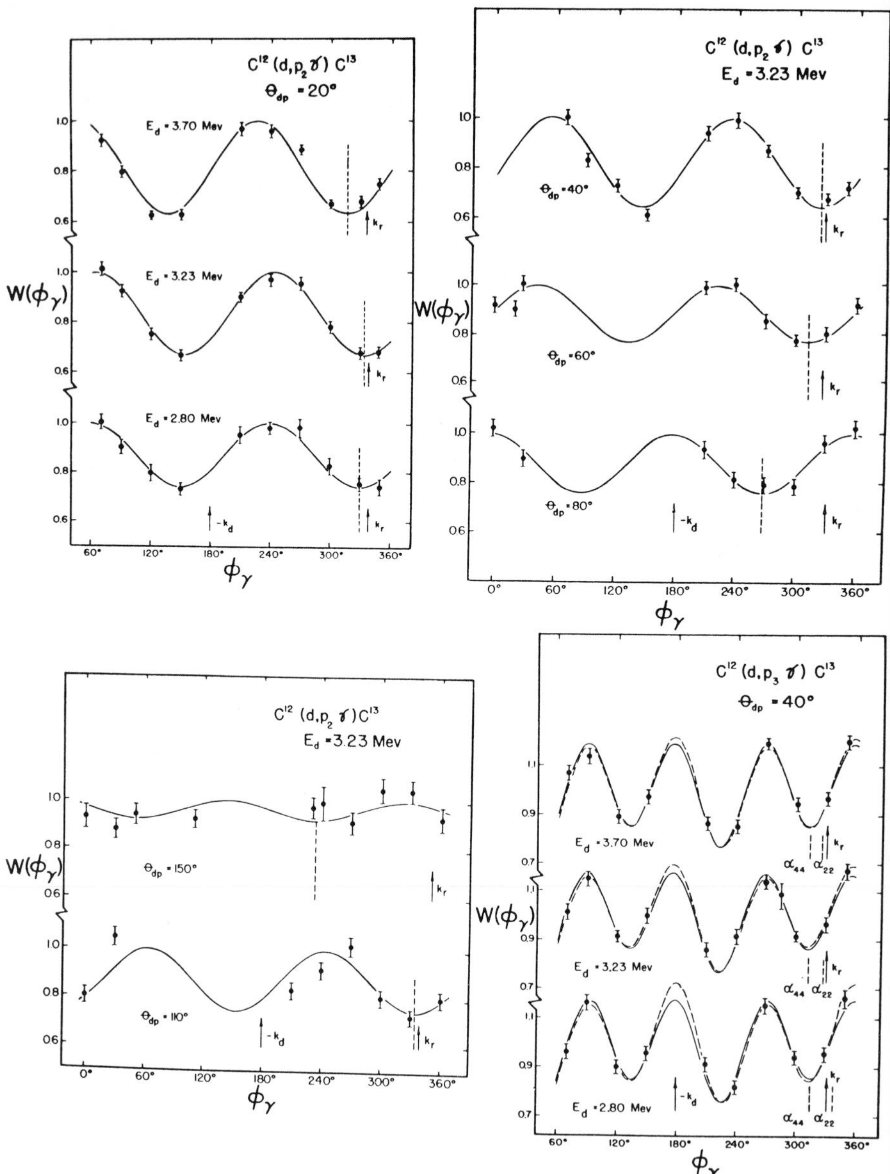

Fig. 2 Reaction-plane measurements[6] of $C^{12}(d,p\ )C^{13}$ angular correlations through the 3.68 and 3.85 MeV states. The recoil angles are indicated by k_r.

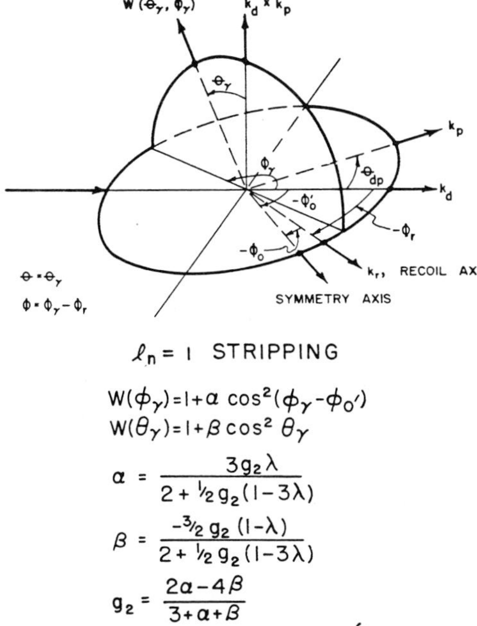

Fig. 3 DWBA angular correlation formalism for the (d,pγ) reaction with $\ell_n = 1$ (Ref. 5).

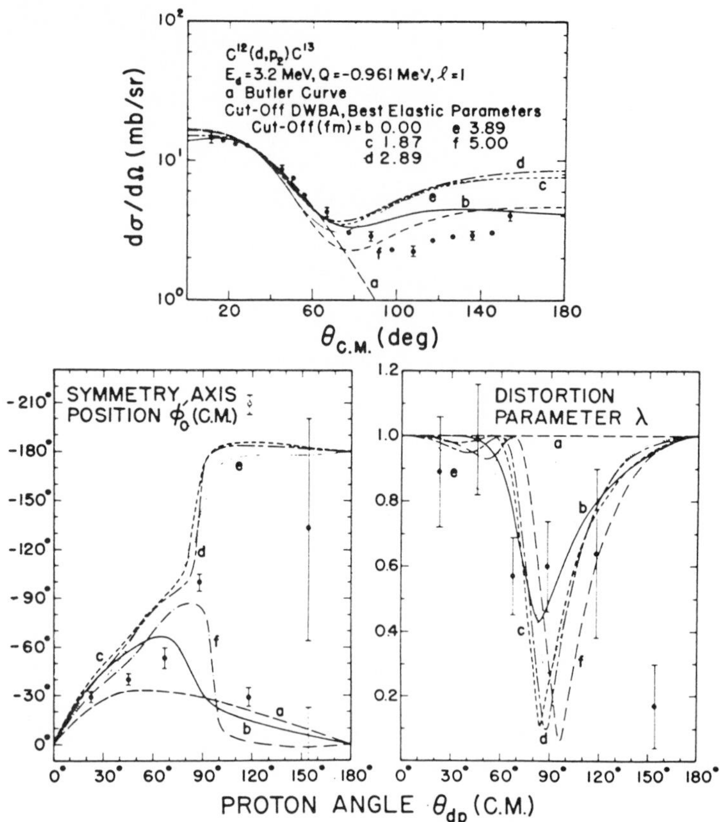

Fig. 4 DWBA fits to the measured differential cross section and p -γ angular correlation parameters for the $C^{12}(d,p\ \gamma_{3.68})C^{13}$ reaction at E_d = 3.23 MeV (Ref. 8).

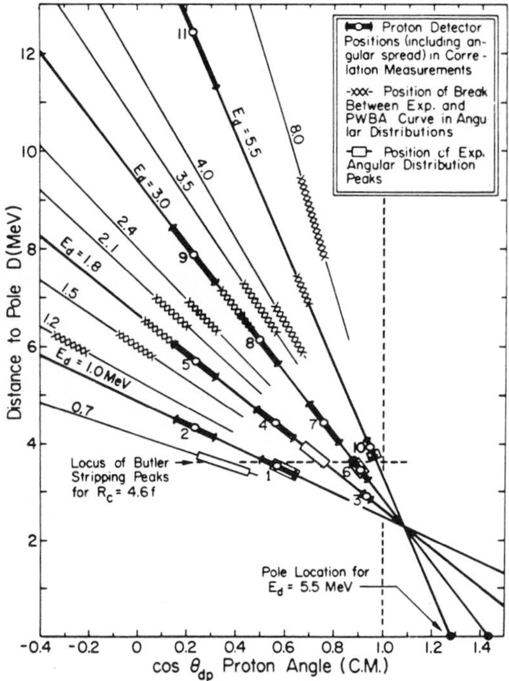

Fig. 5 Distance to the Butler pole vs. proton angle for various laboratory deuteron energies for $B^{11}(d,p\gamma)B^{12}{}_{0.95}$. (Ref. 11).

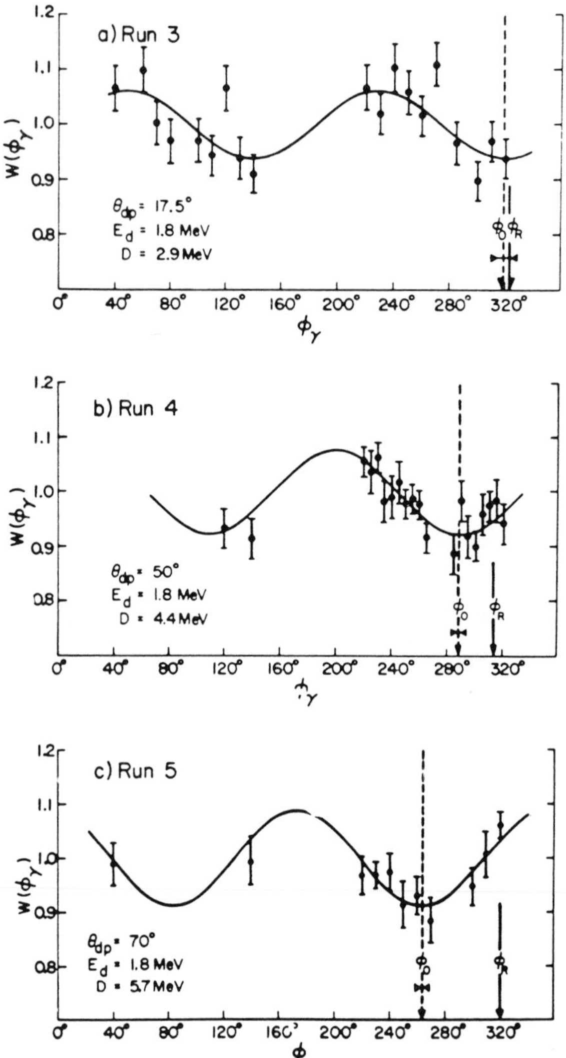

Fig. 6 Proton-gamma angular correlations for $B^{11}(d,p\gamma)$ $B^{12}_{0.95}$.(Ref. 11).

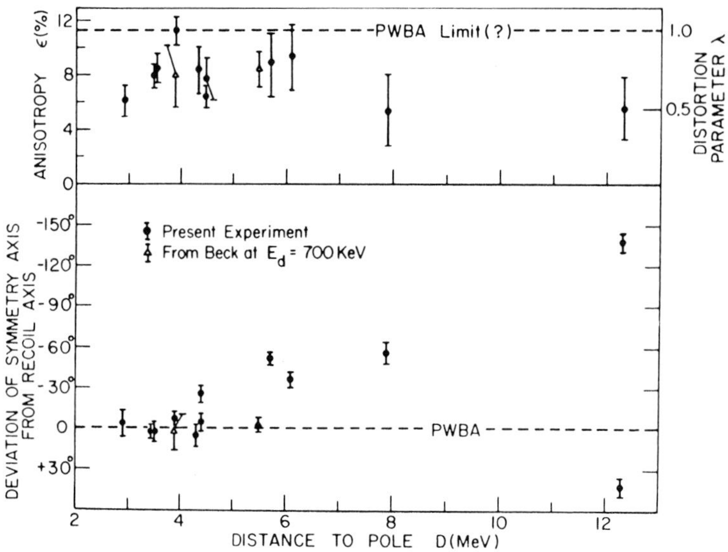

Fig. 7 Measured correlation anisotropy and symmetry axis shift vs. distance to the Butler pole.(Ref. 11).

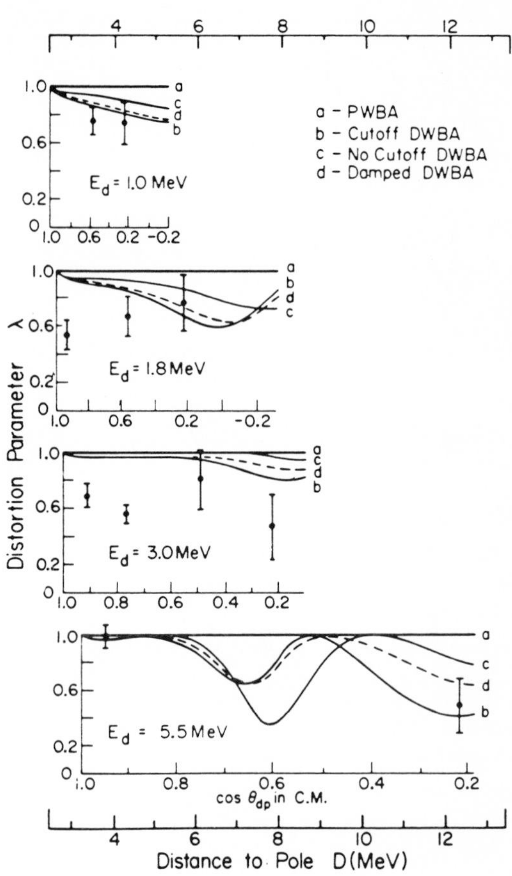

Fig. 8 Distortion parameter vs. distance to the Butler pole. Experimental values and various theoretical curves are shown for the deuteron energies used in the experiment. (Ref. 11).

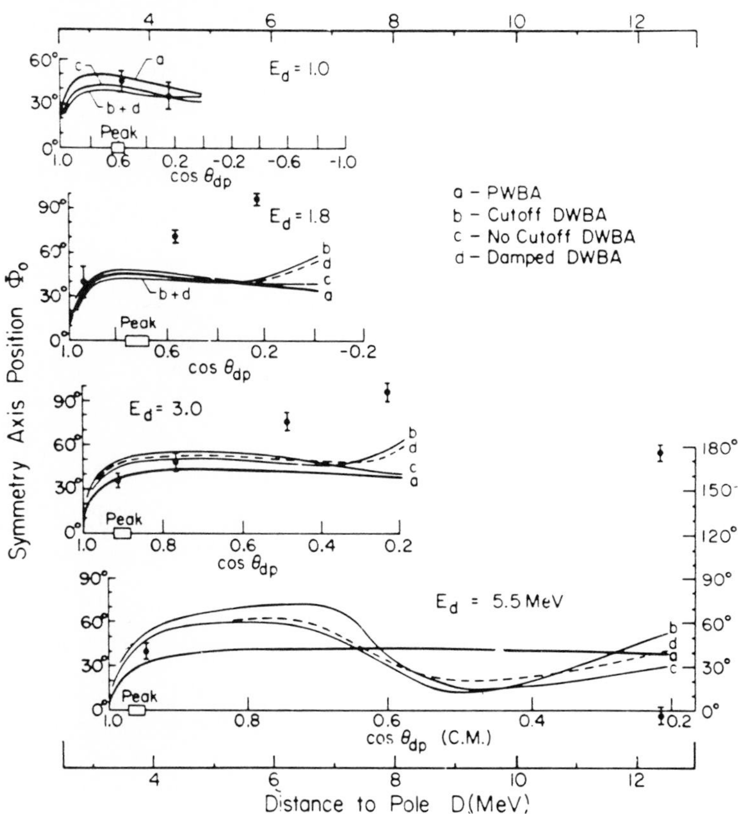

Fig. 9 Symmetry axis vs. distance to the Butler pole. Experimental values and various theoretical curves are shown for the deuteron energies used in the experiment. (Ref. 11).

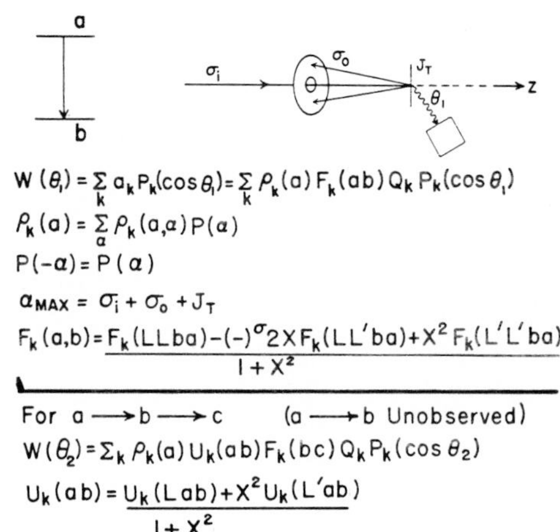

Fig. 10 Angular correlation formalism for particle-gamma techniques of Litherland and Ferguson[1]. (See Ref. 19).

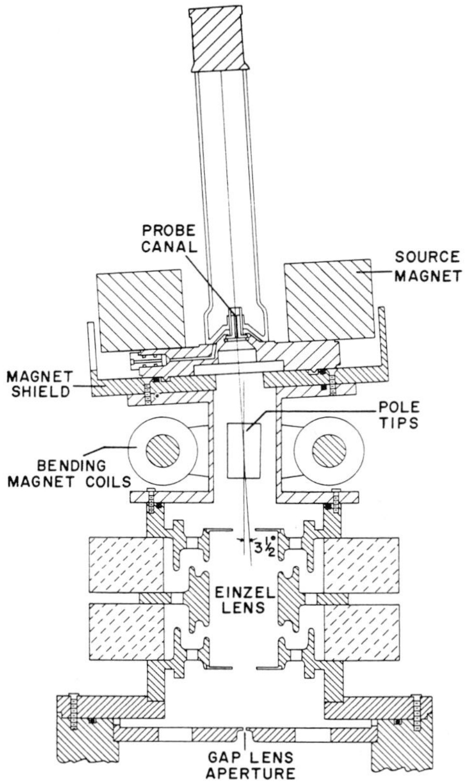

Fig. 11 The He^{++} source used in the Duke 4 MV Van de Graaff accelerator. (Ref. 20).

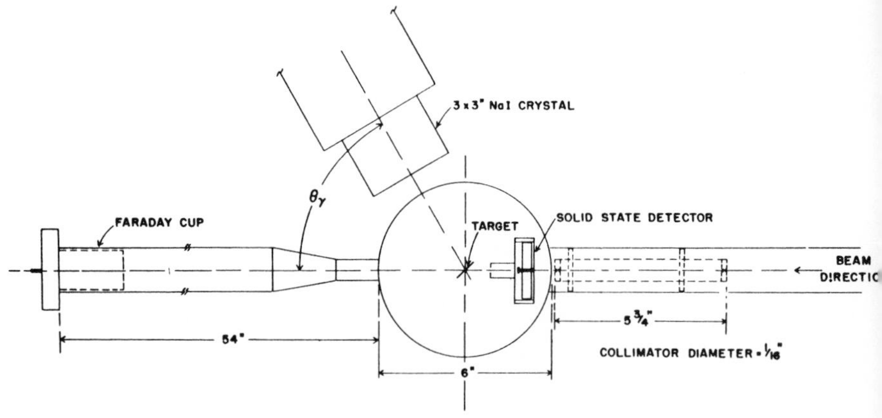

Fig. 12 Target chamber for particle-gamma angular correlation experiments.

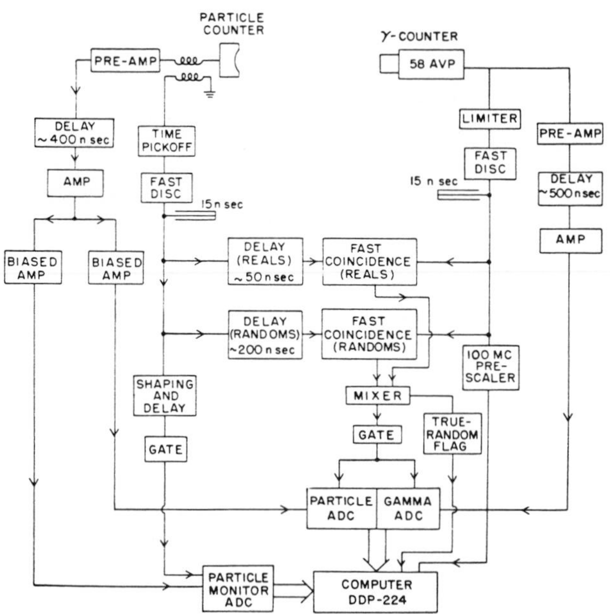

Fig. 13 Block diagram of electronic setup for particle-gamma angular correlation experiments.

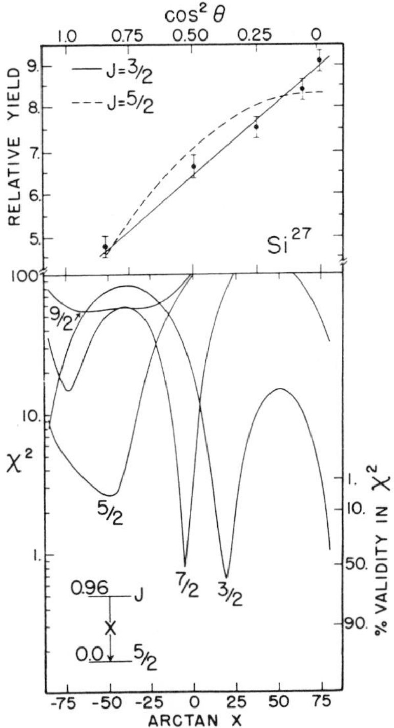

Fig. 14 The (He^3,αγ) angular correlation and analysis for the 0.96 MeV level of Si^{27} populated by the $Si^{28}(He^3,\alpha)Si^{27}$ reaction (from an experiment of Lewis, Roberson, and Tilley).

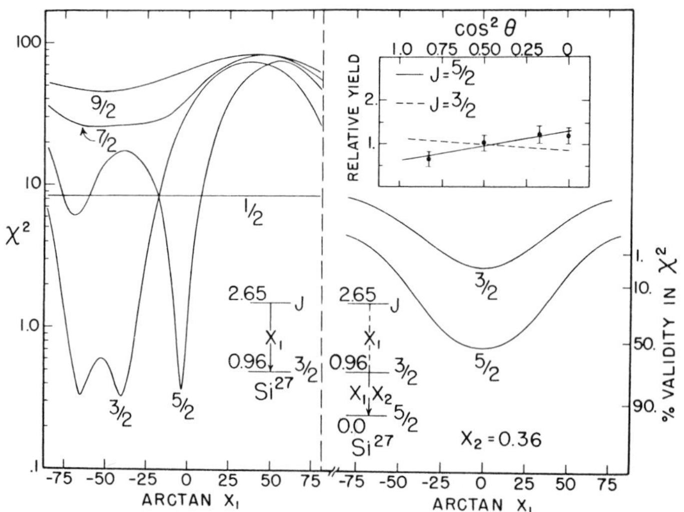

Fig. 15 Angular correlation results for the 2.65 MeV level of Si^{27} populated by the $Si^{28}(He^3,\alpha)Si^{27}$ reaction. The analysis on the left is for the 2.65→0.96 MeV transition. The triple correlation analysis on the right is for the 0.96 MeV transition and was made by taking $x_2 = 0.36$ (from an experiment of Lewis, Roberson, and Tilley).

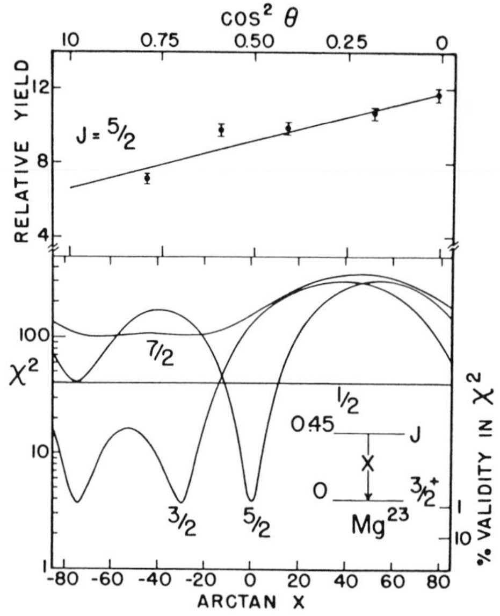

Fig. 16 The $(He^3,\alpha\gamma)$ angular correlation and analysis for the 0.45 MeV state of Mg^{23} populated by the $Mg^{24}(He^3,\alpha)Mg^{23}$ reaction (from an experiment of Haun, Roberson, and Tilley).

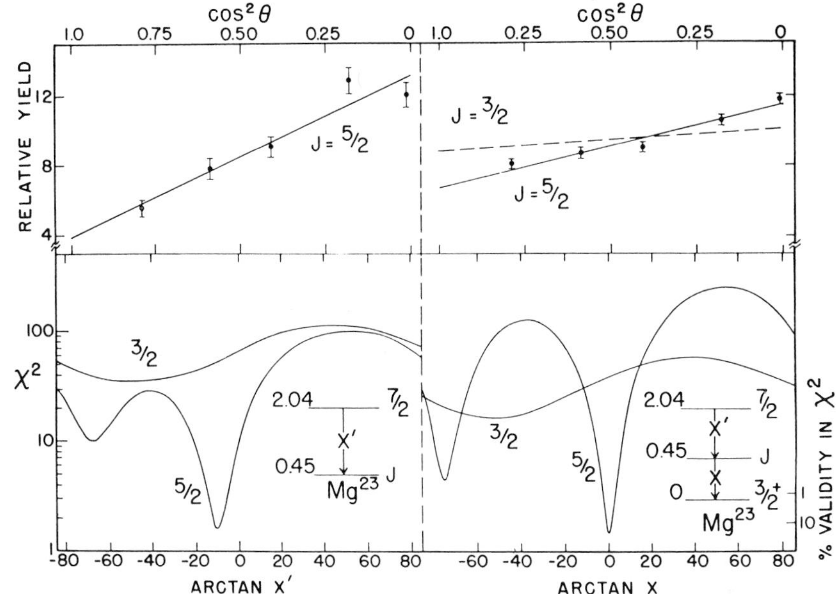

Fig. 17 Angular correlation results for the 2.04 MeV level of Mg^{23}. The analysis on the left is for the 2.04→0.45 transition. In the triple correlation analysis on the right for the 0.45 MeV transition x' was fixed at the value indicated in the analysis on the left (from an experiment of Haun, Roberson, and Tilley).

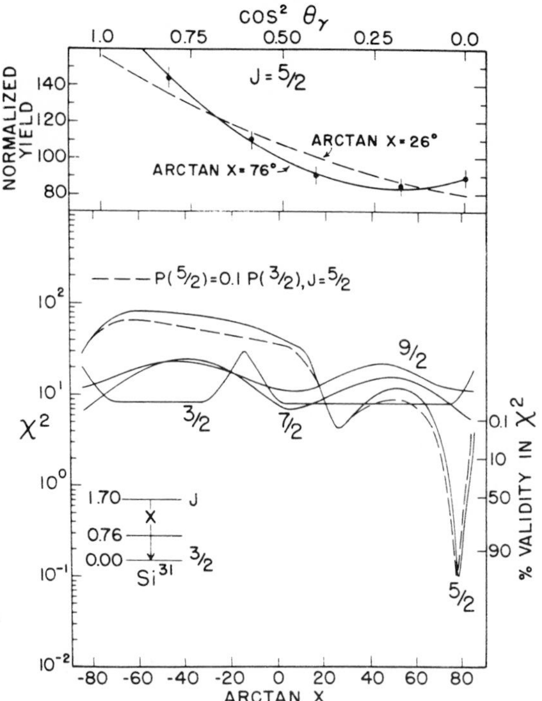

Fig. 18 Angular correlation and analysis for the 1.70 MeV level of Si^{31} populated by the $Si^{30}(d,p\gamma)Si^{31}$ reaction (from an experiment by Webb, Roberson, and Tilley).

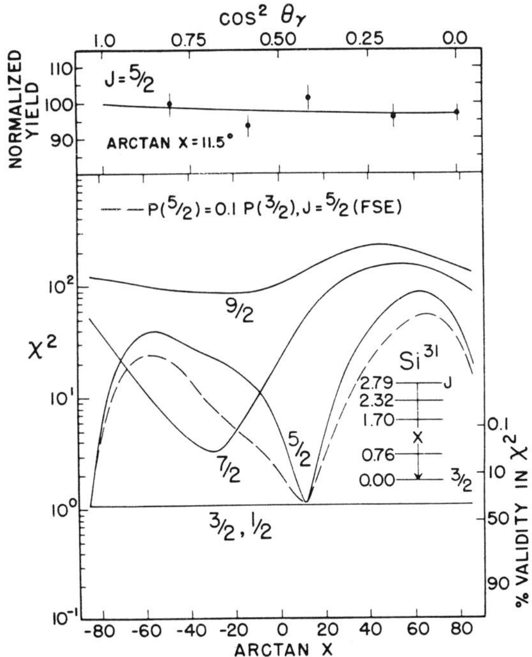

Fig. 19 Angular correlation and analysis for the ground state transition from the 2.79 MeV level of Si^{31} populated by the $Si^{30}(d,p)Si^{31}$ reaction (from an experiment by Webb, Roberson, and Tilley).

SHELL MODEL CALCULATIONS

W. T. Pinkston

Vanderbilt University
Nashville, Tennessee

Abstract

A brief summary is given of nuclear shell model techniques and recent applications of these techniques to nuclei in the 1p-shell and in the (2s,1d)-shell.

Introduction

It is my intent to summarize the status of some shell model calculations of special interest to the participants of this conference. Since a low energy accelerator has been defined to have a maximum energy of 5 MeV, we are compelled by the Coulomb barrier to restrict the discussion to light nuclei. I have arbitrarily chosen Ca^{40} as the upper cut-off, so that we shall be discussing the structure of the 1p-shell and (2s, 1d)-shell nuclei.

In the shell model or independent particle model, nucleons are assumed to move independently in a potential field which, for a given nucleon, represents the averaged effect of all the other nucleons. This, of course, is not an adequate description of the nuclear dynamics, but hopefully it provides a good starting point for a perturbation calculation. In higher orders, interparticle interactions will be included explicitly. The Hartree-Fock or self consistent field theory gives a procedure for calculating the average nuclear field from the interparticle interactions. In this theory the independent particle wave function is a Slater determinant,

$$\Psi = \frac{1}{\sqrt{A!}} \det \{\phi(1)\phi(2)\ldots\phi(A)\} \qquad (1)$$

and the single particle functions, ϕ, are those for which the expectation value of the Hamiltonian is a minimum.

$$\delta \frac{< \Psi | \Sigma\ T\ (i) + \Sigma\ V(i,j)\ | \Psi >}{< \Psi \mid \Psi >} = 0 \qquad (2)$$

Equation (2) implies that the ϕ's should be solutions of the single particle Schroedinger equations,

$$(T + U_a)\phi_a = \varepsilon_a \phi_a, \qquad (3)$$

in which U_a is the average potential energy experienced by a nucleon in the ath level or orbit. It is defined in terms of its matrix elements, viz.

$$<\phi_a | U_a | \phi_a> = \sum_{b \neq a} \{<\phi_a \phi_b | V | \phi_a \phi_b> - <\phi_a \phi_b | V | \phi_b \phi_a>\} \qquad (4)$$

Such calculations are common in atomic structure theory; in nuclear structure theory there are difficulties of both fundamental and practical nature. We shall not have time to discuss the very important work in progress on this subject. We can safely neglect it because the nuclear shell model has gotten along without self consistent field calculations for many years. It appears to be a sufficiently good approximation to replace the fields U_a by a central potential, such as a Woods-Saxon, with a strong spin-orbit term, as proposed by Mayer and Jensen. The potential parameters can be adjuste to give the observed single particle levels, which for light nuclei are sketched in Fig. 1.

Shell Model Calculations

The phrase "shell model calculation" usually means a calculation of the properties of the low lying levels of a nucleus consisting of closed shells plus or minus a few nucleons. The simplest shell model calculations consist of placing the valence nucleons in the lowest states allowed by the exclusion principle. Thus in O^{17} the extra nucleon is in the $1d_{5/2}$ level. In O^{18} there are two neutrons in this level, or $(1d_{5/2})^2$, leading to total angular momenta, J = 0,2 and 4. In O^{19} the configuration, $(1d_{5/2})^3$, leads to J = 3/2, 5/2 and 9/2, and so on. The energy spectra are determined from first order perturbation theory, by calculating the expectation value of the Hamiltonian in these states. Improved calculations employ configuration mixing, which means that the nuclear wave functions are taken to be superpositions of states with the particles in different shells. In O^{18}, for example, the ground state wave function would not be simply $(1d_{5/2})^2$, J = 0. It would be an admixture of

$$\psi(1d_{5/2}{}^2),\ \psi(2s_{1/2}{}^2),\ \text{and}\ \psi(1d_{3/2}{}^2)$$

In general, ψ is written as

$$\psi = \Sigma\, C_\gamma\, \psi_\gamma \tag{5}$$

Then the expectation value of the Hamiltonian is minimized, the C_γ's being the quantities varied. The minimum value of <H> occurs for those values of the C_γ's which are the solutions of

$$\Sigma_{\gamma'}\, H_{\gamma\gamma'}\, C_{\gamma'} = EC_\gamma . \tag{6}$$

Here E is the minimum value of <H>. The matrix elements, $H_{\gamma\gamma'}$, have the form,

$$H_{\gamma\gamma'} = \delta_{\gamma\gamma'}\, \Sigma_a n_a\, \varepsilon_a + \Sigma_{abcd}\,(\text{coefficients})\times \langle ab|V|cd\rangle \tag{7}$$

The first term is the zero order shell model energy; n_a is the number of nucleons in the level, a, and ε_a is the energy of a particle in such a level. The ε's contain the kinetic energy of the particle plus its interaction with the closed shell core; therefore they are just the energies of the low lying levels of nuclei consisting of one particle beyond a closed shell. The second term is written in a highly schematic form but represents the mutual interaction of the nucleons outside the core. These interaction matrix elements are sums over products of two factors. The symbols, $\langle ab|V|cd\rangle$, represent one of these factors, the two-body matrix elements. These two-body matrix elements are independent of the structure--number of particles, angular momentum, isotopic spin, etc.--of the many-particle states ψ_γ and $\psi_{\gamma'}$. The sum in this term runs over the orbits, a and b, which are occupied in ψ_γ and over c and d occupied in $\psi_{\gamma'}$. The coefficients multiplying the two-body matrix elements depend only on the structure of the many-particle states, and not at all on the two-body interactions. These coefficients are tedious to calculate, but straightforward in principle. Their evaluation is best accomplished by using a "multishell" code, either at Oak Ridge, Argonne, or Chalk River. The Oak Ridge Code[1], for example, will set up and diagonalize the matrix of H for any number of particles in levels with $J \leq 5/2$, and up to 4 particles in any level with $j = 7/2$. The maximum number of orbits is 6. Matrices of order up to 400 can be diagonalized without difficulty.

Nuclear shell model calculations have thus become mechanized. The physicist must pick what he considers to be the important configurations. The appropriate single particle matrix elements are usually obtainable from experiment. Most of the physics of the calculation is contained in the V matrix elements.

Two-Body Matrix Elements

Shell model calculations can be divided into three categories, according to the method used to determine the two-body matrix elements.

1. Effective Interactions. The method of effective interactions was introduced into nuclear structure physics by Talmi[2]. In this method the relevant matrix elements, $\langle ab|V|cd\rangle$, are treated as free parameters in least squares fits to the energy levels. The levels of a number of nuclei in the same region are fitted simultaneously so that there are more data than free parameters. The method has been highly successful. A typical example is the study of the oxygen isotopes by Cohen et al.[3] These authors included all states in which particles occupy $1d_{5/2}$ and $2s_{1/2}$ orbits. The inclusion of the $2s_{1/2}$ orbit is necessary since it is only 0.87 MeV above the $1d_{5/2}$ orbit. Configurations in which particles occupy the $1d_{3/2}$ were not included, since the $1d_{3/2}$ is 5.08 MeV above the $1d_{5/2}$. There are 8 two-body matrix elements, and these were used to fit the 13 experimental levels. The known energy spectra of the oxygen isotopes are compared in Table 1 to the theoretical results in order to illustrate the goodness of the fits. Glaudemans et al.[4,5] have treated nuclei in the region, A = 17 through A = 28, with both protons and neutrons in the $1d_{5/2}$ and $2s_{1/2}$ shells, and nuclei in the region, A = 29 through A = 40, assuming a closed $(1d_{5/2})^{12}$ core with the remaining nucleons in $2s_{1/2}$ and $1d_{3/2}$ shells. The fits are satisfactory but not as good as the results in the oxygen isotopes.
2. Realistic Interactions. Ideally the two-body matrix elements should be calculated from the "correct" internucleon potentials--those which reproduce the nucleon-nucleon scattering data. Several potential models exist which satisfactorily account for these data. Unfortunately for the independent particle model, a common feature of these potentials is a repulsive core, i.e. nucleons behave like hard spheres at short distances. With such potentials all the matrix elements discussed thus far are infinite. This means that the independent particle wave functions cannot be good approximations to the true nuclear wave functions. The repulsive cores in V will result in motions which are not

independent but strongly correlated at short distances. On the other hand we know empirically that the shell model works. The theoretical studies of infinite nuclear matter provide the answer to why it works. These studies indicate that the correlations are of such a short range that the nucleons move independently most of the time, so that it is probably reasonable to use shell model wave functions in calculating matrix elements such as quadrupole moments, etc. The nuclear matter studies also indicate how to calculate a quantity, G, the reaction matrix. This is an operator which has the property that its matrix elements between independent particle states is the same as those of V between the correct correlated states. Thus if we wish to do shell model calculations, we must replace $\langle ab|V|cd\rangle$ in Eq. 7 by $\langle ab|G|cd\rangle$. Of course, G can be evaluated only approximately, and even so only with considerable difficulty. Kuo and Brown[6] have developed approximations for calculating G matrix elements for shell model calculations. Figures 2 and 3 give examples of the success of the Kuo-Brown shell model calculations. The spectra of O^{18} and F^{18} are compared there to calculations using the Hamada-Johnston interaction. The single particle functions used in evaluating the two-body matrix elements were taken to be eigenfunctions of an isotropic harmonic oscillator. These functions are probably good approximations to the ϕ's in Eq. 7 except in the tail region. The oscillator energy spacing was taken to be $\hbar\omega$ = 14 MeV, which makes the r.m.s. nuclear radius equal to that obtained from high energy electron scattering.

The nuclei of the 1p-shell have also been calculated[7] using the Kuo-Brown matrix elements. Typical examples are shown in Figs. 4 and 5. In these calculations, $\hbar\omega$ and the $1p_{1/2}$ - $1p_{3/2}$ single particle energy difference were varied to get the best fits possible. In these figures the results of Cohen and Kurath[8] are shown for comparison. Cohen and Kurath calculated the levels of all the 1p-shell nuclei using the method of effective interactions. The fifteen two-body matrix elements and the $1p_{3/2}$ and $1p_{1/2}$ single particle energies were taken as free parameters, and all the known $(1p)^n$ levels were fitted. The r.m.s. deviation between experimental and calculated energies was about 0.5 MeV.

These successes plus others in heavier nuclei force one to conclude that it is possible to predict the properties of finite nuclei using the shell model and matrix elements deduced from realistic internucleon forces.

3. Conventional Interactions. For completeness I would like to mention the oldest kind of calculations, in which two-body matrix elements are calculated with interactions of some conventional shape such as Yukawa or Gauss. These

interactions should be considered to be pseudo reaction matrices, but their matrix elements are rarely good approximations to the G matrix elements. Computations of the two-body matrix elements of conventional interactions are quite simple compared to the evaluation of shell model G matrix elements; thus people will probably continue to use them to some extent. By far the easiest pseudo interaction to use is the surface delta interaction of Moszkowski[9],

$$V(1,2) = V_0 \delta(r_1 - R)\, \delta(r_2 - R) \delta(\theta_{12}).$$

Surprisingly, it also appears to be the most successful. The results[5,10] of using this interaction in the (2s,1d)-shell are quite comparable to those based on the method of effective interactions.

Pseudonium

It would be wrong to give the impression that the study of nuclear structure is in about the same satisfactory state as the theory of atomic structure. I would therefore like to comment briefly on some calculations by Cohen, Lawson, and Soper[11]. These authors have performed a series of shell model calculations in which neutrons populate two levels, $1d_{3/2}$ and $1f_{7/2}$, in some non-existent nuclei, the Pseudonium isotopes. The two levels were made degenerate in order to achieve a maximum amount of configuration mixing. A conventional interaction of Yukawa shape was employed, and energy levels, magnetic moments, quadrupole moments, spectroscopic factors, . . . were calculated. The results of these calculations were treated as experimental data to be fitted by the effective interactions method. In employing the effective interactions method, it was assumed that the $1d_{3/2}$ level fills as N varies from 1 to 4. Thereafter, the low lying Pseudonium levels were assumed to arise from the pure, $(1d_{3/2})^4(1f_{7/2})^{N-4}$ configuration. The N = 4 case is referred to as Ps^{40} because of the similarity of the pseudonium and calcium isotopes. The assumption of a pure $(1d_{3/2})^4$ configuration for Ps^{40} is completely contrary to fact; the contribution of this configuration to the ground state wave function of Ps^{40} is only 9%. Nevertheless, remarkable agreement with pseudo-experiment was obtained. Table 2 is taken from the article of Cohen, Lawson, and Soper. In it the predicted binding energies are compared to the pseudo-experimental ones. The last column lists the contribution of the assumed configurations to the "true" pseudo-wave functions. Energy spectra were also predicted accurately by the model. Even quantities which one might suppose depend sensitively on the wave functions--magnetic moments, transition rates, etc--were predicted fairly well. Apparently the effective interactions method has an amazing ability to absorb the effects of configuration mixing. These calculations pose a dilemma. We have a theory with great predictive power--the shell model--but these results make it impossible for us to conclude that the shell model wave functions are good approximations to the true wave functions.

Deformed Shell Model

Although calculations based on the spherical shell model of (2s,1d)-shell nuclei have been quite encouraging, there is experimental evidence that many of the energy levels of these nuclei can be described in terms of the collective rotational model. As an example some of the energy levels of Ne^{20} are plotted in Fig. 6, in a way which suggests the existence of rotational bands. This type of plot was first suggested by Litherland et al.[12] When plotted against J(J+1) the energies of the levels within these bands fall close to straight lines. Strongly enhanced B(E2)'s connecting levels within the ground state band have been observed, confirming the collective description.

These data should not be taken as evidence against the independent particle model description of (2s,1d)-shell nuclei. Rather it indicates that the average nuclear fields in this region are non-spherical. The shell model still applies, but it is a deformed shell model. The rotational levels can be explained with the time dependent Hartree-Fock approximation. When the static Hartree-Fock solution is deformed, the time dependent Hartree-Fock equations possess solutions which correspond to slow rotations of the static solutions. Even though the nuclei are deformed, it should be possible to describe these motions in terms of the spherical shell model, since the spherical shell model basic states (the ψ_γ's of Eq. 6) span the same region of Hilbert space as the deformed states ordinarily used. The existence of collective rotations means that good results can be obtained with a small number of deformed states, whereas quite a large number of spherical states might be required in an expansion of the wave function. From the stand-point of practical calculations this is an important point. Consider Si^{28}, in the very center of the (2s,1d)-shell. There are 15,385 J=3 states which can be formed by putting 6 protons and 6 neutrons in this shell. This number includes all values of the isotopic spin; therefore it is somewhat larger than the order of the largest matrix to be diagonalized. However, the order of the largest matrix will certainly be several thousand.

There is also evidence for the existence of deformed states in the excited spectra of closed shell nuclei. The fact that the first excited state of O^{16} at 6.06 MeV is 0+ has long been a puzzle, since it would seem that the lowest energy excitations of the O^{16} closed shell would arise from lifting a 1p particle into the (2s,1d)-shell. Such an excitation, however, produces states of negative parity. It is undoubtedly the origin of the 2nd excited level at 6.14 MeV, which is 3-. At least twice as much energy would be required to lift 2 particles into the next shell or to lift one 1p particle into the (2p,1f)-shell. Approximate Hartree-Fock[13,14] calculations indicate, however, that the excitation of 4 particles requires considerably less energy than the excitation of 2. The minimum energy state for 4 holes and 4 particles is strongly deformed and has a much lower energy than one would estimate from considerations based on the spherical shell model. In Fig. 7 are shown the low lying levels of O^{16} with the levels of Ne^{20}--which has 4 particles in the (2s,1d)-shell --superposed, suggesting the presence of a rotational band in O^{16} built on the 6.06-MeV level. This is, of course, what we would expect if the 6.06-MeV level is strongly deformed. Brown and Green[15] have calculated the properties of these states and similar states in O^{17}. Deformed states are believed to occur in Ca^{40}. They have been studied by Gerace and Green[16]. On the other hand, the question as to the nature of the O^{16} states is not completely settled. Philpott and Sydlik[17] have been quite successful in predicting their energies using a 2-particle, 2-hole model.

References

1. French, Halbert, McGrory and Wong, unpublished, and private communications.
2. I. Talmi, Rev. Mod. Phys. 34, 704 (1962)
3. Cohen, Lawson, MacFarlane and Soga, Phys. Letters 9, 180 (1964)
4. P. W. M. Glaudemans, G. Wiechers and P. J. Brussaard, Nucl. Phys. 56, 529 (1964); 56, 548 (1964)
5. Glaudemans, Widenthal, Halbert and McGrory, International Conference on Nuclear Physics, Gatlinburg, Tennessee, September, 1966, Abstract 5.17
6. T. T. S. Kuo and G. E. Brown, Nucl. Phys. 85, 40 (1966)
7. E. C. Halbert, Y. E. Kim and T. T. S. Kuo, Phys. Letters 20, 657 (1966)
8. S. Cohen and D. Kurath, Nucl. Phys. 73, 1 (1965)
9. I. M. Green and S. A. Moszkowski, Phys. Rev. 139, B790 (1965)
10. P. W. M. Glaudemans, B. H. Widenthal and J. B. McGrory,

Phys. Letters 21, 427 (1966)
11. S. Cohen, R. D. Lawson and J. M. Soper, Phys. Letters 21, 306 (1966)
12. Litherland, Kuehner, Gove, Clark and Almqvist, Phys. Rev. Letters 7, 306 (1966)
13. W. H. Bassichis and G. Ripka, Phys. Letters 15, 320 (1965)
14. I. Kelson, Phys. Letters 16, 143 (1965)
15. G. E. Brown and A. M. Green, Nucl. Phys. 75, 401 (1966)
16. W. J. Gerace and A. M. Green, Nucl. Phys. 93, 1 (1967)
17. R. J. Philpott and P. P. Szydlik, Phys. Rev. 153, 1039 (1967)

TABLE 1

Energy Spectra of the Oxygen Isotopes in the Calculations of Cohen, et al. (Reference 3)

Nucleus	Spin	Experiment	Theory
O^{18}	2	1.98	1.93
	4	3.55	3.60
	0	3.63	3.52
	2	3.92	3.87
O^{19}	3/2	0.096	0.04
	1/2	1.469	1.51
O^{20}	2	1.672	1.82
	4	3.568	3.53
	2	4.065	4.02
	0	4.446	4.46

TABLE 2

Binding Energies of the Pseudonium Isotopes Relative to Ps^{40}--from the calculations of Cohen, Lawson and Soper (Reference 13)

	Binding Energies in MeV		
Nucleus	Pseudo-experiment	pure $f_{7/2}$ configuration	Probability of the configuration $(id_{3/2})^4(if_{7/2}{}^{N-4})$
Ps^{41}	-3.47	-3.57	0.173
Ps^{42}	-11.66	-11.66	0.341
Ps^{43}	-16.83	-16.85	0.550
Ps^{44}	-26.56	-26.57	0.658
Ps^{45}	-33.46	-33.38	0.854
Ps^{46}	-44.62	-44.71	0.880
Ps^{47}	-53.13	-53.15	1.00
Ps^{48}	-65.66	-66.11	1.00

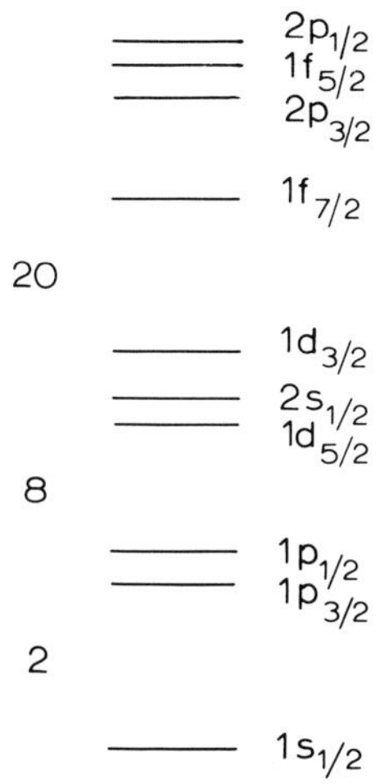

2p1/2
1f5/2
2p3/2
1f7/2
20
1d3/2
2s1/2
1d5/2
8
1p1/2
1p3/2
2
1s1/2

Fig. 1 Shell Model Single Particle Levels for Light Nuclei

O18
MeV
4
3
2
1
0
-1
-2
-3
-4
4+
3+
0+
2+
2+
0+
4+
2+
0+
4+
3+
2+
0+
4+
2+
0+
EXP
KUO - BROWN

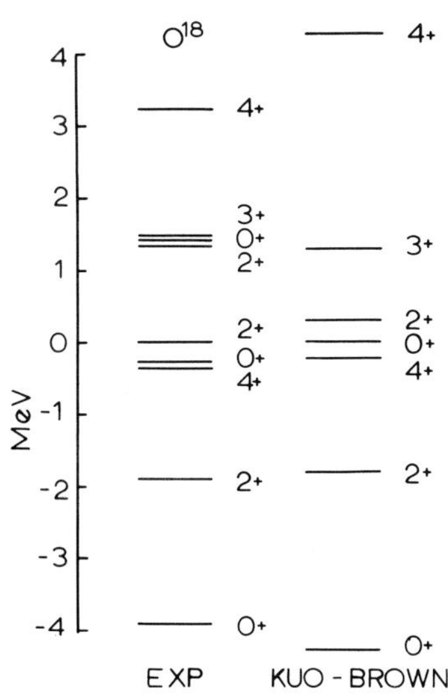

Fig. 2 Energy Levels of O^{18}. Calculated with the Hamada-Johnston Interaction--from Kuo and Brown (Reference 6)

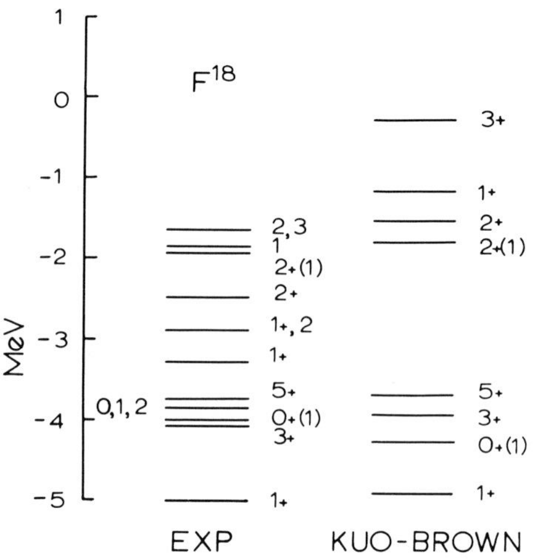

Fig. 3 Energy Levels of F^{18}. Calculated with the Hamada-Johnston Interaction--from Kuo and Brown (Reference 6)

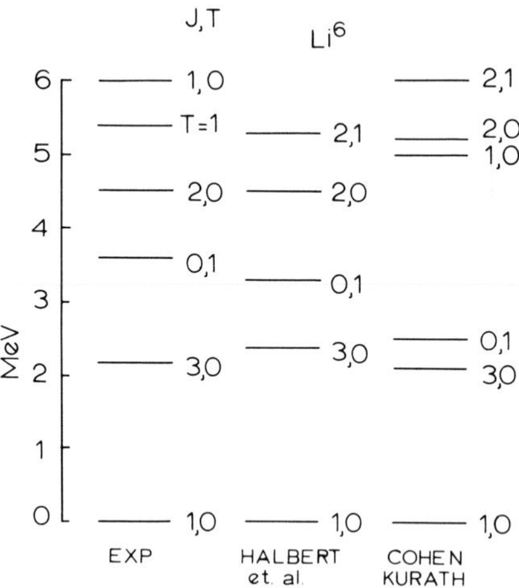

Fig. 4 Energy Levels of Li^6. The 2nd column gives the results of Halbert et al. (Reference 8). The 3rd column gives the results of Cohen and Kurath (Reference 9)

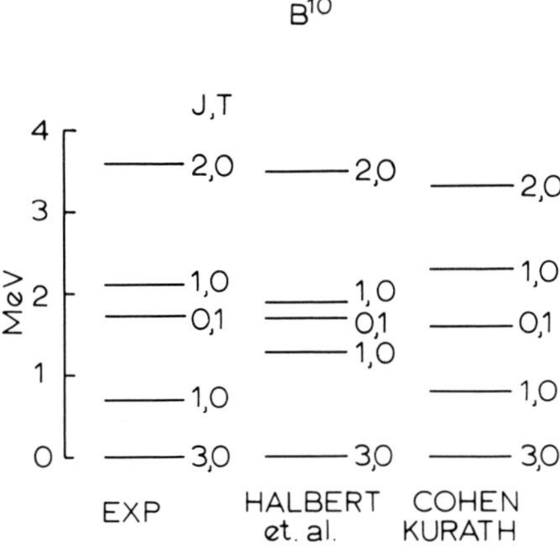

Fig. 5 Energy Levels of B^{10}. The 2nd column gives the results of Halbert et al. (Reference 8). The 3rd column gives the results of Cohen and Kurath (Reference 9)

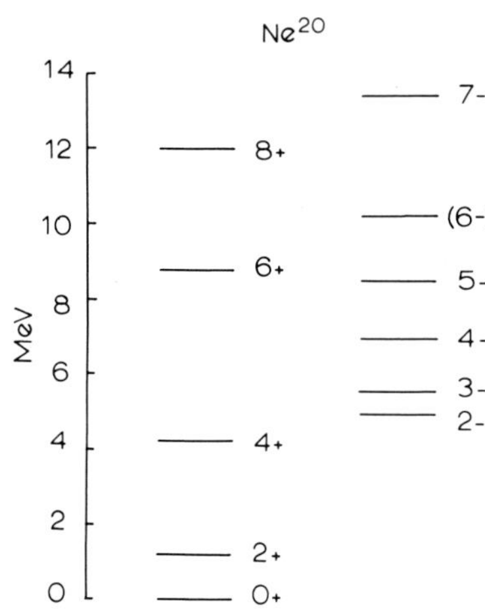

Fig. 6 Rotational Bands in Ne^{20}

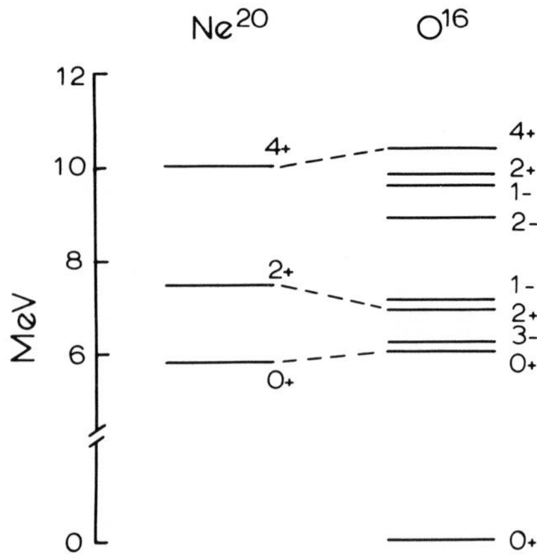

Fig. 7 Energy Levels of O^{16}. The first three levels of the Ne^{20} ground state rotational band are superposed to suggest that a rotational band exists in O^{16} built upon the 6.06-MeV level.

THEORETICAL PROBLEMS IN LOW ENERGY REACTIONS

G. J. Stephenson, Jr.

University of Maryland
College Park, Maryland

Introduction

It is my intention to restrict myself in these remarks to some theoretical problems which can be studied in low energy nuclear reactions and, in particular, to problems related to the study of the intrinsic shapes of light nuclei.

As Dr. Pinkston has pointed out,[1] the nuclear shell model has had considerable success in describing the low lying states of the lightest nuclei, those in the 1p shell and the very beginning of the 2s-1d shell. In addition, it has been shown[2] that one may often obtain a good representation of these shell model states by projecting them from a single deformed shell model, or Nilsson model, state, i.e. from a single determinant of independent particles moving in a non-spherical average potential. This success leads us to the hope that we may obtain a reasonable approximation to the low lying states of light nuclei by performing Hartree-Fock calculations in a body-fixed frame of reference, allowing the density to be non-spherical, and with as realistic two-body forces as possible, to obtain the intrinsic state from which the rotational states of sharp angular momentum may be projected. A great deal of effort is now being spent on this project by several groups.[3]

Symmetries of the Hartree-Fock Wave Functions

The following discussion will be limited to 4n, N=Z even-even nuclei. Recent calculations using the Hartree-Fock-Bogoliubov formalism by Banerjee and his students[4] show convergence to normal Hartree-Fock only for these cases. When performing a Hartree-Fock calculation, it is important to know what symmetries to assume for the wave function, since such symmetries, once assumed, persist throughout the calculation. It is clear, however, that the symmetries of the original two-body Hamiltonian are not necessarily those of the Hartree-Fock effective single-particle Hamiltonian. For example, the original Hamiltonian is invariant under rotations in space, while the solutions which we are seeking correspond to a deformed Hartree-Fock field and are not rotationally invariant.

To determine which symmetries actually do exist, we[5] draw only on those features of the two-body interaction which are common to all of the fits to nucleon-nucleon scattering data, namely the exchange nature of the force and its short range. The exchange nature, the fact that the force is much more attractive in even relative states than in odd relative states, implies that each space orbital is either empty or four times filled with neutron and proton, spin up and down.

From the hierarchy of the multipole terms due to the short range nature of the force, i.e. the monopole-monopole term is greatest, etc., we can deduce that the Hartree-Fock Hamiltonian and density should be invariant under the operations of time-reversal, T, rotation about the z-axis by π, $e^{i\pi J_z}$, and rotation about the x or y-axis by π followed by reflection, $Pe^{i\pi J_x}$ or $Pe^{i\pi J_y}$. The relevant consequence of this is that the orbitals which are filled are real functions of the coordinates, not eigenfunctions of angular momentum. That is to say, the correct orbitals are of the form $x\exp(-r^2/2a^2)$, not $(x\pm iy)\exp(-r^2/2a^2)$ in the 1p-shell, and are of the form $(1-2z^2)\exp(-r^2/2a^2)$ and permutations, or of the form $xy\exp(-r^2/2a^2)$ and permutations in the 2s-1d shell.

Shapes of 1p and 2s-1d Shell 4n Nuclei

From the above remarks, it is straightforward to determine the shapes of 4n nuclei in the 1p shell. For Be^8, all four particles fill some one orbital, say z (for convenience, the exponential damping factor is suppressed), and the Hartree-Fock density clearly has an axis of rotational symmetry and is prolate. In C^{12}, two orbitals are filled, say x and y, and again there is axial symmetry but, in this case, the deformation is oblate. For the ground state of O^{16}, all three orbitals are filled, hence there is complete spherical symmetry.

In Ne^{20}, there is a choice between a prolate deformation corresponding to the filling of the $(1-2z^2)$ orbital or an oblate deformation corresponding to the filling of the xy orbital. The density distributions for these two types of orbital are shown schematically in Figure 1. The density of the $(1-2z^2)$ orbital is more compact, allowing for greater overlaps between the particles occupying the orbital and hence a greater attraction. From this one concludes that the prolate shape is the more tightly bound of the two, a conclusion which is borne out by the Hartree-Fock calculations assuming each symmetry.

When one adds four more particles to make Mg^{24}, another consideration enters. In this case, we also want to maximize the overlaps between particles in different orbits. This is clearly done by filling either the zx or zy orbital, and the corresponding gain in energy more than offsets the difference within the orbit discussed above. The resulting density no longer has any axis of rotational symmetry, being different in each of the three coordinate directions.

Proceeding to Si^{28}, there are again two possibilities, one prolate corresponding to filling $(1-2z^2)$, xz, and yz, and one oblate corresponding to filling $(1-2x^2)$, xy, and $(1-2y^2)$. The same considerations that were applied to Ne^{20} lead us to pick the latter case. Table 1 gives the expectation values of the quadrupole moment operations calculated with the best Hartree-Fock wave functions. The values quoted there bear out the assignments of shapes made above. Other calculations verify the assignments which one makes through the rest of the 2s-1d shell, namely S^{32} is tri-axial, A^{36} is axially symmetric and oblate and, of course, Ca^{40} is spherical.

The energies of the single-particle orbitals obtained in the Hartree-Fock calculations are shown in Fig. 2. A measure of the stability of a given solution is the energy gap between the occupied and the unoccupied orbitals, as this gap enters as an energy denominator in any perturbation. In Fig. 2 the relative stability of the N=Z even-even nuclei is very apparent compared to N≠Z even-even nuclei where the gap for the extra nucleons is very small. This is, of course, consistent with the earlier remark about the convergence of the Hartree-Fock-Bogoliubov solutions to Hartree-Fock solutions only for N=Z even-even nuclei.

The 4-particle 4-hole State of O^{16}

I now wish to describe a particular case where these ideas are relevant in some detail: the case of the low-lying positive parity excited states of O^{16}. The first excited state, 0^+ state at 6.06 MeV, has been a thorny problem for many years. From the appearance of the spectrum, several people[6] suggested that this state was the head of a rotational band and was probably projected from a four-particle four-hole deformed intrinsic state. Bassichis and Ripka[7] were able to show that such a state is a reasonable candidate with a Hartree-Fock calculation assuming a prolate deformation, but the 0^+ state came at about 12 MeV for the correct forces to give the binding energy of the ground state.

From the arguments presented above, we would expect the 8 p-shell particles to form an oblate density by filling, say, the x and y orbitals. The four 2s-1d shell particles would then fill an orbit of the type $(1-2z^2)$. However, to maximize the overlap with the p-shell particles, this density should also be in the x-y plane, so that either $(1-2x^2)$ or $(1-2y^2)$ will be filled. This would then imply that the four-particle four-hole intrinsic state is very ellipsoidal, that is, very non-axial.

To show how this is borne out, Fig. 3 and Table 2 show the results of Hartree-Fock calculations assuming prolate, oblate and ellipsoidal shapes.[8] This was done with a Yukawa force with an exchange mixture taken from good fits in the 2s-1d shell and with a strength adjusted to give the correct binding energy for the ground state, assumed here to be the closed 1p-shell. Choosing the correct shape results in the large gain of energy for the intrinsic Hartree-Fock state shown in the figure. The additional gain of energy for the 0^+ state is due to the increase in total angular momentum content inherent in the more angular shape coupled with the effect of the increased energy gap on the moments of inertia.

The 0^+ state appears at a low enough energy only for the ellipsoidal shape. The experimental spectrum furnishes further evidence that the intrinsic state is triaxial in that the 0^+ to 3^+ spacing is very nearly equal to the sum of the 0^+ to 2^+ and 0^+ to $2^{+\prime}$ spacings, a relation predicted for the band members of a non-axial rotator.[9] The general agreement with the positions of the levels is fairly good, however the incorrect ordering of the 3^+ and 4^+ is an indication that the inertial parameters are not reliable. An attempt to improve this fit, however, should wait for a Hartree-Fock calculation using effective matrix elements obtained from a realistic two-body force. There is one interesting possibility of obtaining additional experimental evidence that the intrinsic shape is ellipsoidal. If the intrinsic is assumed to have axial symmetry, the 2^+ state at 9.85 MeV would be described as the head of a γ band, and the B(E2)'s for transitions to the 2^+ and 0^+ members of the axial band would be in the ratio of Clebsch-Gordan coefficients. With an ellipsoidal intrinsic shape, however, the states are connected by both Q_{22} and Q_{20} operators, leading to the possibility of cancellations and B(E2) ratios which are very different from unity.

Major-Shell Mixing

The discussion thus far, the conclusions which we have reached, and the Hartree-Fock calculations which substantiate these conclusions have all been limited to angular mixing only. That is, we only consider mixing the orbitals in the last unfilled shell to generate the Hartree-Fock orbitals. While this leads to highly deformed density distributions, they are not deformed enough. The clearest experimental evidence for this comes from the intrinsic quadrupole moments which are generally a factor of two greater than the Hartree-Fock wave function can predict in the 2s-1d shell. Consequently, we must include the effects of major-shell mixing.[10] This conclusion has also been reached through shell-model calculations such as those by Kurath on Li^7. [11]

In general, a non-spherical density distribution within a major shell does imply major-shell mixing. This effect appears to be due primarily to the kinetic energy.[12] At saturation the expectation value of the potential energy is most sensitive to a change in the over-all volume. If the density has the right shape, this expectation value is a slowly varying function of additional deformation. Consequently, a deformation at constant volume will not have a large effect on the potential energy.

The kind of additional deformation which we are describing is most easily parametrized by changing the length constants in each of the three directions under the constraint of constant volume. This has the effect of decreasing the kinetic energy of the orbitals whose motion is along the directions which are extended and increasing the kinetic energy of those orbitals whose motion is along directions which are compressed. If the initial density is spherical, the net effect is small and the total energy increases, so there is no deformation of this type. On the other hand, if the density is loaded in some direction, as with Ne^{20}, there will be a large decrease in the kinetic energy of the one filled orbital under a deformation corresponding to the stretching of this one direction and the compression of the other two directions and consequently a large decrease in the Hartree-Fock energy. If we now view these wave functions corresponding to different length parameters in each direction in a spherical representation, we find a particular form of major-shell mixing.

It now becomes very important to seek additional experimental information (in addition to the B(E2) measurements) to test the validity of these arguments. Hartree-Fock calculations including major-shell mixing are very difficult and are still in the early stages.[10] There are, of course, two effects which appear as major-shell mixing; the effect of deformations described above and the mixing required by the fact that harmonic oscillator wave functions are being used to represent orbitals with a finite separation energy. Consequently we need to know experimentally which components of higher shells are admixed.

It is very tempting to turn to direct reactions and look for pick-up reactions proceeding directly from these small components. This is a very dangerous procedure, however, since the reaction which proceeds in two-steps via inelastic scattering to a collective level coupled with the pick-up from the major component of the single-particle orbital has at least as large a cross section and basically the same angular distribution. This phenomenon is discussed, for example, for rotational collective motion by Iano and Austern[13] and for vibrational collective motion by Koslowski and de-Shalit.[14]

Two experiments which do give direct information about major-shell mixing were both done with low-energy machines at Caltech and both studied the decay of a resonance. Christensen and Cocke[15] formed the 2.43 MeV $5/2^-$ level of Be^9 through the $Li^7(He^3,p)Be^{9*}$ reaction and subsequently observed the f-wave neutron decay to the Be^8 ground state. From this measurement, they deduce a reduced width for f-wave neutron emission which is consistent[16] with that which one expects from the type of major-shell mixing described above. Spiger and Tombrello[17] have observed similar f-wave proton strength in the $5/2^-$ state of Be^7 at about 7 MeV in the reactions $He^4(He^3,p)Li^6$ and $He^4(He^3,p)Li^{6*}$. In each of these cases it is clear how the reaction proceeds and the desired information about the resonance level is obtained directly.

Summary

To summarize these remarks, as our understanding of the results of Hartree-Fock and its derivatives, such as Hartree-Fock-Bogoliubov, keeps increasing, we are obtaining a clearer picture of the nature of the low-lying states of light nuclei. We are able to make firm predictions about the shapes of intrinsic states and consequently firm predictions about electromagnetic matrix elements. The resulting shapes force us to conclude that there is major-shell mixing of a very particular type, which in turn leads to predictions about the small components of the single-particle wave functions.

These kinds of predictions place stringent demands upon the experimental evidence which we need. As we have seen, while some of these demands are best met with new, higher energy (i.e. intermediate energy) machines, others are best met by very carefully chosen and executed experiments carried out with low energy machines. All kinds of evidence, from that relating to the structure of the single-particle orbitals to the actual shapes of the intrinsic states, is still needed, especially through the middle of 2s-1d shell, and we may all look forward to a considerable amount of additional light being shed on the structure of these nuclei over the next few years.

TABLE 1

Nucleus	$\langle 2z^2-x^2-y^2 \rangle$	$\langle x^2-y^2 \rangle$
Ne^{20}	7.8	0
Mg^{24}	8.9	4.8
Si^{28}	-10.3	0

Expectation values of the quadrupole moment operations $Q_{20} = 2z^2 - x^2 - y^2$ and $2^{-1/2}(Q_{22} + Q_{2-2}) = x^2 - y^2$ evaluated with Hartree-Fock wave functions. The numbers given are in units of the square of the length parameter for the oscillator wave functions appropriate to each nucleus, ranging from 3-4 $(fm)^2$. Courtesy of M. K. Banerjee.

TABLE 2

	Ellipsoid	Oblate Spheroid	Prolate Spheroid
$\langle J_x^2 \rangle$	3.7	8.7	8.0
$\langle J_y \rangle$	9.9	8.7	8.0
$\langle J_z \rangle$	8.1	0	0
A_x	0.87	0.18	0.33
A_y	0.36	0.18	0.33
A_z	0.31	----	----
Gap(p shell)	12.6	15.3	4.1
Gap(sd shell)	9.5	2.8	10.6
$\langle (2z^2 - x^2 - y^2)/2 \rangle$	7.6	-7.8	9.4
$\langle x^2 - y^2 \rangle$	7.8	0	0

Results of Hartree-Fock Calculations With Different Shapes

The numbers in the lines 4 through 8 are in MeV. The 7th and the 8th lines give the spacings between the last occupied and the first unoccupied p and 2s-1d orbits. The last two lines give the density moments in units of b^2, where b is the oscillator length parameter.

References

1. W. T. Pinkston, preceding paper.
2. D. Kurath and L. Pičman, Nucl. Phys. 10, 313 (1959).
3. For a summary of Hartree-Fock, see, e.g., G. Ripka, "The Hartree-Fock Theory and Nuclear Deformations," Lectures in Theoretical Physics 1965, 237, University of Colorado Press (Boulder, 1966); M. Baranger, "Theory of Finite Nuclei," 1962 Cargèse Lectures in Theoretical Physics, M. Lévy, editor, W. A. Benjamin, Inc. (New York, 1963); and references therein.
4. L. Satpathy and M. K. Banerjee, private communication.
5. J. Bar-Touv and C. A. Levinson, Phys. Rev. 153, 1099 (1967); M. K. Banerjee, G. J. Stephenson, Jr. and C. A. Levinson, to be published.
6. H. Morinaga, Phys. Rev. 101, 259 (1956); G. E. Brown, Congrés International de Physique Nuclèaire, Vol. 1, 129 (Paris, 1964).
7. W. H. Bassichis and G. Ripka, Phys. Letters 15, 320 (1965).
8. G. J. Stephenson, Jr. and M. K. Banerjee, Phys. Letters 24B, 209 (1967); et eratum, to be published.
9. A. S. Davydov and G. F. Filippov, Nucl. Phys. 8, 237 (1958).
10. G. Ripka, "Deformations in Light Nuclei," Proceedings of the International Conference on Nuclear Physics (Gatlinberg, 1966) to be published; R. Muthukrishnan and M. Baranger, Phys. Letters 18, 160 (1965); M. K. Pal and A. P. Stamp, Phys. Rev. 158, 924 (1967).
11. D. Kurath, Phys. Rev. 140, B1190 (1965).
12. A. Lande, Phys. Rev. Letters 18, 496 (1967).
13. P. G. Iano and N. Austern, Phys. Rev. 151, 853 (1966).
14. B. Koslowski and A. de-Shalit, Nucl. Phys. 77, 215 (1966).
15. P. R. Christensen and C. L. Cocke, Nucl. Phys. 89, 656 (1966).
16. G. J. Stephenson, Jr., contributed paper 8.6, Proceedings of the International Conference on Nuclear Physics (Gatlinberg, 1966) to be published.
17. R. J. Spiger and T. A. Tombrello, Phys. Rev., to be published.

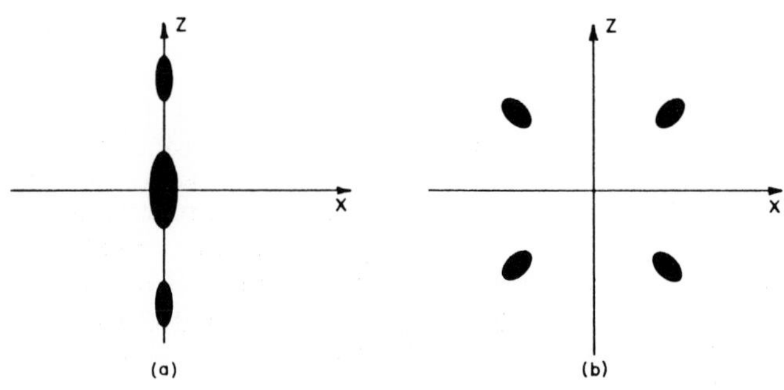

Fig. 1 Schematic density distributions for real wave functions in the 2s-1d shell.

a) $\psi \sim (1-2z^2)e^{-r^2/2a^2}$

b) $\psi \sim xze^{-r^2/2a^2}$

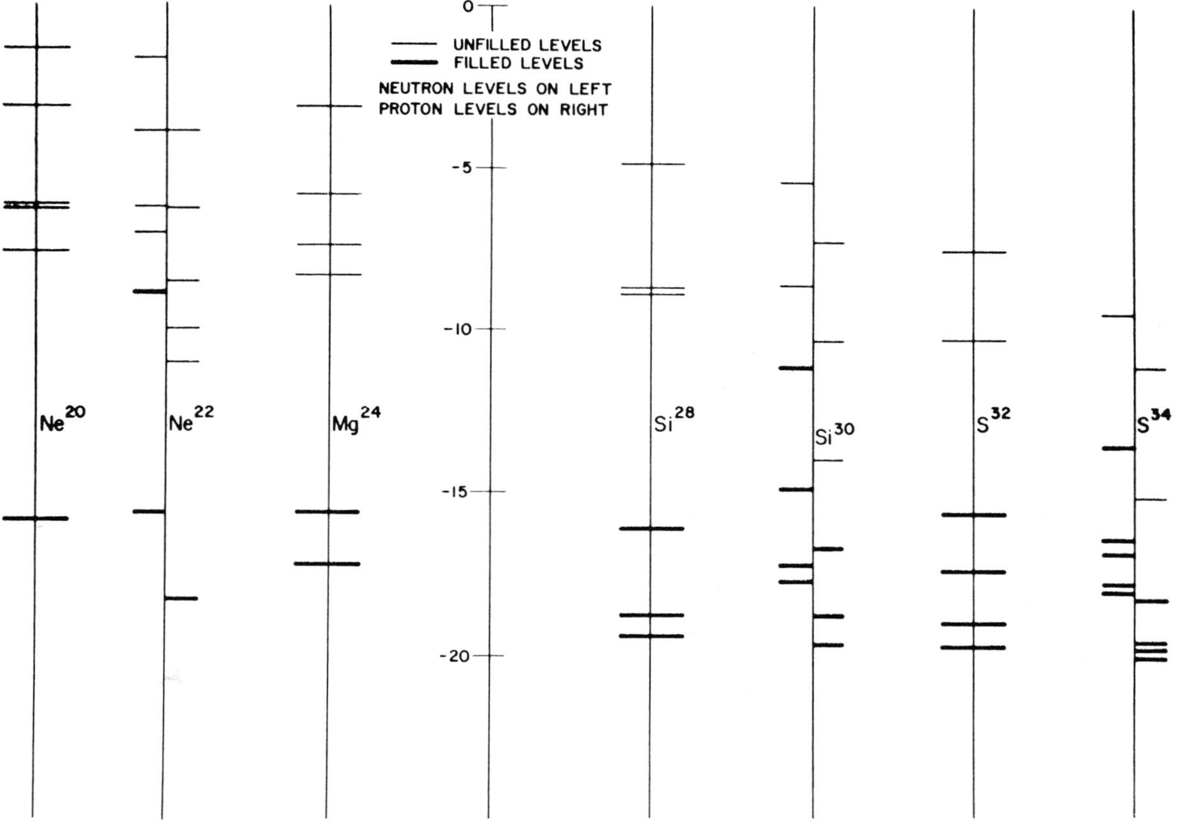

Fig. 2 Energy of Hartree-Fock single-particle orbitals. Courtesy of M. K. Banerjee.

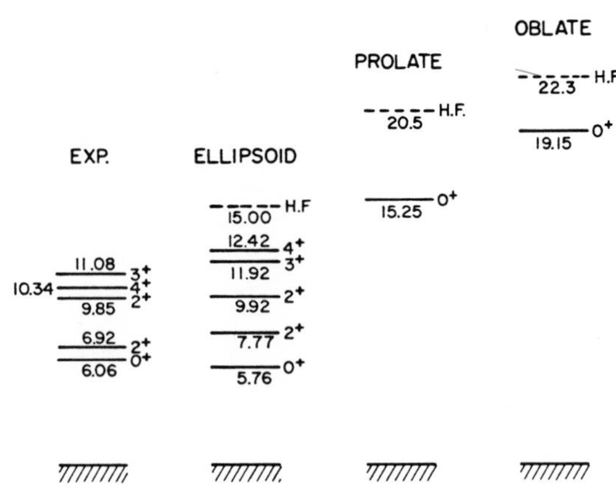

Fig. 3 Energies of the Hartree-Fock intrinsic state and of projected states for different assumed symmetries for the 4-particle 4-hole state of O^{16}. The experimental spectrum of the relevant states is shown on the left.

TRITON-INDUCED REACTIONS

L. F. Chase, Jr.

Lockheed Palo Alto Research Laboratory
Palo Alto, California

INTRODUCTION

At the present time, there seems to be an increase of interest in triton acceleration by electrostatic generators with terminal potentials of the order of or less than 5 MV[1]. Recalling that the triton is the analog nucleus of He^3 and that He^3 has been a most fruitful bombarding projectile[2] in such accelerators, the reason for this interest becomes obvious. For like He^3-induced reactions, triton-induced reactions have relatively high Q-values, which makes it possible for levels in residual nuclei to be excited that otherwise would be accessible only with much higher energy machines. A plot of the Q-values for triton-induced reactions on target nuclei between He and Ca as a function of target atomic mass is shown in Fig. 1. As is readily apparent from the graph, the reactions most useful with lower energy accelerators are the (t,p), (t,α), and (t,n). The relationship of these reactions to other reactions initiated with projectiles having masses ≤ 3 is presented in Table I. These three reaction types are shown in boxes in the table, and their relationships to the other reactions are clearly evident.

In addition, it is worthwhile noting that tritons have higher nuclear penetrabilities and lower stopping powers than He^3 ions with the same energy. Both of these facts represent distinct advantages for tritons over their counterpart He^3 ions. Lower stopping power, for example, makes problems of target preparation considerably easier. Higher penetrabilities allow reactions with reasonable yield to be investigated over a wider range of Z. Coulomb barrier penetrabilities for s-wave He^3 nuclei and tritons are shown in Fig. 2 as a function of target atomic number for several bombarding energies; the considerably higher penetrabilities of the tritons are clearly indicated.

Over the years triton reactions have sometimes been induced by means other than direct triton acceleration. For example, irradiation of Li^6F with neutrons[3] has been used to produce F^{21} by the two-step process of $Li^6(n,\alpha)t$ followed by $F^{19}(t,p)F^{21}$, both reactions taking place directly in the sample. Another such indirect method employs acceleration of the "target" nuclei onto tritiated targets, a technique which has proven useful at tandem facilities for the study of nuclear lifetimes by Doppler shift attenuation measurements. However, for the general study of triton-induced reactions there is no substitute for the acceleration of the tritons themselves. Triton acceleration has been successfully carried out at several facilities, including Chalk River, Los Alamos, the Naval Research Laboratory, the University of Manchester, AWRE (Aldermaston), and, more recently, the Lockheed Palo Alto Research Laboratory. At present other laboratories are actively engaged in the installation of tritium systems, most notably Brookhaven National Laboratory and the University of Texas. The problems involved in modifying a facility for triton acceleration, as well as the general nuclear instrumentation required to perform triton experiments efficiently, are discussed in the following two sections.

Perhaps in concluding these introductory comments, it should be remarked that at bombarding energies of roughly 5-6 MeV, a transition region occurs where direct interaction begins to dominate the reaction mechanism, at least for light nuclei. This observation implies that in general the reaction mechanism below 5 MeV is complex, and hence direct extraction of spectroscopic information is difficult and should be done with extreme care. This subject is taken up further in a later section. Fortunately, however, methods are now employed from which nuclear spectroscopic information can be obtained rigorously without knowledge of the reaction mechanism. These techniques, which require only formation of the desired levels in the residual nucleus, involve the measurement in special geometries of particle-gamma and gamma-gamma angular correlations, the determination of nuclear lifetimes (for example, by gamma-associated particle or Doppler shift attenuation methods), and the measurement of gamma-ray polarization. Such experiments, although particularly well suited for triton work, are complicated and in general suffer from low counting rates. Both of these aspects make almost mandatory sophisticated electronic equipment in order to obtain both accuracy and maximum information from such experiments. Reaction-mechanism-independent experiments are discussed in more detail in a following section.

Finally, a summary of suggested experiments is presented in the last section, lest the reader infer that all useful triton work using low energy machines has been completed.

FACILITIES

Experiments using a beam of accelerated tritons were performed as early as 1951 at Chalk River by Pepper et al.[4] who bombarded Li^6 targets with tritons from a 200-keV accelerator. Since then numerous other laboratories have begun accelerating tritium as it has become readily available and inexpensive. (The cost of tritium is presently $2.00/Curie). Accelerating tritium is hazardous, nevertheless, and some of the problems associated with tritium acceleration are described in a report by Engelke[5]. Acceleration of tritons in the Lockheed 3.5 MeV Van de Graaff accelerator was begun in 1965, and since that time about 75% of the accelerator running time has been with tritium. In the following paragraphs, the tritium-acceleration facility at Lockheed will be described as a more-or-less typical example of such facilities.

Tritium Collection and Disposal

The Lockheed tritium recovery system is similar in principle to others described in the literature, differing mainly in the absence of uranium traps, which trap and purify the tritium for re-use. Tritium which enters the ion source passes down the accelerating tube of the Van de Graaff and is pumped out by the main diffusion pump. When one of the four experimental stations is connected to the accelerator tritium may also enter its vacuum system. Hence, the effluent gases from all pumps must be collected for disposal, and the tritium recovery system performs this function. In operation it serves as a backing pump for the diffusion pumps connected to the recovery system and forces the accumulated gases into reservoirs for disposal. Figure 3 shows schematically the valving arrangement which permits switching the diffusion pumps from the normal system of backing pumps to the recovery system. A representation of the control panel containing the switches for the remotely actuated valves is also shown in Fig. 3. The lines fanning out from beam switching magnets represent beam tubes leading to the four experimental stations. Each station has one or more diffusion pumps which may be connected either to the tritium recovery system or to its own backing pump. A photograph of the actual control panel is shown in Fig. 4.

The recovery pump is a Welch 1402KBG mechanical pump, which has shaft and window seals to prevent escape of the pumped gases on the exhaust side. The reservoirs are standard nitrogen cylinders. To minimize the possibility of gas escaping from a reservoir, the system pressure is never permitted to rise above 1 atm. absolute. There are pressure gauges on each reservoir, and pressure limit switches cause lights to flash in the control room when the reservoir pressure reaches 500 mm Hg. If the pressure rises to 600 mm Hg the pump is automatically shut off. If there were no major leaks in the system, it would take more than a year to fill one reservoir to the maximum allowed pressure. When a reservoir has accumulated about 200 Curies of tritium or has become filled, it is sealed and disposed of as radioactive waste. The cost and rate of consumption of tritium are low enough that re-use of the tritium is not necessary.

The Lockheed 3.5 MeV Van de Graaff accelerator has an R.F. discharge ion source characterized by low gas consumption. With no significant loss of beam output, the source tritium may be diluted with He^4 to a concentration (by pressure) of 10%[6]. Optimum utilization of tritium may occur at even lower concentrations. In practice the tritium is purchased already mixed with helium, the mixture consisting of 1 part H^3 to 9 parts He^4 by pressure. This tritium concentration may be further reduced by admitting additional He^4 to the ion source.

The tritium-He^4 mixture is shipped in special stainless steel containers which have valves adapted to withstand the pressure of the accelerator insulating gas. The shipping containers themselves are used as source reservoirs in the high-voltage terminal of the accelerator. A source reservoir has a volume of 500 ml, and contains 100 Curies of tritium when full, which suffices for up to 500 hours running time. The pressure in the source reservoir is always below 1 atmosphere absolute.

Safety Precautions

The present maximum permissible level of tritium concentration in controlled working areas is 5 $\mu C/m^3$, based on a 40 hour work week. In uncontrolled areas the maximum allowable average concentration during a year is 0.2 $\mu C/m^3$, but any occasion on which the concentration rises to greater than 2 $\mu C/m^3$ is treated as an accidental spillage and must be reported to California State Authorities.

During routine maintenance of the accelerator it is necessary to expose tritium-contaminated components to the atmosphere. The tritium source reservoir must be periodically refilled and the ion source replaced, for example. Inhalation of tritium gas or otherwise coming into contact with gaseous tritium must be prevented. The basic protective measure used during maintenance work is the rapid exhausting of air from the immediate work area. For this purpose a 1000 cfm blower, whose intake is coupled to an 8" dia. flexible hose is provided, the exhaust from the blower being vented to the roof of the building. The intake of the blower is placed as close as possible to the contaminated parts, and there is seldom any detectable escape of tritium into the work area.

Workers wear rubber gloves as a precaution against accidental contact with contaminated parts, and self-contained breathing apparatus is available for use when necessary. Personnel subject to tritium exposure are periodically required to submit urine samples for tritium analysis.

The accelerator room is provided with its own air-conditioning system. The room is maintained at a slight negative pressure to prevent contamination of air in other areas of the laboratory in case a tritium leak should occur. The concentration of tritium in the work areas is monitored continuously. Copper tubes run from a tritium monitor in the control room to various parts of the accelerator room. The tritium entering any one of these tubes can be monitored by appropriately positioning a selector switch (see Fig. 4). Under normal operating conditions, the air-conditioning system exhaust is continuously monitored.

An alarm is provided to signal fialure of any one of a number of critical functions (see Fig. 4). A vacuum failure at any point, a high tritium concentration, and power failure are examples of conditions which may, by choice, cause an alarm to sound. An automatically-dialing telephone may be set to call any experimenter and sound an alarm signal via his telephone when a failure occurs. This alarm system is always set to call someone when the accelerator is unattended.

INSTRUMENTATION

As alluded to in the introduction, considerations regarding the electronic instrumentation which must be integrated into the tritium facility are just as important as considerations of the facility itself. The reason is that most experiments performed with tritons tend to be complex and to require, in addition to statistical accuracy and good reproducibility, efficient methods of data acquisition in order to minimize the duration of the experiments. Of course these same requirements hold for experiments involving reactions induced by other particles. However with tritons from a low energy accelerator the problems are enhanced, primarily because of the high Q-values usually involved coupled with the relatively low cross sections (compared to those for many d,p and p,p reactions), especially in the upper part of the (s,d) shell. As indicated previously, triton-induced reactions often involve the population of many levels in residual nuclei up to quite high excitation energies. The desirability of high resolution in examining the many resulting charged particle groups and γ-rays using solid state detectors, together with the requirement of obtaining all possible data simultaneously, place severe demands on any data acquisition and processing system.

Several types of instrumentation can be used in making angular distribution measurements for reactions such as (t,p) or (t,α) at triton energies below 5 MeV. Arrays of solid state particle detectors with thicknesses appropriate for a particular experiment, and with or without stopping foil covers, are fine where applicable. Furthermore, such arrays can be used in conjunction with mass identification systems, such as E-dE/dx telescopes for higher energy particles or apparatus for measuring E and time-of-flight for lower energy particles. Such systems are particularly effective when interfaced with an on-line computer. However, perhaps the most elegant instrument applicable to these angular distribution measurements is that used over the past several years at the AWRE (Aldermaston) triton tandem facility. This instrument[7)], a multigap broad range magnetic spectrograph, makes it possible to obtain high resolution angular distributions, since measurements are simultaneously made for angles between 5 and 175 deg in 7.5 deg increments. Such a device meets all the above criteria of accuracy, high dispersion, reliability, and efficient data accumulation.

In order to record accurately and completely all the information from the various types of coincidence experiments, a computer-based data acquisition system is a great asset. An example of such a system which was designed with triton experiments in mind is the one used at Lockheed, block diagrams of which are shown in Fig. 5 and Fig. 6. Figure 5 illustrates the apparatus in a configuration suitable for measuring 2-parameter particle-gamma angular correlations[8)] using a movable NaI(Tℓ) γ-ray detector, while Fig. 6 shows a natural extension to a configuration having 5 fixed crystals, which makes possible the complete simultaneous recording of the correlation at five appropriate angles. This latter configuration, a multi-angle goniometer, is presently being assembled. The heart of these systems is an SEL810A computer[9] which uses 16-bit words and has an 8K memory capacity. As indicated in the block diagrams, twin 4096 ADC's are used which allow full 16 x 10^6-element matrix resolution to be obtained. Coincidence events recorded with full resolution are buffered and written onto magnetic tape. At the same time submatrices, appropriately compressed, are stored in a 4K section of core memory reserved for this purpose. A continuous live display of a previously chosen segment of the data can then be generated. Thus, not only is a continuous monitor of the experiment achieved, but in practice a certain amount of on-line analysis is performed during the course of the experiment. It should be noted that in addition to recording true coincidence events, chance coincidence events are "flagged" and recorded simultaneously with the same dispersion. Furthermore, digital stabilizer pulses and x and y singles can be flagged and recorded on magnetic tape if desired. The flags are code bits placed in the ADC word by priority interrupts generated from the logic circuitry. At any time the information stored on magnetic tape can be played back, reanalyzed using different selection criteria, and put into core storage. In practice data which takes a full day to acquire can be played back in a few minutes. Examples of results obtained with this system are shown in the next section.

In addition, because of the flexible computer interfacing employed and the inherent flexibility of software, the Lockheed system configuration can be easily changed to one suitable for the study of short-lived radioactivities. For this type of experiment, the computer controls recording of 2-parameter data as a function of time, beam pulsing, sample transfer, and sequence timing, and simultaneously checks to make sure that proper conditions pertain at all times. The importance of having a computer-based data acquisition and processing system, especially for triton work using low energy accelerators, cannot be over-emphasized.

NUCLEAR STRUCTURE FROM TRITON REACTIONS
MECHANISM INDEPENDENT METHODS

This section deals with measurements whose interpretation does not depend on assumptions about the triton-induced reaction mechanism. Therefore, spectroscopic information obtained from the results of such measurements should be rigorously correct. These techniques are invaluable for use with low energy triton accelerators since the mechanism for reactions induced by tritons with energy less than 5 MeV is generally complex and not well-understood. The disadvantages of such experiments are that they are often tedious and that they do not directly test the structure of the nuclear wave function.

Although the results of the experiments to be described below do not depend on the reaction mechanism, excitation functions are generally measured in order to find the energy at which the yield for production of the level or levels to be investigated is maximized. Population of particular levels in the (s,d) shell, for example, may vary by an order of magnitude or more as a function of triton energy, even over small energy intervals.

The lifetime of a γ-emitting level of a nucleus is a vital piece of spectroscopic information and it is independent of how the level is formed. Two methods are commonly used for measurements of these lifetimes. One is the associated particle technique, in which the distribution of time delays between the particle associated with the formation of the level and the emission of the radiation de-exciting it is measured, and the Doppler shift attenuation methods, of which there are many variations[10]. The former measures lifetimes greater than about 3×10^{-11} sec, and the latter determines lifetimes in the range approaching 10^{-11} sec to 10^{-15} sec. Examples of results obtained for triton-induced reactions using the associated particle technique are shown in Fig. 7 and in Fig. 8. Measurements were made of the time delay between protons and 0.28-MeV gammas in the $F^{19}(t,p_1\gamma)F^{21}$ reaction to give[11] $\tau = (8.31 \pm 0.36) \times 10^{-9}$ sec for the 0.28-MeV F^{21} level (Fig. 7); similar measurements were made for the $Na^{23}(t,p\gamma)Na^{25}$ reaction (Fig. 8) and the $Mg^{26}(t,\alpha\gamma)Na^{25}$ reaction to give[3] $\tau = (7.3 \pm 0.7) \times 10^{-9}$ sec for the 90-keV level in Na^{25}.

The various Doppler shift attenuation methods[10] have been made considerably more powerful with the advent of Ge(Li) γ-ray detectors possessing practical resolutions < 4 keV FWHM for 1-MeV γ rays. Thus, not only can Doppler shifts be accurately measured, but the effect of nuclear lifetimes on the line shapes can be readily observed[10]. Unfortunately, the spectrum of γ-rays emitted when almost any target material is bombarded by tritons is exceedingly complex and therefore difficult to disentangle even when viewed with a Ge(Li) detector. Many of the observed γ rays are produced by high Q-value reactions which compete with the reaction one wishes to observe. This complexity is amply demonstrated in the typical γ-ray spectra obtained from triton bombardment of carbon and oxygen targets, shown in Fig. 9 and Fig. 10, respectively. Since carbon is almost always present either as a target backing or because of carbon build-up, and since some oxide usually will be present in the target used for a particular experiment, γ-ray spectra from such targets will indeed be complex, with many of the lines for which measurements are desired at least partially obscured. Because of these problems of spectral complexity, it is clear that in general some type of coincidence measurement is required to make possible accurate observations of Doppler effects using triton-induced reactions.

Particle-γ and γ-γ angular correlation experiments performed in geometries described by Litherland and Ferguson[8)] are two of the most powerful reaction-mechanism-independent tools for the determination of spins and electromagnetic multipole mixtures. From such measurements accurate γ-ray branching ratios can also be obtained, even for weak branches, either by using the results of the correlations themselves, or by decomposing a composite spectrum consisting of a properly weighted sum of all the individual runs[13)]. There are many examples of the successful application of these correlation techniques to various reactions, and indeed at Lockheed these methods have been very successfully exploited for triton-induced reactions.

Examples of particle-γ angular correlations obtained at the Lockheed facility are presented below. In these measurements the particles were detected near 180 deg in an annular surface-barrier solid state counter, and the γ-rays in coincidence with these particles were detected in a 4-in dia by 4-in long NaI($T\ell$) crystal. The computer data acquisition system described in the preceding section was employed. The formalism used in the analysis of the data has been described by Poletti and Warburton[14)], and is summarized for the case involving a two γ-ray cascade in Table II.

One example of the use of this particle-γ correlation method is the study of the first nineteen levels in O^{18}, using the $F^{19}(t,\alpha\gamma)O^{18}$ reaction[13)]. The alpha particle spectrum observed in coincidence with γ rays of energy greater than 600 keV is shown in Fig. 11, together with the chance coincidence spectrum which was recorded at the same time. The χ^2 plot (refer to Table II for definition) for the simultaneous fit of two γ-ray angular correlations for the 4.45 MeV O^{18} level is shown in Fig. 12. A spin of 1 is uniquely indicated, which is in agreement with the accepted spin and parity assignment of 1^-. The results of this correlation measurement are to be contrasted with the spin value indicated from the measurement of the proton angular distribution obtained from $O^{16}(t,p)O^{18}$ reaction for this level (see next section).

Another interesting example of a particle-γ correlation has been obtained using the $Mg^{26}(t,p\gamma)Mg^{28}$ reaction[15]. The proton spectrum observed in coincidence with γ rays of energy greater than 600 keV is shown in Fig. 13. The p-γ angular correlation for the 1.47-MeV Mg^{28} level is shown in Fig. 14. The χ^2 indicated in the figure allows only J = 2 for the level. For the 4.55-MeV Mg^{28} level, the γ-ray spectrum in coincidence with appropriate protons, the angular correlations of the 1.47- and 3.09-MeV γ rays, and the χ^2 plot for various choices of spin values are shown in Figs. 15, 16 and 17, respectively. As can be seen in Fig. 17, a spin of 2 is uniquely determined, and the γ-ray transition between the two spin 2 levels is essentially pure dipole.

The above examples clearly demonstrate the effectiveness of these coincidence methods when applied to high Q-value triton-induced reactions. There are, however, other mechanism-independent experiments that can be performed. For example, accurate determination of energy level positions using either high resolution spectrographs to detect particle groups or Ge(Li) detectors to observe γ-ray de-excitation, measurement of γ-ray polarizations, and investigation of decay schemes of radioactive nuclei can all readily be carried out using triton-induced reactions. An example of the data obtained in an experiment of the latter type is given in Fig. 18, which shows the γ rays emitted in the decay a T = 2 nucleus, Ne^{24}. The gamma rays were observed using a Ge(Li) detector.

NUCLEAR STRUCTURE FROM TRITON REACTION MECHANISM DEPENDENT METHODS

Finally, let us consider what can be learned from measurements whose interpretation requires at least some assumptions about the mechanism by which the reaction proceeds. Here the investigations referred to are primarily measurements of the angular distributions of the outgoing light reaction products from triton-initiated reactions. For bombarding energies below 5 MeV, both He^3- and triton-induced reactions generally exhibit considerable structure in their excitation functions. These variations with energy may in turn be reflected in marked changes of the shapes of the angular distributions of the emitted particles. A study of these changes with energy and angle is certainly interesting, for in order to explain them, one must understand the competing reaction mechanisms and the interference between them. However, these complications make difficult the extraction of reliable spectroscopic information, although efforts[16)] in this direction have been made. At higher energies the assumption is usually made that the direct reaction process dominates, at least for relatively high yield reactions with well developed distribution patterns. The analysis of such reactions can be made with some validity using plane wave Born approximation (PWBA) calculations, but more satisfying is the analysis made using distorted wave Born approximation (DWBA) calculations involving optical model parameters determined from the appropriate elastic scattering angular distributions. For bombarding energies of about 5 MeV a certain amount of success has been achieved in extracting spectroscopic information, particularly in determining the orbital angular momentum transferred, even using PWBA calculations.

For examples of the successes and difficulties of such work, examination of some of the results obtained from experiments employing (t,p) reactions is most illuminating. In the (t,p) reaction two neutrons in an S = 0 state are transferred with total angular momentum L into a final state with parity given by $\pi_{initial}\ \pi_{final} = (-)^L$. For $J^\pi = 0^+$ target nuclei the spin and parity of the final state are given unambiguously from the determination of L; namely, $J_{final} = L$ and $\pi_{final} = (-)^L$. Examples of the angular distribution of protons emitted in $O^{18}(t,p)O^{20}$ reaction at triton bombarding energies at 10 MeV[17)] and at 5.5 MeV[18)] are shown in Figs. 19 and 20. At both energies analysis of the distribution gives the same L-value. However, the angular distribution of the proton group leading to the level at 4.45 MeV in O^{18} via the $O^{16}(t,p)O^{18}$ reaction at $E_t = 5.5$ MeV[18)] (see Fig. 21) gives an L = 3 assignment, but at $E_t = 10$ MeV[17)] the angular distribution for this same group does not show any stripping-like features (see Fig. 22). Since the level at 4.45 MeV in O^{18} is known to be 1^-, the L = 3 assignment from the $E_t = 5.5$ MeV work is clearly erroneous. The proton angular distribution observed at 5.5-MeV triton bombarding energy evidently results from a mechanism more complex than the simple direct double-stripping mechanism assumed. It is pertinent to recall at this point (previous section) that, even at the relatively low triton bombarding energy of 2.5 MeV, an unambiguous J = 1 assignment for the 4.45-MeV O^{18} level was obtained (Fig. 12) by using the particle-γ coincidence technique.

SUGGESTED AREAS FOR FURTHER INVESTIGATION

The types of experiments to be carried out at a particular laboratory will depend on that laboratory's program for systematic study of nuclear structure and, of course, should not be limited to triton-induced reactions. Nevertheless, it is instructive to point out the areas where further study of triton-induced reaction will be of benefit in such a general program. A list of such investigations, with comments, is given below:

1) Reaction-mechanism-independent angular correlation measurements. Particularly $(t,p\gamma)$ and $(t,\alpha\gamma)$ in the (s,d) shell using both particle-γ and γ-γ correlation techniques. Combinations of NaI(Tℓ) and Ge(Li) γ-ray detectors, together with good resolution particle counters are required. [Example: $O^{18}(t,\alpha\gamma)N^{17}$].

2) Nuclear lifetimes. Associated particle-γ techniques or various types of Doppler shift attenuation method are required. [Example: O^{20*} produced by $O^{18}(t,p)O^{20*}$].

3) Study of (t,n) reactions. Reactions appear to have relatively high cross sections, but have not been systematically investigated.

4) Study of resonance structure. Very marked resonance seem to occur in particle excitation functions using (t,p) and (t,α) reactions.

5) Heavy particle emission studies. Coincidence experiments required, but they may be difficult to interpret. [Example: $Li^7(t,\alpha)He^6(\alpha)2n$].

6) Detailed decay studies of exotic radioactive nuclei. [Example: Ca^{50} from $Ca^{48}(t,p)Ca^{50}$].

7) General study of (t,γ) reactions. An open field.

8) Comparison of certain analog He^3- and triton-induced reactions.

REFERENCES

1) There is a similar interest in the acceleration of tritons by higher energy machines, e.g. tandem accelerator. However, the remarks made in this paper are intended to emphasize the advantages of triton acceleration for the lower energy machines.

2) For a general discussion of He^3-induced reactions at low energies see, D. A. Bromley and E. Almqvist, Repts. Progr. In Phys. 23, 544 (1960).

3) P. Kienle and K. Wien, Nucl. Phys. 41, 608 (1963).

4) T. P. Pepper, K. W. Allen, E. Almqvist, and J. T. Dewan, Phys. Rev. 85, 155 (1952).

5) Morris J. Engelke, Health Problems Associated With the Acceleration of Tritons in a 2.5-MeV Van de Graaff, LAMS-2602.

6) Wayne R. Arnold, AECU 1607, LADC-1037.

7) R. Middleton and S. Hinds, Nucl. Phys. 34, 404 (1962).

8) A. E. Litherland and A. J. Ferguson, Can. J. Phys. 52, 788 (1961).

9) Systems Engineering Laboratory, Ft. Lauderdale, Florida.

10) E. K. Warburton, J. W. Olness, and A. R. Poletti, BNL 11182; E. K. Warburton, J. W. Olness, K. W. Jones, C. Chasman, and R. A. Ristinen, Phys. Rev. 148, 1072 (1966) and references cited therein.

11) R. E. McDonald and J. A. Becker, Phys. Rev. 154, 1101 (1966).

12) R. E. McDonald, J. A. Becker, L. F. Chase, Jr. and D. Kohler (to be published).

13) L. F. Chase, J. A. Becker, D. Kohler and R. E. McDonald, Bull. Am. Phys. Soc. 11, 405 (1966); Proc. Intern. Conf. on Nucl. Structure (1966).

14) A. R. Poletti and E. K. Warburton, Phys. Rev. 137, B595 (1965).

15) L. F. Chase, Jr., J. A. Becker, D. Kohler and R. E. McDonald, Bull. Am. Phys. Soc. 12, 555 (1967).

16) J. D. Silverstein and G. H. Herling, Bull. Am. Phys. Soc 12, 33 (1967).

17) R. Middleton and D. J. Pullen, Nucl. Phys. 51, 63 (1964)

18) R. Moreh, Nucl. Phys. 70, 293 (1965).

Table I. Relationship of triton-induced reactions to reactions initiated by projectiles with masses ≤ 3.

Charge Exchange

n,p	p,n
d,2p	d,2n
He^3,3p	t,3n
t,He^3	He^3,t

One Nucleon Transfer

p-transfer	p-pickup
d,n	n,d
He^3,d	d,He^3
t,2n	t,α

n-transfer	n-pickup
d,p	p,d
t,d	d,t
He^3,2p	He^3,α

Two Nucleon Transfer

"d"-transfer	2n-, 2p-transfer
He^3,p	He^3,n (2p) "proton rich"
t,n	t,p (2n) "neutron rich"

Table II.

TWO CASCADE GAMMA-RAY DISTRIBUTION FORMULA

(γ-ray angular distributions relative to any quantization axis possessing rotational symmetry)

$$a(\gamma_1)b(\gamma_2)c$$

$a(\gamma_1)b$:

$$W(\theta_1) = \sum_k \rho_k(a)F_k(ab)Q_k P_k(\cos\theta_1)$$

$\rho_k(a)$ statistical tensors describing alignment of initial state (a)

Q_k attenuation coefficients

$F(ab)$ depend on γ cascade and independent of nuclear allignment

$$\rho_k(a) = \sum_\alpha \rho_k(a,\alpha)P(\alpha)$$

$$P(\alpha) = P(-\alpha),\ \sum_\alpha P(\alpha) = 1$$

$$\rho(a,\alpha) = (2 - \delta_{\alpha 0})\frac{(a\ \alpha\ a\ -\alpha \mid k0)}{(a\ \alpha\ a\ -\alpha \mid 00)},\ \alpha \geq 0$$

$$F(ab) = \frac{F_k(LLba) - (-)^\sigma 2\delta F_k(LL'ba) + \delta^2 F(L'L'ba)}{1 + \delta^2}$$

(two lowest allowed multipolarities only)

$a \rightarrow b(\gamma_2)C$: (first γ-ray unobserved)

$$W(\theta_2) = \sum_k \rho_k(a)U_k(ab)F_k(bc)Q_k P_k(\cos\theta_2)$$

Least-square fitting procedure:

$$\chi^2 = (1/f)\sum_i \left[Y(\theta_i) - W(\theta_i)\right]^2 \Big/ E^2(\theta_i)$$

For each value of δ the best fit corresponds to those values of P(m) which yield lowest value of χ^2.

$Y(\theta_i)$ gamma ray yield at θ_i

$E(\theta_i)$ uncertainty assigned to γ-ray yield $Y(\theta_i)$

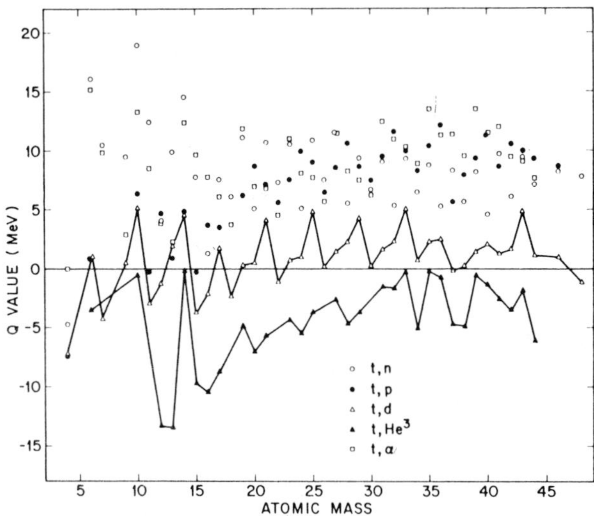

Fig. 1. Q-values for various types of triton-induced reactions as a function of mass number of the target nucleus. Lower solid line (t,He^3), upper solid line (t,d) reaction.

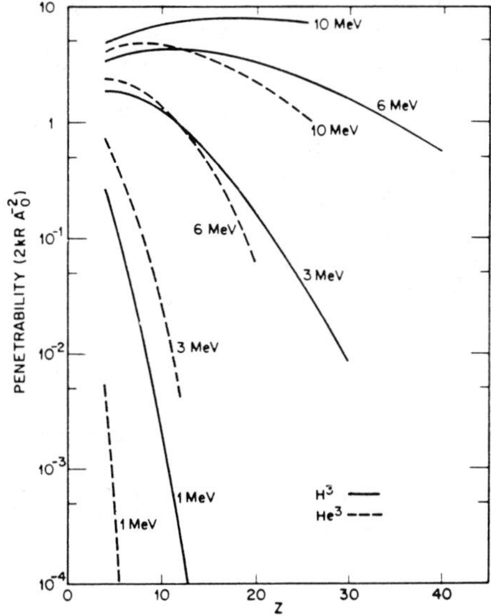

Fig. 2. Coulomb barrier penetrabilities for s-wave He^3 nuclei and tritons as a function of atomic mass.

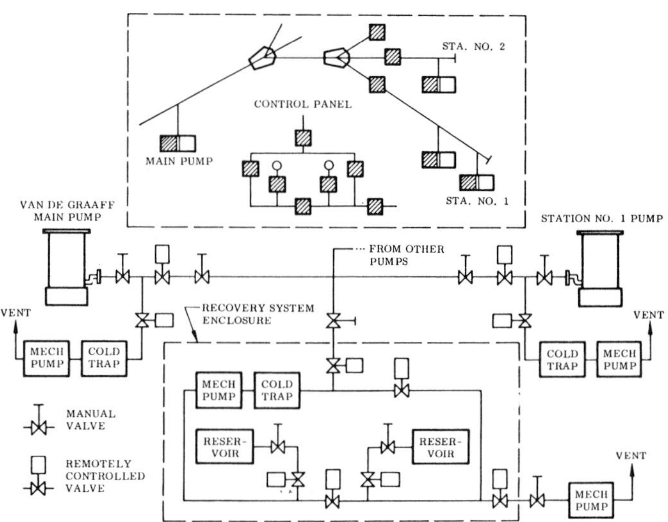

Fig. 3. Schematic diagram of the Lockheed tritium-recovery system.

Fig. 4. Console containing valve-control panel for tritium system pumps, tritium monitor, and control panel for putting automatic-calling safety system into operation.

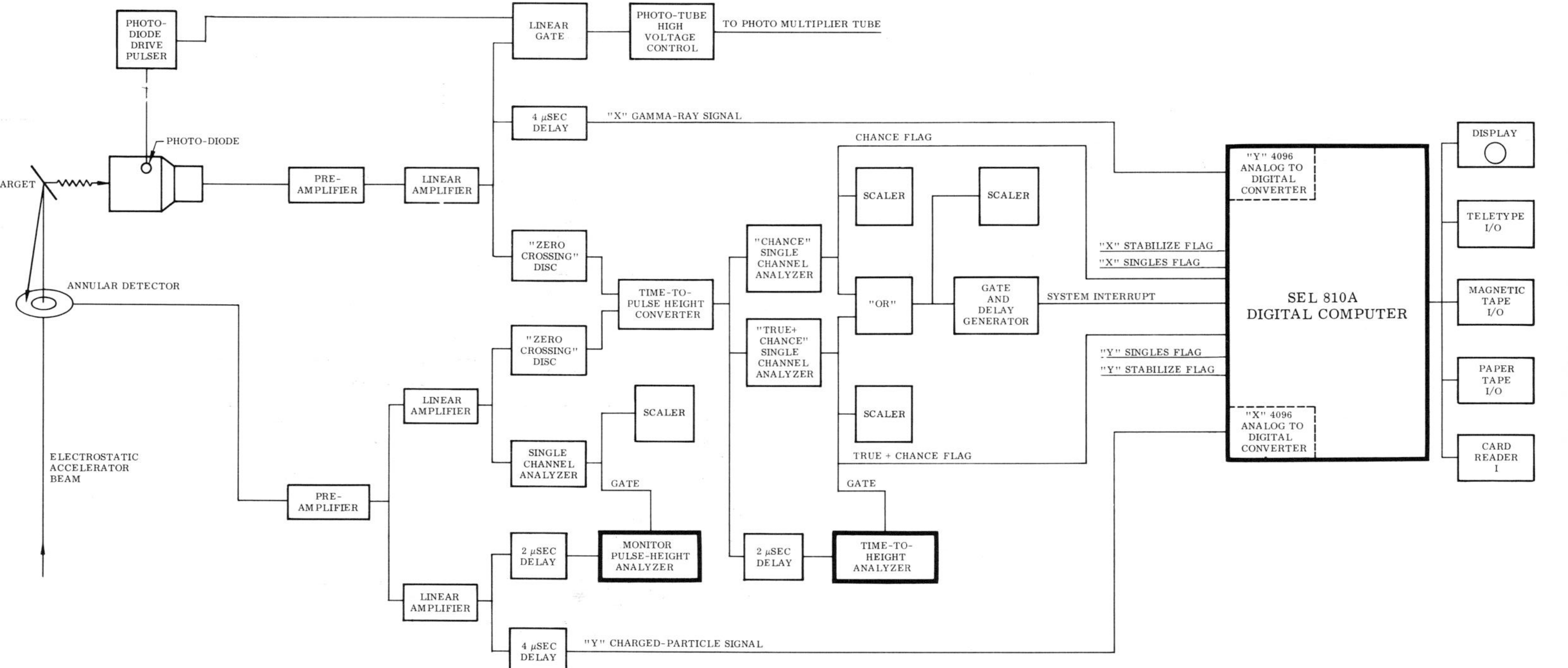

Fig. 5. Block diagram of experimental system configuration used in measuring particle-γ coincidences, showing interfacing with on-line computer.

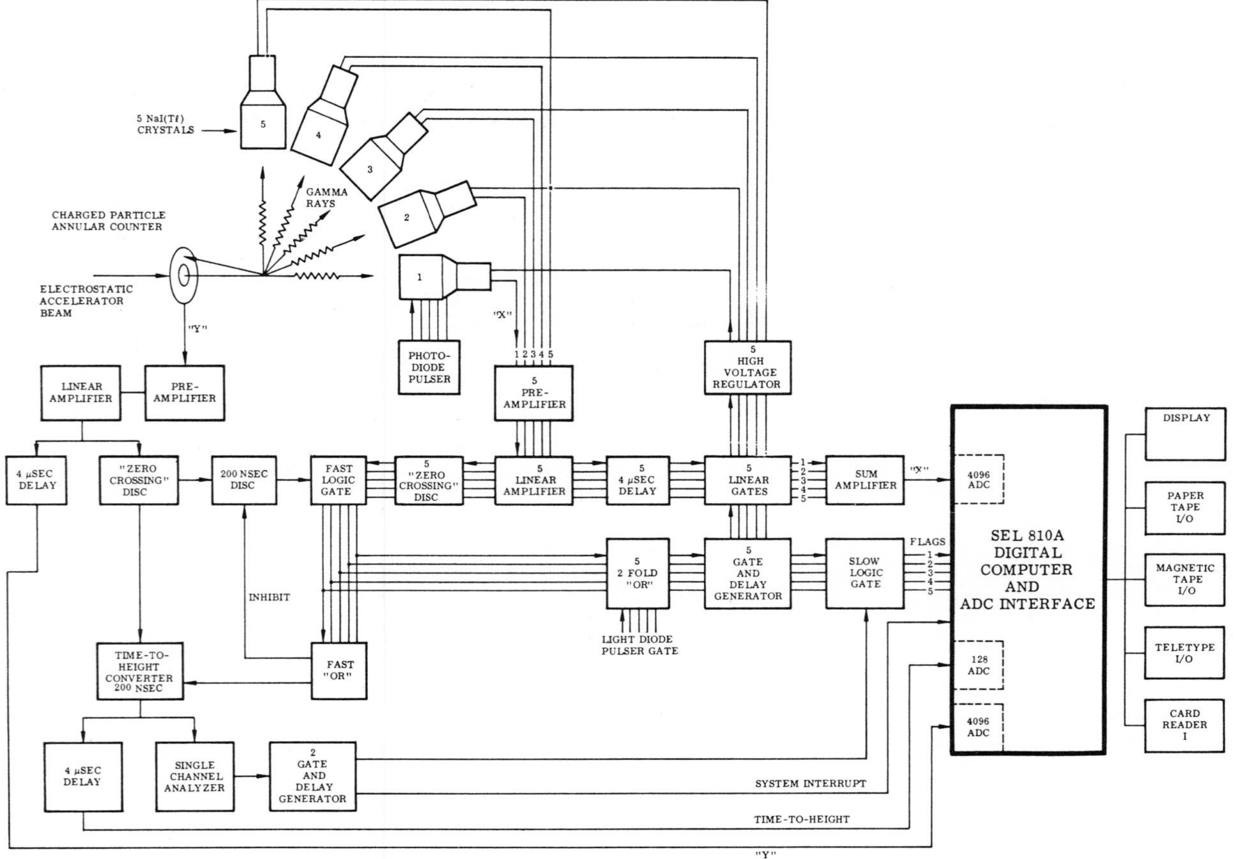

Fig. 6. Block diagram showing experimental system configuration with 5 fixed-crystal gonio-

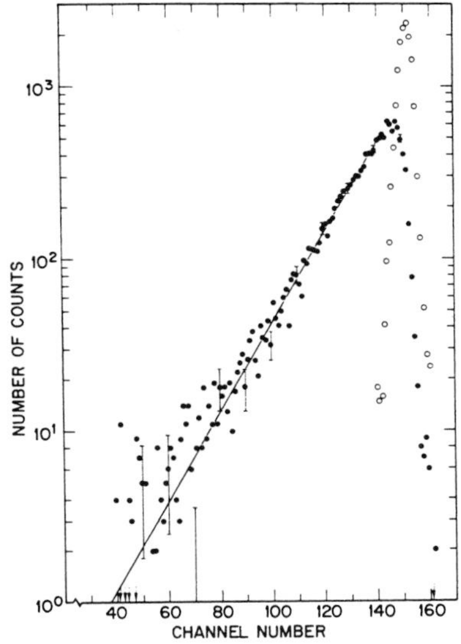

Fig. 7. Distribution of time delays between emission of protons and 0.28-MeV γ rays from $F^{19}(t,p_1\gamma)F^{21}$ reaction.

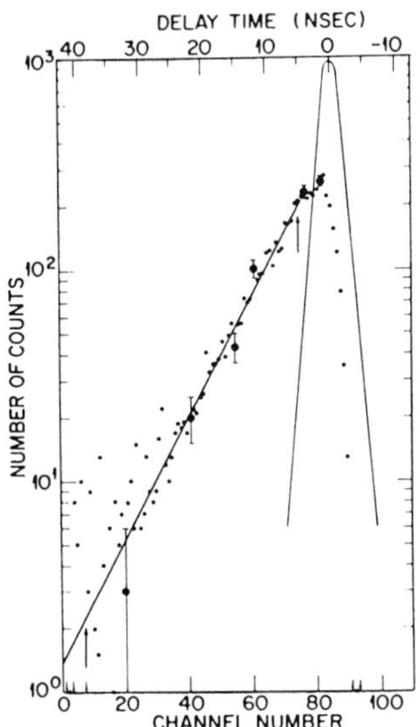

Fig. 8. Distribution of time delays between emission of protons and 90-keV γ rays from $Na^{23}(t,p\gamma)Na^{25}$ reaction.

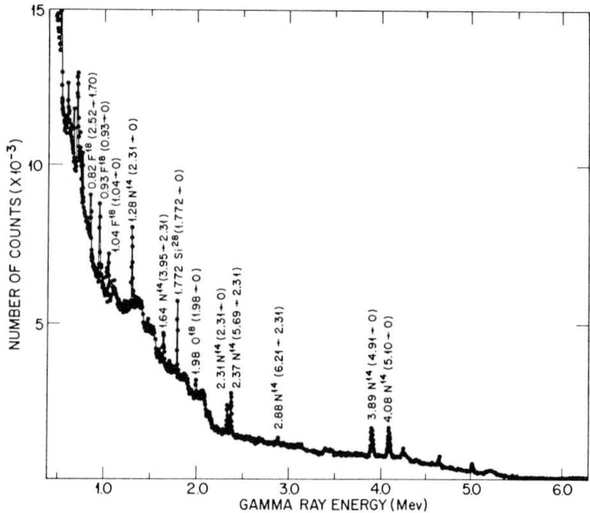

Fig. 9. Gamma-ray spectrum observed in Ge(Li) detector from predominantly carbon target bombarded with tritons.

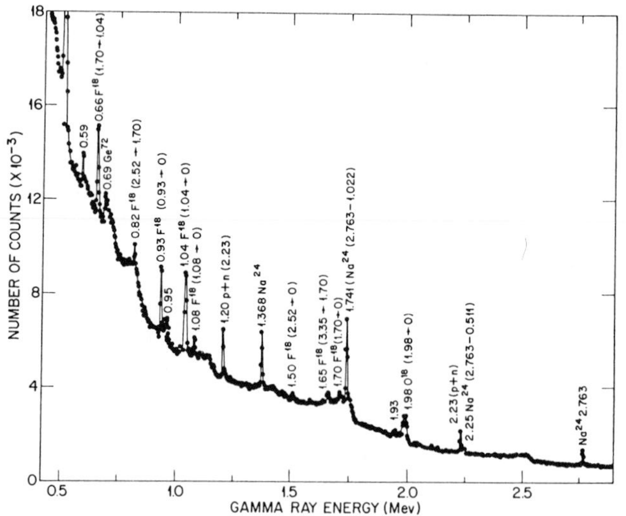

Fig. 10. Gamma-ray spectrum observed in Ge(Li) detector from predominantly oxygen target bombarded with tritons. Gamma rays from a Na^{24} calibration source are superimposed.

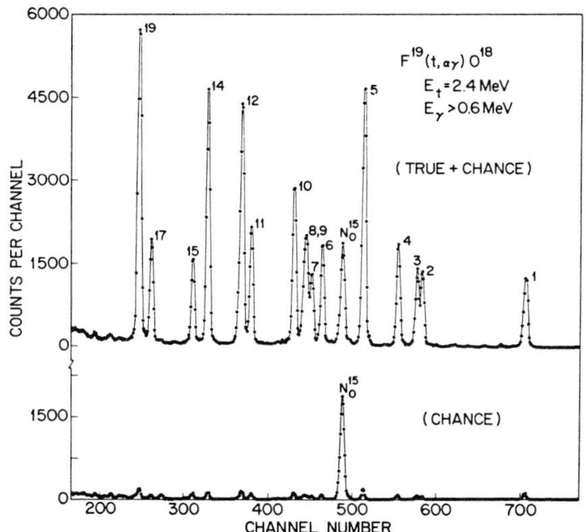

Fig. 11. Alpha-particle spectrum in coincidence with γ rays with $E_\gamma > 0.6$ MeV from $F^{19}(t,\alpha\gamma)O^{18}$ reaction and chance coincidence α-particle spectrum.

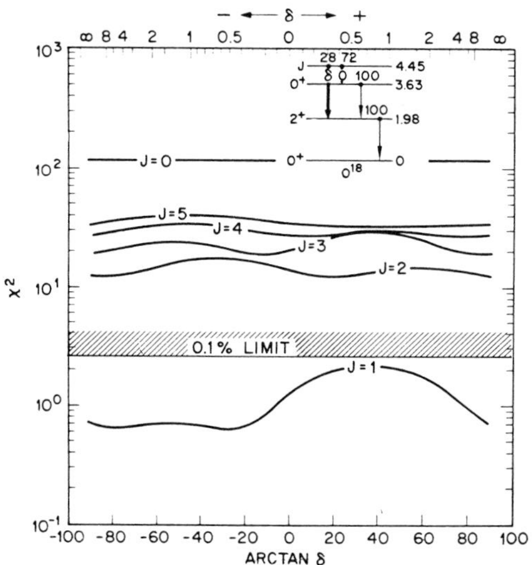

Fig. 12. Chi-squared vs. arctan $\delta_{2.47}$ curves from simultaneous fitting of angular correlations of 2.47- and 0.82-MeV γ-rays emitted in decay of 4.45-MeV level of O^{18}.

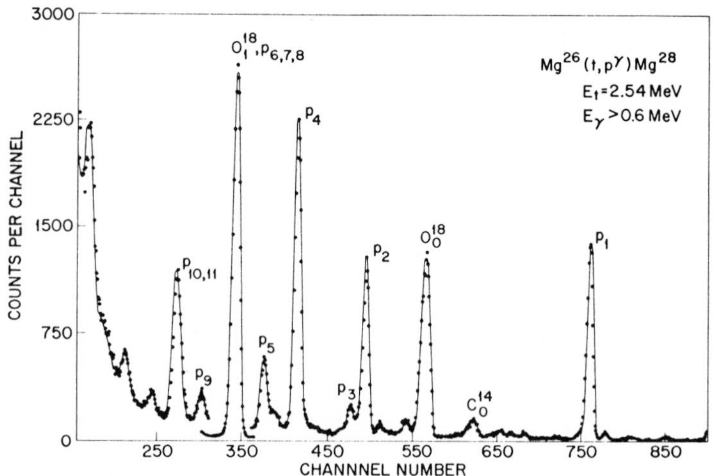

Fig. 13. Proton spectrum in coincidence with γ rays with $E_\gamma \geqslant 0.6$ MeV from $Mg^{26}(t,p\gamma)Mg^{28}$ reaction.

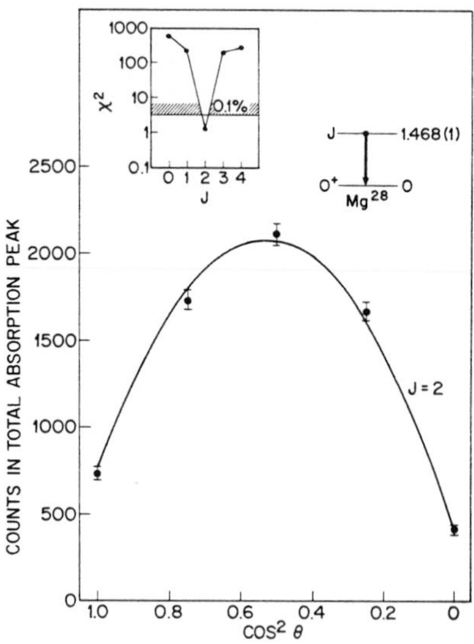

Fig. 14. Proton γ-ray angular correlation for 1.47-MeV level of Mg^{28} produced by $Mg^{26}(t,p\gamma)Mg^{28}$ reaction.

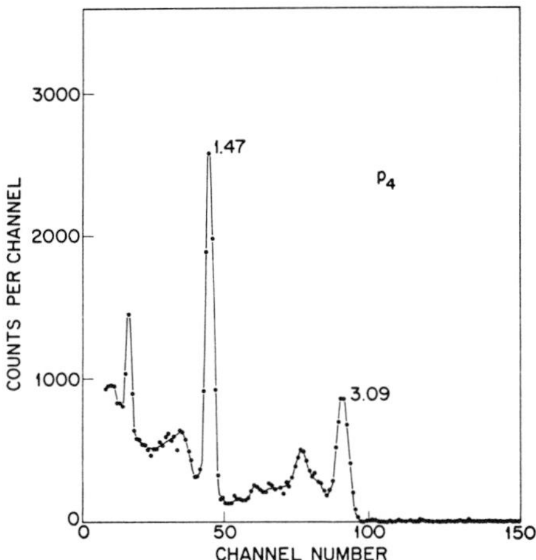

Fig. 15. Spectrum of γ rays in coincidence with p_4 protons from $Mg^{26}(t,p\gamma)Mg^{28}$ reaction.

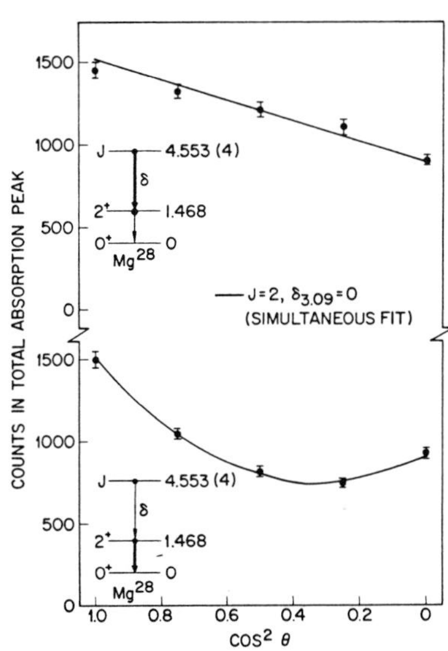

Fig. 16. Proton-γ-ray angular correlations for 1.47- and 3.09-MeV γ rays emitted in decay of 4.55-MeV Mg^{28} level produced by $Mg^{26}(t,p\gamma)Mg^{28}$ reaction.

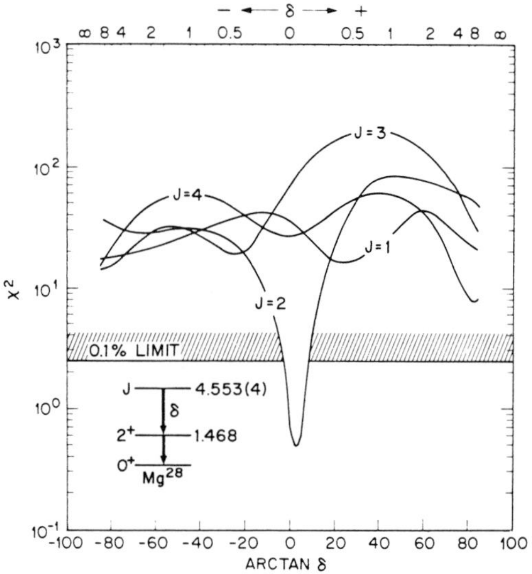

Fig. 17. Chi-squared vs. arctan $\delta_{3.09}$ curves from simultaneous fitting of angular correlations of 3.09- and 1.47-MeV γ rays emitted in decay of 4.55-MeV level of Mg^{28}.

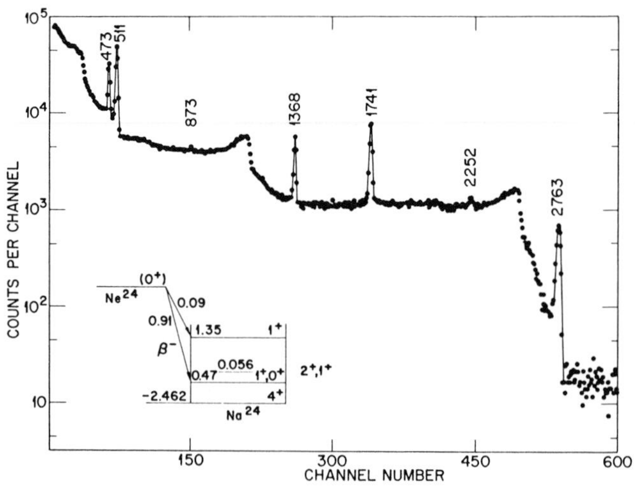

Fig. 18. Gamma-ray spectrum emitted in decay of Ne^{24} observed in Ge(Li) detector.

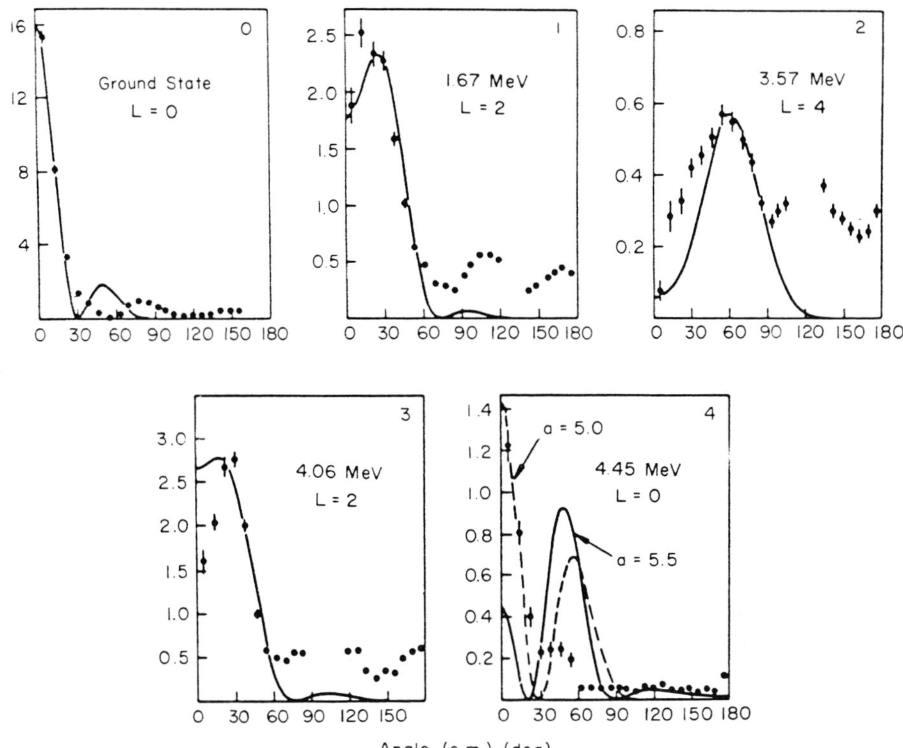

Fig. 19. Proton angular distributions from the $O^{18}(t,p)O^{20}$ reaction for the ground and first four excited states, measured at an incident energy of 10.0 MeV. Taken from Middleton and Pullen[17)].

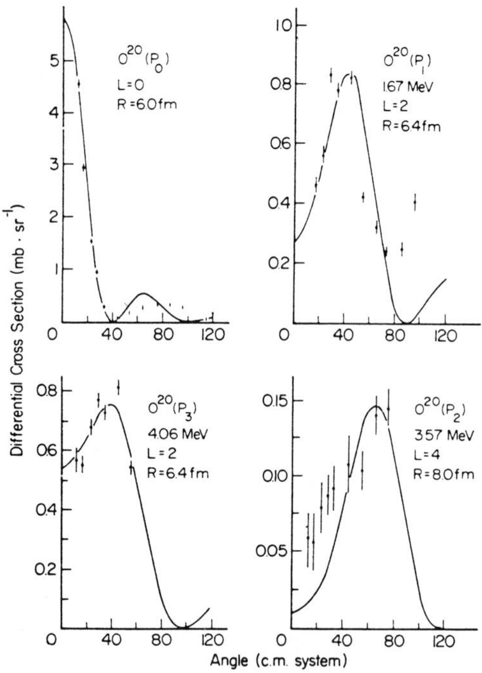

Fig. 20. Proton angular distributions from the $O^{18}(t,p)O^{20}$ reaction for the ground and first three excited states, measured at an incident energy of 5.5 MeV. Taken from Moreh[18].

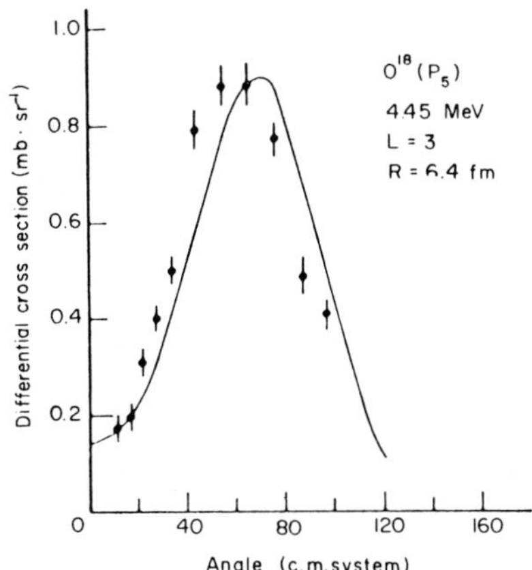

Fig. 21. Proton angular distributions from the $O^{16}(t,p)O^{18}$ reaction for the 4.45 MeV state, measured at an incident energy of 5.5 MeV. Taken from Moreh[18].

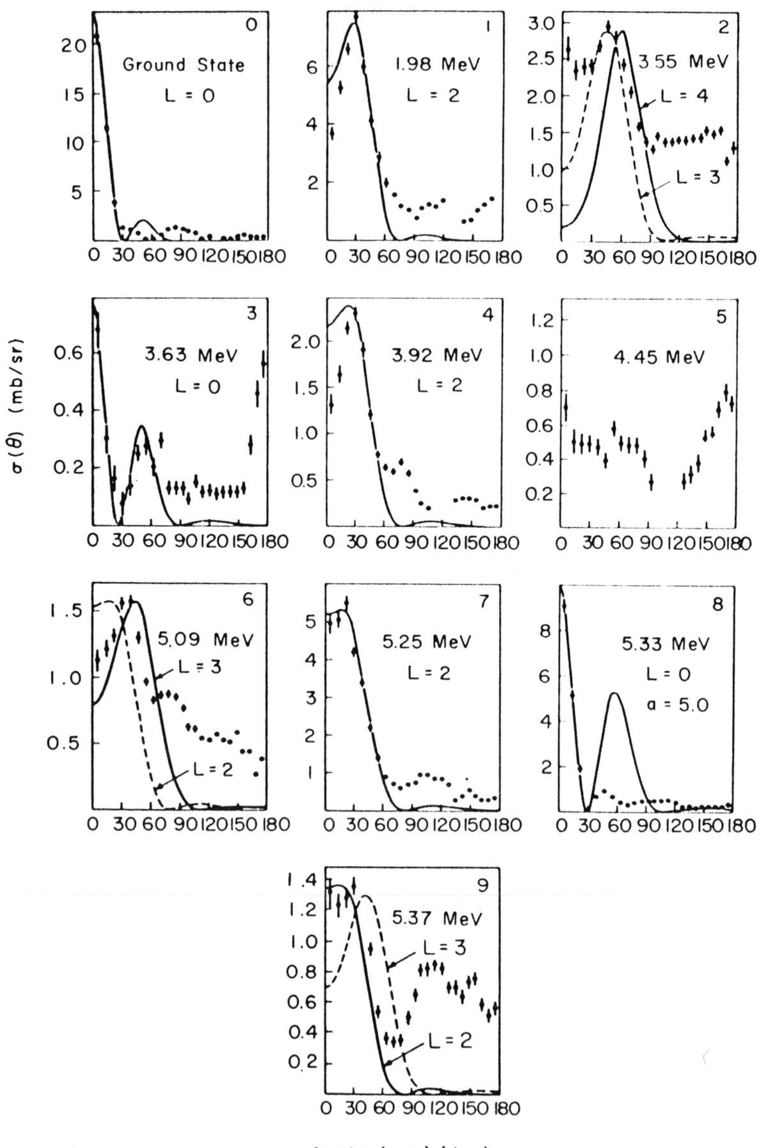

Fig. 22. Proton angular distributions from the $O^{16}(t,p)O^{18}$ reaction for the ground and first nine excited states, measured at an incident energy of 10.0 MeV. Taken from Middleton and Pullen[17].

LITHIUM-INDUCED REACTIONS*

R. R. Carlson

University of Iowa
Iowa City, Iowa

Introduction

The first lithium-induced nuclear reactions were observed by a group working with the late Professor S. K. Allison at the University of Chicago in 1956. This work was done with a 2 MV Van de Graaff modified to accelerate singly charged lithium ions. Most of the work was done on lithium and beryllium targets because of the coulomb barrier for the incident lithium ions. The classical distance of closest approach for lithium on lithium at 2 MV is 13 fermis which is quite large compared to the 2.5 fermi size of the lithium nuclei. Nevertheless, nuclear reactions were observed and cross sections were measured. Some of these results have been reported by Huberman, Kamegai, and Morrison[1)].

Even for this low bombardment energy it was possible to use lithium-7 beams to form exotic nuclei. B^{13} was formed in the reaction Li^7+Li^7; C^{15} was formed in Li^7+Be^9; N^{17} was formed in Li^7+B^{11}. Lithium bombardments make it possible to form unusual nuclei and to form more common varieties in a new way.

Since the first work on lithium reactions, work has been done in Paris at 2 MeV and 5 MeV, at the University of Minnesota from 2 to 4 MeV, at Harwell at 4.5 MeV, and at the University of Iowa from 2 to 4 MeV with our old Van de Graaff and from 2 to 14.5 MeV with our new Van de Graaff. We have used our new model CN 5.5 MV Van de Graaff to extend the study of lithium induced reactions to the bombarding energy range where the incident ions can easily surmount the coulomb barrier in the case of light element targets.

The University of Iowa HVEC machine has a lithium ion source with six filaments--three of Li^6 and three of Li^7 ordinarily. This ion source is mounted on one leg of a Y magnet which is set on top of the accelerator tube. The other leg has a conventional rf ion source supplied with

*Research supported in part by the National Science Foundation.

hydrogen, deuterium, He^3, and boron trichloride. Either source may be switched on from the control console and any beam selected without opening the machine. The rf source has been used for calibration reactions and He^3 reaction studies. There has been no problem in switching back and forth between beams. Operation with the lithium ion source has made it possible to run the machine at voltages in excess of the guaranteed 5.5 MV. We recently took data with 6.7 MV on the terminal. This probably is the result of the fact that the lithium ion source emits only Li^+ ions, making for an improved vacuum.

The University of Iowa CN machine was also supplied with a gap between the 5 ft upper accelerator tube and the 7 ft lower accelerator tube. This gap was meant to house a carbon foil stripping cell. We have recently designed, built, and operated this device. The foils strip the lithium ions after they have been accelerated through the first 5 foot tube. The result is that the machine produces triply charged lithium ions with an energy which is 2.17 times that of the singly charged ions and doubly charged ions with an energy which is 1.58 times as much. By using ions of all three charge states one can cover the bombarding energy range from the lowest energies up to 14.5 MeV. Figure 1 shows a picture of the stripping cell. The semi-circular part forms the wall of the stripping section. The foil wheel itself rotates within an enclosure designed so that the beam hits only the central part of the foil.

The cell holds eleven carbon foils which are 3/8-in in diameter. They are rotated into place by a string controlled pulley and the exact location is determined by sighting up the accelerator tube with a mirror on the flapper at the machine base. A foil lasts about 24 hours and produces about 50 nanoamps of triply charged lithium on target. Ordinary operation is obtained by simply rotating the foil wheel to an open position. No interference with ordinary operation has been found.

Nuclear Structure Studies

While the cross sections for lithium induced reactions are quite small, being only a few millibarns in most cases, it is possible to use them to study states of residual nuclei. This has been done[2)] in the cases of the $Be^9(Li^7,d)C^{14}$ and $B^{10}(Li^6,d)N^{14}$ reactions where gamma decay was detected in coincidence with the deuterons. Three-parameter measurements were made on the particle energy loss-rate and total energy with solid state detectors, to identify the particle, and on the gamma-ray energy with a large NaI crystal. Information on all levels involved in a reaction was collected at the same time, which overcame the effects of small cross section. A Control Data Corp. 160A computer was used to collect these data. Results were in agreement with other studies of these nuclei where comparisons could be made; however, the lithium induced reaction produces the residual nuclear levels with quite different relative populations. The 7.01 MeV state in C^{14} was quite clearly produced in the above reaction whereas it is not clearly produced in other cases.

Figure 2 shows a contour display of E_γ versus E_d for the C^{14} producing reaction. The identification of gamma rays as associated with deuterons is done by the computer from information on particle energy and energy loss rate. From such contours, pulse-height distributions corresponding to individual levels in C^{14} were constructed and branching ratios for decay of the levels was extracted.

The energy levels and decay scheme of N^{17} have also been studied with this three-parameter technique[3]. The work was done on our old Van de Graaff with a 3.3 MeV Li^7 beam on thin B^{11} targets. The reaction is $B^{11}(Li^7,p)N^{17}$ which occurs with an 8.42 MeV Q value. There are also positive Q value reactions producing deuterons, tritons, and alpha particles so particle identification was used as above. The sort of detailed information one can obtain is shown in Figure 3.

The levels of N^{17} have, of course, analogues in F^{17} and O^{17}. These T = 3/2 levels have received a certain amount of attention recently[4] and it is of interest to accurately measure the N^{17} levels for comparison purposes. This has been done with a 20 cc Ge(Li) gamma ray detector in coincidence with a particle detector. Because of the low efficiency of the Ge(Li) detector it was necessary to move the particle detector quite close and use foils to screen out unwanted deuterons, tritons, and alpha particles. Figure 4 shows the coincident gamma rays, which were observed, fitted into the level scheme of N^{17} with the excitation energies obtained from the measured gamma-ray energies. Some of the gamma rays previously seen with the NaI(Tℓ) detector were not seen here because of low intensity. The larger uncertainty in the energies of the higher levels arises because of uncertainty in the correction for Doppler shifts.

Measurements on non-coincident gamma rays from B^{11}+Li^7 showed many other sources of gamma rays besides N^{17} so that only the strongest transitions could be identified. These were the transitions from the 1905.8 keV and 1374.9 keV states. The former showed no detectable Doppler shift for observations at 30°, 90°, and 150° to the beam direction. The latter showed the full Doppler shift and correction for this has been included in the figure given for the excitation energy.

Lithium induced reactions, especially on light weight targets, give a larger Doppler shift than lighter weight projectiles simply because of their greater mass. A 6 MeV lithium-7 bombardment of lithium-7, for instance, will result in a full Doppler shift of 3.3% between 30° and 150° observation. This larger shift makes it useful to look at many lifetimes and the lifetime limits previously set with other reactions in order to set lower values on the errors and extend the limits. Figure 5 shows part of a gamma-ray spectrum taken with this reaction. The mean lifetime for the first excited state in B^{12} at 953 keV was found[5)] to be 0.30 ± 0.04 picosec and the second excited state at 1673 keV was found[5)] to have a mean life which is less than 0.05 picosec. Both of these values are in agreement with earlier work[6)] but have improved errors.

Lifetimes of states formed in lithium induced reactions have also been measured by electronic time delay techniques. The C^{15} first excited state is formed in the $Be^9(Li^7,p)C^{15}$ reaction. The time delay between detection of the proton and the 0.74 MeV gamma ray was measured[7)] giving a mean life of 3.77 ± 0.11 nanosec. This is in good agreement with previous measurements[8)]. Similarly, the $O^{18}(Li^7,\alpha)F^{21}$ reaction was used to form the F^{21} nucleus and the mean life of the first excited state at 0.279 MeV measured[9)] to be 10.1 ± 0.7 nanosec. The mean life of the second excited state at 1.10 MeV was found to be less than 0.3 nanosec. In both of these cases solid state detectors were used to measure particle energy and NaI(Tℓ) detectors were used to measure gamma ray energy. Data were taken in a three parameter mode with the third parameter being the time delay.

The level structure of Be^8 has been investigated by means of the $Li^6(Li^6,\alpha)Be^8$ reaction[10)]. Since the final state of this reaction is a three body system one has to make multi-parameter measurements to distinguish between the first alpha particle and subsequent decay alpha particles. In one measurement at 5.0 MeV bombarding energy, a solid state detector was placed at 12° on one side of the beam and another detector was placed at 35° on the other side spanning an angle of 20°. The large Q value of this reaction and the requirement of coincidence insured that the spectrum contained only contributions from the three alpha final state. The detector angles were chosen to minimize the interference from states in Be^8 with excitations less than 15 MeV. In this way the usual ambiguities of three-body final-state experiments were considerably reduced. The energy spectrum in the 12° counter is shown in Figure 6.

The presence of both the 16.62 and 16.92 MeV states is to be noticed. Considerable interest in these two states has been aroused by the strong isotopic spin mixing these two states display. The angular correlations of the first and the decay alpha particles from these states was measured and found to be the same.

Figure 6 shows clear evidence of the presence of the 19.9 MeV excited state. Since this state must decay by alpha particle emission to be detected its spin and parity must be 0^+, 2^+, 4^+, etc. This state has been seen in other reactions[11)] and is believed to be 2^+ in character.

Nuclear Reaction Mechanisms

Lithium ions have a high mass excess which leads to compound systems with quite high excitation energies even for low bombarding energies. For instance, in the case of Li^6 bombardment of B^{10}, the O^{16} compound system has an excitation of 34 MeV for 5 MeV bombardment. Also, lithium ions have low break-up energies. Lithium-6 requires only 1.47 MeV to break up into α+d and lithium-7 requires only 2.47 MeV to break up into α+t. These features of lithium reactions have led to the expectation that the reactions proceed by way of a direct, or stripping, type reaction. Of course, there are differences between "lithium stripping" and deuteron stripping since the former requires many-particle transfers. Nevertheless, the analogy can be pursued.

The experimental evidence from studies at low bombarding energies (2.0 MeV) seems to argue in favor of a direct interaction mechanism for lithium-induced reactions. This has been summarized by Morrison in his reports to the Gatlinburg Meeting on Reactions between Complex Nuclei in 1960[12)] and to the Padua Meeting in 1962[13)]. He fitted the angular distributions of a number of reactions, involving (Li^6,d) and (Li^7,t), using a direct interaction hypothesis. However, for higher bombarding energies (4.5 MeV) he could find no discernable pattern. This was reported in the 1963 Asilomar Meeting on Reactions between Complex Nuclei[14)].

Recent work[15] at Iowa confirms this result for reactions with large Q values. Measurements were made of the differential cross sections for the charged particles resulting from bombardment of B^{10} and B^{11} by Li^6 and Li^7. This work was done at 5 MeV bombarding energy which is just below the coulomb barrier (5.8 MeV). Many reactions were studied for which the spins and parities of all states involved are known. In these cases the qualitative nature of the angular distributions expected on the basis of a particle transfer, or direct interaction, are known. No consistent pattern could be discerned. It is possible that those reactions in which particles would be transferred with low momenta, i.e., low Q reactions, might fit a direct reaction interpretation but this is not true of the ground and low excited state groups where high momentum transfers are required.

The differential cross sections for the various reactions were integrated to give the total cross-sections for individual states of residual nuclei. When this was done it was found that the total cross sections for a given reaction are proportional to 2J+1 where J is the spin of the particular state of the residual nucleus. A number of cases were found which showed this effect. Figure 7 shows the data for the $B^{10}(Li^6,d)N^{14}$, $B^{10}(Li^7,t)N^{14}$, and $B^{11}(Li^6,t)N^{14}$ reactions.

The formation of a compound nucleus could give rise to a 2J+1 dependence if the compound nucleus were highly excited so that many overlapping levels were formed. In addition to this, the outgoing particles should have high penetrability. The various conditions necessary for the formation of a statistical compound nucleus have been discussed by MacDonald[17].

One feature rather intimately associated with the formation of a highly excited compound nucleus with many overlapping states is the presence of fluctuations in the yield of reactions proceeding by way of this compound nucleus. These fluctuations have been discussed in some detail by T. Ericson[18]. We have looked for and found[19] them in the $B^{10}(Li^6,\alpha)C^{12}$ reaction as shown in Figure 8. The yield of the $B^{10}(Li^6,\alpha)C^{12*}$ reaction is shown in Figure 9 and it also shows fluctuations but as would be expected on a statistical compound nucleus hypothesis there is no cross-correlation between the yields to the ground and first excited states. In this reaction, the excitation studied ranged from 32 to 39 MeV and the average width of the states in the compound nucleus was found to be 1.5 MeV. It was necessary to use multiply charged beams to cover the range of bombardment used.

The $C^{12}(Li^6,p)O^{17}$, $C^{12}(Li^6,d)O^{16}$, and $C^{12}(Li^6,\alpha)N^{14}$ were studied[20] at the University of Minnesota, also making use of multiply charged beams. Figure 10 shows some of their results for the first reaction. The F^{18} compound system is at a much lower excitation energy than is the case above, being formed at 17 MeV excitation with 6 MeV lithium bombarding energy. Fluctuations were observed with the coherence energy, or the average width of the compound nucleus states, being 0.22 MeV. This lower value is expected because of the lower excitation.

Another sign of compound nucleus effects is the appearance of residual states which, because of their spin and parity, cannot be readily formed by a direct reaction. One such state is the 2^- state at 8.88 MeV in O^{16}. Energetically, this could be formed in the $C^{12}(Li^6,d)O^{16}$ reaction. It has been observed with 20 MeV lithium bombardment using the Heidelberg tandem to provide the beam[21]. We have also recently observed[22] the formation of this state with 13 MeV lithium bombardment. Figure 11 shows the spectrum of deuterons. The 8.88 MeV state is not noticeably inhibited in intensity. Interestingly, the $C^{12}(Li^7,t)O^{16}$ (8.88) reaction is noticeably inhibited at tandem energies implying a considerable direct reaction component in this reaction.

Fluctuation studies[23] have also been made on the $O^{16}(Li^6,\alpha)F^{18}$ reaction as shown in Figure 12. The compound system, Na^{22}, is excited to the 18 to 24 MeV range in this reaction. The coherence energy is 0.4 MeV. Angular distributions have been measured at the energies indicated by the arrows in the figure. These are shown in the neighborhood of the lowest energy peak in Figure 13. One would expect the general shape of an angular distribution to persist for changes in bombarding energy equal to the coherence energy and this seems to be the case. The same thing is true at the higher energies.

The yield of the $Li^6(Li^6,\alpha_0)Be^8$ reaction has also been studied[24] as a function of bombarding energy. The final system is one of three alpha particles and in order to study the yield of a particular state of Be^8 it is usually necessary to make measurements on the energy of two of the outgoing alpha particles, as was mentioned above. The ground state alpha group is an exception to this rule because it is at the very upper end of the three-body continuum. The spectrum, measured at 0° with a solid state detector just thick enough to stop the 34 MeV ground-state alpha group, is shown in Figure 14. The number of counts under the upper half of the ground state peak is plotted as a function of bombarding energy in Figure 15.

The peaks shown in Figure 15 occur in the 29 to 35 MeV excitation range of C^{12}. If one interprets these peaks as due to fluctuations having their origin in many overlapping compound nucleus states, the coherence energy is about an MeV. This is not unreasonable for such a light nucleus as C^{12} at this excitation. States of such short duration are hard to understand as compound nucleus states in the ordinary sense; however, one must remember that C^{12} is being formed in a novel manner here, i.e., by inverse fission and, consequently, one has two halves of the compound nucleus established prior to collision. Other signs of compound nucleus effects in the Li^6+Li^6 reaction were described by K. G. Kibler in his study of the angular distributions and total cross sections of charged particles in this reaction[25].

Conclusion

Nuclear structure and nuclear reaction studies with lithium and other heavy ions should serve to provide new information and new tests of old hypotheses. Some nuclear states can be formed with lithium ions in a much more tractable manner than with other beams. The properties found in this way add to the general fund of data necessary for a complete understanding of nuclear physics.

References

1) M. N. Huberman, M. Kamegai, and G. C. Morrison, Phys. Rev. 129, 791 (1963).

2) R. R. Carlson, Phys. Rev. 148, 991 (1966).

3) V. P. Hart, E. Norbeck, and R. R. Carlson, Phys. Rev. 137, 1317 (1965).

4) E. G. Adelberger and C. A. Barnes, Physics Letters 23, 474 (1966); C. A. Barnes, E. G. Adelberger, D. C. Hensley, and A. B. MacDonald, International Nuclear Physics Conference, Gatlinberg, 1966.

5) M. J. Throop, Bull. Am. Phys. Soc. II 12, 484 (1967).

6) E. K. Warburton and L. F. Chase, Phys. Rev. 132, 2273 (1963).

7) R. Mendelson, private communication.

8) J. Lowe, C. L. McClelland, and J. V. Kane, Phys. Rev. 126, 1811 (1962).

9) R. Mendelson and R. T. Carpenter, Phys. Rev. 152, 1002 (1966).

10) M. Mancusi and E. Norbeck, Phys. Rev. 151, 830 (1966).

11) H. E. Conzett, P. Darriulat, H. G. Pugh, E. Shield, and R. J. Slobodrian, Nuclear Chemistry Division Annual Report 1965 (UCRL-16580).

12) G. C. Morrison and M. N. Huberman in Reactions Between Complex Nuclei, ed. by A. Zucker, F. T. Howard, and E. C. Halbert [John Wiley and Sons, Inc., New York 1960], p. 246.

13) G. C. Morrison in Direct Interactions and Nuclear Reactions Mechanisms, ed. by E. Clementel and C. Villi [Gordon and Breach Science Publishers, Inc., New York 1963], p. 878.

14) G. C. Morrison, N. H Gale, and M. Hussain in Proceedings of the 3rd International Conference on Reactions Between Complex Nuclei, ed. by A. Ghiorso, R. M. Diamond, and H. E. Conzett [University of California Press, Berkeley, California, 1963], p. 168.

15) R. L. McGrath, Phys. Rev. 145, 802 (1966).

16) R. R. Carlson and R. L. McGrath, Phys. Rev. Letters 15, 173 (1965).

17) N. MacDonald, Nuclear Physics 33, 110 (1962).

18) T. Ericson, Annals of Physics 23, 390 (1963).

19) W. A. Seale, accepted for publication in Phys. Rev.

20) T. Dzubay, accepted for publication in Phys. Rev.

21) K. Bethge, K. Meier-Ewert, K. Pfeiffer, and R. Bock, On the Mechanism of Lithium-Induced Nuclear Reactions, preprint.

22) D. Johnson, private communication.

23) M. W Greene and E. B. Nelson, Bull. Am. Phys. Soc. II 12, 534 (1967).

24) B. Aldredi, private communication.

25) K. G. Kibler, Phys. Rev. 152, 932 (1966).

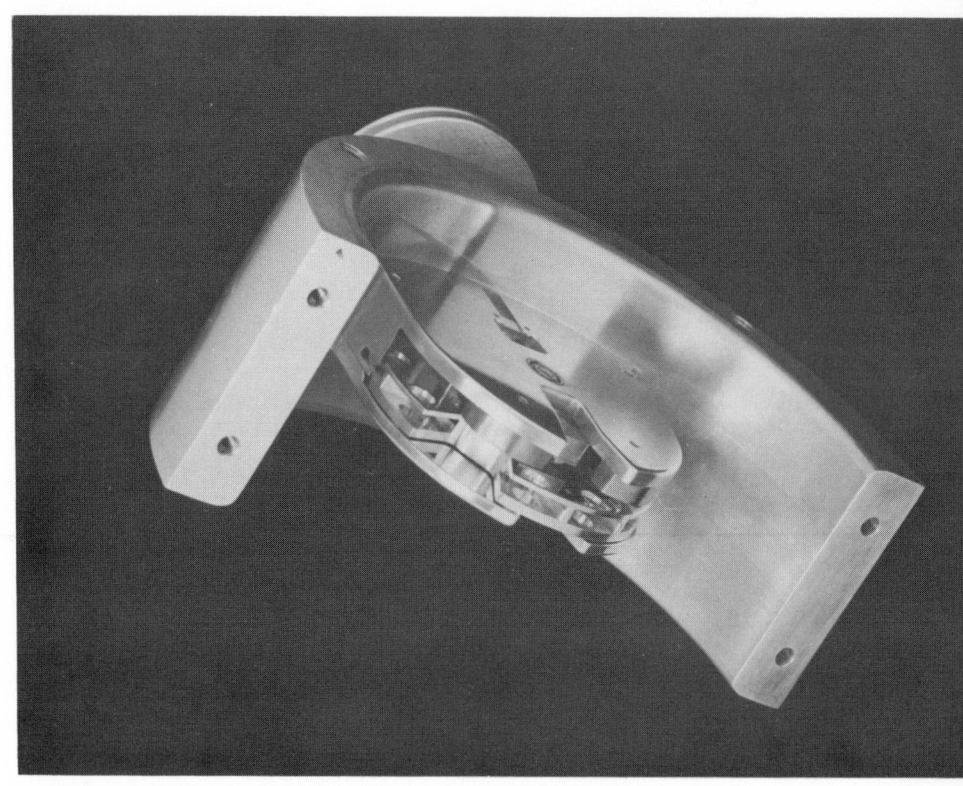

Fig. 1 Carbon foil stripping assembly for 5.5 MV Model CN Van de Graaff.

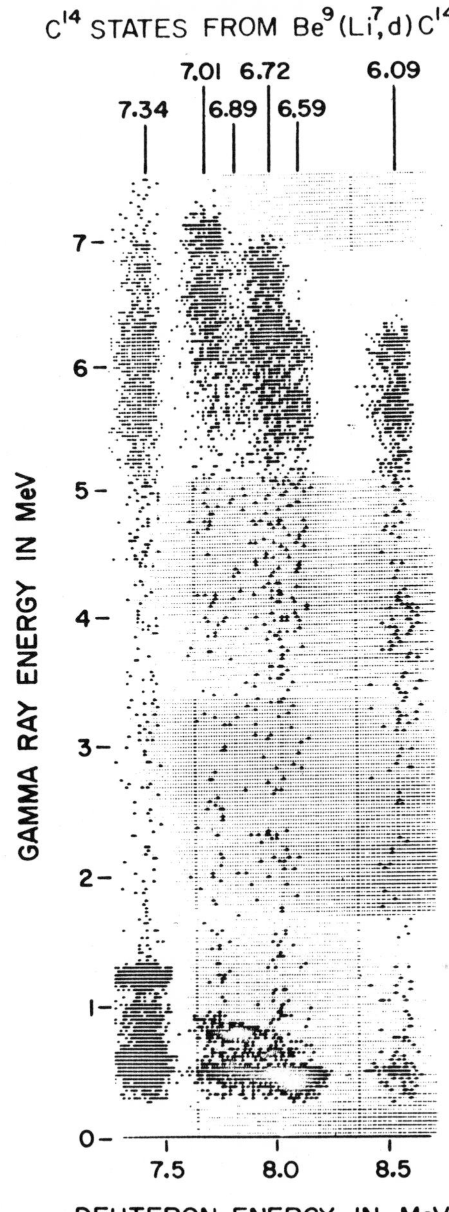

Fig. 2 Contour display of E_γ versus E_d with 256 channels for E_γ and 128 channels for E_d. The 128 channels for E_d are 1/8 of the total 1024 channels in the original data. This display is pieced together out of 5 scans of the data tape. Contour level is 4 counts here.

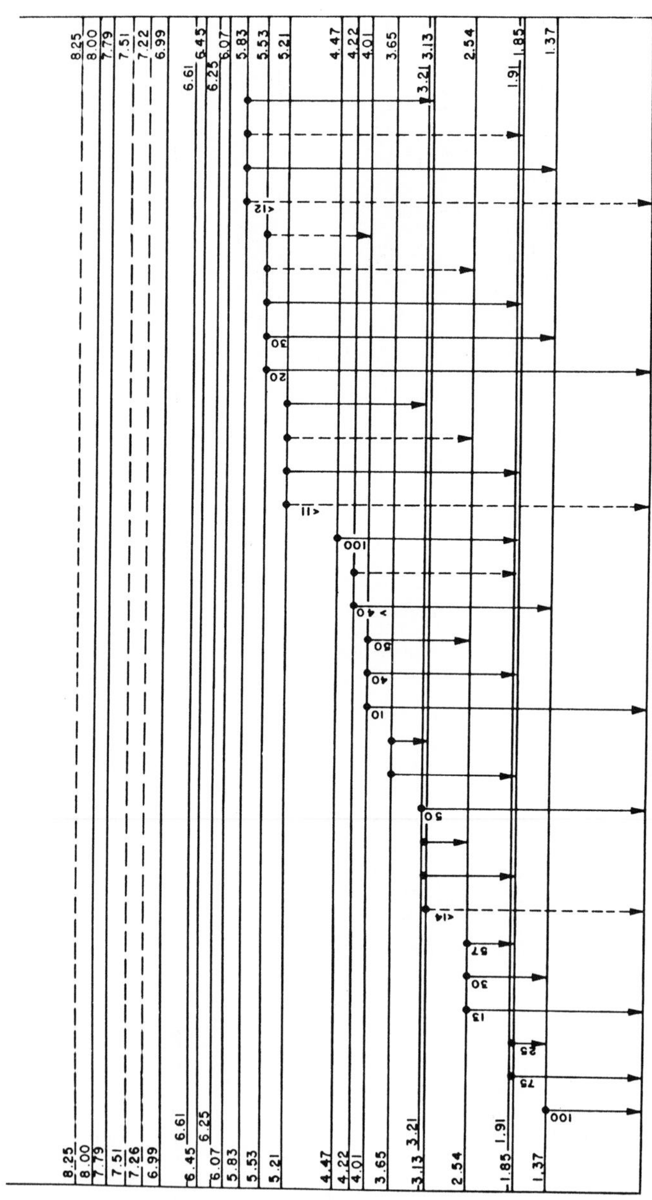

DECAY SCHEME OF N^{17}

Fig. 3 Energy levels and decay scheme of N^{17} obtained with three parameter measurements using solid state detectors and NaI(Tℓ) gamma ray detector.

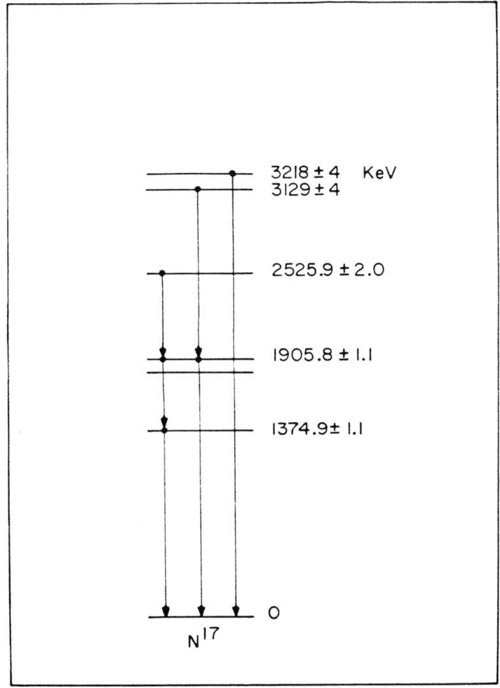

Fig. 4 Energy levels of N^{17} obtained with a 20 cc Gc(Li) gamma-ray detector in coincidence with a proton detector.

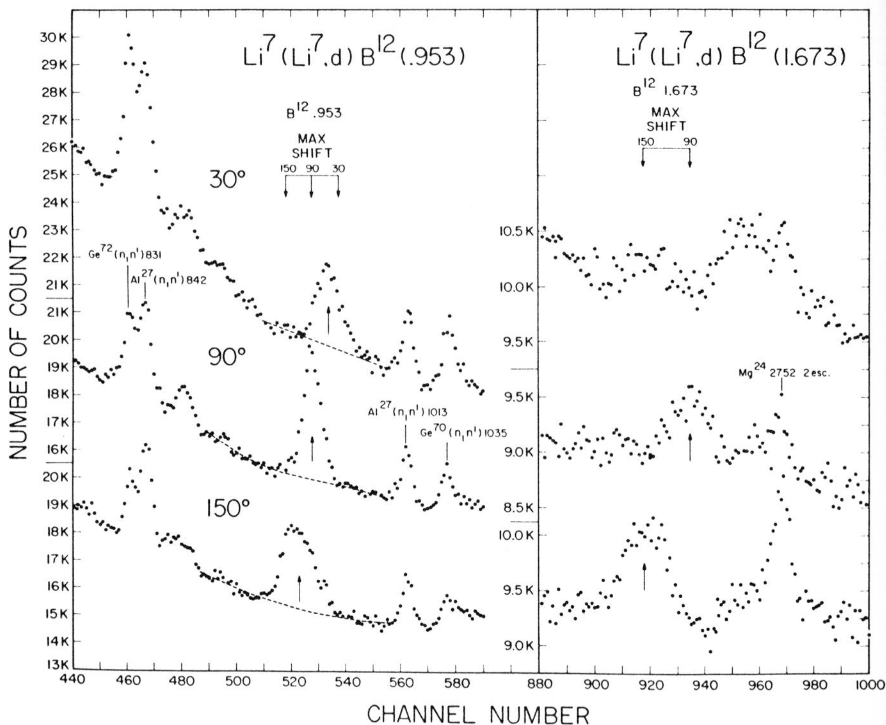

Fig. 5 Portions of gamma-ray spectra from 5.6 MeV Li^7 bombardment of Li^7 target. Partially Doppler shifted lines of B^{12} 953-keV transition and fully Doppler shifted lines of B^{12} 1673-keV transition are shown. $Al^{27}(n,n')$, $Ge(n,n')$ and Mg^{24} lines are due to neutrons produced by the $Li^7(Li^7,n)C^{13}$ reaction.

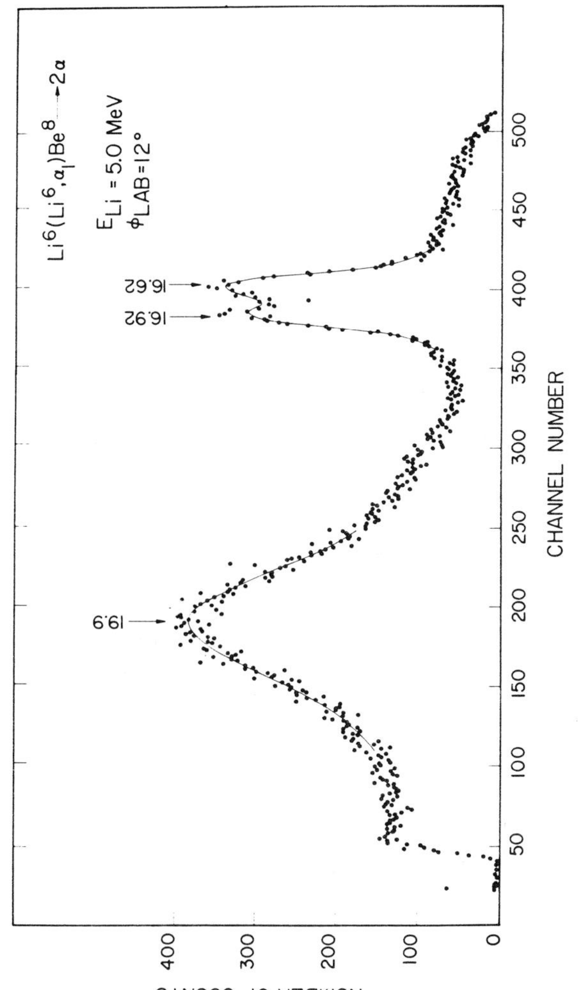

Fig. 6 Coincidence spectrum of alpha particles detected at 12° in the laboratory from $Li^6(Li^6,\alpha)Be^8 \rightarrow 2\alpha$ at 5.0 MeV bombarding energy showing the 16.62-, 16.92 , and 19.9-MeV states in Be^8.

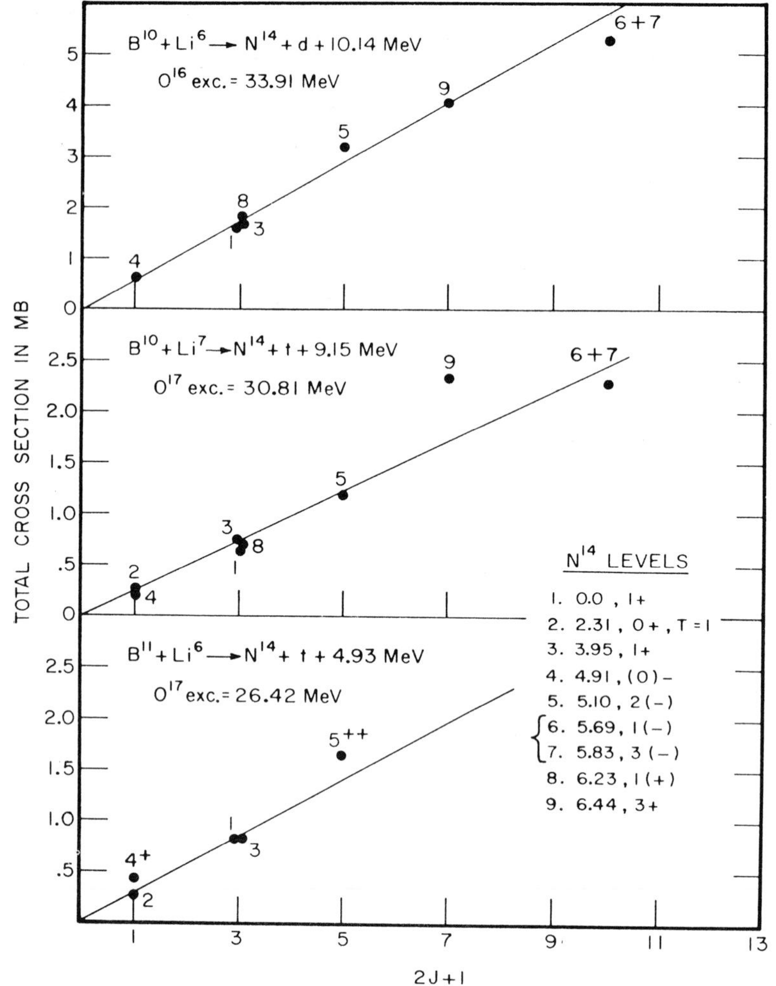

Fig. 7 N^{14} total cross section in mb versus the value of 2J+1. The measured differential cross-sections are integrated and normalized to the range 0°-150°. The (+) and (++) points are observed only over 0° to 40°. Level excitations are given in MeV.

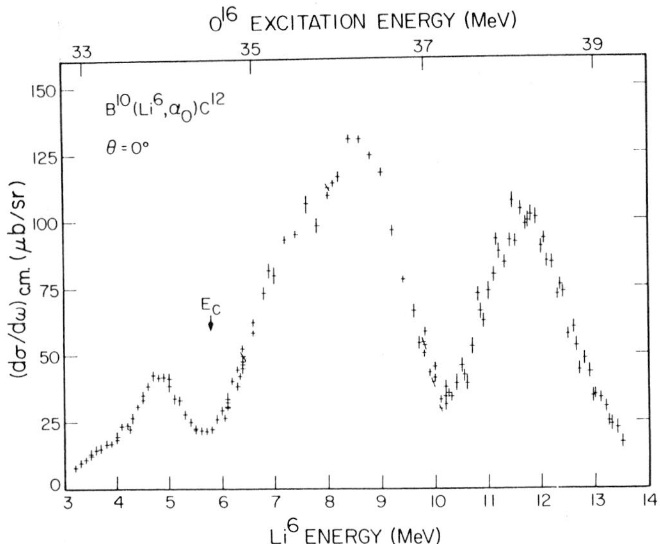

Fig. 8 Center-of-mass differential cross section for the $B^{10}(Li^6,\alpha)C^{12}$ reaction as a function of Li^6 energy in the laboratory. E_c indicates the coulomb barrier. Error bars represent statistical errors only.

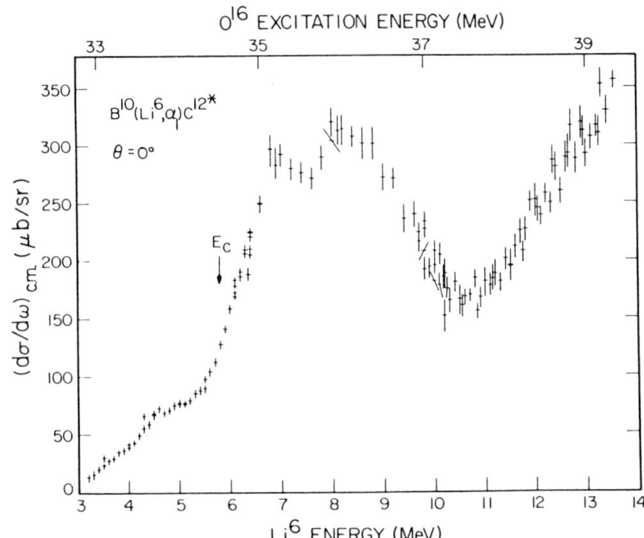

Fig. 9 Center-of-mass differential cross section for the $B^{10}(Li^6,\alpha)C^{12*}$ reaction.

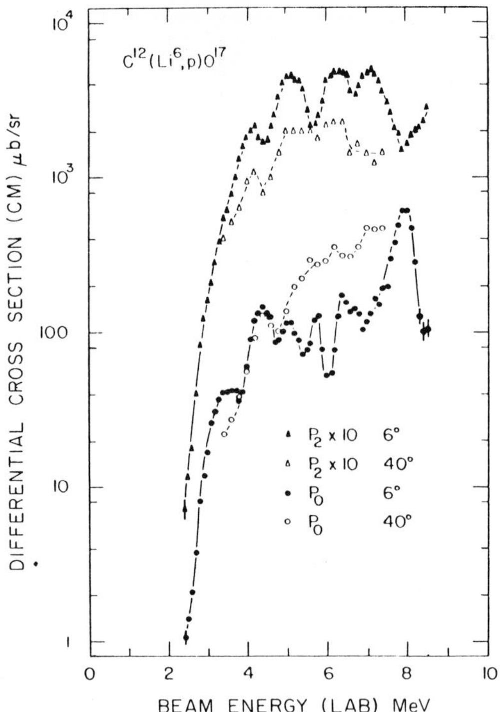

Fig. 10 Center-of-mass differential cross sections for the $C^{12}(Li^6,p)O^{17}$ reactions.

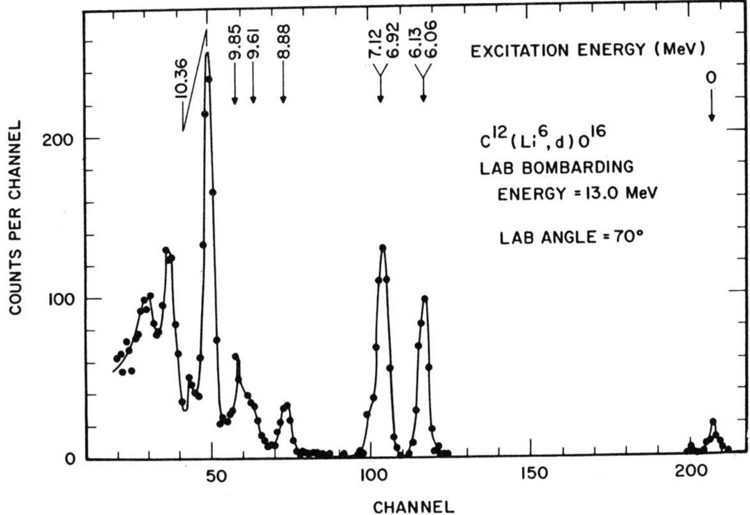

Fig. 11 Deuteron spectrum from $C^{12}(Li^6,d)O^{16}$ reaction with 13 MeV Li^6 ions and 70° angle of observation. Arrows at top indicate expected location of particle groups corresponding to various excitations in O^{16} (in MeV).

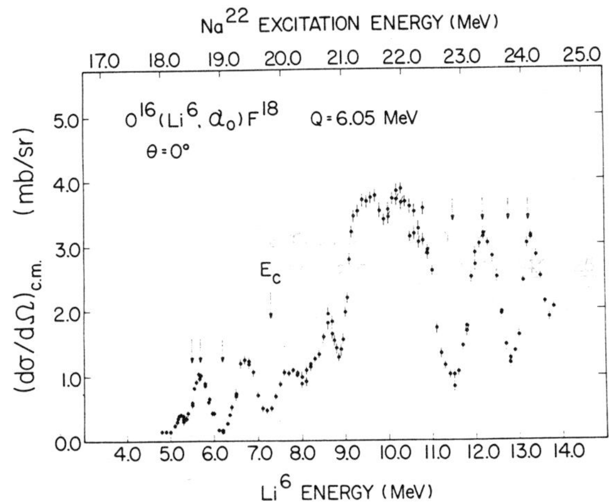

Fig. 12 Center-of-mass differential cross section for $O^{16}(Li^6,\alpha)F^{18}$ reaction as a function of Li^6 energy in the laboratory. Arrows indicate energies at which complete angular distributions have been measured. E_c indicates the coulomb barrier.

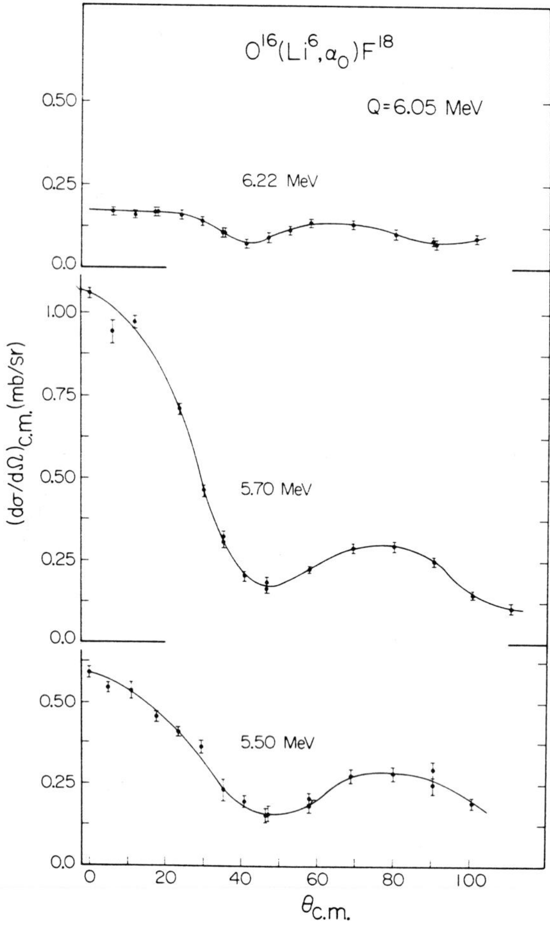

Fig. 13 Angular distributions for the $O^{16}(Li^6,\alpha)F^{18}$ reaction in the neighborhood of the peak in the 0° yield curve at 5.7 MeV.

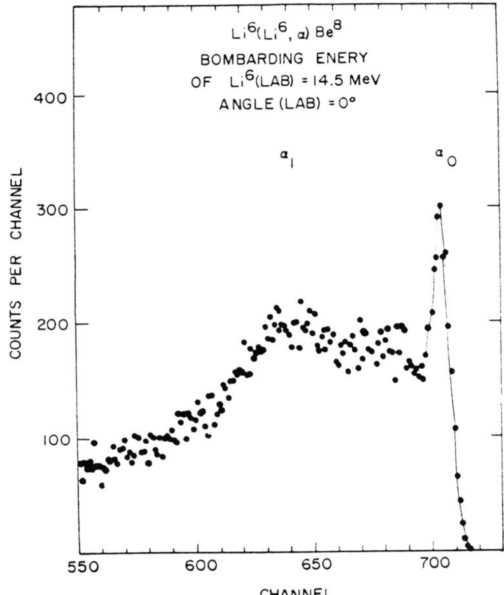

Fig. 14 - Alpha particle spectrum at 0° from 14.5 MeV Li^6 bombardment of Li^6. Positions of ground (α_0) and first excited state (α_1) groups are indicated. Remainder of spectrum is presumably due to break-up alphas from higher excited states of Be^8 and, possibly, three-body break-up.

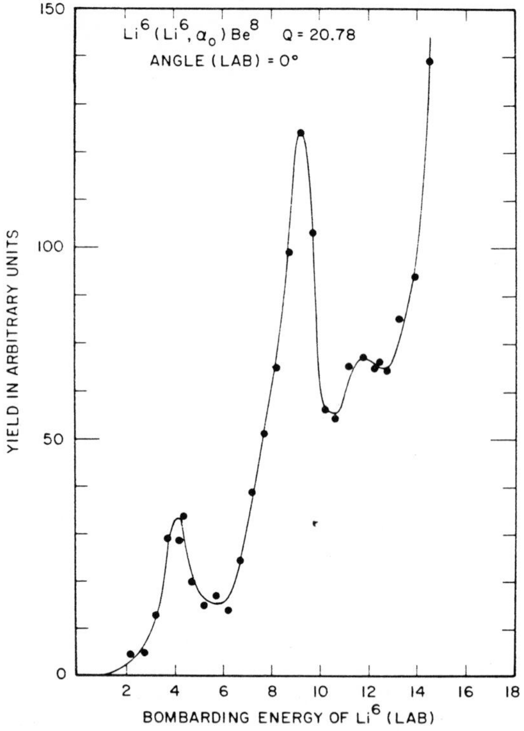

Fig. 15 Yield curve for the $Li^6(Li^6,\alpha_0)Be^8$ reaction.

ISOBARIC SPIN EFFECTS IN NUCLEAR REACTIONS

Jerry B. Marion

University of Maryland
College Park, Maryland

INTRODUCTION

We have heard at this Symposium about some of the effects that isobaric spin has on nuclear reactions, mainly in connection with the so-called analog states. In this paper I will restrict my discussion to a single aspect of isobaric spin effects, namely, the determination of the isobaric spin *impurity*, or *T-mixing*, of nuclear levels.

It is well established that although isobaric spin is an extremely useful concept, T is never a good quantum number in the sense that, for example, angular momentum is; that is, there is always some admixture of T's, albeit very small in some cases, in every nuclear level. The question posed here is: "How precisely do we know the amount of admixture in particular cases?" I am sorry to say that the answer, as we will see, is that there are very few cases for which we can state the isobaric spin impurity with any precision.

I will be discussing only cases of T = 0 and T = 1 mixtures in N = Z nuclei. Because the point is to establish the degree of *mixing*, it is, of course, necessary that at least two levels be involved, one primarily T = 0 and one primarily T = 1. If these levels have the same spin and parity, mixing in isobaric spin will occur. Only in the event that both members of the pair are identified, is there a hope of precisely measuring the amount of mixing; to determine the isobaric spin components in a single level, without reference to its associated level, is virtually impossible to do with precision. (I will elaborate on this point later.)

METHODS OF ANALYSIS

There are basically two types of measurements which are useful for establishing isobaric spin mixing: (a) electromagnetic (E1 and M1) widths and (b) T = 0 particle (d and α) widths.

It is well known that T = 0, E1 transitions in N = Z nuclei are forbidden[1] (in the long-wavelength approximation and neglecting recoil effects) and that $\Delta T = 0$, M1 transitions in these nuclei are strongly suppressed.[2] The status of these selection rules has been reviewed recently.[3] The E1 selection rule is sufficiently strong to provide useful information regarding T-mixing, but the $\Delta T = 0$ part of the M1 matrix element is only suppressed by about an order of magnitude compared with the $\Delta T = 1$ part. Thus, for an M1 transition between two T-mixed levels, or from each member of the pair to a single final state, the strength will be proportional to

$$|M(M1)|^2 = |M_{00} + M_{01} + M_{10} + M_{11}|^2 \qquad (1)$$

where the subscripts refer to the initial and final values of T. Now, $M_{00} \simeq 0.1\, M_{01}$ and $M_{11} \simeq 0.1\, M_{10}$, and because the relative phases of the various parts of the matrix element are not known *a priori*, there is a wide range of uncertainty in the expected value of the transition strength. (It could, in fact, vanish.)

Of course, E1 radiation cannot occur between the members of a mixed doublet because the levels have the same J^π, but we can make use of the strong E1 selection rule in discussing the radiation from the members of a mixed pair to a single lower final state. For example, if we were to find equal values of $|M(E1)|^2$ for each of a pair of $J^\pi = 1^-$ levels radiating to the $J^\pi = 0^+$ ground state of an N = Z nucleus, we would conclude that the two levels had equal T = 1 components, i. e., that they were totally mixed, 50% T = 0 and 50% T = 1. If the levels had $J^\pi = 1^+$, we would not be able to place a sharp value on the amount of mixing because of the latitude in the M1 selection rule.

Deuteron and α-particle widths provide another way of making firm statements regarding T-mixing. If a pair of levels, A and B, are mixed, the wave functions can be expresse in a T-representation as

$$\left.\begin{aligned} |A\rangle &= \alpha|T = 0\rangle + \beta|T = 1\rangle \\ |B\rangle &= \beta|T = 0\rangle - \alpha|T = 1\rangle \end{aligned}\right\} \qquad (2)$$

where the relative phases must be opposite but where the

overall phase is usually unknown. It is easy to show[4] that the ratio of the α-particle or deuteron reduced widths for the two levels is just the square of the ratio of the T = 0 amplitudes in the wave functions:

$$\frac{\theta_\alpha^2(A)}{\theta_\alpha^2(B)} = \frac{\alpha^2}{\beta^2} \tag{3}$$

If the levels A and B can be formed by resonant scattering of α particles or deuterons, the isobaric spin amplitudes are easy to obtain. Also, if the levels can be formed in a non-T-changing reaction, such as (d,α) or (α,α') then the ratio of the formation cross sections is also α^2/β^2. This latter proceudre can be invalidated if the reaction proceeds through a compound nuclear state which has a sufficiently long lifetime that Coulomb effects can mix isobaric spins. This point has been discussed by Browne.[5]

In order for a pair of levels to be appreciably mixed, they must be relatively close in energy--a few hundred keV at most. If, in addition, the levels are unbound with respect to particle emission so that they have appreciable natural widths, some overlap of the levels can occur. In such a case, interference effects can result and any analysis that attempts to extract a precise value for the T-mixing must be carefully done.[4] Asymmetric level shapes that result from this type of interference have been observed[6] in the $B^{10}(d,\alpha)Be^8$ reaction leading to the mixed 2^+ levels near 16 MeV.

Before proceeding to the discussion of T-mixed doublets, let me give one example of the difficulty that one encounters when dealing with a <u>single</u> level. In F^{18}, the 6.23-MeV level is formed[7] in the elastic scattering of α particles by N^{14}. The angular momentum transfer is 3 and J^π is established as 2^-. The reduced width is rather large, $\theta_\alpha^2 \cong 0.5$, and therefore strongly suggests that the 6.23-MeV level has T = 0. On the other hand, this level is observed in the $N^{14}(\alpha,\gamma)F^{18}$ reaction and it is found[8] that the matrix elements for E1 radiation to the $J^\pi = 1^+$, T = 0 level at 1.70 MeV and the $J^\pi = 3^+$, T = 0 level at0.94 MeV are both larger than the average $|M|^2$ for E1, ΔT = 1 transitions in N = Z nuclei. Thus, the strengths of the γ-ray transitions strongly suggest that the 6.23-MeV level has T = 1. It therefore seems clear that this state in F^{18} is highly T-mixed. But until the associated $J^\pi = 2^-$ level is identified and its α-particle reduced width and E1 transition strengths are measured, there is no way to place a precise value on the amount of T-mixing. Since the mixing is apparently quite thorough for this case, one would expect to find the companion level rather close in energy. It is possible that the $\ell_\alpha = 3$ $N^{14} + \alpha$ resonance ($\theta_\alpha^2 = 0.18$) corresponding to $E_x = 6.10$ MeV is the state in question.

THE DOUBLETS IN Be^8

The most extensively studied T-mixed doublet is the pair of levels at 16.6 and 16.9 MeV in Be^8. There is a wealth of information available,[9] but the most significant datum is the ratio of the α-particle widths for these levels. Because these levels are close in energy and are particle unbound only with respect to α particles, the reduced width ratio is equal to the ratio of the total natural widths. These widths have been directly measured[4] with the result $\Gamma(16.6) = 113 \pm 3$ keV and $\Gamma(16.9) = 77 \pm 3$ keV. The values deduced by Browne, Callender, and Erskine[6] from their analysis of the interference effects in the $B^{10}(d,\alpha)Be^8$ reaction are in close agreement with the results above. Therefore, $\alpha^2/\beta^2 = 1.47$, with an uncertainty of only about 5%, and the T-representation wave functions are

$$\left.\begin{aligned} |16.6\rangle &= 0.772|T{=}0\rangle + 0.636|T{=}1\rangle \\ |16.9\rangle &= 0.636|T{=}0\rangle - 0.772|T{=}1\rangle \end{aligned}\right\} \quad (4)$$

One of the more interesting aspects of these levels (which was, in fact, the crucial point in the realization that the levels are highly T-mixed) is the fact that the 16.6-MeV state has a large proton reduced width and a very small neutron reduced width whereas the 16.9-MeV level has just the opposite character. Therefore, in a particle representation we can write approximate wave functions for these states as

$$\left.\begin{aligned} |16.6\rangle &= |Li^7{+}p\rangle \\ |16.9\rangle &= |Be^7{+}n\rangle \end{aligned}\right\} \quad (5)$$

From this alone we can immediately conclude that the levels do not have sharp isobaric spin (in fact, if Eqs. (5) were exact, the mixing would be complete) because any state that is describable as $|(A{=}7){+}(\text{nucleon})\rangle$ cannot be an eigenstate of total isobaric spin. The proton and neutron characters of these states have been established in a variety of reaction studies.[9,10]

Measurements of the M1 matrix elements connecting the states at 17.6 MeV ($J^\pi = 1^+$, ~90% T=1) and at 18.15 MeV ($J^\pi = 1^+$, ~90% T=0) with the $J^\pi = 2^+$ states are consistent with the almost complete mixing of the 2^+ states and the lesser mixing of the 1^+ states.[10,11] Recently, the (presumably) E1 transitions from the $J^\pi = 2^-$ state at 18.9 MeV in Be^8 to the 16.6-16.9 MeV doublet have been identified and the strengths (although only poorly known) are again indicative of the almost completely mixed character of the 2^+ states.[11]

There appears to be a third T-mixed doublet in Be^8 - a pair of $J^\pi = 3^+$ levels near 19 MeV.[12] A search has been made for transitions connecting these states with the 2^+ doublet, but to no avail.[11] The extreme weakness of these transitions (which should be strong M1 transitions and also strong E2 transitions if the $1^+ - 2^+ - 3^+$ doublets have any collective character) remains one of the mysteries of Be^8. We plan to continue these studies by looking for transitions from the 3^+ states to the 1^+ states; in this case we will be seeking enhanced E2 transitions.

THE 1^- DOUBLET IN F^{18}

The scattering of α particles by N^{14} has been used to identify[7] a pair of levels in F^{18} at 5.59 and 5.66 MeV. The angular momentum transfer was found to the one, so that J^π = 0^-, 1^-, or 2^-; only the assignment $J^\pi = 1^-$ for both levels is consistent with γ-ray angular correlation data.[13] These levels have substantial α-particle reduced widths, indicating strong T = 0 components:

$$\left.\begin{aligned} \theta_\alpha^2(5.59) &= 0.09 \\ \theta_\alpha^2(5.66) &= 0.17 \end{aligned}\right\} \quad (6)$$

From the reduced width data, we conclude that

$$\left.\begin{aligned} |5.59\rangle &= 0.53|T{=}0\rangle + 0.81|T{=}1\rangle \\ |5.66\rangle &= 0.81|T{=}0\rangle - 0.53|T{=}1\rangle \end{aligned}\right\} \quad (7)$$

The γ-ray decay properties of these levels have been established by careful measurements recently made at Toronto,[13] supplementing the early results of Price.[14] The Toronto group finds that the two levels have almost identical decays to the $J^\pi = 0^-$, T = 0 level at 1.08 MeV, but that the decays to the $J^\pi = 2^+$, T = 1 level at 3.06 MeV are rather different. From this they conclude[13] that the T = 1 portions of the wave functions are almost the same but that the T = 0 portions are not. I believe we can dispute this conclusion on two counts. First, the use of the similarity in the M1 decays to the 1.08-MeV level does not necessarily mean that the T = 1 amplitudes of the 5.59- and 5.66-MeV levels are the same because of the phase differences that can occur, as we have pointed out earlier. Second, if we rule out the possibility that there are appreciable T = 2 components in the wave functions then we must write these wave functions (in a T-representation) as in Eqs. (2). These wave functions are, of course, the two possible orthogonal combinations of the basis states, and therefore if the T = 1 amplitudes be equal, so also must the T = 0 amplitudes be equal. If there are other $J^\pi = 1^-$ states in the vicinity (some unassigned states do exist in the neighborhood), the situation will be more complicated than the simple analysis presented for the case of a doublet, but the second point just mentioned will not be altered.

It is interesting to note that the Be^8 $J^\pi = 2^+$ doublet has a 40% - 60% T-mixing (in intensity) with an energy separation of about 0.3 MeV, whereas the F^{18} $J^\pi = 1^-$ doublet has only a 35% - 65% mixing and an energy separation as small as 70 keV. Since the T-mixing is due to the Coulomb matrix element connecting the states, one would expect a stronger mixing in states that are closer together. Perhaps the fact that the position of O^{17} + p binding in F^{18} occurs <u>between</u> the levels in question has some importance which we do not yet understand.

THE 1^- DOUBLET IN O^{16}

The decay properties of the $J^\pi = 1^-$ states at 12.43 and 13.09 MeV in O^{16} have been thoroughly studies by Hebbard[15] using the $N^{15}(p,\alpha)C^{12}$ and $N^{15}(p,\gamma)O^{16}$ reactions. From the results of these experiments, we have three ways to assess the T-mixing of the levels, all of which should be equally valid: (a) the ratio of the α- particle reduced widths leaving C^{12} in the ground state, (b) the ratio of the α-particle reduced widths leaving C^{12} in the first excited state, and (c) the ratio of the E1 strengths to the ground state of O^{16}.

The results are:

$$\frac{\theta^2_{\alpha_o}(12.43)}{\theta^2_{\alpha_o}(13.09)} = 4.6 \qquad (8)$$

$$\frac{\theta^2_{\alpha_1}(12.43)}{\theta^2_{\alpha_1}(13.09)} = 3.7 \qquad (9)$$

$$\frac{|M(E1)|^2_{12.43}}{|M(E1)|^2_{13.09}} = \frac{1}{5.9} \qquad (10)$$

(The ratio of E1 matrix elements, since they connect the T=1 parts of the wave functions, should equal the <u>inverse</u> of the ratio of α-particle reduced widths which connect the T=0 parts.)

The agreement among these three numbers is only fair; one would hope that our understanding of isobaric spin mixing is better than this! Taken on average, these results indicate that the intensity of T-mixing between the 12.43 and 13.09-MeV states is about 20%, a value that is not far from that expected from the magnitude of the Coulomb matrix element corresponding to the observed energy splitting.

THE 1^+ DOUBLET IN C^{12}

I would like to conclude this discussion of T-mixed doublets by mentioning a very interesting case, but one for which we do not yet have all of the essential information.

The 12.7- and 15.1-MeV states in C^{12} have both been assigned $J^\pi = 1^+$. The assignment for the lower state is derived primarily from the observed lack of α-decay to the ground state of Be^8 (which is forbidden by angular momentum and parity considerations if $J^\pi = 1^+$) and by the agreement of the measured log ft value[16] for the β decay of N^{12} to this state with that computed on the basis of the Cohen and Kurath model[17]. The assignment for the upper state again rests on the lack of ground-state α-decay and on the magnitude of the M1 resonance absorption cross section, which is a ΔT=1 process from the T=0 C^{12} ground state to the (presumably) T=1 15.1-MeV state.

It has been generally accepted that the T=1 assignment for the 15.1-MeV level is correct because this state fails to decay by α-particle emission to the 2.9-MeV, $J^{\pi} = 2^{+}$ state of Be^{8} (experimentally, $\Gamma_{\alpha}/\Gamma < 0.05$, ref. 18). This argument is not correct, however, and the lack of α-decay actually has no bearing on the T assignment. R. F. Christy originally made an unpublished argument to the effect that a $J^{\pi} = 1^{+}$ state of C^{12} could not decay, because of symmetry considerations, to a Be^{8} state, such as the 2.9-MeV state, which is in a α-α configuration. Christy's argument is quite complicated, but a simple and elegant proof has been constructed by G. J. Stephenson, Jr.[19] The argument is as follows. First, consider the states of Be^{8} which, in L-S notation, have the partition [44]. From this partition, <u>only</u> three states can be made: ${}^{11}S_{0}$, ${}^{11}D_{2}$, and ${}^{11}G_{4}$. These correspond to the $J^{\pi} = 0^{+}$ ground state and the well known $J^{\pi} = 2^{+}$ and 4^{+} states at 2.9 and 11 MeV, respectively. Now, a grouping [4] outside of the S-shell (i.e., [44] = Be^{8}) is formally equivalent to a [4] "hole" in the closed P-shell (i.e., [4444] - [4] = [444] = C^{12}). Therefore, we expect the [444] partition to produce only C^{12} states with $J^{\pi} = 0^{+}$, 2^{+} and 4^{+} --- <u>not</u> $J^{\pi} = 1^{+}$. Of course, none of the Be^{8} or C^{12} states are purely combinations of [4] partitions, but the 2.9-MeV state in Be^{8} consists predominantly of [44]. Thus, any decay from a C^{12} state with $J^{\pi} = 1^{+}$, which cannot be predominantly [444], to the Be^{8} 2.9-MeV state must proceed via a small component of the Be^{8} wave function. Consequently, the lack of α-decay connecting the C^{12} 15.1-MeV state with the Be^{8} 2.9-MeV state does not constitute evidence for the T=1 assignment of the 15.1-MeV level.

Any α-decay of the 15.1-MeV state (which has not yet been observed) does, of course, furnish evidence of the T=0 impurity in this level. It is therefore of some interest to pursue the search for this decay mode; to do so will require the refinement of present techniques.

We also need more information concerning the properties of the 12.7-MeV state. The γ-ray to α-particle branching ratio has recently been measured with reasonable precision[16], but we still have only a crude upper limit on the total width (<15 keV). A value for Γ is, of course, required before we establish a value for Γ_{α}, the relevant quantity. Since the width is probably only a few hundred eV, it will clearly require a sophisticated experiment to measure this quantity. Perhaps we can persuade the practitioners of the resonance absorption art to tackle this formidable problem.

CONCLUSIONS

As advertised earlier, information on T-mixed doublets is scant. I have discussed 6 cases and for only 4 of these is there sufficient data to allow a reasonable assessment of the amount of T-mixing. Perhaps we will soon have new results for doublets in Be^8, B^{10}, and F^{18}. But it is clear that more experiments are needed and that more consideration of these problems by theorists is required before we will have an adequate understanding of the role that Coulomb effects play in these interesting levels.

REFERENCES

1. L. A. Radicatti, Proc. Phys. Soc. A66, 139 (1953); ibid. A67, 39 (1954); W. M. MacDonald, Phys. Rev. 100, 51 (1955).

2. G. Morpurgo, Phys, Rev. 114, 1075 (1959).

3. D. H. Wilkinson, in Nuclear Spectroscopy, F. Ajzenberg-Selove, Ed., Academic Press, New York, 1960, Part B, p. 852; E. K. Warburton, in Isobaric Spin in Nuclear Physics, J. D. Fox and D. Robson, Eds., Academic Press, New York, 1966, p. 90.

4. J. B. Marion, P. H. Nettles, C. L. Cocke, and G. J. Stephenson, Jr., Phys. Rev. 157, 847 (1967).

5. C. P. Browne, in Isobaric Spin in Nuclear Physics, J. D. Fox and D. Robson, Eds., Academic Press, New York, 1966, p. 136.

6. C. P. Browne, W. D. Callender, and J. R. Erskine, Phys. Letters 23, 371 (1966).

7. E. A. Silverstein, S. R. Salisbury, G. Hardie, and L. D. Oppliger, Phys. Rev. 124, 868 (1961).

8. W. R. Phillips, Phys. Rev. 110, 1408 (1958).

9. G. J. Stephenson, Jr., and J. B. Marion, in Isobaric Spin in Nuclear Physics, J. D. Fox and D. Robson, Eds., Academic Press, New York, 1966, p. 766.

10. G. J. Stephenson, Jr., and J. B. Marion, to be published.

11. W. E. Sweeney, Jr., Ph.D. Thesis, University of Maryland, 1967; W.E. Sweeney, Jr., and J. B. Marion, to be published.

12. F. C. Barker, Nucl. Phys. 83, 418 (1966).

13. A. M. Charlesworth and R. E. Azuma, Bull. Am. Phys. Soc. 12, 53 (1967); A. M. Charlesworth, R. E. Azuma, K. Cassel, and J. A. Kuehner, Bull. Am. Phys. Soc. 12, 663 (1967); and private communication.

14. P. C. Price, Proc. Phys. Soc. (London) A68, 553 (1955).

15. D. F. Hebbard, Nucl. Phys. 15, 289 (1960).

16. D. E. Alburger and D. H. Wilkinson, Phys. Rev. 153, 1061 (1967).

17. S. Cohen and D. Kurath, Nucl. Phys. 73, 1 (1965).

18. D. E. Alburger and P. F. Donovan, Rev. Mod. Phys. 37, 448 (1965).

19. G. J. Stephenson, Jr., private communication.

SUMMARY AND OUTLOOK

J. H. Gibbons

Oak Ridge National Laboratory*
Oak Ridge, Tennessee

I. It would be foolhardy for me to attempt a comprehensive review of the two dozen papers presented during this week. We've heard some very practical "hardware" discussions in experimental techniques but these were properly balanced by rich reviews of the status and outlook of whole sub-fields of study, perhaps best exemplified by Professor Peck's thoughtful paper. The flavor of the meeting has, by design, been weighted toward experimental physics but we were graced (and kept more or less honest) by sympathetic theorists. In fact I am left with the distinct impression that despite the remarkably rapid advances in experimental nuclear structure physics our theorist brothers are nipping close at our heels with valid requests for new information and with testable predictions. It is a wholesome, efficient condition for empirical testing and associated theoretical speculation to be in dynamic equilibrium.

My strongest impression is that nuclear structure physics is recently flowering because of the addition of new, basic tools. Unlike particle physics the new tool is not ever-higher energy -- but greater sophistication in ion sourcery, radiation detection, data handling, and calculational aids. In fact there was little reference during the conference to a need for more particle energy, *per se*. I think this should not be surprising because the range of nuclear excitations available to even a 5 megavolt accelerator includes most of the "real world" of radioactivity, reactors, bombs, and stars -- even supernovae.

What are the new tools?

---

*Operated for the U.S. Atomic Energy Commission by Union Carbide Corporation.

(A) Ion Sourcery

1. Pulsed beams. We now have widely available techniques and commercially available hardware that can dependably produce pulses of ions to less than one nanosecond in duration with peak current of the order of 10 milliamps. Two general applications of this technique are being fruitfully pursued. First, the high resolution timing enables us to measure energies by time-of-flight. This technique has resulted in important information on MeV range neutron inelastic scattering (nuclear models and reactor design), keV range neutron capture (nucleosynthesis and reactor design) and (p,n) reactions (isobaric analogue states), to name only a few. A second general application of the pulsed beam technique is the use of the time information for event discrimination. For example, the study of gamma rays from neutron capture or inelastic scattering is greatly facilitated by the time separation of the gammas from the neutron-producing target from those arising from (n,γ) or $(n,n'\gamma)$. Another use of pulsed beams, not yet exploited is the study of low cross section/high background reactions wherein the use of a high instantaneous ion current allows better signal-to-noise, yet allows for a modest target current easily handled by available techniques.

The question of the optimum technique for producing ion pulses is clearing up a bit, although still somewhat muddy. Certainly it is agreed that the first pulsing, by sinusoidal sweeping, should be performed in the injection end of the accelerator. The beam quality, i.e. energy and angular spread, of the ion beam from the source is all-important, thus strongly favoring the duoplasmatron source over rf sources. When terminal space and power permit, it seems quite clear that bunching by velocity modulation, sometimes referred to as "klystron bunching," provides a much more flexible, less complicated system subject to less maintenance and, in fact, less expensive than Mobley bunching.

2. High resolution beams. Studies of nuclear reactions with very high resolution continue to prove fascinating and valuable. This is exemplified by the remarkable measurements at Duke of isobaric analogue resonances in K^{41} via $Ar^{40}(p,n)$ and $Ar^{40}(p,p)$ reaction studies. The unique identification of fine-structure state spins which collectively give overwhelmingly clear evidence for isobaric analogues, was possible because of their fine energy resolution. The likelihood of MeV-range charged particle energy resolutions approaching 1:50,000 is fascinating.

3. Heavy ions. Advances in ion source techniques now allow us to use virtually any ion we choose. Further, by electron stripping we can obtain higher energy beams with the same voltage accelerator. Incidentally, the tandem accelerator was once labelled the "swindletron" by Alverez in recognition of such potential. Heavy ions are a boon to Coulomb excitation, to studies of high angular momentum states, to Doppler shift measurements of excited state lifetimes, to several aspects of solid state physics such as channeling (interatomic potentials and impurity locations), and to nuclear astrophysics (helium, carbon, and oxygen burning mechanisms).

4. Dependability. Too frequently we think of progress only in terms of new techniques. Of equal importance, I think, is the lifetime and freedom from maintenance of a given technique. For example, early experiments using pulsed beam techniques were, per force, planned to be accomplished in a few hours because that was the average dependable life of the system before maintenance. What good would automatic, computer controlled, operation of an experiment such as the impressive work of A. B. Smith be if the ion source lifetime were 20 hours? The current dependability of ion sources, pulsers, and bunchers of hundreds of hours, achieved by tedious engineering development, is directly reflected in the new kinds of studies undertaken and in the greatly enhanced efficiency of accelerator operation.

(B) Detectors and Associated Electronics

The relatively recent advent of silicon and germanium detectors, accompanied by the development of field-effect transistors, integrated circuits, and other solid state devices has swept over some areas of experimental nuclear structure physics like the life-giving spring floods of the Nile river. Also, not to be outdone by the solid state crowd, the already impressive characteristics of magnetic analyzers are being constantly improved and still hold their own, particularly for analysis at higher energies, for low background counting, and for studies of reaction products near zero degrees. It is too early to know how great the impact the improved detection systems will be but it is apparently as great as the advent of fast digital computers as a new tool for the theorist. We can list, for example, some consequences of this order of magnitude resolution enhancement in charged particle and γ-ray spectroscopy.

1. The new energy resolution permits Doppler shift measurements of nuclear lifetimes down to $\lesssim 10^{-14}$ seconds,

which gives us a window on multipole order and magnetic moments of many excited nuclear states. Earlier lifetime measurements were not only restricted to longer times but also were inherently less trustworthy because they were more indirect.

2. Energy level locations and resolution of previously unresolved states, particularly in complex nuclei, are now possible.

3. Measurements of angular correlations, Q values, decay schemes, and new techniques such as stripping studies with preserved axial symmetry are resulting in much more nearly complete quantum mechanical descriptions of nuclear states.

4. Multibody process studies are now feasible, through the combined use of semiconductor detectors and advanced techniques in data handling. Who of us will ever forget the hour with Harry and his "Holmgren diagrams"?

The flowering field of solid state detectors, still under rapid development, is only a component of the new art, for they would be of little value without the new, low noise, highly stable, linear and logic electronics that condition and process the detector information. Here, too, we have witnessed over the past several years an impressive advance, actively contributed to by our colleagues in private industry. The establishment of AEC Nuclear Instrument Modules has proven to be a tremendous aid to the experimenter. Experiments can be set up or modified vastly more easily and reliably than before. More sophisticated measurements can be made because of the greater dependability and lower unit cost of the equipment. Incidentally the next large contribution of the nuclear electronics manufacturers to nuclear physics, which we should urge upon them, is to develop a fool- and people-proof microphone and audio-amplifier system for use at nuclear physics conferences! A final point on the new nuclear electronics. The value of highly trustworthy, well designed electronics should not be overlooked when optimizing investment in an accelerator program. Too frequently we forget the high cost of a loss of a few days of accelerator time due to poor or insufficient data taking or handling equipment. We, too, are sometimes penny-wise and pound-foolish.

The increasingly easy access to fast digital computers has been another vital ingredient in our new tool inventory. More sophisticated raw information is obtained due to solid state detectors, beam pulsing, etc. and the experimenter must have means of transforming the massive amount of raw data into an interpretable set in short time in order to feedback into the experiment. Otherwise expensive accelerator time can easily be consumed for naught. Secondly, an increasing number of multiparameter experiments are being performed. This requires either an expensive, large core multichannel analyzer or a computer (if for nothing more than to transform the information, buffer the rate, and store it on magnetic tape). Thirdly, processing of information (such as extraction of first, second, and third moments of peaks in a pulse height spectrum) after an experiment is finished can be greatly facilitated with a small computer coupled to the experimenter through a light pen and memory storage scope. Last, given the basic dependability of accelerator and data acquisition system, a computer for executive control of an experiment involving repetitious steps can relieve the experimenter of a great deal of drudgery; also, in such experiments computer control can often result in more accurate results since it doesn't tend to become careless, forgetful, or sleepy.

(C) Theoretical Tools

While we obviously concentrated on hardware we surely all recognize the powerful new tools of the theorist. First and foremost the large, fast, cheap (per operation) digital computer continues to be the great new slave of the theorist, allowing him to make fewer of those simplifying assumptions previously needed in order to shorten calculations. The impressive success of the distorted wave Born approximation (DWBA) analysis in fitting angular distributions and correlations is a good case in point. Equally impressive is the recent success of the Hartree Fock method in understanding the structure of low lying states in light nuclei and in predicting, for example, shapes of light nuclei and magnetic moments of excited states. The study of the deformed shell model, deriving intermediate structure information from configuration mixing, is helping guide the experimental study of these remarkably simple aspects of complicated nuclei. It is always surprising to me that complicated, heavy nuclei can display such simple features as analogue resonances on the one hand and statistical features such as Porter-Thomas distributions of reduced level widths on the other.

Summary

Granted all these new tools, where do we now find

ourselves? We certainly are building a storehouse of information on gross nuclear properties, such as the location and quantum mechanical description of states in nuclear matter -- over the range of simplicities from single particle states, isobaric analogue states, intermediate resonances, to compound nucleus resonances. We are beginning to understand some regularities such as lifetimes, moments, level density, cross sections, collective motions, and shell effects. We are near a microscopic theoretical basis for gross nuclear structure effects and we are beginning to understand or at least visualize collective effects in simple nuclei. We have measured enough angular correlations and polarization distributions to think we're beginning to understand some reaction mechanisms.

But lest we transmit, even to ourselves, the feeling that we might rest on our laurels let's not forget that memorable curve shown by Professor Finley on (D,D) polarization versus energy, where four experiments give one well-defined curve, three another curve differing by up to a factor of two from the first, and, lest the theorists guffaw at the experimenters, where is sufficient guidance from the theory to say who is probably right?

Likewise let's remember the studies reported by Carlson of (Li,Li) reactions where 1-2 MeV broad resonances are observed in the excitation function (corresponding in time to only a few transits across the nucleus) but where cross-correlation studies of the several reaction channels clearly show that the cross section fluctuations must be "compound nucleus" type! This quandary is aptly described in the classic New Orleans jazz tune, "It must be jelly 'cause jam don't shake like that."

We might also pause to remember that we know basic quantum numbers of literally only a few of the hundreds of excited states in nuclei below 6 MeV excitation.

I don't hesitate to mention cross sections in this summary even though that remarkable Scotsman, George Morrison, feels they are "commercial." After all we have some industrial sponsors. We've made great progress in both measuring cross sections and understanding nuclear cross section regularities by analyzing the results through, for example, the non-local optical model. In fact it is widely felt that we can now predict some neutron scattering cross sections (MeV range) at least as accurately as we can measure them. However true this may be we must remember also how little we know. Remember Professor Tombrello's testimonial that only this spring, with the cross section measurement of $(He^3 + He^3) \rightarrow He^4 + 2p$, have we finally arrived at an understanding of how the hydrogen burning cycle of solar energy generation works! Let's also recall that the excitation function for $C^{12} + C^{12} \rightarrow Mg^{24}$, thought to be smooth, has just been found to vary with energy by up to a factor of ten. Let's recall how little we know about neutron capture cross sections, or the reaction mechanism of fission.

In short, while our knowledge about the nature of nuclei is, in many ways, beautifully refined, we don't need to look very far before we become acutely aware of how much we don't know. Additional information is not only needed to test and help develop a unified theory of nuclear matter, but also to aid understanding in stellar nucleosynthesis problems, geochemical investigations, and the very practical problems of nuclear reactor and shielding design.

II. Over-View. Rather than attempt an "outlook" I choose to try an "over-view." It is well for practitioners in every field to, from time to time, re-examine their work and raison d'etre, in the context of the total scientific enterprise. Therefore I want to end this conference with a set of summary arguments that hopefully will describe why so many of us feel that nuclear structure physics remains so vital, so worthy and such an exciting field in which to work.

1. Nuclear structure physics remains "good science" in that, despite great advances, new and unifying -- even simplifying -- fresh insight is being gained into the basic properties of nuclear matter. The science is ripe for exploitation because of new, powerful experimental and theoretical tools. New information, which reveals a remarkably simple nature even in very complex systems, gives promise of much more detailed understanding of heavy nuclei than previously thought.

2. Nuclear structure physics is a superb area in which to train future scientists. A student working in this area must by necessity develop a first-hand expertise in vacuum systems, accelerator components, solid state devices including detectors, linear and logic electronics, digital computers, and cryogenic systems. He must learn to work in a group of people, yet has a chance to do solo work, basically because the equipment is cheap enough to allow one-man operation and direct manipulation by the novice. The relatively low cost is also an important factor since it allows a large number of universities to participate

directly in the enterprise. By contrast, I understand that one distinguished physicist recently lamented "high-energy" physics as a place for graduate student training partially because of the large (about $1 million) cost per thesis! My guess is that a typical thesis in nuclear structure physics, in addition to being basically a better area for graduate student training, is nearly an order of magnitude less expensive.

3. Nuclear structure physics is tightly coupled to the "real world." The energy range we're concerned with is where the action is -- radioactivity, reactors (thus power, water, and the whole energy revolution), bombs, and stars. Society, our ultimate source of support, is properly interested in the relatedness of knowledge gleaned by us to social need -- both practical and aesthetic. One could make many statements about the practical values already received by society from nuclear structure physics research but I remember one statement by Dr. Seaborg that personifies the case for continued vigorous support of research in "low-energy nuclear physics." The investment in nuclear reactors for power production in the US over the next 30 years will be greater than $100 billion. The efficiency of these reactors is strongly dependent upon knowledge, used in design, of nuclear cross sections and systematics of nuclear structure. A one percent change in efficiency, easily envisaged, resulting from better nuclear information, could thus effect a savings to society of $1 billion in this area alone during this relatively short period of time.

4. Nuclear structure physics is spilling over into other fields, illuminating other disciplines. Just because it deals in energies so often encountered in the "real world," the results and tools of nuclear structure physics research are intimately related to other fields of research. For example: (a) Our explosive advance in the understanding of astrophysics, stellar evolution and nucleosynthesis, the origin and distribution of the elements and isotopes of elements, largely stems from our knowledge of nuclear reaction cross sections and the theory of nuclear structure. Some of the best customers for nuclear structure information nowadays are astrophysicists. (b) The Mössbauer effect, only a few years old, is already one of the most promising new tools in the study of solid structure and chemical physics. Some of the greatest successes have been the cross-disciplinary work of nuclear researchers with chemists -- a fascinating area for graduate student training. (c) The study of ion channeling in thin single crystals, one of several techniques in channeling studies, promises to

provide a powerful new tool for measuring interatomic potentials, for locating impurity positions in crystal lattices, and other solid state and metallurgical problems.

In short, the light of knowledge in nuclear structure physics not only further illuminates the subject itself but also clearly and directly illuminates other fields and disciplines in an exciting way. Our chosen field remains a cornucopia, the fruits of which are not only sweet to our own taste, but also to others.